FUNDAMENTALS OF
APPLIED ENTOMOLOGY

FUNDAMENTALS OF

With Chapters by

W. DON FRONK | *University of Wyoming*

DEANE P. FURMAN | *University of California at Berkeley*

ROBERT F. HARWOOD | *Washington State University*

B. AUSTIN HAWS | *Utah State University*

CARL JOHANSEN | *Washington State University*

JOHN A. NAEGELE | *Cornell University*

JOHN V. OSMUN | *Purdue University*

ROBERT E. PFADT | *University of Wyoming*

WM. M. ROGOFF | *South Dakota State College*

DONALD A. WILBUR | *Kansas State University*

APPLIED ENTOMOLOGY

Edited by Robert E. Pfadt

Professor of Entomology

University of Wyoming

The Macmillan Company | *New York*

Library of Congress catalog card number: 61–10775

The Macmillan Company, New York
Brett-Macmillan Ltd., Galt, Ontario

Printed in the United States of America

Preface

As insecticides and methods of control mushroom in number and variety and as our store of information on the biology of both destructive and beneficial insects grows, the study of applied entomology tends to encompass greater masses of data—far greater than any teacher can present and any student can assimilate in a single course. To overcome the difficulty of so much specific information, the authors have attempted to write a text based on principles.

Since many instructors offer service courses to agricultural students who have had no previous training in entomology, the first part of this book presents modern summaries on insect structure, function, growth, and classification. These topics consist of information essential for any student who has an interest in safeguarding from insect attack all man's possessions—his crops, his livestock and their feed and shelter, his own food and clothing, and his home.

After these basic subjects we include chapters on the principles of insect control, insecticides, and application equipment to provide the student with a general concept of how to combat destructive insects.

Then we discuss in separate "host" chapters the details of how growers protect various crops, livestock, stored grain, and other properties from insects and related pests. Rather than treat each individual pest that affects a host—this would certainly be too lengthy—we summarize and generalize by first presenting a list of the important pests of a given host, then the nature of their injury, methods of cultural control, biological control where applicable, and chemical control, and finally the kinds of insecticide application equipment suitable for treating the host.

In each host chapter we treat in detail four or more representative pests. These we have selected on the basis of their importance to the crop, their distribution, and their usefulness in illustrating different kinds of injury, life cycles, and control methods. Although the selected pests may not cover all the instructor wishes his students to study, he can readily assign others for library research or present them in lecture.

To keep this text within reasonable limits it has been necessary to delete much detailed information, to reduce the number of hosts covered, and to focus on basic principles. We feel this has been a difficult but wise decision, and that the material included will provide the student with an adequate background in applied entomology and with an understanding and appreciation of the principles of insect control.

Because common names of insects are becoming quite familiar to both farmers and students of agriculture and are generally accepted by entomologists, we have resorted to such names extensively in this text. For the most part, the list of common names of insects approved by the Entomological Society of America has been followed. Some common names used here have not been acted upon or approved. In order to provide the student with a reference to corresponding scientific names, we have included an appendix which lists the common-scientific names of all insects and mites noted in this book. For names of mites of veterinary importance, we have not necessarily followed the approved list, but rather the recent publications of Gordon K. Sweatman and of E. W. Baker, *et al.*

In describing the size of insects and mites we have used both U.S. linear and metric measures (inch and millimeter), whichever seemed most appropriate and easiest for the student to comprehend.

We are grateful for the help and encouragement given to us by many colleagues and friends who have supplied us with illustrations and have reviewed our manuscripts. We especially wish to acknowledge the entomologists who have read the following chapters: Drs. Leigh Chadwick and Maurice T. James, Chapter 2; Dr. Maurice T. James, Chapter 3; Drs. Maurice T. James and R. W. Strandtmann, Chapter 4; Dr. H. S. Telford and Mr. H. B. Busdicker, Chapter 5; Dr. Reginald H. Painter and Mr. Roy Pickford, Chapter 8; Professors R. T. Everly and G. E. Gould and Mr. Harold H. Dodge and Mr. B. J. Fitzgerald, Chapter 9; Dr. Dial Martin, Chapter 11; Dr. Leland G. Merrill, Jr., Chapter 12; Mr. E. J. Newcomer, Chapter 13; Mr. B. J. Landis, Chapter 14; and Dr. H. O. Deay, Chapter 17. Dr. H. C. Chiang reviewed the section on the European corn borer and Mr. John A. Begg the section on the black cutworm. Dr. Robert Lavigne read several chapters, while he and the editor travelled together investigating the ecology of grasshoppers. We also wish to thank Dr. W. W. Middlekauff for his help in checking scientific names, and Dr. Jean L. Laffoon for bringing us up-to-date on common names. Thanks are also due Mr. James Bebermeyer of the Wyoming University Agricultural Information Office who gave freely of his time in advising on editorial matters.

Robert E. Pfadt

Laramie, Wyoming
September, 1961

Contents |

Preface   v

Chapter

1 | Insects and Man | *Robert E. Pfadt*   1

2 | Insect Structure and Function | *Robert F. Harwood*   22

3 | Insect Growth | *Robert F. Harwood*   64

4 | Classification of Insects and Their Relatives | *Carl Johansen*   81

5 | Principles of Insect Control | *Carl Johansen*   138

6 | Chemical Control | *W. Don Fronk*   159

7 | Insecticide Application Equipment | *W. Don Fronk*   191

8 | Insect Pests of Small Grains | *Robert E. Pfadt*   213

9 | Insect Pests of Corn | *Robert E. Pfadt*   249

10 | Insects of Legumes | *B. Austin Haws*   282

11 | Insect Pests of Cotton | *Robert E. Pfadt*   315

12 | Vegetable Crop Insects | *W. Don Fronk*   346

13 | Insect Pests of Tree Fruits | *Carl Johansen*   376

14 | Insect Pests of Small Fruits | *Carl Johansen*   408

15 | Insect and Other Pests of Floricultural Crops | *John A. Naegele*   430

16 | Stored Grain Insects | *Donald A. Wilbur*   466

17 | Household Insects | *John V. Osmun*   495

x | Contents

18 | Livestock Insects and Related Pests | *Robert E. Pfadt*   526

19 | Poultry Insects and Related Pests | *Deane P. Furman*   561

20 | Insects of Medical Importance | *Wm. M. Rogoff*   585

Appendix | Common-Scientific Names   609

Glossary   629

Index   656

FUNDAMENTALS OF
APPLIED ENTOMOLOGY

Chapter 1 | INSECTS AND MAN | Robert E. Pfadt

The history of man is the record of a hungry creature in search of food, van Loon concluded in *The Story of Mankind*. In America, a land of plenty, indeed a land of vexing surpluses, few people appreciate the vital importance of food in maintaining the health and life of man. Today, more than a third of the world's population is hungry, and with rising birth rates and the prolongation of life by the humane application of medical science, the problem of raising sufficient food to fill all human wants appears to be increasing. This problem is not a new one; history is filled with evidence of man's precarious position in the face of famine and disease. Causing much of this trouble have been the insects, those small six-legged animals that devour man's crops, feed on his livestock, suck his blood, and infect him with disease.

Insects inhabited the earth long before man appeared. Somewhat doubtful fossils indicate insects may have been around for 300 million years; certainly by Carboniferous times, 200 million years ago, insects had extended their world and become numerous. When man arrived, approximately 500,000 years ago, insects had evolved into nearly all of their present diversity. Although we have little proof, primitive man presumably was harassed by blood sucking insects that not only fed on him but also spread pestilence. There is evidence that human lice, vectors of typhus and other diseases, infested ancient peoples; the dried-up remains of these pests have been found in the hair of prehistoric mummies from many parts of the world.

Yet we should not conclude that all insects, or even many, were enemies of ancient man. Just as do primitive tribes today, he likely ate many kinds of insects including caterpillars, grubs, and grasshoppers. The ancient Chinese practiced silk culture; according to Chinese tradition, this craft goes back to Emperor Fu-hsi who lived at the beginning of the third millennium B.C. The people of ancient Egypt knew about honey bees and put them to good use. A hieroglyphic honey bee is inscribed on a sarcophagus dating back to 3633 B.C., and a bas-relief describing the process of extracting honey is depicted in the temple of Ne-user-re, built around 2600 B.C. Cuneiform inscriptions record the introduction of bees into Assyria for the production of honey and wax, and clear representations of flies and of preserved locusts that were used as food appear in the seals and sculptures of ancient Assyria and Babylon.

Ancient man not only used insects to satisfy his physical wants; he also brought them into his rituals and made them symbols of worship. To the ancient Egyptians, dung beetles [*Scarabaeus sacer* Linnaeus (Fig. 1:1)

Fig. 1:1. The sacred scarab beetle, *Scarabaeus sacer* L., of the ancient Egyptians. *Courtesy USDA.*

and several other species] were sacred and symbolized eternal life. The image, carved in jade, emerald, and other stones, symbolized their sun-god Khepera who was the "Creator" and the "Father of the Gods." These images, known as scarabs, were used widely as sacred ornaments and as symbols of resurrection in burials. When a man died his heart was removed and a scarab inserted in its place. Scarabs, along with figures of gods, were placed on mummies lying in their sarcophagi.

Why did the Egyptians come to revere dung beetles—a reverence that seems strange at first thought? They held the beetles sacred because they associated these insects with their kings. Interring their deceased monarchs in tunnels cut into cliffs, they concealed the tombs from robbers with piles of refuse. The decomposing organic matter served as breeding places for the beetles which the early Egyptians related mistakenly to their kings rather than to the refuse.

We find vivid accounts of the ravages of insect enemies in the literature of the ancient Egyptians, Hebrews, and Greeks. The Bible mentions them many times, and eleven insects have been specifically identified in the Bible by F. S. Bodenheimer, an Israeli entomologist. Among these are the body louse, *Pediculus humanus* L., the human flea, *Pulex irritans* L., the webbing clothes moth, *Tineola bisselliella* (Hum.), the honey bee, *Apis mellifera* L., and the desert locust, *Schistocerca gregaria* Forsk. Joel 2:3 describes the destructiveness of locusts in these words:

. . . the land is as the garden of Eden before them, and behind them a desolate wilderness; yea, and nothing shall escape them.

Of the ten plagues visited upon Egypt preceding the Exodus, insects caused three and were involved in two or three others. The eighth plague was one of locusts:

For they covered the face of the whole earth, so that the land was darkened; and they did eat every herb of the land, and all the fruit of the trees which the hail had left: and there remained not any green thing in the trees, or in the herbs of the field, through the land of Egypt.

Even in present times the peoples of Africa and the Middle East have grave trouble with periodic outbreaks of this migratory grasshopper, known commonly as the desert locust (Fig. 1:2).

During the Middle Ages insects as vectors of disease were responsible for some of the worst epidemics that have struck the human race. The Black Death, mainly bubonic plague, is one of the major calamities of history. In

Fig. 1:2. A swarm of the desert locust, *Schistocerca gregaria* Forskål, in the Ogaden desert of Ethiopia. *Courtesy ICA.*

the middle of the fourteenth century the disease claimed the life of one quarter of the population in Europe—at least 25 million victims. Although bubonic plague is essentially a bacterial disease of rodents transmitted by the oriental rat flea, *Xenopsylla cheopis* (Rothsch.), at times it causes serious epidemics among human beings. When rats die of the disease the fleas will leave the dead animals and migrate to other hosts including man. In feeding on blood the flea directly introduces the infection with its bite. This disease remains with us still, but it no longer kills in such great numbers.

We could continue relating the histories of fateful human diseases carried by insects—epidemic typhus by the human louse, malaria by the anopheles mosquito, yellow fever by the aedes mosquito, sleeping sickness by the tsetse fly, and still others—but this would take us deeply into the field of medical entomology and divert us from our main objective, the study of agricultural entomology. Let us skip over these interesting but diverting medical stories and take a look at applied entomology in North America beginning with the period of colonization.

INSECTS IN COLONIAL AMERICA

Fortunately not nearly as many insect pests attacked the crops of the early colonists in America as attack crops nowadays. The flood of plant materials from the Old World and of their insect enemies, which inevitably accompanied them, had not yet begun. But there were native and a few introduced insect species that caused much trouble. Agriculture in America during colonial times consisted of growing a few grains, fruits, and vegetables that the English had been accustomed to producing at home, corn and tobacco adopted from the Indians, and in southern colonies, where the climate was favorable, rice and indigo.

As early as 1632 armyworms caused serious damage to the settler's corn. Fruit insects were injurious too, for a Mr. John Hull recorded in 1661, "the cankerworm hath for four years devoured most of the apples in Boston, so that the trees look in June as if it were the ninth month." In 1740 grasshoppers seriously attacked the crops of the Massachusetts Colony. The colonists, applying the best control they knew, armed themselves with bundles of brush and drove millions into the ocean. In 1743 an outbreak of armyworms caused extensive damage to grains throughout the North Atlantic states.

Insects, principally mosquitoes, brought a sea of troubles to the colonists by transmitting serious human diseases. Because of malaria the death rate of slaves working the rice swamps was high; still more slaves had to be imported as replacements. Yellow fever felled thousands of America's pioneers. In 1699 it killed one-sixth of the population of Philadelphia and in 1793, when the population numbered 50,000, 11,000 persons contracted the disease and 4,000 died.

Besides the native insects, colonists had to contend with those that they brought with them. Stored-grain insects infested grain and animal parasites annoyed and sucked the blood of livestock. The colonists transported to their homes clothes moths, bed bugs, and cockroaches. Peter Kalm, a Finnish naturalist, noted in 1748 the great havoc of the pea weevil. He stated that peas were no longer cultivated in Pennsylvania and to only a limited extent in New Jersey and New York because of the work of this insect. In 1779 the Hessian fly, supposedly introduced from Europe in the straw bedding of Lord Howe's Hessian troops, caused extensive destruction to the wheat crop on Long Island.

The colonists introduced honey bees into New England early, at least by 1640, to provide themselves with honey and wax. After 1670 bee culture declined in the colonies, presumably due to American foulbrood, a devastating bee disease. The Indians were unfamiliar with honey bees and called them the "white man's fly."

VOLUNTEER ENTOMOLOGY

As America grew and agriculture expanded, insects increased their injurious attacks and forced recognition of the problem upon the populace. During these early times there were no agricultural experiment stations or federal laboratories to study any of the distressing plant and animal problems confronting both farmers and city people. A keenly observant group of men—farmers, ministers, physicians, and teachers—became interested in insects and their economic importance and began to study and write about them. One of the most prominent of the early workers was **William D. Peck,** a Massachusetts naturalist who in 1795 wrote *The Description and History of the Cankerworm.* In 1805 he became the first professor of natural history at Harvard and in this position was able to pursue his interest and study of insects. Born in Boston in 1763, Peck became known as America's first native entomologist.

Thaddeus William Harris, a student of Professor Peck, became a distinguished early economic entomologist (Fig. 1:3). Harris received a medical degree in 1820 and took up the practice of medicine for a short while. His interest in insects probably arose early in life as both of his parents were fascinated by natural history. In 1831 he became librarian at Harvard and while a member of a commission to study the geology and botany of

Fig. 1:3. Thaddeus William Harris (1795–1856), pioneer economic entomologist, published the first comprehensive report on destructive insects in America in 1841. *From the National Archives.*

Massachusetts wrote what is now regarded as a classic in applied entomology, *Report on Insects Injurious to Vegetation*, first published in full in 1841. The third edition (1862) is a book beautifully illustrated with wood engravings of insects and contains seven chapters with over 600 pages.

PROFESSIONAL ENTOMOLOGY

There were other studies and other publications on insects during the volunteer period but we shall turn to the year 1854, a significant milestone in entomology, for it was in this year that the profession of entomology is considered to have begun in the United States. Recognition of the need for insect control led to the appointment of two entomologists to government positions. One was Townend Glover, who accepted a position with the new United States Bureau of Agriculture, and the other was Asa Fitch who went to work for the state of New York.

Townend Glover began his duties of collecting "information on seeds, fruits, and insects of the United States" on June 14, 1854. Though Glover's chief interests were in his drawings of insects and in his agricultural museum, field activities took him into the South where he studied insect pests of crops, particularly those of the orange and of cotton.

Fig. 1:4. Asa Fitch (1809–79), first state entomologist, investigated the injurious insects of New York and described many of the economic species of America. *Courtesy New York State Museum and Science Service.*

Fig. 1:5. Charles Valentine Riley (1843–95), a dynamic investigator and organizer of agricultural entomology in America. *Courtesy University of Missouri.*

Dr. **Asa Fitch,** a medical doctor, gave up the practice of his profession in 1838 and began the study of insects in 1840 (Fig. 1:4). In 1854 the New York State Agricultural Society, authorized by the state legislature, appointed him to investigate the injurious insects of New York, thus making him the first state entomologist. Fitch made thorough studies of the life histories of many insect pests of New York and described many of the important economic species of America. He described, for example, the grape phylloxera, *Phylloxera vitifoliae* (Fitch), the corn leaf aphid, *Rhopalosiphum maidis* (Fitch), and the wheat jointworm, *Harmolita tritici* (Fitch). Much of his work was published in the Transactions of the New York State Agricultural Society in the form of fourteen annual reports.

From these modest beginnings entomology in America, through the research and study of many diligent entomologists, has gradually risen to the position of an important and respected science. The developments came in two streams that often intermingled. One consisted of the advances made by the federal organization, the other, of contributions from the state experiment stations and universities. In recent years a third stream consisting of the teams of entomologists and of other scientists in industry and commerce has risen to great importance.

Because a full account of this century of entomological progress would fill a volume in itself, we shall only consider a few of the highlights, first taking up the contributions made in the federal service by the chiefs of entomology.

Entomology in federal service

Upon the retirement of Townend Glover in 1878, **Charles Valentine Riley** (Fig. 1:5) accepted the post. Riley was already a well-known entomologist; he had been state entomologist of Missouri for ten years and had published nine annual reports. These reports were sound pieces of research illustrated by admirable woodcuts of insects. Riley was a man with a difficult but driving temperament. He was troubled with insomnia and though he found it hard to sleep in his bed at home he could sleep on a long railway journey or in a barber's chair. In addition to his Missouri reports, he is remembered for four other important accomplishments.

1. He was largely responsible for the founding of the **United States Entomological Commission** in 1877. The job of the commission was to study how to control the hordes of the Rocky Mountain grasshopper, *Melanoplus spretus* (Walsh), that had developed in the eastern foothills of the Rocky Mountains, flown eastward in 1874, and descended upon the farmlands of the Midwest creating a national disaster. Growing crops were devoured, farms were abandoned, and the trek of settlers toward Kansas and neighboring states was halted. Three entomologists, Riley, A. S. Packard, and Cyrus Thomas, made up the commission. The results of their studies were published in five reports, the first two on the Rocky Mountain grasshopper and the other three on a variety of insects. In June 1881 the activities of the commission ceased.

2. He began the building of the organization that grew into the Bureau of Entomology.

3. Based on his research in Missouri, he suggested the use of American resistant rootstocks to control the ravages of the grape phylloxera in France. For this he received a gold medal from the French Government.

4. He conceived and directed the successful biological control of the

cottony-cushion scale, a serious pest of citrus in California, by introducing a predaceous enemy of the scale, the lady beetle, *Rodolia cardinalis* (Muls.), from Australia.

Although Riley's accomplishments are now recognized universally by entomologists, his career was not without disappointments. In his eagerness to promote work in entomology, he went directly to Congress for obtaining increased funds rather than through regular channels. This lack of bureaucratic ethics inflamed Riley's superior, the Commissioner of Agriculture. In the heat of the argument Riley resigned and J. H. Comstock of Cornell University was appointed federal entomologist, a position Comstock held for two years, 1879 to 1881. Upon the election of President Garfield, Riley's friends were able to persuade the new administration to reappoint him to his former position in 1881.

Fig. 1:6. Leland O. Howard (1857–1950), brilliant promoter of entomology in America and world authority in medical entomology. Howard was chief of the Bureau of Entomology from 1894 to 1927. *Courtesy USDA.*

Fig. 1:7. Edward F. Knipling (1909–), present Director of the Entomology Research Division of the United States and world renowned for studies on insect pests of man and animals. *Courtesy USDA.*

Riley retired in 1894 and his assistant, **Leland O. Howard,** stepped in as chief (Fig. 1:6). This was a happy selection, as Howard was both a brilliant scientist and a leader and a man of action. He graduated from Cornell University (B.S., 1877; M.S., 1883), received his Ph.D. from Georgetown

(1896), and M.D. from George Washington (1911), LL.D. from Pittsburgh (1911), and Sc.D. from Toronto (1920). He made lasting contributions to medical entomology, biological control, insect taxonomy, and perhaps most important of all, to the tremendous growth, efficient operation, and sound research of the Bureau of Entomology. With Dyar and Knab as collaborators, he wrote an ambitious monograph, *The Mosquitoes of North America, Central America, and the West Indies.*

In 1927 **Charles L. Marlatt,** succeeded Howard as chief of the Bureau of Entomology. Marlatt had been associate chief to Howard and had labored long and perseveringly to have Congress pass federal quarantine laws. Such laws were badly needed to put an end to the thoughtless introduction of foreign pests. Though the United States had suffered most from stowaway insects, it was one of the last countries to pass a satisfactory quarantine law. In 1912 the Plant Quarantine Act finally became a reality.

Under **Lee A. Strong,** chief from 1933 to 1941, the quarantine work of the federal government became more highly organized and more efficient. He was largely instrumental in the merger of two bureaus in 1934 that formed the Bureau of Entomology and Plant Quarantine.

Upon the sudden death of Strong in 1941, Dr. **P. N. Annand** became chief of the bureau and held this office through the war years. Annand's great contribution was organizing and channeling the resources of the bureau into insect control studies to help increase food and fiber and to provide the military with new methods of controlling the insect vectors of such diseases as typhus, malaria, and yellow fever. Upon Annand's death in office in 1950, **Avery S. Hoyt** succeeded him and remained chief until January 2, 1954 when the Bureau of Entomology and Plant Quarantine was abolished.

The recent reorganization within the USDA was begun in 1952 and apparently is still going on. The reason given for these changes is to organize the department along functional lines rather than according to scientific disciplines. Under the able leadership of **Edward F. Knipling** (Fig. 1:7), Director of the Entomology Research Division of the Agricultural Research Service of the USDA, entomology in the federal government is again moving forward. Here is a skeleton outline of the major subdivisions in the Entomology Research Division as of 1961.

Entomology Research Division, E. F. Knipling, Director

1. Pioneer Research Group
   a. Insect Physiology Laboratory, W. E. Robbins, In Charge
   b. Insect Pathology Laboratory, A. M. Heimpel, In Charge

2. Cotton Insects Research Branch, S. E. Jones, Chief
3. Fruit and Vegetables Research Branch, B. A. Porter, Chief
4. Grain and Forage Insects Research Branch, R. G. Dahms, Chief
5. Insects Affecting Man and Animals Research Branch, A. W. Lindquist, Chief
6. Insect Identification and Parasite Introduction Research Branch, W. H. Anderson, Chief
7. Pesticide Chemicals Research Branch, S. A. Hall, Chief
8. Bee Culture Research Investigations, C. L. Farrar, Leader

Work on insects of stored products was shifted to the Agricultural Marketing Service and forest entomology to the Forest Service. Plant Quarantine is now set up as a separate division under the Agricultural Research Service as is also the Plant Pest Control Division.

Entomology in the states

Entomologists working in state departments and in the universities of America have contributed brilliantly to the science of entomology. Besides Asa Fitch of New York, other early state entomologists were **B. W. Walsh,** hired in 1866 by Illinois, and **C. V. Riley,** hired by Missouri in 1868. Walsh was born in England and went to Cambridge University where he worked with Charles Darwin. He came to America at the age of thirty, but not until after a varied career as a farmer and lumberman, did he begin the earnest study of insects, this when he was fifty years old! Though his career in entomology lasted only eleven years, he greatly influenced the standards of research and writing of a young science. Riley admired the older Walsh greatly and learned and profited much from their associations. State entomologists of this early period headed research and educational organizations, while present-day state entomologists are principally regulatory officials.

The need for research in agriculture, not just entomology, was recognized by agricultural societies, state boards of agriculture, and numerous individuals throughout the country. From 1840 on, there was continuous activity to obtain public support for agricultural colleges. This movement culminated in the **Morrill Land-Grant College Act** of 1862 which donated to each state 30,000 acres of federal land for each of its United States Senators and Representatives, for the endowment, support, and maintenance of at least one college where the leading subjects would be related to agriculture and the mechanic arts, and provided for professorships in botany and entomology. This act, together with the **Hatch Act** of 1887, which established state agricultural experiment stations throughout the nation, became the *point d'appui* for the phenomenal growth and development of entomological research and teaching by the states.

The teaching of entomology in America, so vital for the training of new entomologists, was begun by Peck and Harris in an informal way at Harvard University. The first regular teacher of entomology was **Hermann Hagen** who was brought to Harvard in 1867 from Germany through the invitation of Louis Agassiz, Director of the Harvard Zoological Museum. Hagen was an enthusiastic teacher and had a kindly, helpful way with fellow workers. Many students came to him for instruction, including Herbert Osborn and J. H. Comstock. At Harvard he founded the first entomological museum in this country.

The teaching of entomology got its real impetus from the newly formed agricultural colleges. Among the prominent early teachers in these institutions were B. F. Mudge at Kansas State University, A. J. Cook at Michigan State University, T. J. Burrill and S. A. Forbes at Illinois University, C. H. Fernald at the University of Maine and University of Massachusetts, and J. H. Comstock at Cornell University.

Fig. 1:8. John Henry Comstock (1849–1931), one of America's great, early teachers of entomology. *From the National Archives.*

J. H. Comstock (Fig. 1:8), who became one of the leading teachers of entomology in the world, greatly influenced the science not so much by his excellent research on the morphology of insects as by the many fine students he turned out. He graduated from Cornell University (B.S., 1874) and for forty years thereafter worked and taught at his alma mater. He founded there the first department of entomology in a university anywhere.

The student of entomology today is greatly indebted to these pioneer teachers, for it was through their efforts and dedicated lives that we now have so many fine teachers in so many splendid departments of entomology in America.

Entomological research, particularly the applied phases, in the states is conducted principally by the agricultural experiment stations. Since these are usually located in the agricultural college, both teaching and research are performed by one and the same department of entomology. Generally the faculty's teaching load is light, so that most entomologists spend the larger share of their time doing research.

A significant development for agricultural entomology was the creation of the **Federal-State Extension Service** by the Smith-Lever Act of 1914. The first extension entomologist was **T. H. Parks** who was hired by the University of Idaho in 1913 a year before the act was passed. The circumstance that led to his employment was the presence of the alfalfa weevil in Idaho and the concern of hay growers over quarantine laws enacted by California and Montana against them. How well the extension entomologists of the nation have performed their function of taking the discoveries made by the entomologists of the experiment stations and quickly making the information available to county agents and farmers is indicated by their number in 1960—75 extension entomologists employed in 46 states!

Commercial entomology

Just as the appointments of Glover and of Fitch to federal and state positions in 1854 is considered the beginning of professional entomology in the United States, so the appointment of Dr. **Otto H. Swezey** (Fig. 1:9) in 1904, fifty years later, as assistant entomologist in the experiment station of the Hawaiian Sugar Planters Association is considered the beginning of commercial entomology. Dr. Swezey came from Ohio State University and continued in active service for thirty years. Soon other grower's organizations began to recognize the need for specialists on insect control and began to hire entomologists. Though their achievements in applied entomology have been many, we have time to mention only a few of the outstanding workers. In 1910 **Asa C. Maxon** was made director of the experiment station of the Great Western Sugar Company at Longmont, Colorado. He carried on research there for thirty-five years and became the leading authority on insects affecting sugar beets. In the citrus industry, Sunkist Growers since 1920 have had a progressive group of entomologists who have greatly

Fig. 1:9. Otto Herman Swezey (1869–1959), first commercial entomologist in America and a devoted student of insects. *Courtesy Hawaiian Sugar Planters Association.*

improved insect control measures on the organization's extensive citrus plantings in Arizona and California. One of the most brilliant records in agricultural entomology has been made by the entomologists of the Pineapple Producers Association in Hawaii. In 1930 Dr. **R. N. Chapman,** the eminent insect ecologist, left the University of Minnesota to become director of the association. In the same year Dr. **Walter Carter** became head of the department of entomology of the Pineapple Research Institute and is still active in both conducting and directing research on pineapple pests. For many years the United Fruit Company has carried on investigations in tropical agriculture and on the insects that affect their extensive plantings.

The biggest employer of commercial entomologists today is the insecticide industry, which comprises more than fifty basic manufacturers and more than 500 formulators and processors. The industry employs hundreds of entomologists to work in laboratories, on experimental farms, and in company organizations as administrators, technical representatives, and salesmen. A recent estimate of entomologists in industry puts the number at about 500, and a survey by the National Agricultural Chemicals Association indicates considerably increased employment of entomologists during the next few years due to an expected expansion of the industry.

Other areas in which the numbers of commercial entomologists have grown can be seen by the following categories of employment.

Beekeeping and associated supplies industry
Structural pest control operators
Supervised pest control services
Commercial crop spraying and dusting
Forest products industry
Grain and milling trade
Seed growers
Canning companies
Tree experts and arborists
Nurserymen
Dairy industry
Biological supply houses
Consulting entomologists

ENTOMOLOGY IN CANADA

Our historical review of applied entomology in America would be incomplete if we did not call attention to the history of the science in Canada. An early period, before the 1850's, existed as in the United States, when knowledge of insects depended on the observations of a few people who were interested in these animals as a hobby. They noticed the beautiful butterflies, the tormenting mosquitoes, and the devastating grasshoppers. By their encroachments on the economy of Canada, insects forced the development of entomology just as they had done in the United States.

The beginnings of Canadian agriculture stressed the exportation of lumber and wheat, and when in 1856 the Hessian fly and wheat midge caused destruction of the crop to the tune of over two million dollars, the people became greatly alarmed. Because the pest problem intensified as agriculture expanded and increased, insects made the entomologist one of the most important scientists in Canadian society. Famous Canadian entomologists included **James Fletcher,** the first Dominion Entomologist, and his successors, **Charles Gordon Hewitt** and **Arthur Gibson.**

The science of entomology is now firmly founded in Canada with over 400 professional entomologists, more than fifty well-equipped research centers, sixteen institutions giving formal instruction, and eight professional societies. Because a system similar to the state agricultural experiment stations was not adopted in Canada, most entomological research, over 85 per cent, is conducted by entomologists of the Dominion Department of Agriculture both in the field and in the research institutes and laboratories that have been established widely throughout the country.

ENTOMOLOGICAL SOCIETIES

Entomological societies have played an important part in the development of the science by bringing people of common interests together, by creating a contagious enthusiasm for the study of insects, by providing a strong organization to enlighten public opinion and to sway governmental decisions and actions, and by sponsoring journals in which members can publish their research. Entomological societies started in England with the founding of the **Aurelian Society** in London about 1745. The society did not last long, for the fire that burned its library and insect collections also caused its dissolution in 1748. A succession of societies followed, until finally the present and distinguished **Entomological Society of London** was formed in 1833.

In America the first society of this kind was the Entomological Society of Pennsylvania founded at York in 1842. Short-lived, it disbanded around 1844. The oldest existing entomological society in America is the **American Entomological Society,** founded in Philadelphia in 1859 and called the Entomological Society of Philadelphia until 1867. It is a strong organization with an excellent insect collection and several periodical publications, notably the *Transactions, Entomological News,* and *Memoirs.*

Another important early society was the **Entomological Society of Canada,** founded at Toronto in 1863. This association immediately led to an increase in the number of articles on insects, and in 1868 the society began its now famous journal, *The Canadian Entomologist.*

The federal acts of 1862 and 1887, which established the state agricultural colleges and experiment stations, opened the door for the employment of large numbers of entomologists who shortly felt the need for an association. In July 1889 James Fletcher, the Dominion Entomologist of Canada, came to Washington where he and L. O. Howard drafted a constitution for an Association of Economic Entomologists. The next month the Association was organized at Toronto. In 1908 the organization began publishing the *Journal of Economic Entomology* and in the following year changed its name to the **American Association of Economic Entomologists.** As entomology grew in America, those primarily interested in the basic rather than the applied phases of the science organized the **Entomological Society of America** in 1906. This society began publishing its annals in 1908. Because many entomologists in the United States belonged to both organizations, they decided to merge into one strong society in 1953 and to retain the name Entomological Society of America. Today this society has 4,300 members with world-wide representation, an annual budget of well over $100,000, and its own headquarters building at College Park, Maryland. The society now publishes or underwrites nine publications.

Annals of the Entomological Society of America
Journal of Economic Entomology
Index of American Economic Entomology
Monographs of the Thomas Say Foundation
The Annual Review of Entomology
Miscellaneous Publications of the Entomological Society of America
Bulletin of the Entomological Society of America
Entoma—Pest Control Directory
Opportunities in Professional Entomology

A WORD OF EXPLANATION

At this point and before we state what this text is all about, we should reveal what it isn't. It is not a "cookbook" with chemical recipes to rid plants, livestock, or even oneself of noxious insects. Control recommendations are largely a state responsibility, and they often change from year to year depending on research, experience, new chemicals, new crop varieties, and—extremely crucial these days—federal laws governing pesticide residues on food.

Because these laws are important and because they are a lively topic not only among farmers and agriculturalists but also among housewives whose menus may change as a result of them, we shall digress momentarily to discuss the topic of laws and insecticides. The first federal law concerning insecticides was passed in 1910 to protect the farmer and other users of these chemicals. Before this date many fake remedies were advertised and sold to farmers. Even effectual ones like paris green were often adulterated. In the 1860's Benjamin D. Walsh carried on a crusade against these malpractices and addressed himself to one of these dishonest purveyors in the following language:

We fear greatly that, instead of being a decently good entomologist, tolerably well acquainted with the noxious insects of the United States, you are a mere entomological quack; and that, instead of talking good, common, horse sense to us, you are uttering all the time nothing but bosh.

The **Federal Insecticide Act** of 1910 served its purpose well; it quickly put an end to nearly all the fraud in the sale of insecticides. The act set standards for existent insecticides and fungicides, forbade false claims on labels, and prohibited the inclusion of substances that would injure vegetation.

There were several state laws covering insecticides before the federal act became law. The first pesticide law was adopted by New York State in 1898 to regulate the sale of paris green. Similar legislation was enacted the following year by Oregon and Texas and in 1901 by California, Louisiana, and Washington.

In 1947 the **Federal Insecticide, Fungicide, and Rodenticide Act** supplanted the act of 1910. The new law covers the marketing of rodenticides and herbicides as well as insecticides and fungicides, expands on the regulations governing labels, and requires registration with the United States Department of Agriculture of any economic poison marketed in interstate commerce. The purpose of the 1947 act, which is currently in effect, is to protect not just the buyer of agricultural chemicals but the whole public from any sort of misuse of them. The U.S. Department of Agriculture administers the act and provides inspectors to examine economic poisons marketed in interstate commerce. These men take samples from warehouses, drug stores, grain and feed stores, and other outlets and submit them to department laboratories where they are analyzed and studied. Whenever a chemical is found in violation of the law, officials may seize it by court action and may also initiate prosecution of offenders.

In addition to the 1947 act, another law, the **Federal Food, Drug, and Cosmetic Act** of 1938 and an amendment to it, called Public Law 518 or the **Miller Amendment** after Congressman A. L. Miller who introduced the bill, regulates the use of insecticides and other pesticide chemicals. The purpose of the law, which is administered by the Food and Drug Administration of the U.S. Department of Health, Education, and Welfare, is to make sure that the food supply is safe for human consumption.

Besides having one of the richest diets and the most varied menus on earth, Americans daily consume an assortment of around 400 chemicals added to foods as preservatives, mold inhibitors, antioxidants, coloring agents, bleaches, thickeners, thinners, emulsifiers, moisteners, and—the substances of main interest to us—pesticides. Unfortunately, the latter, applied to growing crops and to livestock for control of destructive insects and diseases, may leave residues of the toxicant. The problem that faces us, and especially the Food and Drug Administration, is what residues are safe and how much. This is not an easy problem to solve, for prohibiting use of pesticides could well lead to famine in America. Yet certainly no one is willing to advise the consumption of dangerous amounts of poison. Since no sharp line exists between poisonous and nonpoisonous chemicals, for common salt can be a poison in excess, and arsenic can be a lifesaver, a compromise solution has been reached by applying the old Paracelsus' law. The Swiss alchemist-physician Paracelsus (Fig. 1:10) put it this way: "Poison is in everything, and no thing is without poison. The dosage makes it either a poison or a remedy."

The method by which the FDA guards our food from harmful amounts of residues is to establish "tolerances." A **tolerance** is the amount of a pesticide that may safely remain as a residue on a food crop or in meat or fat.

Fig. 1:10. Paracelsus (1493–1541), Swiss-born scientist who helped guide medical men away from mistakes of Galen and Avicenna and directed their thoughts toward rational research and advocated the use of pure chemicals in medical practice. *Courtesy of Parke, Davis & Company.*

Scientists of the FDA first consider available data on safety and on amount of residue that remains when the insecticide is used according to directions on the label. FDA then sets a tolerance that will be safe and can be met if the grower follows label directions. Though the majority of presently used insecticides bear tolerances, there are some, such as pyrethrum, rotenone, and petroleum oils, that are exempt from this requirement because, properly used, they present no hazard; there are still others, such as calcium cyanide, dinitrocresol, and TEPP, that have a zero tolerance because they are too dangerous to allow on food even in small amounts.

Like the USDA, the FDA has its team of inspectors. They check on the residues of toxicant on fresh produce, meat, milk, and other agricultural products rather than on packaged pesticides. When excessive residues from a particular area are suspected, samples are examined from outgoing shipments of the product. If unlawful residues exist, a federal court order removes the shipment from the market. The law also provides for action against persons and business firms responsible for violations.

Because the agricultural industry has a responsibility for producing healthful, wholesome food and for producing this food within the law, agricultural leaders have emphasized the importance of following official recommendations and label directions in controlling insect pests. The FDA advises the grower to follow three simple rules:

1. Use a pesticide only on the crops for which its use is recommended by the manufacturer on the registered label.
2. Use the pesticide in the amounts specified on the label.
3. Apply the pesticide only at the time specified on the label.

Most state agricultural colleges publish insect control recommendations each year that not only conform with federal and state laws, but also explain local variations which must be reckoned with to achieve the best control.

WHY THIS BOOK

As one may surmise from what has been said, textbooks are not the best places for anyone to seek the latest in insect control recommendations. On the other hand, texts do serve an important role in providing both a background of information on insects, their habits, life histories, and ecology and an appreciation of the insect problems on various crops and how we go about solving these problems.

An attempt has been made to develop principles in this book so that once learned, the student can handle specific insect problems himself or will know where to get the information he needs. As many students, principally "ag" students, will not have had a previous course in entomology, we have begun the main part of this book with modern treatments of Insect Structure and Function, Insect Growth, and Insect Classification. In order to provide the student with prerequisite information for intelligent study of the host chapters, these topics are followed by short chapters on the Principles of Insect Control, Insecticides, and Application Equipment.

Host chapters have been written to present a panorama of the insect problems that affect specific crops. First, we discuss the number and importance of the pests of the crop, second, how these pests cause injury, and then, in general, how they are controlled. After these introductory sections we consider a limited number of pests of the crop, usually four or five, in detail. The choice of pests may not include all insect species that a student should study for a particular area, but he may add other species to those treated and with the help of his teacher dig out the necessary information, a task that is both edifying and rewarding.

Selected References

Essig, E. O., *A History of Entomology* (New York: Macmillan, 1931).

Howard, L. O., *A History of Applied Entomology*, Smithsonian Misc. Coll., Vol. 84, 1930.

Leonard, M. D., "The Development of Commercial Entomology in the United States," Proceedings Tenth International Congress of Entomology, 3:99–106 (1958).

Montgomery, B. E., "Arthropods and Ancient Man," *Bul. Ent. Soc. Amer.*, 5:68–70 (1959).

Pellett, F. C., *History of American Beekeeping* (Ames, Iowa: Collegiate Press, 1938).

Zinsser, Hans, *Rats, Lice and History* (Boston: Little, Brown, 1935).

Chapter 2 | INSECT STRUCTURE AND FUNCTION | *Robert F. Harwood*

Insects invade and thrive in more environments than any other group of animals. Although they essentially dwell on the earth's surface, they have also mastered the subterranean world and the realms of air and water. They inhabit deserts and rain forests, hot springs and snow fields, dark caves and sunlit surroundings. They eat the choicest foods on man's table—and can eat the table too! It seems obvious that organisms with abilities such as these must have extreme structural and functional diversity. It is truly amazing that such diversity is found in animals as small as insects. Though as a group they are much smaller than mammals, their anatomy and physiology for performing their many commonplace activities are just as complex. The extreme range of environments utilized by insects is accompanied by an equal range of structural and functional variations.

GENERAL EXTERNAL FORM

Insects, like mammals, are **bilaterally symmetrical** animals, that is the external structures and most internal structures are divided into left and right halves that are mirror images. Only minor variations of this scheme occur, with occasional subtle differences in the mouthparts and genital structures and major asymmetry possible in the digestive tract.

Both sexes often resemble each other, particularly in the immature forms. However **sexual dimorphism** of adults may be very marked. There is a tendency for female insects to be larger than males, though with beetles the males are often bigger and are armed with large mandibles or horns. In several species of moths the antennae of the males are decidedly fringed and in mosquitoes and related Diptera the males have very bushy antennae.

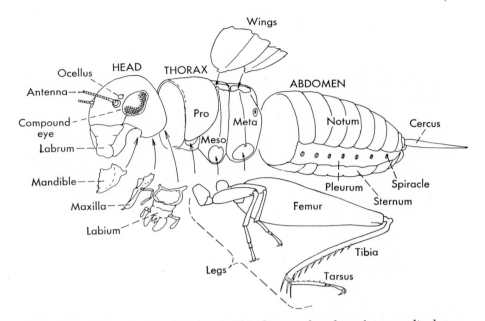

Fig. 2:1. External structure of an insect. This diagram, based on the generalized structure of the common cricket, shows the body regions and their associated structures.

Females of many insects can be clearly distinguished by well-developed ovipositors, males by prominent genital claspers. Extreme differences are found in the scale insects, where the females are flattened, inactive, and featureless, the males active, with well-developed legs and wings (Fig. 13:23). More subtle differences occur, such as in higher Diptera where the compound eyes of males are practically contiguous in front, those of females separated.

Adult insects have three distinct body regions, **head, thorax,** and **abdomen** (Fig. 2:1). Each region results from a variable degree of **fusion of segments** distinctly separate in embryonic development. Clearly separate segments in postembryonic stages are usually evident in the abdomen, a structure which retains a certain amount of flexibility. The thorax, bearing three pairs of legs, is obviously a fusion of three segments. Fusion is most complete in the head region. On the basis of the presence of appendages, and on embryological evidence, most investigators agree that the head is a fusion of six or seven primitive segments. It is frequently difficult to distinguish three separate body regions, particularly in immature insects. A case in point is the house fly larva (Fig. 2:2G), which has no distinct and hard head capsule and bears no appendages clearly separating the thorax from the abdomen. In specially adapted forms, such as adult female scale

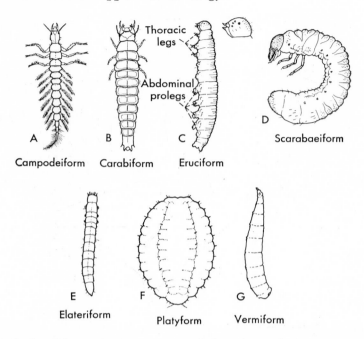

Fig. 2:2. The larval forms of insects. A, campodeiform, larva of an aquatic neuropteran, *Sialis;* B, carabiform larva of a carabid or ground beetle; C, eruciform caterpillar, the larva of a butterfly; D, scarabaeiform, white grub, the larva of a June beetle; E, elateriform, wireworm, larva of a click beetle; F, platyform, flattened larva of an uncommon moth; G, vermiform, a fly maggot. *Redrawn from Peterson,* Larvae of Insects, *1951, by permission Alvah Peterson.*

insects, legs may be absent and the thorax and abdomen more or less fused into a single unit.

The progenitors of modern insects possessed a pair of appendages on each segment, and this situation remains in many modern arthropods. In insects **segmented appendages** may now be present in a largely unmodified condition (**legs**), in structures highly modified for a particular function (**mouthparts** and **genitalia**), in a temporary condition (**abdominal appendages** of larvae—which may actually be secondary developments not homologous to true segmental appendages), or they may be entirely lacking. The primitive structure of an appendage, possibly homologous with the two-branched appendage of crustaceans, consists of a several segmented organ allowing movement in a number of directions. The leg, derived from seven segments, but with five segments commonly recognized, is an example of this highly articulated type of structure (Fig. 2:3).

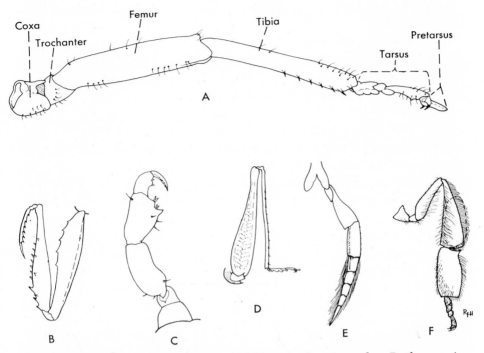

Fig. 2:3. Insect legs. A, commonly observed features of an insect leg; B, the grasping and heavily spined foreleg of a mantid, which preys on other insects; C, the clinching leg of a hog louse, adapted for seizing the hairs of its host; D, the long and well-muscled hind leg of a grasshopper, adapted for jumping; E, the swimming hind leg of a diving beetle; F, the hind leg of a honey bee, adapted for carrying pollen (outlined mass is the position of the pollen ball).

HEAD

The insect head is a hardened capsule with form and position generally dependent on the mouthparts and type of food ingested. A heavy head structure is found among insects with chewing mouthparts. Commonly this type of mouthparts has the head directed downward, as in grasshoppers; or the head protrudes forward as in predaceous insects which have the mouthparts developed for seizing prey in front of them; or mouthparts face down and backward as in the cockroach. Insects with piercing-sucking mouthparts do not require as heavy a frame for the attachment of large muscles that operate chewing mandibles and consequently may have smaller heads. Head position is again governed by location of mouthparts which may be directed forward in mosquitoes, downward in horse flies, and back-ward in aphids.

There are a number of quite constant features on the insect head. In addition to mouthparts there is a pair of antennae, a pair of compound eyes, and three, two, or no simple eyes (Fig. 2:1). The compound eyes are often prominent, in some cases comprising the major area of the head.

Antennae

Antennae are sensory structures located between or just below the compound eyes. In various insects they are known to perceive odors, humidity changes, vibrations, and wind velocity and direction. Their great differences in form may be a useful tool for separating families of insects. Two basal segments, the **scape** and **pedicel,** and a series of similar segments, the **flagellum,** are a common feature (Fig. 2:4). The simplest form

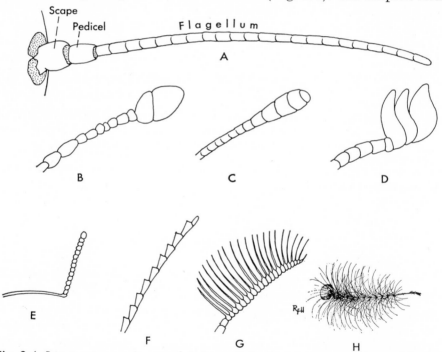

Fig. 2:4. Insect antennae. A, general features of the insect antenna, represented by the filiform of filamentous type such as that of the grasshopper; B, capitate or head-shaped form, such as that found on some adult clerid beetles; C, clavate or club-shaped, typical of adult tenebrionids or darkling beetles; D, lamellate or platelike, found in scarabaeid beetles such as June beetles; E, geniculate or elbowed, this example being moniliform or necklacelike at the end, as represented by some adult weevils; F, serrate or sawlike, typical of many cerambycid beetles; G, pectinate or comblike, especially developed in males of several moths; H, plumose or plumelike, the antenna of a male mosquito.

is the threadlike or filiform antenna. Variations include club-shaped or clavate, head-shaped or capitate, elbowed or geniculate, platelike or lamellate, comb-shaped or pectinate, and plume-shaped or plumose antennae.

Mouthparts

Mouthparts of insects are very specialized structures believed, with the exception of the labrum-epipharynx and hypopharynx, to be derived from segmental appendages. Types of mouthparts have developed to permit the ingestion of a variety of foodstuffs. Among separate groups of insects, mouthparts quite different in structure are adapted for utilizing the same type of food. Thus, although mosquitoes, horse flies, stable flies, and fleas all feed on blood, their mouthparts are very different from a structural standpoint.

The basic and most primitive type of mouthparts is the **chewing** type, such as is found in grasshoppers and beetles. Here is thought to be the pattern from which much more specialized types of organs of ingestion are derived. In order of appearance, from front to back, chewing mouthparts consist of a single **labrum** or upper lip, a pair of **mandibles** or jaws, a pair of **maxillae** or second jaws, and a **labium** or lower lip derived from the fusion paired appendages (Fig. 2:1). A single structure, the **hypopharynx** or tongue-like organ is located centrally. The inner surface of the labrum is referred to as the **epipharynx**, an area frequently membranous and inconspicuous. Sensory structures, the palps, functioning as organs of taste and smell, are found on the maxillae and labium. The mouthparts of adult weevils may superficially appear to be piercing and sucking in nature, but actually consist of an elongated portion of the head bearing chewing mouthparts (Fig. 2:5).

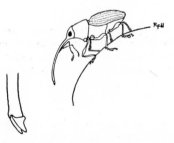

Fig. 2:5. A weevil. The snout of this beetle superficially resembles many piercing-sucking mouthparts, but note the enlargement of the tip showing chewing mandibles to be present.

There is a considerable variety of mouthparts not of the chewing type. In honey bees a combination of chewing and lapping structures is well suited for the gathering of solid and liquid food. Thrips suck up juices that ooze from plant tissues abraded by the points of short stylets. In stable flies a spongy though greatly reduced labellum on the tip of the labium, similar to that found on the proboscis of the house fly, contains hard rasping teeth.

Piercing-sucking mouthparts, developed for withdrawing fluids from animals and plants, are a very important type. They are best known in Hemiptera and Homoptera and in mosquitoes and horse flies, though they are present with different modifications in several other insect groups. The parts that enter tissue consist of a group of piercing stylets that work as a unit called a **fascicle**. There is generally a strong pumping mechanism developed in the foregut for removal of fluids, though in some aphids it has been demonstrated that pressure from within the conductive tissues of plants is sufficient to explain the rate of removal of sap.

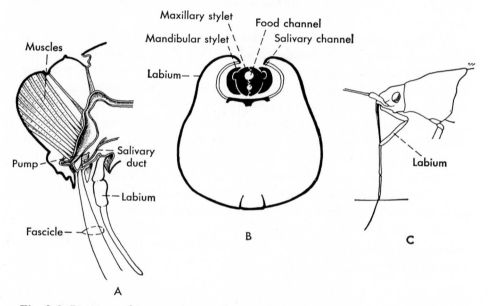

Fig. 2:6. Piercing-sucking mouthparts of Hemiptera and Homoptera. A, sectional view of cicada head, note well-muscled pump; B, cross-section of cicada mouthparts, note that the labium forms a sheath around the maxillary and mandibular stylets, which intermesh to form a fascicle; C, fascicle of milkweed bug entering tissue, the labium folding back and not piercing the surface. A, B, *redrawn from Snodgrass, Smithsonian Misc. Coll. 104, No. 7;* C, original.

Fluid is taken up by the Hemiptera and Homoptera through a food channel, and there is also a duct for ejection of salivary secretions (Fig. 2:6). Both passages are located between a pair of stylets developed from the maxilla. These **maxillary stylets** are grooved to slide on one another, and **mandibular stylets** outside of them are functionally connected by interlocking grooves, the four stylets comprising the fascicle. In some plant feeders the salivary fluids contain enzymes or toxins that can dissolve or distort plant cell walls. The tips of the stylets may have minute teeth for tearing tissues. The labium forms a jointed sheath that holds the other mouthparts when at rest; it does not enter the tissue during feeding.

Mouthparts of mosquitoes (Fig. 2:7) likewise consist of stylets, but their component parts are different from those of Hemiptera. The labrum-epipharynx and hypopharynx form a food channel. The posterior portion of this channel is closed by the hypopharynx which has a salivary duct. Salivary fluid contains anticoagulins that reduce the clotting of blood. The maxillae and mandibles form paired piercing stylets that may bear fine

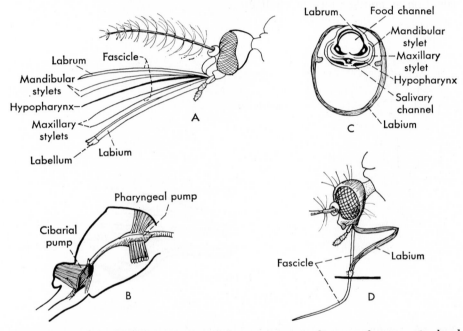

Fig. 2:7. Piercing-sucking mouthparts of the mosquito. A, diagram of a mosquito head in lateral view; B, sectional view of the head showing two well-muscled pumps for withdrawing blood; C, cross-section of mouthparts, indicating the fascicle lies within a sheath formed by labium; D, diagram of fascicle entering tissue, with labium flexed backwards. *Redrawn from Snodgrass, Smithsonian Misc. Coll. 104, No. 7.*

teeth at their tips. The labium has a lobed and soft sensory structure, the **labellum.** The labium is unjointed and serves as a container for the remainder of the mouthparts, flexing back during feeding and not actually entering into animal tissue. The relative position of the mouthparts in horseflies is similar, but the stylets are relatively heavier cutting structures, and the labium is large and fleshy, aiding in sponging up the blood.

Ticks and mites have mouthparts that are piercing and sucking in nature (Fig. 2:8). The main cutting structures are a pair of **chelicerae.** In ticks and many mites each chelicera is composed of a jointed appendage with pincer-like cutting structures. In some mites, such as the common red spider mite, the chelicerae are simple sharp stylets that serve as piercing organs. Ticks possess a distinct median structure called the **hypostome** which anchors in tissue through the presence of barbs that face downwards. An outer pair of segmented structures, the **pedipalps,** is also present. In ticks the pedipalps are grooved to fit protectively against the chelicerae; in mites the pedipalps may be toothed on their tips or may be modified to function as another pair of chelicerae.

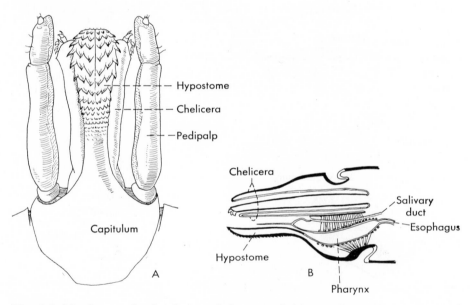

Fig. 2:8. Mouthparts of ticks. A, ventral diagram of the capitulum and mouthparts of an *Amblyomma* tick; B, section of the head of a tick, note pump for withdrawing blood. *A, original; B, after Snodgrass, Smithsonian Misc. Coll. 110, No. 10.*

THORAX AND ASSOCIATED STRUCTURES

The thorax serves as a center for bearing structures of transportation. It is composed of three segments which are usually fused into a single unit. Each segment bears a pair of legs, and the last two segments bear wings when both pairs are present. The thorax is often box-shaped, having a distinct dorsal surface (**notum**), ventral surface (**sternum**), and a pair of sides (**pleura**). Internally there may be strong skeletal ridges at the site of sutures, helping to brace the thorax and serving as sites of muscle attachment.

Legs

Insect legs are constructed on a similar basic plan. Though the leg is derived from seven segments, only five are clearly apparent. From point of attachment to the body, these five are the **coxa, trochanter, femur, tibia,** and **tarsus** (Fig. 2:3). The first two segments are generally short, the next two long, and the terminal segment small and usually subdivided into three to five subsegments. The tarsi may bear adhesive pads on their under surface, and a terminal portion called the **pretarsus** usually bears claws and pads. Legs have undergone amazing structural modifications to fit an insect's manner of living. Notable examples are the swimming legs of aquatic beetles, clutching forelegs of mantids, jumping hindlegs of grasshoppers, grasping legs of lice, and pollen-carrying hindlegs of honey bees (Fig. 2:3).

Wings

Though all insects do not possess wings, these are the only organs of true flight among invertebrates. Insects lacking wings, such as the Thysanura (silverfish) and Collembola (springtails), belong to a primitive group (**Apterygota**) that never developed flight structures. Other insects are or were winged (**Pterygota**), though many present-day forms lack these structures. Loss of wings has occurred in whole orders of insects, such as fleas and lice, through the development of a parasitic habit where travel by flying is not required and where superfluous structures such as wings might even be disadvantageous for remaining on a host. In some cases, for example the fly family Hippoboscidae, wings are present on some species but are absent on others. Thus the sheep ked is without wings, whereas a related hippoboscid attacking deer still possesses them. Some insects have lost their wings because they live in a very restricted environment such as under bark or in caves, and do not need to fly. Aphids are remarkable in that wingless forms are commonplace, but winged forms develop to enable them to change plant hosts.

Wings are located only on the second and third thoracic segments. Though some fossil insects have flat outgrowths on the first thoracic segment, these outgrowths were never functional wings, and it is uncertain whether they are homologous with the wings of the succeeding two thoracic segments. In Diptera, where a single pair of wings is used for flight, the second pair has been modified into small knobbed vibrating

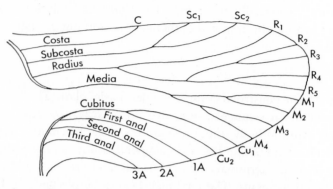

Fig. 2:9. The basic plan of wing venation in insect wings. This system is based on the tracheae that precede longitudinal veins in the developing wing pads of immature insects, and on a comparison of wing structure in fossil insects. In present day insects the number of longitudinal veins is generally reduced, and crossveins are common. *After Comstock, 1906,* A Manual for the Study of Insects, *by permission Cornell University Press, Ithaca, N. Y.*

guidance organs, the **halteres.** Beetles have the first pair of wings, known as **elytra,** modified as a tough protective cover playing no part in flight. The forewings of grasshoppers are quite leathery and are referred to as **tegmina.** In Hemiptera the basal half of the first pair of wings is leathery, the terminal half membranous and they are known as **hemelytra.** Wings may be fringed (thrips, Fig. 3:11) or may bear scales (Lepidoptera and mosquitoes).

A basic pattern of **wing venation** has been determined to underlie the system of veins in insect wings (Fig. 2:9). Each principal longitudinal vein is always preceded by a trachea during formation of the wing in a bud or wing pad. Using this evidence and that obtained by detailed comparison of wing venation in fossil insects, it has been possible to construct a hypothetical system. Despite great structural differences between orders and families of insects, it is possible to determine correctly homologies in wing veins and to apply universally accepted names to such veins.

Though there is much variation in wing size, shape, and structure, some generalizations are possible. The more advanced insects can fold their wings close to the body, giving them the advantage of being able to explore small spaces for obtaining food and to seek shelter from a harsh environment and many of their enemies. Insects that have a profusion of veins in the wings, particularly an excess of cross veins, are generally slow and unskilled flyers. The fast and highly maneuverable fliers tend to have wings that are relatively short and wide, with only a few well-developed longitudinal veins and reduced number of cross veins.

ABDOMEN AND ASSOCIATED STRUCTURES

In most insects the abdomen, composed of distinct segments, has maintained a flexible condition. As many as eleven segments are found, though this number is commonly reduced to about eight or fewer clearly recognizable ones. A large portion of the digestive tract, the reproductive system, and other vital organs are located internally. Quite possibly the supple nature of the abdomen is required for expansion as eggs enlarge in the female. Certainly flexibility is a requisite for copulating, ovipositing, and stinging.

With the exception of genital structures, segmental appendages of the abdomen are seldom retained in adult insects. Larvae may possess prominent abdominal appendages, and frequent transitory and vestigial structures of such a nature may occur during embryonic development. Thysanura have simple abdominal appendages called **styli** (Fig. 2:10), abdominal **prolegs** (locomotory structures) are present in caterpillars (Fig. 2:2C) and sawfly larvae, and abdominal appendages may be prominent respiratory structures in aquatic insects such as mayfly nymphs and aquatic Neuroptera (Fig. 2:2A).

External Genitalia

The external reproductive structures of insects are often highly specialized and complicated. This is particularly true of male insects, where special hardened structures, setae, and membranous areas have been found useful characters to distinguish otherwise similar appearing species. Typically there is an intromittent organ, the **aedeagus**, and paired **claspers** (Fig. 2:11).

Fig. 2:10. A thysanuran in which abdominal appendages called styli are evident. *From Snodgrass, Smithsonian Misc. Coll. 122.*

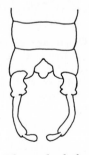

Fig. 2:11. The end of the abdomen in a male mayfly. The aedeagus is in the center, with claspers to either side.

Female insects frequently have well-developed **ovipositors** for placing eggs in a site that is desirable for egg survival (Fig. 2:12). Whole families possess characteristically distinctive ovipositors. Long-horned grasshoppers have long and flat, bladelike ovipositors, crickets have a round, lance-shaped structure. Some of the parasitic wasps are endowed with an amazingly slender and flexible ovipositor that can enter tough materials such as the bark of a tree. The ovipositors are generally composed of three or less pairs of valves that may fit together to form a single functional unit. The so-called ovipositor of insects, such as muscoid flies, is functionally such but structurally different; the end of the abdomen is developed into a narrow telescoping tube that can extend to form what is called more properly the **pseudovipositor.**

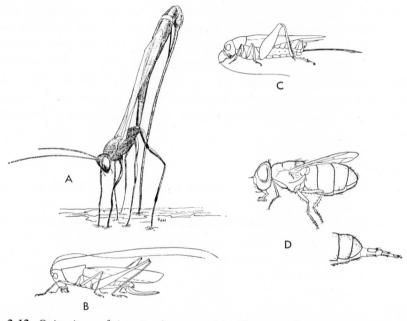

Fig. 2:12. Ovipositors of insects. A, a parasitic ichneumonid wasp starting to pierce the bark of a tree with its ovipositor, in order to reach a woodboring larva; B, the bladelike ovipositor as found in longhorn grasshoppers (Tettigoniidae); C, the lance-shaped ovipositor of crickets (Gryllidae); D, the pseudovipositor of a muscoid fly, in which the terminal abdominal segments are narrow and normally retracted.

INTEGUMENT AND DERIVATIVES

The outer covering of insects is one of their most distinctive features. It is this hard **exoskeleton** (Fig. 2:15A) that helps identify them as being related to the crustaceans, spiders, millipedes, and other arthropods. It may serve as armor, skeletal support for muscles and other internal organs, and as a barrier retarding loss of water from the body. Knowledge of the structure and composition of integument provides an understanding of how it is able to serve its many important functions.

The integument is composed of a sheet of living epithelial cells which produces the outer layers of cuticle (Fig. 2:13). This layer of epithelial cells, the **epidermis**, rests on a noncellular **basement membrane**. Occasional wax-secreting cells are found in the epidermis, as are cells which secrete a molting fluid that softens the old cuticle at time of molting.

Cuticle lying just above the epidermis comprises the major structural portion of the integument, separable into a relatively thin outer layer or **exocuticle**, and a thick and inner **endocuticle**. The exocuticle is composed of protein and the flexible and nearly indestructible substance called **chitin**, and here **pigments**, if present, are found. This portion is thinner, but generally harder and less flexible than endocuticle. The endocuticle is also composed of chitin and protein, but lacks pigment.

The outermost layer of integument, the **epicuticle**, is much thinner than exo- and endocuticle, but may be composed of several distinctly different layers. In forms having a highly specialized epicuticle there is an outermost cement layer or **tectocuticle**. The cement layer serves as an outer protective covering for a very thin wax layer which is an important barrier guarding against water loss. A **polyphenol layer** and an innermost **lipoprotein layer** composed of fatty substance in chemical combination with protein may be present.

The three regions above the epidermal cells are laid down in stratified

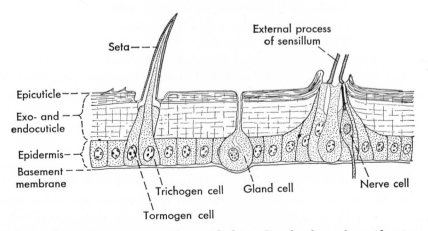

Fig. 2:13. The insect integument. The cuticle lying directly above the epidermis consists of the unpigmented endocuticle, and above it the thinner and pigmented exocuticle. *Redrawn and modified from Richards, 1951,* The Integument of Arthropods, *by permission University of Minnesota Press.*

layers. Vertical passages are found through these strata, in the form of **channels** for sensory nerve fibers and **ducts** of wax glands. In addition, in some insects, plentiful and extremely fine **spiral pore canals** of uncertain function traverse the cuticle vertically.

The complex chemical nature of integument is of great importance to insects. This structure acts as a selective barrier to the passage of liquids and gases. Consequently some groups of organic solvents and contact insecticides are more able to pass through the cuticle than others. Some exchange of respiratory gases takes place through the integument in terrestrial forms, but this feature is more important in aquatic insects that have the cuticle especially adapted for gas passage, it being formed in some cases into thin-walled gills (Fig. 2:14).

Prevention of water loss is particularly important to terrestrial insects. In soil inhabitants the wax layer is continually abraded in passage through soil particles. If these insects are placed in a dry atmosphere they soon undergo fatal loss of water. It is believed that the early Egyptians discovered the fact that dusts protect stored grain from the depredations of insects. More recently, very fine particulate materials, such as silica aerogel, that both abrade and adsorb the cuticular waxes of insects have been found to effectively and safely control household pests such as cockroaches and structural pests such as termites.

Because of the relatively rigid nature of the outer covering of insects, growth is accomplished by shedding or **molting** of the cuticle to form a new and larger covering. A definite series of changes takes place in the integument prior to molting. The epidermal cells become detached from the layers of cuticle, they generally increase in number by cell division, and they consequently become wrinkled and folded under the restricting outer layers. **Molting fluid**, containing enzymes that attack chitin and protein, digests away the thick endocuticle. The digested substances are resorbed and most likely are used in forming new exocuticle. Since the exocuticle and epicuticle remain virtually intact, there may be little or no externally visible change in the integument.

Internal pressure is used to split the old cuticle along the back. Muscular contractions of the body accomplish this, accompanied in terrestrial insects by the swallowing of air and in aquatic forms by the swallowing of water. A structurally weaker middorsal line is usually the site of fracture of the cuticle. The lining of foregut, hindgut, and tracheae is cuticular in nature and is consequently to be found attached to the shed cuticle.

Molting generally takes place in a rather secluded and protected site because the newly molted insect is quite immobile and defenseless, and because a short time is necessary for the new cuticle to become fully formed. The new integument is white or clear, but in forms possessing a dark cuticle the darkening takes place very shortly by a **tanning process** and by the deposition of pigment. The outermost protective cement layer of the epi-

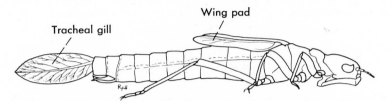

Fig. 2:14. The nymph of a damselfly (Odonata). During its growth stages this insect lives in water, respiration being aided by three leafshaped tracheal gills at the end of the abdomen.

cuticle is deposited soon after molt, and the thick endocuticle develops over a longer period. Expansion of the new covering takes place by the insect's swallowing air or water.

Hardening of the cuticle is called **sclerotization** and is largely due to the interaction of proteins with tanning agents which are polyphenols or quinones. It was previously believed that hardening was due to the presence of the polysaccharide chitin, but it is now known that the soft intersegmental membranes may actually have a higher proportion of chitin than the hardened areas.

The hard portions of the integument may be divided into distinct platelike areas called **sclerites.** These sclerites are separated from each other by flexible cuticle or by indented lines called **sutures.** Sutures are generally the external evidence of an internal ridge that serves as a point of attachment for muscles. In some instances, as in the head, the sutures may simply indicate a point of fusion between what were originally separate and distinct segments.

There may be a number of cuticular modifications in the form of hairs, spines, and spurs. The hairs are called **setae** and have a particular mode of formation (Fig. 2:13). There is a **trichogen cell** that secrets the seta and a **tormogen cell** that develops into the socket. A nerve cell may be closely associated with the seta (see Nervous System), and in some specialized instances the seta is hollow and serves as a channel for products produced by glandular cells. The seta itself is generally a simple, hairlike structure; but it may be plume-shaped in forms such as the honey bee, or in Lepidoptera and mosquitoes it may be modified in the form of a scale. **Spines** are composed of heavy inflexible outgrowths of the integument derived from several epidermal cells. **Spurs** are socketed outgrowths formed by several epidermal cells and are connected to the body wall by a joint. The outer surface of the cuticle may be made up of very fine structures, called **microtrichia,** which bear no direct relationship to the number of epithelial cells. In some insects a loose, powder-like substance may be present on the outer surface of the cuticle.

RESPIRATORY SYSTEM

Insects, for the most part, are small, active animals requiring a large amount of oxygen to support their metabolism. A butterfly at rest requires about three times as much oxygen per equivalent weight of tissue as a man under similar conditions. A butterfly in flight increases its oxygen consumption about 160 times, approximately 25 times the amount on an equivalent-weight basis required by a man running. It is obvious that insects, particularly flying insects, must have a rather efficient respiratory system that will provide them with the oxygen they require during periods of high activity. Since carbon dioxide diffuses through tissue about 25 times as fast as oxygen, the essential problem is to supply enough oxygen to tissues, the removal of carbon dioxide thereby being more or less automatically solved by the same system.

Oxygen is directly taken up by insect tissues without the aid of respiratory pigments such as hemoglobin (see Circulatory System for exceptions). The distribution system consists of main trunks called **tracheae.** These subdivide into fine **tracheoles** which ramify among the tissues, terminating in a **tracheal end cell.** The system also includes large **air sacs** found particularly among flying insects (Fig. 2:15D). The tracheal network is derived embryonically from the integument, and consequently it has an epithelium, like cuticular epidermis, that secretes an inner lining (**intima**) similar in chemical and structural constitution to the cuticle. The tracheal tubes are braced against collapse by the presence of spiral thickenings of the intimal lining called **taenidia** (Fig. 2:16B).

Air enters the tracheal system through specialized openings, called **spiracles,** on the sides of the thorax and abdomen. These spiracles are usually able to close, thus conserving water when air is not being taken up. Basically there is a total of ten pairs of spiracles, eight on the abdomen and two on the thorax. However, there may be a great deal of variation in number and location of spiracles in various insects. Thus the mosquito larva has a single

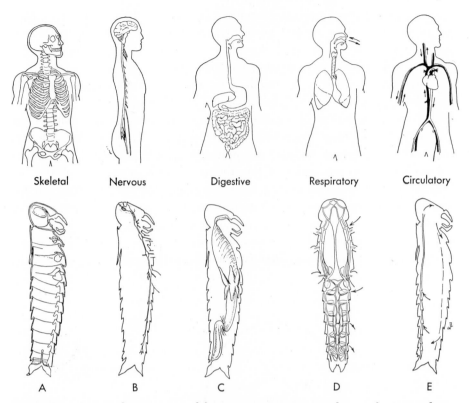

Skeletal	Nervous	Digestive	Respiratory	Circulatory
A	B	C	D	E

Fig. 2:15. A structural comparison of five important systems in the grasshopper and man. A, skeletal. Though the insect skeleton is largely external, note internal ridges and processes for the attachment of muscles. B, nervous. The nerve cord is located dorsally in man, ventrally in insects. The brain is proportionately larger in man. C, digestive. The gut is more complex in many insects. D, respiratory. In man the respiratory system is relatively small, with gases transported by the circulatory system; insects have tracheae and air sacs that ramify throughout the tissue to exchange gases directly with the tissues. Arrows indicate direction of flow of respiratory gases. E, circulatory. The insect circulatory system is much simpler than that of man, because it is not required to carry the respiratory gases. Arrows indicate direction of blood flow.

pair on an air tube near the tip of the abdomen; the pupa has a single pair on the thorax; and spiracles are located on thorax and abdomen in the adult.

Despite the ubiquitous nature of tracheae in insect tissue, an over-all plan can be discerned for the respiratory system (Fig. 2:16A). The spiracles are located along each side of the body. Short branches lead in from these to a principal **lateral longitudinal trunk.** Branches connect the lateral trunk of each side to a major **dorsal longitudinal trunk,** a **ventral trunk,** and a **visceral trunk** that is closely associated with the digestive and reproductive systems. Rather small tracheal commissures connect the system from each side in the dorsal and ventral body regions. This basic tracheal pattern is often modified, for example in larvae of many Diptera the dorsal longitudinal trunk is the main functional trunk.

A large insect, such as a grasshopper, can be seen to make rhythmic **respiratory movements** with the abdomen. In Coleoptera and Hemiptera these movements consist of a raising and lowering of the upper part of the abdomen; in Odonata, Diptera, and Hymenoptera the whole abdomen lengthens and shortens slightly; in Lepidoptera and Trichoptera the upper and lower surfaces and sides of the abdomen move in and out. Close observation of the spiracles during such movements shows that they do not open or close simultaneously. Experiments have shown that respiratory movements place pressure on the air sacs resulting in a **directional flow of gas** due to the control of spiracular opening. Thus in the grasshopper air enters the two thoracic and first two abdominal spiracles and leaves the

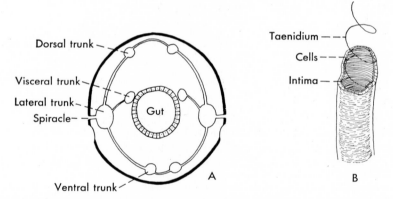

Fig. 2:16. The respiratory system. A, diagrammatic cross-section of the insect body to show the location of spiracles and main longitudinal tracheal trunks; B, structure of the trachea showing the spiral thickenings called taenidia which brace the inside of the tube.

body through the posterior abdominal spiracles (Fig. 2:15D). In flight, or other extreme activity, all spiracles remain open in order to allow maximum uptake of oxygen. Rhythmic opening and closing of spiracles are under control of the central nervous system, but individual spiracles can be made to open in response to an increased local concentration of carbon dioxide.

One particular advantage of the tracheal respiratory system of insects is that it is well suited for such diverse environments as the air, soil, the internal environment of hosts, and water. Obviously a number of special adaptations are necessary to permit adequate oxygen consumption under these circumstances. In very small insects inhabiting wet environments, such as some Collembola and some parasitic larvae, spiracles are actually lacking, and sufficient gas exchange takes place by **general diffusion** through the body surface. Aquatic insects obtain atmospheric oxygen directly, or by diffusion of oxygen dissolved in water through a gill. A gill may have an abundance of tracheae (**tracheal gills** of damselfly nymphs, Fig. 2:14), or be filled with body fluids (**blood gills** of Chironomid larvae). Gills are often utilized only during high activity and stress, sufficient gas diffusion normally taking place through the general body surface. Oxygen may be obtained through a **physical gill** consisting of an air bubble held at spiracular openings. The bubble supplies oxygen in greater amount than is originally entrapped because the nitrogen present in the initial air bubble (about 80 per cent) diffuses more slowly than oxygen. Consequently, oxygen is replenished in the bubble by diffusion of dissolved oxygen from water into the oxygen-depleted bubble. Notonectid bugs and diving beetles are typical examples of insects breathing with the aid of an air bubble.

It is evident that a very efficient aquatic respiratory system could be developed if there were some means of perpetually maintaining a gas film around an aquatic insect into which dissolved oxygen from the surrounding water could diffuse and be utilized. A few aquatic Coleoptera and Hemiptera have achieved this ideal condition through a structural development of the epicuticle called a **plastron.** The plastron consists of extremely fine hairs or scales on the integument surface that permanently hold a thin film of gas to the body. Gaseous connection is maintained between this trapped film and the spiracles, making this system functionally similar to a tracheal gill.

A further adaptation to aquatic respiration consists of obtaining oxygen from air-filled cells of aquatic plants. The best known example occurs among mosquito larvae in the genus *Mansonia.* Here the air tube at the terminal end of the body is modified to form a piercing organ. Some internal parasites of insects maintain a connection with a trachea of their host.

DIGESTIVE SYSTEM

In its simplest form the digestive system of insects consists of a tube that is rather poorly differentiated into foregut, midgut, and hindgut (Figs. 2:15C and 2:17). Closer examination reveals that there is generally a valve, the **stomodaeal** or **cardiac valve,** that separates foregut and midgut. The midgut and hindgut are separated by a **proctodaeal valve.** There is a tendency for the system to be structurally simple in larvae and more complicated in adult insects.

There are often marked modifications of major sections of the digestive tract. In many insects that imbibe liquids one or more reservoirs, often connected with the foregut by only a narrow duct, have evolved for storage of food. The midgut, particularly in some sucking insects, can consist of as many as four structurally distinct regions and may possess a large

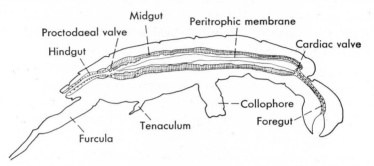

Fig. 2:17. The simple digestive system of a collembolan or springtail. Gastric caeca or other outpocketings of the gut are lacking, and simple valves separate the three gut regions. The peritrophic membrane is clearly visible. Malpighian tubes, found in most insects at the junction of mid and hindgut, are lacking in this insect. *After Folsom and Welles.*

number of accessory outgrowths or chambers (Fig. 2:18). The hindgut is generally rather simple with the terminal portion enlarged. In dragonfly nymphs the hindgut is modified into a large and complicated structure which also serves in respiration and locomotion, as well as its usual functions. In many Homoptera the hindgut loops back alongside of the midgut to form a special filter chamber where liquids and excess food components of plant sap directly bypass the absorptive areas of the midgut.

The **foregut** functions primarily as a storage organ, but may perform a limited grinding and mixing of food. A distinct and narrow **pharynx** and **esophagus** may be present at the anterior end, followed by the main storage area or **crop,** and the latter may be followed by a muscular, gizzard-like area called the **proventriculus.** In the proventriculus there may be a fine screen of hairs to prevent the return of solid food particles (honey bees), or there may be heavy, toothlike structures that serve both in a screening and grinding capacity as in many chewing insects. The internal lining of the foregut is similar to cuticle, often bearing setae, spines, or roughened ridges. No digestive enzymes are produced in the foregut, though limited digestion takes place in some cases from carbohydrate-splitting enzymes already mixed with the food and originating in the salivary glands, or by the regurgitation of enzymes from the midgut. Most food constituents are not absorbed through the wall of the foregut, though fats apparently can be.

The **midgut** is the main site of digestion and absorption. At its anterior end, just behind the cardiac valve, it often possesses a series of outpocketings, the **gastric caeca** (Fig. 2:19), that are areas of high digestive enzyme activity. Similar outpocketings occur in other locations in many insects, but though these are also referred to as caeca, they appear to be chambers possessing microorganisms that aid in digestion. Digestive enzymes are richly present throughout the midgut, but, as has been shown for the larvae of flesh flies, these enzymes and areas of absorption may be limited to specific regions of the gut, or even to specific cells. Contents of the midgut are generally more alkaline than contents of the foregut. The acidic or basic nature of these contents, of importance in the function of digestive enzymes, may be limited to quite specific regions.

There is no cuticle-like armature or lining connected with the cells of the midgut. However in many insects, particularly those partaking of solid food, a semipermeable structure, the **peritrophic membrane,** lies between food and the surface of the epithelial cells (Fig. 2:17). This membrane is perpetually replaced, passing on with the food into the hindgut. It may be formed as a continuous tube, like a sausage casing, by specialized cells in the region of the stomodaeal valve (fly and mosquito larvae), or in successive layers by cells comprising the entire midgut (grasshoppers). The peritrophic membrane is extremely thin, composed of chitin and protein as is cuticle, and permits passage of liquids and solutes while retaining fragments of food.

The **hindgut** is generally a rather simple tube which enlarges to form the rectum at its terminal end. At the anterior end, near the juncture of the proctodaeal valve, the **Malpighian tubes** empty their excretory products. A thin, internal, cuticle-like lining occurs in the hindgut, generally without spines or other conspicuous armature. Often there are structures called **rectal pads** or **papillae.** The function of these structures is not entirely settled, though in terrestrial insects they appear to be a device for conserving water by removing it from the gut contents and returning it to the body.

Insects possess a wide variety of **digestive enzymes.** These enzymes split

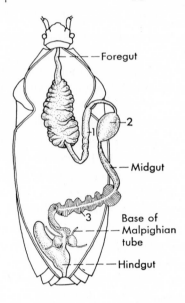

—Foregut

—2

—1

—Midgut

3

Base of
—Malpighian
tube

—Hindgut

Fig. 2:18. Digestive tract of a hemipteran, the squash bug. There are several outpocketings of the gut, and the midgut can be seen to consist of three distinct segments. *After Breakey.*

large molecules of foodstuffs into smaller molecules that are then able to pass through the gut wall to be utilized. As in most animals, there are enzymes for the common foods, namely **proteases** for protein, **carbohydrases** for carbohydrates, **lipases** for fats. In insects that undergo complete metamorphosis, there is usually a quite different type or activity of the digestive enzymes between larvae and adults, reflecting differences in the diets of these stages. Species that eat food possessing a large proportion of nutrients in the form of solutes, such as plant sap or blood, generally have a smaller variety of enzymes than those species that partake of solids which require greater enzymatic breakdown.

Symbiotic microorganisms in the insect often aid in breaking down foodstuffs which are particularly hard to digest. These symbionts benefit from their life in the insect by having an ideal environment for their growth. The host provides ample food and ideal conditions of moisture and oxygen tension. Symbionts in turn, in the process of breaking down largely indigestible food materials into simpler molecules, benefit their insect host by providing it with usable nutrients that are in excess of their own requirements or are by-products of their metabolism. Striking examples are symbiotic Protozoa that utilize wood cellulose in the gut of termites, and bacteria that aid in the digestion of beeswax ingested by larvae of the wax moth *Galleria.* The widespread possession of symbionts by insects as a group indicates a cooperative association with microorganisms that has taken place over a long period of time.

NUTRITION

The nutritional requirements of all insects are not adequately known. Detailed studies have been made primarily on insects feeding on grain and other stored products. Much more information is needed for insects that feed on blood, plant sap and leaves, wood, and inside other insects. In many cases where information is lacking, accurate analyses have not been possible for want of synthetic diets with nutrient elements which are acceptable in taste and consistency to the insect in question.

Where known, the nutritional requirements of insects are found to be similar to those of other animals. The require the same ten **amino acids** found essential for protein synthesis in mammals. **Carbohydrates** are required for energy and can usually be supplied in the form of sucrose or glucose. However, unlike mammals, the only vitamins required are the water soluble ones of the **vitamin B complex** and, for some plant-feeding species, **ascorbic acid. Sterols** are essential in small amounts, and either those of animal or plant origin appear to be satisfactory. **Fats** and **oils** are not considered to be an absolute requirement, though a few plant-derived oils seem beneficial in synthetic diets prepared for plant feeders. The **minerals** required by insects can be supplied by several salt mixtures found satisfactory for the diet of vertebrates.

There is little doubt that those insects which can thrive on foodstuffs lacking in essential nutrients are aided by the presence of symbiotic microorganisms. These symbionts may be in the digestive tract (see Digestion), or in specialized bodies called **mycetomes,** believed to have been originally derived from the gut. **Symbionts** are often yeasts or yeastlike organisms that provide B complex vitamins. They are typically found in blood-, wood-, and sap-feeding insects. Symbionts in the fat body of cockroaches have been well studied, and symbiotic yeasts from some beetles have been cultured on artificial media.

The majority of plant-feeding insects confine their attacks to a single plant or to a few closely related plants. Chemical analyses of plant leaves indicate that in general they all contain rather similar nutrients. It is now evident that particular plants may be attacked by a limited group of insects because of the presence of substances that are attractive or the absence of substances that are repellent, and not because such plants are particularly well suited from a nutritional standpoint. Apparently these **attractants** and **repellents** have developed in plants during their close and prolonged evolutionary association with insects and mites. Undoubtedly plants and insects have thus greatly influenced each other to contribute to the evolutionary changes resulting in the present complex of plant-insect relationships. Entomologists have speculated that plants developed repellent or toxic substances which prevent excessive attack by insects, but that very specific factors peculiar to a group of plants may be the signposts which indicate to an insect a satisfactory host plant. For example the mustard oils of cabbage and other cruciferous plants have been demonstrated to be the key attractive factors for the diamond back moth and some other pests of crucifers.

EXCRETION

The organs of excretion in insects, functionally equivalent to kidneys in vertebrates, are the **Malpighian tubes** (Fig. 2:19). These tubes are located at the juncture of mid- and hindgut. They have a hollow center which empties into the digestive tract, but the remainder of each tube is a closed structure that generally lies free in the body cavity. In some insects, notably certain Coleoptera and Lepidoptera, the distal end of the tube is attached to the surface of the rectum, but the tubes are not open at this end and they do not discharge their contents into this region of the gut. The tubes may lie passively in the body cavity, or may undergo writhing movements due to the presence of muscle strands. There is great variation in the number of tubes present in various groups of insects. Aphids, Collembola (Fig. 2:17), and some Thysanura lack these structures, two to six tubes are typical of the majority of insects, and the honey bee and some Orthoptera possess as many as 150. If an exceptionally large number of tubes are present, this is due to the branching of a much lesser number, so that only a few ducts actually enter the digestive tract.

Malpighian tubes take waste products in solution from the insect blood or hemolymph. Usually the soluble nitrogenous wastes are converted into highly insoluble **uric acid** (frequently in association with **inorganic salts**) which is discharged into the hindgut. The excretion of uric acid is a water-conserving mechanism, water returning to the hemolymph through the wall of the tube near its base. The uric acid mechanism of conserving water is typical of some other animals such as reptiles and birds; but by way of contrast, man and other mammals largely excrete urea in solution in water. Insects that do not need to conserve water because they inhabit a wet environment excrete their nitrogenous wastes in soluble form. Thus blow

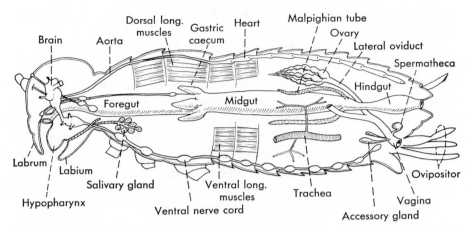

Fig. 2:19. The major internal structures of insects. *After DuPorte, 1959,* Manual of Insect Morphology, *by permission Reinhold Publ. Corp., N.Y.*

fly maggots and many aquatic insects excrete **ammonia** directly, and insects feeding on moist foods generally excrete some **urea.**

Initially the nitrogenous waste products are formed away from the excreting organs, being transported to these organs by the blood. Recently it has been shown that the enzymes necessary for formation of uric acid and other nitrogenous waste products are found in high concentration within the **fat body** of several insects. We have then a situation that operates in a manner similar to nitrogenous excretion in vertebrates. Vertebrates produce urea and other waste products in the liver while insects produce uric acid in the fat body; in both the waste products are released to the blood; in vertebrates the kidneys filter them out, while in insects the Malpighian tubes do this job.

A certain amount of what is termed **storage excretion** takes place quite commonly in insects. In some cases uric acid in solid concretions is packed in specialized **urate cells** in the fat body (cockroaches, Collembola). Blow fly maggots have a pair of posterior Malpighian tubes for normal excretion, but have an interior pair which store granules of **calcium carbonate** and **calcium phosphate.**

CIRCULATORY SYSTEM

The circulatory system provides a means of chemical exchange between organs. In insects it is composed of a fluid, blood or **hemolymph,** containing **blood cells;** a dorsal pulsatile tube, the **heart** (Fig. 2:19), which functions to circulate the blood; and **accessory pulsating structures** which may be present to aid circulation.

In insects the circulatory system is referred to as an **open system.** In man this system is termed a closed one because blood is completely channeled from heart to arteries, to capillaries, to veins, returning to the heart. In insects the heart and forward extension of it, called the **aorta,** are the only real blood vessels (Fig. 2:15E). Blood is released forward in the region of the head (Fig. 2:25), passes more or less freely through the body, returning to the heart through openings along its side called **ostia.** **Dorsal** and **ventral diaphragms** are present to help channel the blood along the upper and lower body surfaces, but these are frequently missing or poorly defined. Accessory pulsating organs may be present at the base of appendages such as the legs, and a membrane may divide tubular appendages to distribute blood in one side and out the other (Fig. 2:20).

The blood of insects is not an effective carrier of oxygen to tissues. Respiratory pigments are for the most part lacking, though larvae of some chironomid midges and horse bots (both Diptera) contain **hemoglobin.** In the former this hemoglobin is in the fluid portion of blood and not in specialized cells such as the red blood cells or erythrocytes of vertebrates. In the latter the hemoglobin is in special fat cells. In these insects the hemoglobin serves as an emergency reserve during a shortage of oxygen in the surrounding medium rather than as the normal means of respiration.

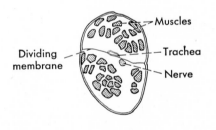

Fig. 2:20. Cross-section of a femur, leg of the pomace fly *Drosophila.* The dividing membrane does not continue all the way to the tip of the appendage, and thus permits the outward flow of blood on one side and its return on the other. *From a photomicrograph by Miller, in Demerec, 1950,* Biology of Drosophila, *by permission John Wiley & Sons, Inc., N.Y.*

Blood cells contain a nucleus and are so variable that they are difficult to classify into groups. As many as ten classes of blood cells divided into 32 types have been described for the larva of a noctuid moth, but most authorities recognize five or six classes. Many of the blood cells are phagocytic, and may be particularly useful in engulfing disintegrating tissue fragments during metamorphosis. There is no doubt that blood cells play some part in growth and metamorphosis, since the ratio of blood cell types changes between molting intervals. The cells may function in clotting at wound sites, in some cases serving as the center of formation of the clot.

It is important that blood maintains an osmotic pressure optimal for the body cells. The correct ratio of sodium and potassium is also necessary for proper nerve and muscle function. The **osmotic pressure** of insect blood is largely due to amino acids, whereas in mammals inorganic chlorides are of greater importance. In insect blood there is also a higher amount of phosphates than in that of mammals. In vertebrates a relatively high ratio of sodium to potassium in blood serum and a high potassium content of body cells provide proper ion balance for nerve impulse propagation and muscle activity. The same relationship holds for carnivorous insects, but in many of the forms whose ancestors were plant feeders, or who are themselves plant feeders, the amount of blood sodium relative to potassium is very low. A **low blood sodium level** is found in many Lepidoptera, Hymenoptera, Phasmidae or walking sticks, and plant feeding Coleoptera. Though nerve propagation has not been explained in these cases (see Nervous System), it is notable that in all instances the body cells maintain a high concentration of potassium. Evidently the partially permeable nerve sheath helps to maintain the ionic environment around the nerves at levels similar to those required for vertebrate nerve function.

MUSCULAR SYSTEM

Although the muscular system of insects is complex, practically all the body muscles of adults, nymphs, and more primitive larvae can be homologized throughout the various orders. However, the musculature of high holometabolous larvae has yet to be compared successfully in detail with that of other insects. Within a species, the muscle groups in each segment are often similar. Origin and insertion of muscles are modified by the motion requirements of the insect in question. Differences in muscular patterns are largely the result of loss of muscles from an over-all "original" arrangement. The total number of muscles is often very large, and as simple an organism as a moth larva may have roughly three times as many muscles as are found in man.

All insect muscles are of the **striated** variety. They may be divided into a skeletal and visceral group according to whether they move the body wall and its appendages, or are associated with internal organs. The **skeletal muscles** are clearly recognizable as separate bundles of fibers with a definite origin and insertion. **Visceral muscles** consist of the circular and longitudinal muscles of the gut and the sheaths of interconnecting muscle fibers associated with the reproductive system and ventral diaphragm. The striated nature of insect muscle is quite like that of vertebrates.

Four subdivisions of muscle type are possible, chiefly based on the location and nature of nuclei and muscle sheaths. Particularly noteworthy are the **giant mitochondria** observable in the indirect flight muscles. These structures are sites of high enzymatic activity required for energy transformations in this very active group of muscles.

REPRODUCTIVE SYSTEM

Insects are **bisexual,** that is there are males and females. Reproduction without benefit of males occurs (**parthenogenesis**), but usually the combination of sperm and egg is required to produce a new individual. The reproductive system consists of paired gonads with the common duct from each combining into a median duct that leads to the outside of the body. In conjunction with these ducts are found specialized glands and organs for storage of spermatozoa.

Each **ovary** consists of a group of egg tubes or **ovarioles** (Fig. 2:21A). The ovarioles are loosely grouped together, held in position by a **terminal ligament.** The number of ovarioles varies from one in some aphids to several hundred in other insects. Each ovariole is a tube of epithelial cells contain-

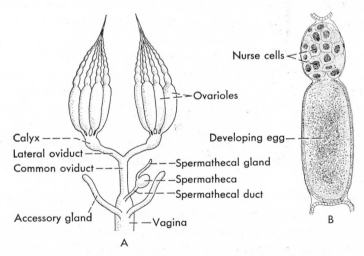

Fig. 2:21. The female reproductive system. A, diagram of the whole system; B, section of an egg follicle in the honey bee, showing nurse cells associated with the developing egg. A, *after several investigators; B, original.*

ing eggs in varying stages of development. This tube is divided into chambers, with primordial germ cells or **oogonia** at the narrow end, and eggs in various stages of development in succeeding chambers. Enlargement of the eggs is primarily due to the formation of yolk granules which are a food reserve. In many insects **nurse cells** are associated with the eggs to aid in their development (Fig. 2:21B). By the time the eggs are fully developed the epithelial cells of the ovariole have deposited a shell or **chorion.** It is the imprint of these cells that leaves the sculptured pattern readily visible on the chorion after oviposition (Fig. 2:22). At one end of the egg an opening through the chorion, the **micropyle,** permits entrance of the sperm.

Fertilization generally takes place after an egg leaves the ovary. The egg passes down the **lateral oviduct** and enters the **common oviduct.** As it passes the duct of the sperm storage organ or **spermatheca,** fertilization takes place. In some insects entrance of the sperm can be controlled by the female, for example, in the honey bee. The unfertilized eggs develop into drones and fertilized eggs into workers or queens. Sperm can be maintained for very long periods in the spermatheca of female insects. A small gland sometimes located on the spermathecal duct may produce secretions responsible for the longevity of sperm (Fig. 2:21A).

The male intromittent organ is generally placed during copulation in that portion of the median oviduct called the **vagina.** However in many insects a special chamber for deposition of spermatozoa, the **bursa copulatrix,** is developed to one side of the median oviduct. There is particularly clear

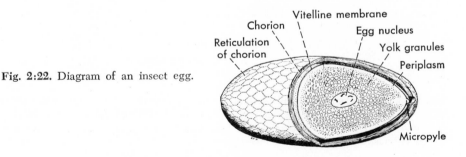

Fig. 2:22. Diagram of an insect egg.

Chorion
Vitelline membrane
Reticulation of chorion
Egg nucleus
Yolk granules
Periplasm
Micropyle

separation in the higher Lepidoptera, where the external opening of the bursa is on the segment in front of that bearing the median oviduct. In this case a **seminal duct** is present to permit sperm to enter the true reproductive system of the female, and ultimately to reach the spermatheca.

There are usually **accessory glands** that discharge their contents into the median oviduct. These are known as **colleterial glands** if they produce a sticky substance which glues the eggs to objects. In the cockroach they produce protein and a tanning substance which form the hard brown cover for the **ootheca,** which is an egg packet containing several eggs (Fig. 17:12). In grasshoppers the functional glands are extensions of the upper portion of each oviduct, and should be referred to as **oviducal glands.**

The gonad of the male consists of a few to several tubular **testicular follicles** (Fig. 2:23A). These follicles are enclosed in a sheath, and frequently both **testes** are enclosed in this sheath as a single unit. Each follicle is a tubular sheath of epithelial cells containing male germ cells in varying stages of development. At the upper end are the primordial germ cells or **spermatogonia,** followed by packets of sperm in succeedingly advanced stages of development. The **spermatozoa,** each possessing a head and flagellum, are located at the lower end of the follicle (Fig. 2:23B).

Ducts lead from the testes to outside the body wall (Fig. 2:23A). From each testis a duct, the **vas deferens,** unites to form a median **ejaculatory duct.** There is frequently a **seminal vesicle,** an enlargement of each vas

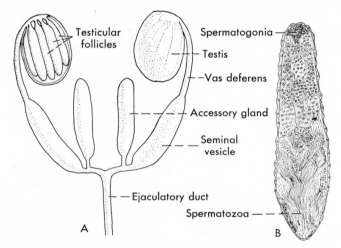

Fig. 2:23. The male reproductive system. A, diagram of the whole system; B, section of the testicular follicle in a grasshopper showing the growth and differentiation of germ cells into mature flagellated spermatozoa. Note that groups of developing cells are contained in packets. A, *after several investigators; B, original.*

deferens, which serves as an area of sperm storage. **Accessory glands** are usually present, and though their function is uncertain it seems likely that they produce seminal fluid for additional volume and for the nutriment of spermatozoa.

Physiological aspects of the reproductive system in insects are not well known. All experimental evidence shows that this system does not produce sex hormones affecting secondary sexual characteristics, such as are found in vertebrates. Hormonal mechanisms seem responsible for initiating the development of eggs and, in some social insects, for preventing their development. There is also some means of controlling numbers of eggs, and excess eggs undergoing development can be resorbed if sufficient food reserves are lacking. Food reserves for egg formation may be derived from nutrients recently consumed, or from reserves of fats and proteins already present within the body.

NERVOUS SYSTEM AND SPECIALIZED RECEPTORS

The central nervous system of insects differs in location from that of mammals. The main **nerve cord** is located in the ventral body region beneath the gut, and the **brain** is situated in the head above the digestive tract (Figs. 2:15B and 2:19). It is quite apparent that the ganglionic masses of the central nervous system have fused to varying degrees. Both the brain and the **subesophageal ganglion** consist of three fused ganglia. Generally there are three thoracic ganglia and as many as eight abdominal ganglia, yet in many insects there is a further migration and fusion of ganglia toward the front of the body. This condition is characterized in

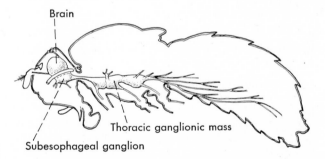

Brain

Thoracic ganglionic mass

Subesophageal ganglion

Fig. 2:24. Central nervous system of a fly, *Drosophila.* Though the thoracic and abdominal ganglia consist of a fused mass, their separate origin is indicated by the segmental nerves passing to the segments of thorax and abdomen. *After Miller, in Demerec, 1950,* Biology of Drosophila, *by permission John Wiley & Sons, Inc., N.Y.*

Hemiptera and muscoid Diptera (Fig. 2:24) for example, by a large thoracic ganglionic mass that innervates the thorax and abdominal segments. Segmental nerves branch from each ganglion into the muscles and other body structures of their segment. Even when ganglia migrate anteriorly, or fuse in a mass, it is possible to determine their segmental origin by tracing the peripheral nerves that connect to them.

A system associated with the digestive tract, the **stomatogastric system,** is located on the foregut (Figs. 2:19 and 2:25). From the third or tritocerebral portion of the brain a pair of connectives attaches to the **frontal ganglion** on the esophagus. A short and relatively thick nerve, the **recurrent nerve,** runs under the brain from the frontal ganglion to connect with the **occipital** or **hypocerebral ganglion** in back of the brain. The occipital ganglion has a single nerve or pair of nerves connecting with a single or paired **ingluvial ganglion** on the upper wall of the crop. Finer nervous connections are made between the ganglia of this stomatogastric system and the gut, certain mouthparts, salivary gland, and aorta.

A **sympathetic nervous system** is frequently present in the form of median nerves, being particularly well developed in caterpillars. These nerves may be a simple connection between suboesophageal and succeeding ganglia of the nerve cord, or may branch in each succeeding segment to the lateral body areas. Where present they connect with the spiracles, though spiracular innervation is supplied by lateral nerves from ganglia of the nerve cord in forms lacking median nerves. The terminal ganglion in the abdomen innervates the posterior portions of the gut and the reproductive system.

The enzyme and ion interchanges occurring in insect **nerve transmission** resemble the situation found in vertebrates. **Cholinesterase** and **acetyl choline** are usually considered necessary for transmission across the synapse, which may be inhibited by drugs and poisons affecting vertebrates. **Sodium ions** and **potassium ions** are likewise of primary importance in propagating

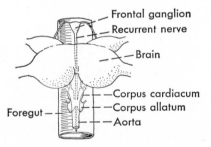

Frontal ganglion
Recurrent nerve
Brain
Corpus cardiacum
Corpus allatum
Foregut
Aorta

Fig. 2:25. The brain and associated endocrine structures of a cockroach. The termination of the aorta and the anterior portion of the stomatogastric nervous system are also indicated. *After Cazal.*

an electrical charge along the axon, though the specific amounts or ratios may differ from vertebrates. Where drugs or toxicants do not affect the nerve transmission of insects to the same degree as in vertebrates, it is likely that differences in the nerve sheath are responsible for permitting or preventing these substances from reaching the site of activity. This nerve sheath or **neurilemma** is a thin structure of chemically combined fat and protein molecules that are oriented and have characteristics similar to those of the myelin sheath of vertebrate nerves.

Sensory receptors

There is a wide variety of specialized sensory structures that serve to acquaint the insect with conditions surrounding it, and with internal conditions. **Sensory hairs** on the body surface are quite similar in structure to ordinary setae, but with the addition of one or more **sensory neurones** attaching to some point on their inner surface (Fig. 2:13). Similarly there are other sensory structures on the body surface which resemble sensory hairs in internal structure, but in place of setae are found thin walled pegs, domes, or pits. Such receptors can serve to detect stimuli of taste, smell, touch, motion, temperature, or humidity. Frequently these sensory organs are concentrated on structures in close contact with the external environment such as palpi, tarsi, antennae, or cerci.

Insect eyes

The eyes of insects merit special mention, not only because of their elegant structure, but because the visual ability of some insects is second only to that of advanced vertebrates. In addition to the high degree of visual acuity which may be present, other characteristics make them particularly suited for vision during flight. In discussing the visual organs both simple eyes or ocelli, and compound eyes must be considered.

As many as three **dorsal simple eyes** or **ocelli** (Fig. 2:26A) are present in insects, though these structures are frequently reduced to two or none. Structural details suggest that these are not organs of particularly acute vision. There may be a few or several receptor units behind a single corneal area, with no clear separation of such units to permit division of the image received. Thus it appears that the ocelli are suited for determining levels of light intensity, and it has in fact been shown that these structures are used to modify over-all behavior of the insect based on amount of light present. **Lateral simple eyes** or **stemmata** are found in many larvae (Fig. 2:2C). These also are not considered to be organs of acute vision. Some insects without eyes, fly maggots, for example, may distinguish between high and low light intensity by means of a general light sensitivity of the body surface.

The **compound eye,** as its name implies, is made up of a large number of separate receptor units (Fig. 2:26). Each unit, an **ommatidium,** is quite a complex structure. The ommatidium can be divided into the outermost optical elements consisting of a clear **cornea** and a light-gathering device called the **crystalline cone.** In back of these the **retinula cells,** which are sensory neurones, form a rod-shaped structure possessing an internal **rhabdom** or light receptor unit. Photochemical reactions must take place within the retinula, but pigments undergoing such reactions have not been isolated.

The compound eyes of many nocturnally active insects are able to adapt to conditions of high and low light intensity. **Adaptation of compound eyes** takes place through the migration of pigment granules within cells that form a sheath around each ommatidium. In dim light the pigment migrates towards the outermost part of the eye, leaving the retinula receptor elements uncovered. Under these circumstances a maximum quantity of light

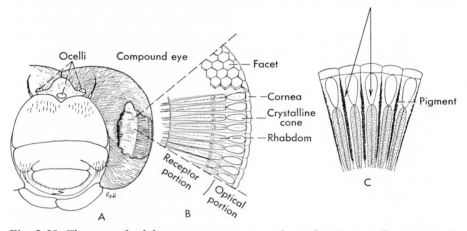

Fig. 2:26. The eyes of adult insects, as seen in a dragonfly. A, over-all position and size of ocelli and compound eye; B, enlargement diagrammatically showing how each receptor unit or ommatidium of compound eye is located beneath a hexagonal facet. Many cells within the ommatidium are deleted for simplification; C, pigment in the light-adapted position permits light, indicated by arrows, to reach only the receptor units or rhabdoms in direct line with the ommatidium.

can reach the retinula since rays of light entering the optic portion at an angle can impinge on the bared receptors of adjacent ommatidia. Pigment ensheaths the receptors during periods of high light intensity, and therefore the retinula cells only receive light entering the optic portion directly in front of their own ommatidium (Fig. 2:26C). While the dark adapted eye has increased sensitivity because of maximal light activation of each receptor unit, it seems obvious that under such circumstances vision must be less acute.

A number of features enhance the **perception of movement** by insects. This ability is particularly advantageous in flying and in predaceous insects.

Like man, many insects can distinguish a maximum of about fifty flickers of light per second as separate events, yet the honey bee can distinguish a maximum of 300 flickers per second. In flying insects the **facets** (cornea) are arranged much closer together in portions of the eye most necessary for vision in flight. By this means more receptor units are stimulated per unit of time during movement, and finer distinctions of movement are possible.

FLIGHT

Flight is perhaps the most distinctive feature of insects, since they are the only invertebrates capable of true flight. Not only are they able to fly, but the best insect fliers are as good or better than birds at this skill. Some insects, such as the house fly and other higher Diptera, have extreme maneuverability in flight; others, such as locusts, can sustain flight for prolonged periods of time and for distances of hundreds of miles.

A definite series of events take place in an insect for the **initiation and maintenance of flight.** Loss of tarsal contact with a surface can be shown as the stimulus initiating flight movement of the wings in a great many species. There are certain signals that indicate to an insect that flight can be economically continued; thus an airstream must continuously hit receptors on the front part of the head in locusts, and various flies will sustain flight for much longer periods in such an air stream. When the velocity of the air stream becomes too high, equivalent to a loss of forward motion in flight, wing movements cease. The mosquito relies on a moving pattern being visible to the bottom portion of the eye, indicating forward movement, in order to maintain flight. Under experimental conditions flight can be maintained in flies and bees until the energy reserves in the form of sugars or glycogen are depleted, and can be started again by feeding them sugar. The prolonged flight of locusts has been shown to be maintained by the utilization of fats rather than sugars.

Flight direction is controlled by varying the angle of the wings. The basic up and down movement of wings is provided by muscles extending between the top and bottom of the thorax thereby depressing it and providing the upstroke, and by longitudinal muscles (indirect flight muscles) that compress the thorax lengthwise to provide the downstroke or power stroke (Fig. 2:27). Other muscles, attached to small plates in the wing base, cause changes in the angle of the stroke. In flies the second pair of wings are modified into the knobbed halteres which serve as vibrating gyroscopic guidance organs.

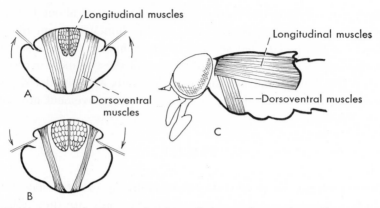

Fig. 2:27. Diagram of the direct and indirect flight muscles in a horse fly, in cross-section and as seen on the median plane. A, upstroke, caused by contraction of the dorsoventral muscles; B, down or power stroke, caused by the contraction of the longitudinal muscles; C, relationship of large flight muscles in the right half of the thorax. *Based on findings of several investigators.*

Perhaps the **frequency of wing beat** is most remarkable. This varies from about five beats per second in butterflies, to over 1,000 beats per second in a ceratopogonid fly. Muscle contracts in response to an impulse from the stimulating nerve, and a ratio of one contraction of flight muscle per impulse can readily be demonstrated in insects with a relatively slow wing beat. But in fast-flying insects the flight muscle may contract as many as forty times in response to a single nerve impulse, thus making very fast wing beats possible. This extremely fast type of wing beat is typical of Diptera, Hymenoptera, Coleoptera, and some Homoptera.

HORMONAL MECHANISMS

The role of hormones in controlling growth of insects is being rapidly clarified. Much exciting research has determined the endocrine structures involved, the role they play, and to some extent the chemical nature of hormones produced. The interplay of hormonal events is best understood in growth and metamorphosis.

Endocrine structures operative during growth and metamorphosis are associated with the head and thorax (Figs. 2:25 and 2:28). A **trigger mechanism** is required to initiate growth, and this may be supplied by circumstances normally taking place in the life of an insect. Thus the trigger mechanism for nymphal growth in the blood-sucking bug *Rhodnius* is distension of the gut after feeding; the hibernating pupa of a species of moth requires cold temperatures to trigger completion of development; mosquitoes require extension of the gut by a blood meal to cause eggs to develop. These triggering stimuli are relayed to the brain where nerve cells called **neurosecretory cells,** begin secretion of a substance that can be stained or otherwise demonstrated. Prior to molting the neurosecretory substance builds up in a storage organ in back of and beneath the brain, the **corpus cardiacum,** where it is released into the blood to further affect other endocrine structures.

Molting and growth are controlled by hormones released from the **corpora allata** near the corpus cardiacum in the head, and the **prothoracic glands** in the region of the thorax. The corpora allata release **juvenile hormone** which maintains the immature form of an insect during early molts. The corpora allata degenerate or stop secretion at the end of immature growth resulting in an adult insect in the next stage. Miniature adults can

Fig. 2:28. Corpora allata and prothoracic glands in the larva of a honey bee. *After Formigoni.*

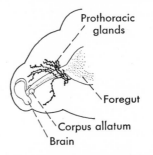

Prothoracic glands

Foregut

Corpus allatum

Brain

be developed by removal of the corpora allata in early growth stages. Strangely enough, the juvenile hormone produced by the corpora allata may again be present in relatively large amounts in insects after the adult condition has been achieved and this suggests that this hormone has still other as yet incompletely determined functions in the insect.

Hormones causing molting and differentiation of tissues are produced by the prothoracic glands. Differentiation into the adult does not take place in larvae and nymphs in spite of molting because of the presence of juvenile hormone from the corpora allata, but once the adult condition is achieved the prothoracic glands disappear. An exception occurs in Thysanura (silverfish) and Collembola (springtails) which retain the prothoracic glands and molt as adults. Two hormones involved in growth and differentiation have been isolated from insects in pure form, and juvenile hormone has been obtained in highly purified form.

The corpora allata, so important in maintaining the larval or nymphal condition in early stages of growth, have been found to be important in adult insects as well. They appear to control metabolism of insects in general, and specifically to control the development of eggs in female insects. Thus implantation of corpora allata from a mosquito that can develop eggs without feeding on blood into one that normally requires blood results in egg development in the host without the necessity of a prior blood meal.

There are other hormonal substances, **ectohormones** or **pheromones,** that appear particularly important in controlling the growth of social insects. The queen honey bee produces a substance (or substances) which in sufficient concentration inhibits workers that ingest it from producing eggs and building queen cells. At least one source of this substance is the mandibular glands of the head. Similar growth effects have been found between ovarian-inhibiting substances in insects and in crustaceans, and it seems likely that similarities in hormonal mechanisms exist between insects and other invertebrates. Indeed there even appear to be substances in certain mammalian tissues that have biological properties akin to those of the juvenile hormone of insects!

STRUCTURE AND FUNCTION IN MITES AND TICKS

External form

Mites and ticks have a body consisting of two regions, the **cephalothorax** and the **abdomen.** There are variations of this basic plan, particularly in mites, whereby the body may appear to consist of a single unit, or the abdomen subdivided into segments. There may be a distinct headlike region, but this is not structurally similar to the head of insects. This area, bearing the feeding organs, is called the **gnathosoma** (jaw body). When it is definitely developed into a headlike structure such as in ticks, it is frequently called the **capitulum** (Fig. 2:8A). Often there is a distinct demarcation of the body between the second and third pair of legs (Fig. 2:29). The anterior portion is then called the **proterosoma** (preceding body), the posterior portion the **hysterosoma** (behind body).

There are normally four pairs of legs in adults. The form emerging from an egg is called a larva and has but three pairs of legs. At the first molt a hindmost pair of legs is added, making a total of four pairs, and the immature form is now called a nymph. Three nymphal stages are thought to be typical of mites, though there are many variations. The nymphs may closely

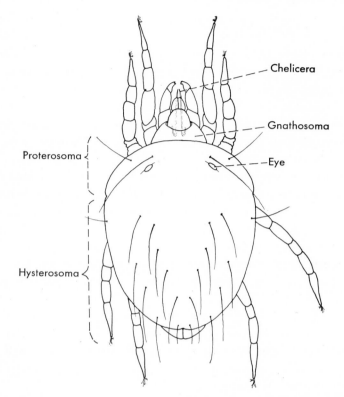

Fig. 2:29. General external form of a tetranychid or spider mite. *After Malcolm.*

resemble adults, or differ markedly in appearance. Adult mites are especially variable in form, frequently being adapted for their mode of existence. Many parasitic mites have developed bizarre adaptations in form, and the phytophagous eriophyid or blister mites have become narrow and elongate with only two pairs of legs (Fig. 4:5A). The legs are usually six segmented, but subdivision to form seven segments occurs, and fusion may result in as few as two segments.

The integument, similar to that of insects, is composed of several layers secreted by a sheet of epidermal cells. The chemical nature and microstructure of these layers is largely unknown. There is often a very rich sculpturing of the cuticle which is distinctive enough to be of aid in classifying mites. The integument may have areas that are thicker, forming sclerites or plates. Setae are often limited to specific locations, and they vary so widely in form as to be of prime importance in classification. Special sensory setae are common, especially on the ends of appendages.

Internal form and function

For reasons of brevity, description of internal structures and their functions will be limited to mites. Knowledge in this area is extremely meager, and can be supplemented by reference to Baker and Wharton's *An Introduction to Acarology*. The internal organization of the two-spotted spider mite, *Tetranychus telarius* (L.), is illustrated (Fig. 2:30), not because it is particularly typical, but it is the most widely encountered mite of agricultural importance.

The digestive system consists of fore-, mid-, and hindgut. Each of these areas may be relatively simple, or further subdivided into definite regions. In the two-spotted spider mite the spot markings are due to the presence of dark food in each side of the midgut being readily visible through the integument. Though detailed studies on the digestive enzymes present in all forms are lacking, limited determinations indicate mites have enzymes similar to those of insects, and certainly the wide variety of foodstuffs utilized leads one to believe that they possess the necessary enzymes.

Excretion takes place by means of a variety of structures. There are usually excretory tubes in connection with the hindgut. Certain of the cells composing the digestive tract are excretory in function, and a gland on the coxa of the leg appears to be excretory in function. The main nitrogenous waste product is **guanine.**

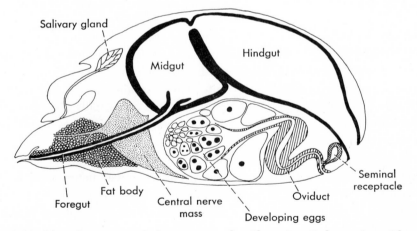

Fig. 2:30. Internal anatomy of the two-spotted spider mite. *Redrawn from Blauvelt.*

The circulatory system is extremely simple. A simple heart is located dorsally in only a few mites. In others there is a free circulation of blood consisting of a clear hemolymph with cells.

The muscles, as in insects, are striated. They are located so as to perform the required movements, and there are muscles within appendages which cause their movements, and between appendage and body causing changes in body position.

Reproduction takes place by sexual means. The males possess a pair of testes, with ducts leading outward much as in insects. Females have a pair of ovaries, or a single ovary, and ducts and glands similar to those in insects are present. Sperm is frequently transferred in a sperm packet or **sperma- tophore.** There are several species of mites for which males are unknown, and parthenogenesis occurs frequently in many species that have males.

The nervous system appears to be relatively simple. Ganglia of the central nervous system have fused into a mass that surrounds the foregut. From this mass nerves radiate to the eyes, mouthparts, legs, and interior organs. Motor fibers connect with the muscles, and sensory fibers lead from the often elaborate external sensory setae to the central system. Eyes are often lacking, and when present they are simple in structure. They are prob- ably only sensitive to changes in light intensity, and do not form clear images. From one to five eyes may be present on the upper anterior por- tion of the body.

The respiratory system is quite variable in form. Tracheal tubes with branching tracheoles may be present for internal distribution of gases, but these are often lacking. External breathing openings, the **stigmata,** are important structures for identifying mites. These are characteristic in their form and location. The tracheae ramify from stigmata, or there may be a number of sacs leading from the stigmata into the tissues.

Hormonal mechanisms in ticks and mites are virtually unknown. Since molting occurs it seems likely that this event, as in insects, is under hormonal control. The diapause forms of some mites are known to be controlled by day length, and in such cases it is likely diapause is mediated by hormonal events.

Selected References

Baker, E. W., and G. W. Wharton, *An Introduction to Acarology* (New York: Macmillan, 1952).

Hughes, T. E., *Mites or the Acari* (London: University of London, The Athlone Press, 1959).

Pringle, J. W., *Insect Flight* (Cambridge (Eng.) University Press, 1957).

Roeder, K. D., *Insect Physiology* (New York: Wiley, 1953).

Snodgrass, R. E., *Principles of Insect Morphology* (New York: McGraw-Hill, 1935).

Wigglesworth, V. B., *The Physiology of Insect Metamorphosis* (Cambridge (Eng.): University Press, 1954).

———, *The Principles of Insect Physiology* (New York: Wiley, 1950).

Chapter 3 | INSECT GROWTH | *Robert F. Harwood*

The growth of insects, both as individual organisms and as exploding populations, is a subject of interest and much speculation. The uninitiated observer is amazed by a sudden appearance of insects where previously they seemed lacking or unimportant. It is small wonder that insects were used as evidence for man's erstwhile belief in spontaneous generation, the development of living things from inanimate substance.

Great variation in type of development of insects never ceases to interest even the trained entomologist. Differences in the body shape and behavior of various stages of an insect may make it hard for one to realize without detailed study that a single organism is being observed.

We shall discuss the growth of the individual insect as an orderly process which proceeds in a set pattern. Growth is a continuous increase in size, but in insects this increase is accompanied by wide variations in form.

THE EGG

Insects develop from eggs which are usually deposited by the female in places favorable for their survival. In assessing insect populations the potential present in their eggs is often overlooked. For the most part they are small, often being one half millimeter or less in their greatest dimension. Furthermore **egg sites** are frequently hidden from view. For example, many leafhoppers, long-horned grasshoppers, and weevils deposit their eggs inside plant tissues. Here they remain moist and out of sight. Locusts, crickets, and a number of beetles deposit their eggs beneath the surface of the soil. Parasitic insects, particularly parasitic wasps, may lay eggs inside their host.

Eggs that are laid in water are seldom noted. Some caddisflies and damselflies oviposit in plant stems beneath the water surface. Dragonflies and mayflies may drop their eggs on the water while flying. Gelatinous egg masses are deposited in water by several midges and caddisflies.

Some insects place their eggs in quite conspicuous locations. The prominent egg masses of mantids that have been glued to a twig are particularly noticeable. Lacewings attach single, small, light green eggs to foliage by means of a slender stalk. Many true bugs lay eggs that have bizarre shapes and gaudy colors in conspicuous masses.

The external **appearance of insect eggs** is extremely diverse (Fig. 3:1). They range in shape from spherical to elongate. Outgrowths for their attachment to objects or for respiration may be present, as well as ridges and caplike structures. They may be held in a case called an **ootheca** (cock-

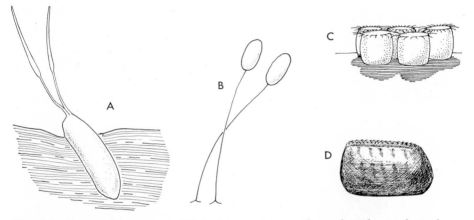

Fig. 3:1. Shapes of insect eggs. While insect eggs are often relatively simple in form, the egg of the water scorpion *Ranatra* (A) is in plant tissue with respiratory filaments in the surrounding water; B, lacewings lay eggs attached to surfaces by a long stalk; C, eggs of stink bugs and other Hemiptera are frequently bizarre in appearance and laid in groups; D, the cockroach lays its eggs in a packet or ootheca, each surface indentation indicating the position of an egg. A, *after Hungerford; B, C, D, original.*

roaches), or in a so-called **egg pod** (grasshoppers). A fine reticulation of the surface of the chorion or shell can usually be seen at high magnification. This surface structure is the imprint of cells lining each egg chamber in the ovary, left there as these cells secreted the chorion.

The **numbers of eggs** produced by females of different species are extremely variable, and are related to the chances for survival to the adult stage or to the production of large colonies in the case of social insects. Among parasitic forms that spend their entire life on a host, there is little danger of loss during development. Accordingly the sheep ked produces a single offspring at a time, and the total number in a lifetime is small.

Parasitic flies that deposit their eggs on vegetation or other sites where there is only a slight change of contact with a host lay over 1,000 eggs. The female of sexual forms in aphids may lay only a single egg directly onto the host plant. Among the social insects the queen honey bee can lay more than 2,000 eggs a day during periods of peak production, and over a million eggs during a five-year period of productivity. Perhaps 100 to 200 eggs can be cited as the usual range for number of eggs produced by most insects. Some parasitic Hymenoptera, notably Braconidae and Chalcididae, solve the problem of attrition by a phenomenon called **polyembryony.** Whereas normally a single individual develops from each egg, in these insects early divisions within the egg result in as many as a hundred embryos which grow into the same number of individuals (Fig. 3:2).

When fully developed within the ovary (Fig. 2:22) the egg is ready for fertilization. The shell or **chorion** at this time is completed and consists mainly of tanned proteins as in cuticle. Further subdivisions into layers of varying chemical composition often occur. The chorion is a relatively impermeable structure and therefore has an opening or openings for the entrance of sperm, called the **micropyle** if single, or **micropylar pores** if

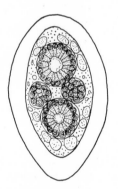

Fig. 3:2. Polyembryony. Section of an egg of *Platygaster vernalis* Myers, a wasp that parasitizes the Hessian fly. Four embryos in an early stage of development are visible. *After USDA.*

multiple. The yolk granules may be surrounded by a very thin **vitelline membrane,** lying beneath and next to the chorion. A limiting vitelline membrane cannot be demonstrated in some insect eggs. Yolk granules, as well as fat globules, fill the egg in a matrix of clear protoplasm. The granular material is usually lacking in the periphery, forming a poorly defined clear outer area termed the **periplasm.** Prior to fertilization the nucleus of the egg (**female pronucleus**) may be situated in almost any position.

Among insects the act of mating usually takes place quite some time before fertilization of the eggs. This is possible because sperm is stored inside the female, generally entering the egg only at the time of egg-laying or oviposition. Longevity of sperm within the female may be remarkably long, evidence suggesting that the period may be as much as five years in queen honey bees. In such cases sperm stored in the spermatheca of the female become active only when they pass through the spermathecal duct to fertilize a passing egg. The female may be able to selectively prevent entrance of sperm into the egg. Drone bees are produced from eggs that develop without the stimulus of sperm. The drone thus has the genetic constitution of its mother, the queen, a fact which has been used in apicultural research to get sperm for artificial insemination from drones produced by queens that have particularly desirable characteristics.

FERTILIZATION OF THE EGG

Ordinarily, as with most forms of animal life, the development of a new insect begins with the process of fertilization. The combining units are called **eggs** (produced by female) and **sperm** (produced by male). Combination of egg and sperm starts the process of normal cellular division, the development of a new individual. This new individual is a combination of two units each possessing half the usual number of chromosomes. The resultant body cells of the newly developing insect then have the normal double or diploid number of chromosomes and contain genetic components of each parent.

Exceptions to the process of fertilization just outlined occur in many cases. Insects are known for which no males exist, and in a large number of species, though males are usually required, the females can produce offspring in their absence. This development of young without benefit of males is termed **parthenogenesis.** Several species of cockroaches can produce offspring without males, and some weevils (notably white-fringed beetles) have been found to have females only. An intermediate condition exists, such as in aphids, where summer offspring are produced in the absence of males, but normal sexual reproduction occurs in the fall. Whether we refer to the production of young with or without males, the process is **sexual reproduction.** The egg is an element essential to sexual reproduction, and it matters little whether a sperm is required to initiate development or whether this can be induced by other means.

Fertilization usually takes place as the egg traverses the common oviduct past the point where the spermatheca enters it. Following fertilization the micropylar openings seal off to prevent the loss of water from this region after the egg leaves the body of the female. The egg nucleus (female pronucleus) generally shifts toward the micropylar end to join the sperm nucleus (male pronucleus). Several extra sperm cells may enter the egg, but these disintegrate.

EARLY ORGANIZATION AND TOPOGRAPHY

Before fertilization, and with the first cell divisions, the insect egg often shows evidence of **presumptive organization** into the regions of the developing individual. Eggs in the oviduct are lined up in the same relative position as the mother, there being a presumptive head end, right and left sides, and top and bottom. At the first few divisions following fertilization the resultant cells may be committed toward development of structures or body regions of the forming insect. Investigators have shown that limited cellular destruction during early development by such means as ultraviolet light or a needle prick will cause specific defects in the insect that emerges from the egg. In some cases early injury causes defects in the larva and not the adult, later injury affects adult structure and not the larva. Thus the mechanism controlling organization appears different for larval and adult structures.

Following fertilization the first cell divisions typically take place near the center of the egg. Since there is a relatively large amount of yolk present the cells divide by **meroblastic cleavage,** a situation where the whole egg does not divide but rather divisions are limited to a local region. This meroblastic cleavage is common in animal eggs possessing much yolk, the usual situation in insects. The dividing cells migrate to the periphery to form a single layer of cells, the **blastoderm.** A region on the ventral surface consists of cells that are thicker, and makes up the **ventral plate** or main area of embryonic development (Figs. 3:3A,B,C).

A second layer of cells forms beneath the surface of the cells comprising the ventral plate, a process called **gastrulation** (stomach formation). This inner layer of cells develops by (1) the infolding and separation of a trough on the midventral line (Figs. 3:3D,E,F), (2) or by a lateral overgrowth and fusion of cells at the lateral margins of the ventral plate, (3) or by simple division of cells in the midventral area in a manner leaving an inner sheath of cells. The two layers of embryonic tissue formed are the raw material from which organs and organ systems are derived. The outer layer or **ectoderm** will form the outer covering and derivatives in the embryo. The inner layer or **mesoderm** will form many of the inner structures of the developing individual. (See p. 73 for a discussion of endoderm.)

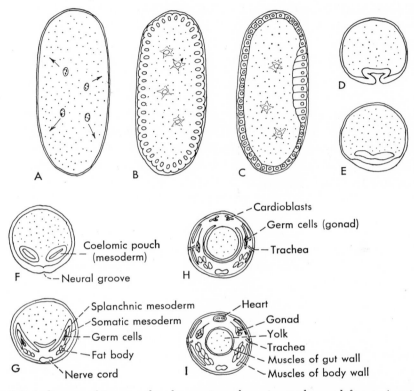

Fig. 3:3. A diagram of insect embryology, extraembryonic membranes left out. A, migration of the first cleavage nuclei to the surface; B, blastoderm with vitellophag cells remaining in the yolk; C, formation of the ventral plate; D, E, F, formation of mesoderm; G, H, I, development of internal organs. *Redrawn from Hagan, 1951,* Embryology of the Viviparous Insects, *by permission Ronald Press Co., N. Y.*

Segmentation of the embryo, a subdivision into distinct body parts, becomes apparent soon after the development of ectoderm and mesoderm. This separation is indicated by thickening of the mesoderm tissue in the middle of each segment, and by its remaining thin at the margin between segments. More distinct evidence of segmentation soon occurs by growth of the head region and appearance of appendages (Fig. 3:4). The front portion of the head forms two enlarged lobes, and just behind these lobes appendages delimiting five more segments of the head appear, making a total of six segments comprising the head. Behind the head three slightly wider segments with larger appendages form the thorax. A maximum of twelve narrow succeeding segments indicates the extent of the abdomen. Appendages may form on the abdominal segments, remaining on the individual after hatching or disappearing during further embryonic growth.

The developing embryonic area becomes covered by the lateral blastoderm layer which forms two **extraembryonic membranes.** In the simplest mode of formation this occurs by a direct growth of blastoderm over the embryo. The outer membrane closest to the chorion is called the **serosa.** Within the serosa the membrane covering the embryo alone is called the **amnion.**

In most insects a radical migration of the embryo into the yolk forms the amnion and serosa (Fig. 3:5). During later development the embryo returns to the surface. The process of involution of the embryo and its subsequent return to the surface is called **blastokinesis.** The function of blastokinesis is uncertain, since shifts in position of this magnitude hardly

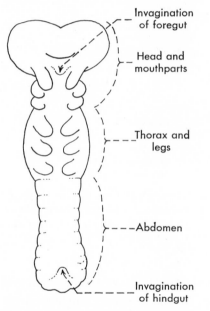

Fig. 3:4. General diagram of the external appearance of an insect embryo when body segmentation is just completed.

Fig. 3:5. Diagrammatic representation of the extraembryonic membranes of an insect, formed by involution of the embryo into the yolk.

seem necessary to develop the extraembryonic membranes. In some insects, notably the grasshopper, embryonic growth ceases for the duration of harsh seasonal conditions such as winter's cold or summer's drought, with the embryo remaining inside protected by both membranes. When favorable climatic conditions resume, growth recommences and the embryo returns to the surface. In this case it appears that blastokinesis is a mechanism for protection of the embryo.

The extraembryonic membranes undergo a variable fate in different insects. In the majority of cases, as the lateral margins of the embryo expand after blastokinesis, the membranes are pushed toward the dorsal surface and are finally engulfed within the body where they disintegrate. In some instances the serosa remains next to the chorion, develops a fine structure similar to insect cuticle, and therefore is a potent barrier preventing loss of water. This serosal membrane may adhere to the chorion and be readily mistaken for a vitelline membrane, as seems to be the case in mosquito eggs. In grasshoppers the serosa is retained as a loose bag around the nymph at time of hatching. The new grasshopper nymph wriggles in this bag to the soil surface, and there sheds it in what amounts to a second hatching (Fig. 3:8D,E).

THE DEVELOPMENT OF ORGANS AND ORGAN SYSTEMS

Formation of the ectoderm and mesoderm sets the stage for the **differentiation** of these tissues into the structures that develop into the insect which emerges from the egg. Let us follow the further development of ectoderm tissue into definite organs.

Ectodermal derivatives

The central nervous system is derived from ectoderm. Shortly after the mesodermal layer has differentiated, two **neural ridges** form, parallel to one another making a central trough, the **neural groove** (Fig. 3:3F). This groove sinks below the surface and forms a tube of tissue, the **nerve cord,** that separates from the surface ectoderm which then closes back over it. The nerve cord remains in this relative position (the ventral surface of the developing animal) further forming its various subdivisions as the body regions become distinct. Accordingly this cord eventually forms the main ganglionic complex that comprises the **brain,** a ganglionic mass that becomes the **subesophageal ganglion,** three **thoracic ganglia,** and eight **abdominal ganglia.** The nerve cord does not remain a single tube, but separates into two **connectives** that span the space between ganglia along its whole length.

As we have seen, the nerve cord and ganglia are derived from a groove in the midventral region of the ectoderm. In further development **efferent nerves** pass from the segmental ganglia to the muscles and glands within their respective segments. What of the **afferent nerves** that receive stimuli of touch, taste, smell, light, and sound for transmission to the central nervous system? These also develop from ectoderm, but as specialized cells within the integument. At appropriate areas a special cell such as a sensory hair, or receptor organ such as the eye, grows inwardly to form a nerve connecting with the nearest ganglion of the central nervous system.

The **tracheal tubes** of the respiratory system also develop as invaginations of the ectoderm. These invaginations take place along the lateral areas of the animal in a segmental region. From the first invaginations the longitudinal tracheal trunks interconnect, and further ramifications of the tracheae develop to form a complete respiratory system by the time of hatching.

Ectoderm also forms the anterior and posterior portions of the digestive tract. As the head and posterior end of an embryo become distinct, near each extremity an invagination develops into the **foregut** and **hindgut** (Fig. 3:4). The ectodermal derivation of these regions of the gut is later apparent by their structural resemblance to the integument, as they possess an epithelial layer which forms an inner cuticle-like lining. Although there is some question about the formation of **Malpighian tubes,** it is generally conceded that they are formed from the anterior end of the hindgut.

Other relatively minor structures are derived from ectoderm. The terminal portion of ducts connecting the reproductive system with the outer surface of the animal are formed by invaginations of this tissue. Much glandular tissue, such as the **salivary glands,** is also ectodermal in origin.

Mesodermal derivatives

The mesoderm develops into many of the important internal structures of insects. After separating from the ectoderm, this layer soon divides into right and left halves. Each solid block of tissue hollows out and extends laterally, forming an inner and outer sheet of tissue on each side. The outer layer is the **somatic mesoderm,** which forms the **skeletal muscles** of the body wall and appendages. The inner layer is the **splanchnic mesoderm,** which forms the **visceral muscles** associated with the digestive tract and reproductive system (Figs. 3:3F–I).

The circulatory system is derived from somatic mesoderm. Advancing upper margins of the somatic layer fuse to form the tubular **heart** and **aorta** in the middorsal line (Figs. 3:3H–I). **Blood cells** are initially derived from cells remaining in the hollow formed between the inner and outer layers of mesoderm. Further blood cells are produced by division of these primordial cells. Cells of the **fat body** are first noted in the same region as the primordial blood cells.

Most of the reproductive system develops in association with the somatic mesodermal layer. Though the primordial germ cells may have been formed in the first few cellular divisions, the gonads (ovaries and testes) which develop from these come to lie in the abdomen against the upper and inner surface of the somatic mesoderm (Figs. 3:3G–I). Germ cells, namely spermatozoa and ova, develop from these primordial germ cells, as do nurse cells in the ovary when they are present. The enveloping tissue which forms **sperm tubes** and **ovarioles,** and the first portion of the **ducts** leading from them, is derived from mesoderm.

Endodermal development

Vertebrates and many other higher animals have a well-defined inner layer of embryonic tissue, the **endoderm.** There is some question whether such a tissue is present in insects. If it is present, it forms the **midgut.** At the very first divisions after fertilization, a few cells scatter within the yolk. These cells aid in consuming the nutritive reserves in yolk, and accordingly are called **vittelophags** (yolk eaters). In some insects groups of cells among the vitellophags are thought to migrate at the appropriate time to connect with the advancing midgut and hindgut to form the central tubular section of midgut. In other cases cells forming the midgut are first noted to be present at the advancing ends of the foregut and hindgut, and presumably have come to lie in this position after early derivation from mesodermal cells. For this reason the mesoderm tissue at time of formation can also be called the mesentoderm layer. At any rate it seems likely that the midgut is of different origin from portions of gut in front and in back of it. The fully developed midgut differs in structural details from digestive tract at its either end since it lacks a well-defined, cuticle-like lining. The midgut is developed in the embryo around the time of completion of the lateral margins of body wall, the remaining yolk being contained in this portion of digestive tract at the time of hatching.

HATCHING

When embryonic development is finished there are a variety of **hatching mechanisms** which aid a new individual to emerge from the egg. For example in Hemiptera there may be a point of structural weakness in the chorion forming a cap or **operculum** which breaks off at a distinct line of fracture (Fig. 3:6C). In some insects, and notably in grasshoppers, a pair of glandular structures called **pleuropodia,** which resemble appendages of the first abdominal segment in the mature embryo, secrete enzymes which partially destroy the surrounding membranes (Fig. 3:6B). Most mature embryos increase their internal pressure by swallowing surrounding fluids and air.

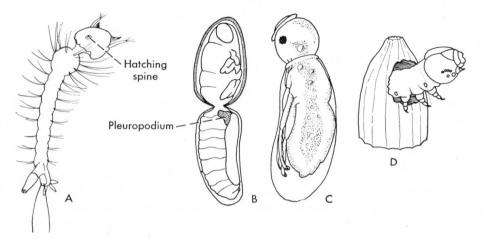

Hatching
spine

Pleuropodium

A

B

C

D

Fig. 3:6. Mechanisms of hatching. A, the mosquito larva has a spined egg-burster for applying pressure to the egg shell at the site of fracture; B, in grasshoppers a secretion from the glandular pleuropodia digests the inner portion of the shell just before hatching. If the egg is tied off in the middle, the portion lacking pleuropodia is not digested; C, many insect eggs have a cap portion which is popped off during hatching. An emerging nymph of the bed bug, *Cimex*, swallows air to expand the body; D, many insects, such as the larva of the European cabbage butterfly, simply chew through the egg shell. *B, after Slifer; C, after Sikes and Wigglesworth; D, after Essig, 1947,* College Entomology *by permission The Macmillan Company, N. Y.*

Such internal pressures may swell the head, or evert **special vesicles** which in turn fracture the chorion. In many insects a **hatching spine** is present on the head for cutting the chorion, or for applying the pressure at one point (Fig. 3:6A). In Lepidoptera the new larva simply chews its way out of the shell (Fig. 3:6D).

There is a wide variation in external structure of insects at the time of hatching. Some are legless, some are quite inactive, others possess well-developed organs of locomotion and actively seek food. Such major differences in development and activity suggested to early investigators that insects hatching with poorly developed locomotory structures had really emerged prematurely, and subsequent growth consisted of a sort of delayed embryonic development. Active and well-developed insects were thought to have completed embryonic growth by hatching time. It was difficult of course, to explain that while most insects laid eggs, many flies deposited larvae, aphids bore nymphs, and the sheep ked laid larvae which almost immediately formed puparial cases. We now realize that variations in post-embryonic growth are involved, since even legless larvae generally have later-larval or presumptive adult structures present within their body in rudimentary and undeveloped form.

METAMORPHOSIS

Upon hatching, insects grow by a series of molts, shedding the old cuticle and expanding into a new and larger one. When the adult stage is reached, molting in most insects ceases. At each molt externally visible changes occur, which have caused this type of growth to be termed **metamorphosis,** a change in form or transformation. There is considerable variation in the amount of bodily change at molting and the degree of this change is used to classify insects into three generally accepted types of metamorphosis: no metamorphosis, simple metamorphosis, and complex metamorphosis. From a physiological standpoint, since similar hormonal mechanisms control postembryonic growth, there is a tendency to refer to all development which follows hatching as larval growth.

In describing the events of metamorphosis several special terms, such as stadium, instar, imago, and stage, are often used. The **stadium** is the time interval between the molts of insects, and **instar** is the form assumed by

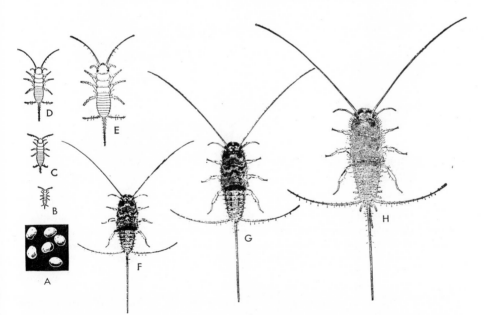

Fig. 3:7. No metamorphosis. Development of Ametabola, as represented by a thysanuran. Group of eggs, A; the nymphs, B to G, quite closely resemble the adult, H, and there is scarcely any major difference between the external appearance of the oldest nymph and the adult. *From Metcalf, Flint, and Metcalf, 1951,* Destructive and Useful Insects, *by permission of McGraw-Hill Book Co., Inc., N. Y.*

an insect during a particular stadium. When an insect emerges from the egg it is said to be in its first instar; at the end of this stadium the insect molts and becomes a second instar, etc. The final instar is the adult insect or **imago. Stage** is a distinct, sharply different period of an insect's life, for example, the egg stage, larval stage, pupal stage, and adult stage.

In what is considered the most primitive type of postembryonic growth, the structural changes are almost imperceptible (Fig. 3:7). Insects exhibiting this type of development are said to undergo **no metamorphosis,** and they are referred to as **Ametabola.** Molting may continue throughout their adult life. Collembola (springtails) and Thysanura (silverfish) are the insects most commonly encountered in this group. Immature Ametabola are called nymphs.

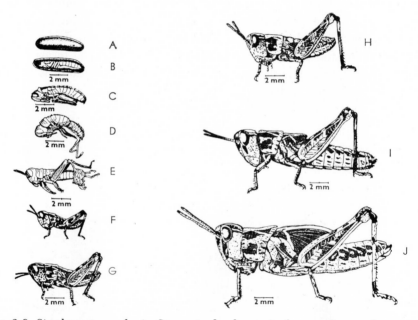

Fig. 3:8. Simple metamorphosis. Stages in development of a grasshopper from egg to last nymphal instar. A, newly laid eggs; B, embryo within egg; C, hatched nymph inclosed in serosa; D, E, nymph shedding serosa; F to J, first to fifth nymphal instars. *Courtesy Commonwealth Scientific and Industrial Research Organization, Australia, original drawing by Mr. D. C. Swan.*

Insects which undergo **simple metamorphosis** belong to the **Heterometabola.** In this type of growth there is a relatively gradual change in external appearance in the molting steps from egg to adult (Figs. 3:8 and 3:9). The immature forms are called **nymphs,** and have feeding habits usually similar to those of the adult. In the final molt functional wings, when present, are developed. Grasshoppers, termites, chewing and sucking lice,

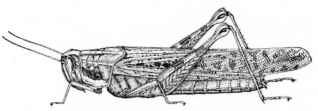

Fig. 3:9. Adult grasshopper with fully developed, functional wings. *Courtesy University of Arizona.*

and true bugs are common examples of insects in this group. A greater deviation of metamorphosis occurs among the Heterometabola whose immature stages are aquatic. These are sometimes called **Hemimetabola,** and their nymphs can be referred to as **naiads.** The aquatic insects in this category are the mayflies, dragonflies and damselflies, and stoneflies.

The greatest external and internal structural changes take place among insects with **complex metamorphosis,** the **Holometabola** (Fig. 3:10). These are regarded as the most advanced insects, or most recent in an evolutionary sense. The postembryonic form is a **larva** which feeds actively and may have locomotory appendages developed to varying degrees. Fly larvae (maggots), for example, are completely legless, whereas many beetle larvae have well-developed legs. After several molts the **pupa** is formed. The pupa is often considered as being an inactive stage. This is true of feeding, and generally true of locomotion (mosquitoes being a notable exception), but major structural reorganizations are taking place internally. At the termination of the pupal stage a highly active adult results. These great variations in structure during the growth of holometabolous insects are often paral-

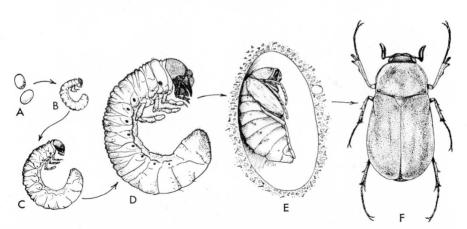

Fig. 3:10. Complete metamorphosis, as found in a May beetle. From eggs (A), three larval instars develop (B, C, D,), pupation occurs in a cell in the soil (E), and finally the adult beetle (F) emerges.

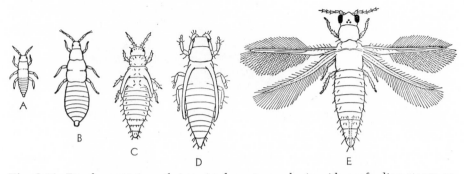

Fig. 3:11. Development in a thrips, simple metamorphosis with nonfeeding stages resembling pupae. A, B, first and second instar nymphs; C, propupa; D, pupa, E, adult female. *From Snodgrass, 1954, Smithsonian Misc. Coll. 122.*

leled by different habits. Thus larvae and adults may eat radically different foods and occupy different environments. Beetles, flies, fleas, moths and butterflies, and bees and wasps are common representatives of the Holometabola.

There are several instances where insect transformation does not fit neatly into the ordinary classifications of metamorphosis. Thrips belong to the Heterometabola, yet the last two nymphal instars do not feed and may be inactive (Fig. 3:11), a situation resembling the pupal stage in Holometabola. Some insects, among which the Meloidae or blister beetles provide an example, undergo what is termed **hypermetamorphosis.** In this case growth is by complete metamorphosis, but there are distinct changes in external form and habits at each successive larval molt.

The pupae of insects, being inactive and defenseless, frequently have some means of protection and concealment (Fig. 3:12). Such protection is

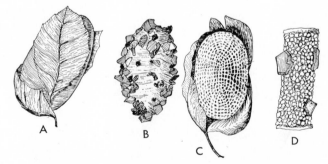

Fig. 3:12. Various types of insect cocoons. The cocoons of many moths are encased in leaves of the host plant (A), debris sticks to the cocoons of a flea (B), the alfalfa weevil spins its lacy cocoon among leaves of the host plant (C), and many caddisflies simply seal off the case of cemented particles in which the larva developed (D). *C, courtesy USDA; A, B, D, original.*

sought by the last larval instar. In fact this last larval form does not feed just prior to pupation, often has a distinct appearance, and is known as the **prepupa.** In many insects, particularly Neuroptera, caddisflies, fleas, and many Lepidoptera and Hymenoptera, a **cocoon** of silk is woven by the larva. Pupation takes place within the cocoon. Insects which pupate in soil often do so in an **earthen cell.** Trichoptera larvae build cases by gluing together pebbles, sticks, or other fragments in which they live and subsequently pupate. Some moths cover the silken cocoon with body hairs.

LARVAL FORMS

Larval form is extremely variable in insects, but there are sufficient similarities in over-all structure to permit a classification of type that is useful in describing their appearance. (1) **Campodeiform** (Fig. 2:2A) larvae have a flattened body with long legs, and usually with filaments on the end of the abdomen. Larvae of diving beetles in the family Dytiscidae and many other beetles, Neuroptera, and Trichoptera afford typical examples. (2) **Carabiform** larvae (Fig. 2:2B) are similar to the campodeiform type, but the legs are shorter and filaments are lacking on the end of the body. They receive their name from the larvae of carabid beetles. Chrysomelid beetle larvae are of the same type. (3) **Eruciform** larvae (Fig. 2:2C) are cylindrical, have a well-formed head, thoracic legs, and abdominal prolegs. Larvae of Lepidoptera and of sawflies are typical examples. (4) **Scarabae-iform** larvae (Fig. 2:2D) are "C-shaped," have a well-developed head and usually possess thoracic legs but lack prolegs. The type is named after larvae of scarabaeid beetles (dung beetles, May beetles), and is also represented by the larvae of weevils and furniture beetles. (5) **Elateriform** larvae (Fig. 2:2E) are cylindrical, smooth, relatively toughskinned larvae with short legs. They are named after larvae of elaterid or click beetles (wireworms). Larvae in the beetle family Tenebrionidae also have this appearance. (6) **Platyform** larvae (Fig. 2:2F) are broad and flat with legs short or absent. Isolated examples are found among larvae of some syrphid flies, certain caterpillars, and blister beetles. (7) **Vermiform** or wormlike larvae (Fig. 2:2G) are cylindrical and elongate, without appendages of locomotion. This form is represented by the larvae of higher Diptera (maggots), many woodboring beetles, fleas, and many parasitic wasps.

PUPAL FORMS

Pupal form can be classified by means of the appearance of developing appendages. (1) In **obtect** pupae the appendages are close to the body, being held there by a tight fitting outer envelope (Fig. 3:13A). Pupae of this type are found in Lepidoptera and many Coleoptera, as well as the less advanced Diptera. The obtect pupa of butterflies is often angular and metallic colored, and is called a **chrysalis**. (2) When the appendages develop free of the body the pupa is called **exarate** (Fig. 3:13B). This type

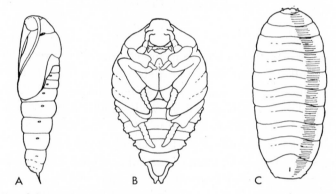

Fig. 3:13. Pupal form of insects. A, the obtect pupa of a moth; B, the exarate pupa of a scarabaeid beetle; C, the coarctate pupa of a fly. *Redrawn from Peterson,* Larvae of Insects, *1951, by permission Alvah Peterson.*

of pupa is characteristic of Neuroptera, Trichoptera, and most Coleoptera. (3) If the visible pupal case is smooth with no appendages apparent it is referred to as **coarctate** (Fig. 3:13C). This condition is typical of the more advanced or cyclorraphous Diptera. The pupal case in reality is a hardened and expanded skin of the third larval instar. Within this shell a fourth larval instar molts to form an obtect pupa.

Selected References

Hagan, H. R., *Embryology of the Viviparous Insects* (New York: Ronald, 1951).
Johannsen, O. A., and F. H. Butt, *Embryology of Insects and Myriapods* (New York: McGraw-Hill, 1941).
Ross, H. H., *A Textbook of Entomology* (New York: Wiley, 1956).

Chapter 4 | CLASSIFICATION OF INSECTS AND THEIR RELATIVES | *Carl Johansen*

The animal kingdom is divided into a number of large groups known as **phyla.** The following is a list of the ten most important phyla of animals, including a few examples of each:

Invertebrates
1. Protozoa—single-celled animals, as amoeba
2. Porifera—sponges
3. Coelenterata—jellyfishes, corals
4. Platyhelminthes—flatworms, flukes, tapeworms
5. Aschelminthes—roundworms, trichina
6. Mollusca—snails, slugs, clams
7. Echinodermata—starfish, sea cucumbers
8. Annelida—segmented worms, earthworms, leeches
9. Arthropoda—insects, spiders, crayfish, millipedes

Vertebrates
10. Chordata—fishes, amphibians, reptiles, birds, mammals

In this book, we are mainly concerned with Arthropoda, which is the largest group of animals. More than three-fourths of the total number of species belong to this phylum. Other invertebrate phyla which contain agricultural pests are the Aschelminthes, Platyhelminthes, and Mollusca. These include, respectively, plant- and animal-infesting roundworms, flukes and tapeworms that parasitize higher animals, and slugs and snails which are crop pests.

ARTHROPODA

Arthropods are quite variable in structure. They include such diverse animals as millipedes, spiders, crayfish, and insects. However, all arthropods have certain characteristics in common, as follows:

1. Series of ringlike segments—each animal in this group has a body formed of a number of segments.
2. Jointed appendages—they have legs and other appendages which are made up of segments jointed together.
3. Exoskeleton—they possess an outer covering of a hardened, horny material, an external skeleton.
4. Bilateral symmetry—the arrangement of body parts is such that they can be split down the middle so as to form two equal portions.
5. Ventral nerve cord—the nerve cord (more or less equivalent to spinal cord of man) is found within the lower part of the body.

In order to classify animals into groups and subgroups which can be more easily studied and understood, a system of nomenclature has been developed. The largest groups in the animal kingdom, as already mentioned, are the phyla. Each phylum is divided into a number of classes; each class into a number of orders; each order into a number of families; and so on. Let us take the codling moth, the familiar "worm in the apple," as an example and see how this classification system works:

Kingdom—Animal
Phylum—Arthropoda
Class—Insecta
Order—Lepidoptera
Family—Olethreutidae
Genus—Carpocapsa
Species—pomonella

We derive the **scientific name** of the codling moth, *Carpocapsa pomonella* (Linnaeus), by combining the generic and specific names. Note that this scientific name is italicized in print; when written by hand it is underlined to indicate italics. Correct style also includes capitalizing the genus but not the species. You will see that sometimes a man's name, either abbreviated or in full, is listed after the scientific name of an insect. This is the person who first described the species in question. If his name is in parentheses, it indicates that the scientific name has been changed in some way since the species was first described.

Farmers and entomologists alike have a tendency to use common names for important crop and livestock insects. This practice has become so entrenched that the Entomological Society of America regularly publishes a list of approved common names. In this book we shall often refer to insects only by their common names. Yet for scientific accuracy and as a key to the literature of an insect, the scientific name is indispensable. For this reason we have included an appendix of common-scientific names which the student may consult.

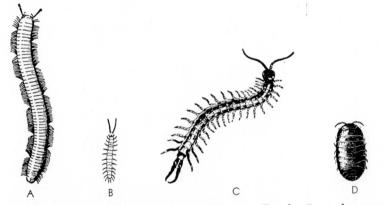

Fig. 4:1. Representative arthropods (not to scale). A, millipede; B, garden symphylan (greatly enlarged); C, centipede; D, sowbug. *A, C, D, courtesy USDA; B, courtesy Waterhouse, Wash. Agr. Exp. Sta.*

Characteristics of the major classes of arthropods are presented in Table 4:1 and representatives of four of these classes are illustrated in Fig. 4:1. Only the classes Arachnida and Insecta will be discussed in greater detail in this chapter.

Recognition of the pest species involved in an agricultural problem is of utmost importance. Different control measures are often required even for two closely related kinds of insects due to variations in their life cycles or in their reactions to insecticidal materials. There are about 700,000 species of insects and 9,000 species of mites and ticks which have been described and catalogued and many more remain to be discovered. Obviously, no person can learn to recognize more than a small portion of the total. An entomologist who has worked in one region for most of his life is not

Table 4:1 | Major Classes of the Phylum Arthropoda and their Characteristics.

Class and Examples	Body regions	Pairs of legs	Pairs of antennae	Breathing organs	Eyes	Agricultural importance
CRUSTACEA Crayfish, crabs, sowbugs, etc.	2 Cephalothorax and abdomen	5 or more	2	Gills	Compound	Sowbugs are a minor pest, esp. on greenhouse crops
ARACHNIDA Spiders, scorpions, daddy-long-legs, mites, ticks, etc.	2 Cephalothorax and abdomen	4	None	Book-lungs or tracheae	Simple	The mite and tick group contains major pests of both animals and plants and some beneficial predators
DIPLOPODA Millipedes	2 Head and body (rounded form)	30 or more (2 pr. per segment)	1 (short)	Tracheae	Simple	Few species feed on roots and tubers, esp. vegetable crops, mostly minor
SYMPHYLA Symphylans	2 Head and body (flattened form)	12 (1 pr. per segment)	1 (long)	Tracheae	None	Garden symphylan is extremely damaging to all types of crops in some areas, feeds on roots
CHILOPODA Centipedes	2 Head and body (flattened form)	15 or more (1 pr. per segment)	1 (long)	Tracheae	Usually simple	Feed on insects; rather insignificant agriculturally
INSECTA Bugs, beetles, butterflies, bees, etc.	3 Head, thorax and abdomen	3	1	Tracheae	Compound, often possess simple eyes also	Greatest number of major agricultural pests; also many beneficial species

likely to be familiar with more than a few hundred insects out of the thousands of kinds which are present.

We shall discuss the groups of insects, mites, and ticks that are of major agricultural importance and stress a limited number of families which contain almost all of the major pest species. By studying the characteristics of these families, you can attain a practical background which you may apply to the agricultural pest species throughout the United States, indeed most of the world.

CLASS ARACHNIDA

Almost all members of the class Arachnida are air-breathing arthropods. The body is usually divided into two regions, the **cephalothorax** and the **abdomen;** however, the sun spiders appear to have three regions, while the mites and ticks have the entire body more or less fused into one region. Antennae are absent and eyes are simple. Four pairs of legs are attached to the cephalothorax in the adult stage. Most forms breathe by means of **book-lungs**—pouchlike organs containing membranous flaps resembling the pages of a book—situated in the underside of the abdomen. Mites and ticks breathe by means of **tracheae.**

The order **Araneida** contains the spiders (Fig. 4:2). They are generally beneficial, since they feed mainly upon insects. **Scorpionida** are the scorpions which are most common in the Southwestern states. The sting of the common species is painful but not dangerous. Pseudoscorpions belong to

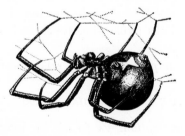

Fig. 4:2. The black widow spider, a poisonous species. *Courtesy Utah Agr. Exp. Sta.*

the order **Chelonethida.** These unusual little animals are commonly found under bark or stones and inside buildings. They feed upon mites and small insects. **Phalangida** are the daddy-long-legs. Their food consists of plant juices, dead plant and animal material, and possibly live insects.

Order Acarina: mites and ticks

Acarina is by far the most important of the arachnid orders. It contains the mites which attack both plants and animals and the ticks which are pests of animals. Most newly-hatched acarina have six legs; while most later stages have eight. The cephalothorax and abdomen are fused into a single body region. Mouthparts are adapted for biting, piercing, and sucking. They breathe by means of tracheae or (apparently) through the body surface. Mites and ticks range in size from less than 1 mm. (as small as 1/300 in.) up to 15 mm. (⅗ in.) long.

Ticks

Ticks are major agricultural pests because they suck the blood of domestic animals and also transmit disease organisms. One can distinguish ticks from mites by their larger size, leathery skin, and spiracles located behind the third or fourth pair of legs.

FAMILY ARGASIDAE—SOFT-BACKED TICKS (FIG. 4:3A)

Description: ⅕ to ½ in. long; leathery, wrinkled, granulated integument; no dorsal shield; head capsule (capitulum) ventral; pedipalpi (palpi) are leglike; sexual dimorphism not marked; spiracles anterior to fourth pair of legs.

Bionomics: active throughout the year in warm climates; eggs laid in large masses on ground or in sheltered places, 500 to 1,000 per female; each female lays several batches of eggs; six-legged larval stage lasts about 5 to 12 days; two or three nymphal stages take several weeks to several months to complete, nymphs are eight-legged; adults hide during day in burrows, nests, or homes of hosts and feed on host at night (ear tick adult does not feed); adults are long-lived and feed a number of times—"many-host ticks"; relapsing fever and other diseases are transmitted by certain species.

Examples: fowl tick, relapsing-fever tick, and ear tick.

FAMILY IXODIDAE—HARD-BACKED TICKS (FIG. 4:3B)

Description: ⅓ to ⅗ in. long; dorsal shield (scutum) present; head capsule (capitulum) anterior; male is much smaller than distended female, giving marked sexual dimorphism.

Bionomics: may reproduce throughout the year in sheltered places; eggs usually laid on ground, 2,000 to 6,500 per female; larval stage may be several weeks to 11 months long, winter tick larvae remain dormant during summer; unfed larvae may live a considerable time; after feeding, larva drops to ground and molts; nymphal stage is several weeks to several months long, unfed nymphs may live for more than a year; after feeding on second host individual, the nymph drops to ground and molts; new adult finds third host and feeds, then mating occurs and female drops to ground, lays all of her eggs, and dies; usually three host individuals are required for completion of the cycle, although some species are "one-host ticks" or

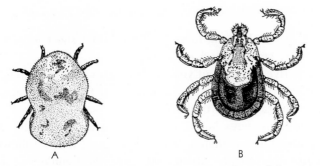

Fig. 4:3. Ticks. A, ear tick, Argasidae; B, Pacific Coast tick, Ixodidae. *Courtesy USDA.*

"two-host ticks"; Rocky Mountain spotted fever, Texas cattle fever, and several other important diseases of domestic animals and man are transmitted by this group. Tick paralysis caused by the Rocky Mountain wood tick and other species is due to a toxin, not a microorganism.

Examples: cattle tick, lone star tick, brown dog tick, Gulf Coast tick, winter tick, American dog tick, and Rocky Mountain wood tick.

Mites

Mites also are major agricultural pests. Various kinds attack both plants and animals and a few are beneficial predators upon pest species. Mites are smaller than ticks, some of them being microscopic in size. The skin is not leathery and the tracheal openings (stigmata), when present, are near the head region or the bases of certain legs.

FAMILY PHYTOSEIIDAE—PREDATOR MITES (FIG. 4:4A)

Description: 0.2 to 0.5 mm. long; usually pale in color and oval in shape; body flattened above and with few short curved hairs.

Bionomics: winter as adult females in disease cankers on tree limbs, in dead lecanium scales, in plant debris or soil, or in bark cavities; usually found on undersides of leaves or in duff on ground when active; pass through larva, protonymph, and deutonymph stages; generation completed in 10 to 20 days under favorable conditions; adults may live about 30 days during growing season; usually complete three to four generations per season; predators of injurious spider mites, rust mites, and the cyclamen mite; may also feed upon pollen and other materials.

Examples: many important predators of phytophagous mites, especially in the genus *Typhlodromus.*

FAMILY DERMANYSSIDAE—DERMANYSSID MITES, CHICKEN MITES (FIG. 4:4B)

Description: 0.5 to 1.5 mm. long; leathery body; short legs; eyeless; eggs are pearly white, smooth, and elliptical.

Bionomics: active throughout year under warm conditions; eggs deposited in crevices, under debris, or on host animal; pass through larva, protonymph, and deutonymph stages; life cycle requires minimum of 7 to 17 days under favorable conditions; eggs laid 2 to 10 days after female has fed, several eggs laid for about a day, then another blood meal taken, followed by more egg-laying; usually produce about 100 eggs per female and females live about two months.

Examples: chicken mite, northern fowl mite, tropical fowl mite, tropical rat mite.

FAMILY DEMODICIDAE—FOLLICLE MITES (FIG. 4:4C)

Description: 0.1 to 0.4 mm. long; wormlike, weakly colored, annulate, eight-legged mites; legs short and stumpy, five-segmented, located on anterior portion of body; no setae on legs or body.

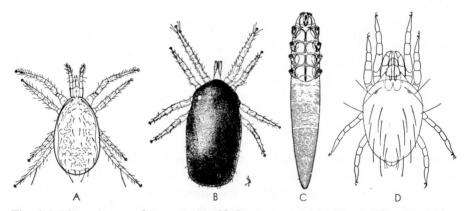

A   B   C   D

Fig. 4:4. Mites. A, a predator mite *Typhlodromus cucumeris,* Phytoseiidae; B, chicken mite, Dermanyssidae; C, follicle mite, Demodicidae; D, Banks grass mite, Tetranychidae. *A after Cunliffe and Baker; B, from USDA; C, from Baker et al., 1956, Parasitic Mites by permission National Pest Control Association; D, courtesy Malcolm, Wash. Agr. Exp. Sta.*

Bionomics: entire life cycle spent on host animal; inhabit sebaceous glands and hair follicles, all stages found in pustules of skin pores; go through egg, larva, protonymph, and deutonymph stages to reach adult stage; demodectic mange of several domestic animals is a serious problem.

Examples: cattle follicle mite, sheep follicle mite, follicle mite, horse follicle mite, hog follicle mite, dog follicle mite.

FAMILY TETRANYCHIDAE—SPIDER MITES (FIG. 4:4D)

Description: 0.2 to 0.8 mm. long; more or less oval in shape, the male usually tapering posteriorly; vary in color from yellow to green, red, or brown.

Bionomics: most overwinter as bright yellow, orange, or red adult females in debris on ground or under bark of trees (some winter as eggs); stages— egg, larva, protonymph, deutonymph, adult; some species spin silken webbing on plants; most injurious family of plant-feeding mites.

Examples: European red mite, clover mite, two-spotted spider mite, yellow spider mite, McDaniel spider mite, grass mite, brown wheat mite, strawberry spider mite, spruce spider mite, southern red mite, citrus red mite, four-spotted spider mite, brown spider mite, Schoene spider mite.

FAMILY ERIOPHYIDAE—ERIOPHYID MITES, BLISTER MITES, RUST MITES, GALL MITES (FIG. 4:5A)

Description: 0.08 to 0.2 mm. long; two major types—elongate, wormlike, soft-bodied forms and wedge-shaped, harder bodied forms; two pairs of legs at anterior end of body; abdomen finely striated and bearing long setae.

Bionomics: mostly winter as immatures or adults under bud scales or bark (sometimes as eggs); spherical eggs laid singly or in groups, hatch in two to four weeks; wormlike type causes formation of galls, blisters, or erinose patches on leaves or fruit in which they live; wedge-shaped type are free-living "leaf vagrants" which often cause a "rusting" of the foliage; several plant virus diseases are transmitted by eriophyids.

Examples: pear leaf blister mite, apple rust mite, peach silver mite, dryberry mite, redberry mite, wheat curl mite, grain rust mite, fig mite, walnut blister mite, cotton blister mite, currant bud mite, grape erineum mite, citrus rust mite, filbert bud mite, tomato russet mite.

FAMILY TARSONEMIDAE—TARSONEMID MITES,
THREAD-FOOTED MITES (FIG. 4:5B)

Description: 0.1 to 0.3 mm. long; males much smaller than females and
differing in form, females typically ovoid (cyclamen mite type has dorso-
ventrally flattened body, "almond-shaped"); integument of adult relatively
hard and shiny and with few hairs or spines; color opaque white to light
green, tan, or pink.

Bionomics: overwinter in all stages in crowns of plants or under bulb
scales, active throughout the year in greenhouses; eggs laid singly; six-
legged larvae are opaque white or "glassy"; quiescent nymphal stage; one
generation completed in about two weeks under favorable conditions;
feeding causes discoloration, curling, and distortion of plant parts.

Examples: cyclamen mite, broad mite, bulb scale mite.

FAMILY TROMBICULIDAE—CHIGGERS, REDBUGS, HARVEST MITES (FIG. 4:5C)

Description: adults about 1 to 2.5 mm. long, oval or more usually "figure-
8-shaped"; larvae are red to pale yellow and 0.2 to 0.3 mm. long; these mites
have legs separated so that 2 pairs are anterior and 2 pairs posterior.

Bionomics: six-legged larval trombiculid mites are widespread parasites
of vertebrate animals; later stages are free-living, mainly in soil, feeding on
eggs and early larval instars of small arthropods; stages include egg, six-
legged larva, nymph, and adult; eggs usually laid in soil; larvae crawl about
until find suitable host animal, do not usually burrow under skin of host;
often attach to restricted areas of host's body; feed on lymph and skin tissues;
entire life cycle 2 to 12 months long; one to three generations per season in

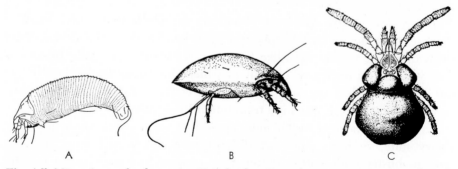

Fig. 4:5. Mites. A, peach silver mite, Eriophyidae; B, cyclamen mite, Tarsonemidae; C,
adult chigger mite, Trombiculidae. *A, courtesy Ohio Agr. Exp. Sta.; B, courtesy Univ.
Calif.; C, courtesy USDA.*

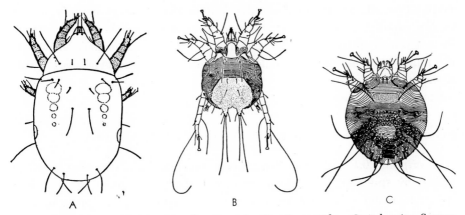

Fig. 4:6. Mites. A, bulb mite, Acaridae; B, scab mite, Psoroptidae; C, itch mite, Sarcoptidae. *A from Conn. Agr. Exp. Sta.; B from Baker and Wharton, 1952,* An Introduction to Acarology, *by permission The Macmillan Company; C from Baker et al., 1956,* Parasitic Mites, *by permission National Pest Control Association.*

temperate climates; about 20 species are important as the cause of dermatitis or in the transmission of diseases such as scrub typhus.

Examples: chiggers.

FAMILY ACARIDAE—ACARID MITES, CEREAL MITES, ROOT MITES, FUNGUS MITES (FIG. 4:6A)

Description: 0.4 to 1 mm. long; body stout, white or fawn; integument usually smooth and shiny with a few long, spinelike hairs; body distinctly divided by transverse groove.

Bionomics: many have migrating stage known as hypopus or wandernymph during which no food is eaten, attach to insects by suckers, release and begin feeding when suitable place is reached; stages include egg, larva, first nymph, hypopus, third nymph, adult; chiefly injurious to cereal, food products, and plant roots or bulbs; several of the cereal-infesting species can produce a severe dermatitis in humans known as "grocers' itch."

Examples: grain mite, bulb mite, mushroom mite, dried fruit mite.

FAMILY PSOROPTIDAE—SCAB MITES (FIG. 4:6B)

Description: up to 0.5 mm. long; body rounded, longer than wide; all legs long and strongly developed, except fourth pair small in some cases; third or fourth pair of legs may have whiplike setae.

Bionomics: spend entire cycle on host animal; do not burrow in skin, but may be protected by scabs caused by their feedings; they prick the skin to feed and usually are found near edges rather than beneath centers of scab lesions; produce severe itching, causing animals to scratch or bite infested areas; cause scab in cattle, sheep, goats, and horses, ear canker in rabbits, also found in certain wild animals; can damage wool and even cause death of sheep.

Example: scab mite.

FAMILY SARCOPTIDAE—ITCH MITES, MANGE MITES (FIG. 4:6C)

Description: 0.1 to 0.4 mm. long; body round and globose, skin striations broken by spineline projections; legs very short and sometimes clawless; first and second pairs of legs end in long, stalked, flaplike pretarsi, third and fourth pairs end in single, long whiplike setae, two anterior pairs are distant from two posterior pairs.

Bionomics: stages include egg, larva, nymph, adult male, and immature and mature female (maturation of female believed to take place after fertilization); fertilized female begins laying eggs a few hours after starting to burrow into outer layer of host skin; larvae and nymphs also burrow, but are commonly found in hair follicles or surface of skin; life cycle is about ten to 14 days long; sarcoptic mange in domestic animals can cause serious reduction of meat, milk, or wool and even cause death.

Examples: depluming mite, scaly-leg mite, itch mite.

CLASS INSECTA

Insects represent the largest and most diverse class of animals. Adult insects differ from other arthropods in usually having two pairs of wings, three distinct body regions (head, thorax, and abdomen), and three pairs of legs. The antennae are variable in form and most adult insects possess both compound and simple eyes. Insects breathe by means of an air-tube system (tracheae). Table 4:2 presents a brief résumé of the 26 orders of insects.

Insects are divided into two subclasses, the **Apterygota** or wingless insects and the **Pterygota** or winged insects. The Apterygota contain small, primitive insects which grow and develop with little or no metamorphosis. They include three orders: Protura, Thysanura, and Collembola.

The Pterygota contain the other 23 orders of insects. Some of these may lack wings, but the condition is a secondary one, for their thoracic structure definitely places them in the winged subclass.

The Pterygota are further divided into the **Paleoptera** or ancient, winged insects, in which the wings are held permanently at right angles to the body, and the **Neoptera** or modern winged insects in which the wings can be folded and held close to the body. Paleopterans were abundant in ancient times and included many orders now extinct. Today they are represented by two orders, the Ephemeroptera and the Odonata. The Neopterans, being able to fold their wings, have an advantage for they can escape from enemies not only by flying away but also by running fast and by hiding in crevices. It is an interesting fact that although wingless species occur in all of the Neopteran orders, none of the living or extinct Paleoptera is wingless.

Since immature insects, larvae and nymphs, are often the major active feeding stages, knowledge of them is especially important to agricultural entomology. In the early days of the development of insect classification only the adult insects were studied. Even today, the adults are much better known than the nymphs or larvae. Characteristics of the immature stages of the insect orders of major agricultural importance are presented in Table 4:3.

If one can learn three "key" things about an insect order plus another typical feature, he will be able to separate them fairly well. The three basic characteristics are: type of mouthparts, type of wings, and type of metamorphosis. Discussion of fourteen insect orders and 87 families of major agricultural importance now follows:

Order Orthoptera: grasshoppers, katydids, crickets, cockroaches, mantids, walkingsticks

Mouthparts—typical chewing mouthparts.

Wings—forewings elongate and narrow, modified into somewhat hardened tegmina, hindwings membranous with extensive folded area.

Metamorphosis—simple.

Additional features—wingless and shortwinged forms common; mainly terrestrial with good powers of running or jumping.

FAMILY BLATTIDAE—COCKROACHES (FIG. 4:7A)

Description: ⅖ to 1½ in. long; oval, flattened body; head largely concealed by prothorax; slender antennae longer than body; wingless or with two pairs that fold flat over back; legs are long and spiny, fitted for running.

Bionomics: active throughout the year in protected places; eggs are enclosed in capsules which usually remain attached to tip of female abdomen

Table 4:2 | Characteristics of Insect Orders

Order	Appearance	Examples	Metamorphosis
1. PROTURA		Telsontails	None
2. THYSANURA		Silverfish and allies	None
3. COLLEMBOLA		Springtails	None
4. EPHEMEROPTERA		Mayflies	Simple
5. ODONATA		Dragonflies, damselflies	Simple
6. PLECOPTERA		Stoneflies	Simple
7. ORTHOPTERA		Grasshoppers, crickets, cockroaches, etc.	Simple
8. DERMAPTERA		Earwigs	Simple
9. EMBIOPTERA		Embiids	Simple
10. ISOPTERA		Termites	Simple
11. PSOCOPTERA		Booklice and psocids	Simple
12. ZORAPTERA		Barklice	Simple
13. MALLOPHAGA		Biting lice, bird lice	Simple
14. ANOPLURA		Sucking lice	Simple

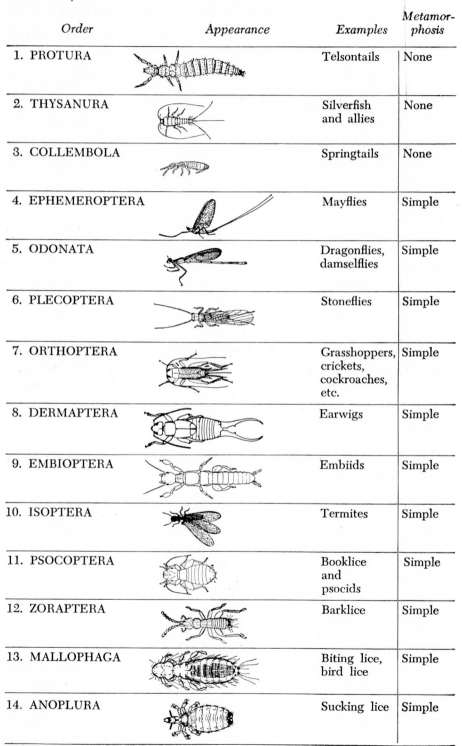

Wings	Mouth Parts	Antennae	Tarsal Segments	Habitat	Agricultural Importance [1]	
					Beneficial	Injurious
None	Sucking	None	1	Terrestrial and semi-aquatic	—	—
None	Chewing	Long, many-segmented	2–3	Terrestrial and semi-aquatic	—	—
None	Chewing	Short to long	fused to tibia or 1	Terrestrial and semi-aquatic	—	+
2 pr. membranous	Chewing	Bristlelike, short	3–5	Aquatic as nymphs	—	—
2 pr. membranous	Chewing	Bristlelike, short	3	Aquatic as nymphs	+	—
2 pr. membranous	Chewing	Threadlike, long	3	Aquatic as nymphs	—	+
Tegmina & membranous	Chewing	Threadlike, short to long	0–5	Terrestrial	—	++++
Short tegmina & membranous	Chewing	Threadlike, long	3	Terrestrial	—	++
2 pr. membranous or none	Chewing	Threadlike	3	Terrestrial and semi-aquatic	—	—
2 pr. membranous or none	Chewing	Beadlike, short to long	4–5	Terrestrial	—	++
2 pr. membranous or none	Chewing	Threadlike, generally long	2–3	Terrestrial	—	—
2 pr. membranous or none	Chewing	Beadlike, long	2	Terrestrial and semi-aquatic	—	—
None	Chewing	Threadlike or clublike and short	1–2	Terrestrial, ecto-parasitic	—	++
None	Piercing-sucking	Bristlelike, short	1	Terrestrial, ecto-parasitic	—	+++

[1] Dash indicates minor agricultural importance; pluses indicate extent of major agricultural importance.

Order	Appearance	Examples	Metamorphosis
15. THYSANOPTERA		Thrips	Simple
16. HEMIPTERA		Bugs	Simple
17. HOMOPTERA		Aphids, scales, leafhoppers	Simple
18. NEUROPTERA		Lacewings and allies	Complex
19. COLEOPTERA		Beetles, weevils	Complex
20. STREPSIPTERA		Twisted-winged insects, stylopids	Complex
21. MECOPTERA		Scorpionflies	Complex
22. TRICHOPTERA		Caddisflies	Complex
23. LEPIDOPTERA		Butterflies, moths, skippers	Complex
24. HYMENOPTERA		Ants, bees, wasps, etc.	Complex
25. DIPTERA		Flies	Complex
26. SIPHONAPTERA		Fleas	Complex

Figures 3, 11, and 17 from Essig, Insects and Mites of Western North America, 1958, by permission The Macmillan Co.; Figures 1, 9, 12, 20, 21 from Essig, College Entomology, 1947, by permission The Macmillan Co.; Figure 14 from Handbook of the Insect

Wings	Mouth Parts	Antennae	Tarsal Segments	Habitat	Agricultural Importance [1] Beneficial	Injurious
2 pr. slender, fringed with hair	Rasping-sucking	Short	1–2	Terrestrial,	+	+++
Hemelytra & membranous or none	Piercing-sucking	Threadlike, short to long	2–3	Terrestrial and aquatic	++	++++
2 pr. membranous or none	Piercing-sucking	Bristlelike or threadlike	1–3	Terrestrial	—	+++++
2 pr. membranous	Chewing	Usually threadlike	5	Terrestrial and aquatic	+++	—
Eltyra and membranous	Chewing	Variable, short to long	1–5	Terrestrial and aquatic	++++	+++++
Front vestigeal, hind membranous, none in ♀	Chewing	Short, none in ♀	2–5	Terrestrial, most parasitic in insects	—	—
2 pr. membranous or none	Chewing	Threadlike, long	5	Terrestrial	—	—
2 pr. membranous with hairs or scales	Chewing	Threadlike, long	5	Aquatic as larvae and pupae	—	—
2 pr. membranous with scales	Siphoning, chewing in larvae	Variable, short to long	5	Terrestrial	—	+++++
2 pr. membranous or none	Chewing or chewing-lapping	Usually threadlike, elbowed	Usually 5	Terrestrial	+++++	++
membranous and halteres or none	Piercing-sucking or sponging; chewing in larvae	Threadlike or aristate, usually short	5	Terrestrial, many aquatic larvae and pupae	++++	+++++
None	Piercing-sucking; chewing in larvae	Knobbed and short	5	Terrestrial, ecto-parasitic as adults	—	++

Insect World, 1956, by permission Hercules Powder Company; *Figure 19 courtesy* Ohio Agricultural Experiment Station; *other figures courtesy* USDA.

Table 4:3 | Characteristics of Immature Insects in Agriculturally Important Orders

Order	Type of Young	Number of instars	Wing pads	Mouth-parts	Thoracic legs	Abdominal prolegs	Eyes
ORTHOPTERA	Nymph	Usually 5 or 6	Usually in late instars	Chewing	Well developed	None	Compound and simple
DERMAPTERA	Nymph	4–5	Usually present	Chewing	Well developed	None	Compound and simple
ISOPTERA	Nymph	6	In late instars of sexual forms	Chewing	Well developed	None	Compound and simple; or none
MALLOPHAGA	Nymph	3	None	Chewing	Special form	None	Compound, poorly developed
ANOPLURA	Nymph	3	None	Piercing-sucking	Special form	None	Compound, small when present
THYSANOPTERA	Nymph	4	Usually present	Rasping-sucking	Short	None	Compound, sometimes simple
HEMIPTERA	Nymph	Usually 5	Usually present	Piercing-sucking	Well developed	None	Compound, sometimes simple
HOMOPTERA	Nymph	3–5	Often present	Piercing-sucking	Well developed	None	Compound, sometimes simple
NEUROPTERA	Larva (antlion, aphidlion, others)	3 or more	None	Chewing, jaws modified for sucking	Well developed	1 caudal pr. in some aquatics	Usually 5–7 pr. simple
COLEOPTERA	Larva (grub, white grub, wireworm, others)	Usually 5 (3–25)	None	Chewing	None to well developed	None	1–6 pr. simple
LEPIDOPTERA	Larva (caterpillar)	Usually 5–6	None	Chewing	None to well developed	5 pr. with crochets (also 2–4)	1–8 pr. simple
HYMENOPTERA	Larva	Usually 4–5	None	Chewing	None to well developed	None or 8 pr. without crochets (also 6–7)	1 pr. simple or none
DIPTERA	Larva (maggot, wriggler, others)	Usually 4–6	None	Chewing, maggot has mouth hooks	None	None (several have false legs)	None, sometimes simple (eye spots)
SIPHONAPTERA	Larva	3	None	Chewing	None	None	None

for several days; five to seven nymphal instars; nocturnal, hiding in cracks during day; feed on all sorts of materials, including starchy substances; contaminate human food and produce unpleasant odors.

Examples: oriental cockroach, German cockroach (crotonbug), American cockroach, brown-banded cockroach, common wood cockroach.

FAMILY TETTIGONIIDAE—LONGHORN GRASSHOPPERS, KATYDIDS (FIG. 4:7B)

Description: mostly large (1 in. or more long) insects with slender or stout bodies; antennae nearly as long or longer than body; laterally flattened, bladelike ovipositor; arboreal forms usually green, those living in or on the soil usually gray or brown.

Bionomics: usually winter in the egg stage; the egg is usually inserted into or laid on plant tissue, Mormon cricket lays eggs singly in soil; one generation per season; most species are plant feeders, a few prey on other insects; the Mormon cricket is gregarious, migrating in enormous bands and often causing serious damage to range in the West.

Examples: Mormon cricket, coulee cricket, angular-winged katydid, broad-winged katydid, fork-tailed bush katydid.

FAMILY GRYLLIDAE—CRICKETS (FIG. 4:7C)

Description: mostly ½ in. or more long, a few tiny species less than ¼ in. long live in ant nests; the tree crickets are flattened and whitish or pale green; the ground-dwelling crickets have large heads, cylindrical bodies and dark colors, often black; antennae are long and threadlike.

Bionomics: mostly winter as eggs or nymphs; tree crickets insert eggs in twigs, field crickets lay eggs in soil; males chirp by vibrating forewings together; feed on plant foliage but are partially carnivorous, eating other insects and small invertebrates; field crickets may damage cereal and garden crops during occasional outbreaks, tree crickets injure fruit and berry twigs by their egg-laying habit.

Examples: field cricket, house cricket, black-horned tree cricket, four-spotted tree cricket, snowy tree cricket.

FAMILY ACRIDIDAE—GRASSHOPPERS (FIG. 4:7D)

Description: variable in size from ⅗ to 2⅗ in. long; short antennae; greatly enlarged hindlegs fitted for jumping; narrow forewings (tegmina); large "ear drum" present on first segment of abdomen.

Bionomics: usually overwinter as eggs laid in masses (pods) of 2 to 100

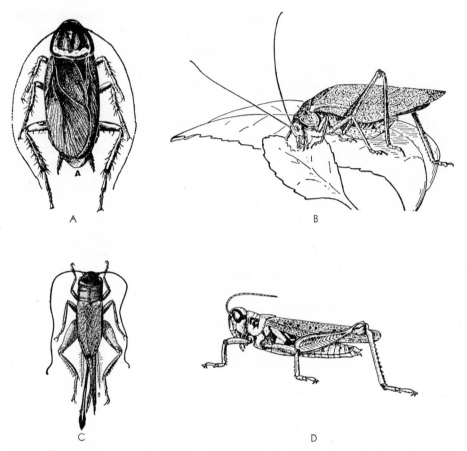

Fig. 4:7. Orthoptera. A, American cockroach, Blattidae; B, broad-winged katydid, Tetti-goniidae; C, field cricket, Gryllidae; D, migratory grasshopper, Acrididae. *A, B, C, from Essig, 1958,* Insects and Mites of Western North America, *by permission The Macmillan Company; D, courtesy Ariz. Agr. Exp. Sta.*

in the soil; four to eight nymphal instars and usually one generation per season; general feeders on all types of plant materials, most destructive to field and forage crops.

Examples: migratory grasshopper, two-striped grasshopper, red-legged grasshopper, clear-winged grasshopper, differential grasshopper, devastating grasshopper, Rocky Mountain grasshopper.

Order Dermaptera: earwigs

Mouthparts—typical chewing mouthparts.
Wings—forewings are hardened covers over hindwings and are quite

short, hindwings are membranous and rounded with radiating veins; some lack wings.

Metamorphosis—simple.

Additional feature—large forceps-like cerci at end of abdomen.

FAMILY FORFICULIDAE—EUROPEAN EARWIG AND OTHERS (FIG. 4:8A)

Description: 3/10 to 3/5 in. long; elongate and flat-bodied; heavy beadlike antennae may exceed half the length of the body; abdominal glands exude an evil-smelling liquid.

Bionomics: winter as adults; eggs laid in burrows in ground and protected by female; young nymphs are also cared for by the female; four to five nymphal instars; largely nocturnal, hiding in cracks, etc., during the day; primarily scavengers, but also attack other insects and snails, and feed on plant material.

Example: European earwig.

Order Isoptera: termites

Mouthparts—chewing.

Wings—two pairs membranous of equal size and shape, both winged and wingless forms occur in a colony.

Metamorphosis—simple.

Additional features—termites are social insects with two or more forms or castes occurring in each species (reproductives, supplementary reproductives, soldiers, workers, and nasuti); termites are sometimes confused with ants and called "white ants," they are easily distinguished from ants in that they are light colored and soft bodied, with the abdomen broadly joined to thorax and with the antennae not elbowed.

FAMILY RHINOTERMITIDAE—SUBTERRANEAN TERMITES (FIG. 17:20)

Description: winged forms about 1/3 in. long to the tips of the wings; workers are dirty white and lack compound eyes; soldiers have large heads and mandibles; winged forms are dark, often black.

Bionomics: more or less active throughout year depending on protection from weather; nests are in ground often connected by mud-covered passageways to wooden structures upon which they feed; six nymphal instars require two years; winged males and females swarm out of nests in spring, mate and start new colonies (wings are shed soon after swarming flights); feed on timbers, roots of plants, furniture, and carpets; ability to utilize cellulose of wood is dependent upon protozoans in gut.

Examples: eastern subterranean termite, western subterranean termite.

Order Mallophaga: chewing lice

Mouthparts—chewing.

Wings—wingless.

Metamorphosis—simple.

Additional features—small or minute, flat, broad-headed external parasites; compound eyes not well developed; no ocelli.

FAMILY MENOPONIDAE—POULTRY BODY LICE (FIG. 19:1)

Description: ⅟₂₅ to ⅕ in. long; head broadly triangular; antennae concealed, tarsi with two claws.

Bionomics: entire cycle completed on host animal, active the year round; eggs glued to feathers of host.

Examples: chicken body louse, shaft louse, goose body louse, large duck louse.

FAMILY PHILOPTERIDAE—FEATHER CHEWING LICE (FIG. 4:8B)

Description: ⅟₂₅ to ⅟₇ in. long; head and body quite variable in shape; antennae threadlike and exposed; tarsi with two claws.

Bionomics: active throughout year on hosts; eggs laid singly on feathers; largest family, contains species parasitizing a wide variety of birds, several important pests of poultry.

Examples: slender goose louse, chicken head louse, small pigeon louse, fluff louse, large chicken louse, wing louse, large turkey louse.

FAMILY TRICHODECTIDAE—MAMMAL CHEWING LICE (FIG. 18:10D)

Description: ⅟₂₅ to ⅟₁₀ in. long; antennae usually three-segmented; antennae threadlike and exposed; tarsi with one claw.

Bionomics: remain on host throughout life, active 12 months of year; eggs glued to hairs of host; contains the parasites of mammals, including domestic animals.

Examples: cattle biting louse, horse biting louse, angora-goat biting louse, sheep biting louse, cat louse, dog biting louse.

Order Anoplura: sucking lice

Mouthparts—piercing-sucking.

Wings—wingless.

Metamorphosis—simple.

Additional features—small, external parasites of mammals; compound eyes reduced or absent; no ocelli.

Family Haematopinidae—wrinkled suckling lice (Fig. 4:8C)

Description: 1/14 to 1/4 in. long; both adults and nymphs bear a superficial resemblance to a crab, owing to the flattened body and clawed, crablike legs; wingless; mostly about 1/8 in. long; gray, brown, or yellow in color; short antennae; and no eyes.

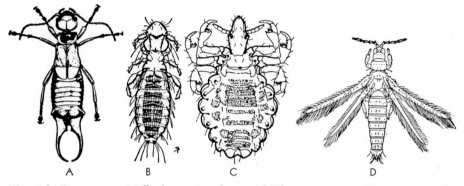

Fig. 4:8. Dermaptera, Mallophaga, Anoplura, and Thysanoptera. A, European earwig; B, chicken head louse, Philopteridae; C, hog louse, Haematopinidae; D, pear thrips, Thripidae. *A, courtesy Wash. Agr. Ext. Serv.; B, courtesy USDA; C, after Ferris; D, courtesy Calif. Agr. Exp. Sta.*

Bionomics: entire life cycle completed on host animal, active the year round; eggs (called nits) are glued to hairs of the host; nymphs feed frequently; usually three nymphal instars and a number of generations per season.

Examples: short-nosed cattle louse, hog louse, horse sucking louse, cattle tail louse.

Order Thysanoptera: thrips

Mouthparts—rasping-sucking.

Wings—similar in form, long, very narrow, and fringed with long hairs; wings sometimes absent.

Metamorphosis—intermediate between simple and complex.

Additional features—cerci absent; small, slender-bodied insects.

Family Thripidae—narrow-winged thrips (Fig. 4:8D)

Description: minute, 1/25 to 1/17 in. long; two pairs very slender, linear wings fringed with long hairs; compound eyes fairly large; legs stout, tarsi with bladder-like adhesive organs; mouthparts, cone-shaped, far back on underside of head.

Bionomics: usually overwinter as adults in soil or plant debris; white eggs inserted into plant tissues or in crevices; some species parthenogenetic; two to four nymphal instars and one to seven generations per season; last one or two nymphal instars are nonfeeding, resting forms which aestivate in soil or plant debris during late summer and transform to adults during the fall; feeding destroys buds or blossoms, whitens or curls leaves, and deforms or scars fruits.

Examples: pear thrips, onion thrips, western flower thrips, gladiolus thrips, greenhouse thrips, grass thrips, iris thrips, tobacco thrips, flower thrips, bean thrips, grain thrips, citrus thrips, red-banded thrips, chrysanthemum thrips.

Order Hemiptera: bugs

Mouthparts—piercing-sucking.

Wings—overlapping on abdomen, forewings are hemelytra (with hardened basal portions and membranous tips), hindwings membranous.

Metamorphosis—simple.

Additional feature—base of rostrum usually not touching anterior coxae ("beak" arises at front of underside of head).

FAMILY PENTATOMIDAE—STINK BUGS (FIG. 4:9B)

Description: ⅕ to ¾ in. long; broad, shieldlike body; large triangular scutellum between forewings at rest; five-segmented antennae usually about one half the length of body; compound eyes relatively small, only two ocelli; thoracic glands give off strong odor; eggs are squat and barrel-shaped.

Bionomics: winter as adults; eggs laid in groups, usually glued to a leaf; five nymphal instars; many species feed on plants, some feed on other insects, and a few feed on both plants and insects.

Examples: green stink bug, conchuela, Say stink bug, harlequin bug, southern green stink bug, spined soldier bug, rice stink bug.

FAMILY COREIDAE—COREID BUGS, SQUASH BUGS (FIG. 4:9A)

Description: ⅖ to ⅘ in. long; elongate body; large compound eyes; four-segmented antennae; membranous portion of forewings have many parallel, longitudinal veins; some species, the "leaf-footed bugs," have the hind legs flattened and leaflike.

Bionomics: most winter as adults; eggs are laid on host plants; usually five nymphal instars; some species phytophagous, others predaceous; have an odor which is strong, "over-sweet."

Examples: squash bug, horned squash bug, leaf-footed bug.

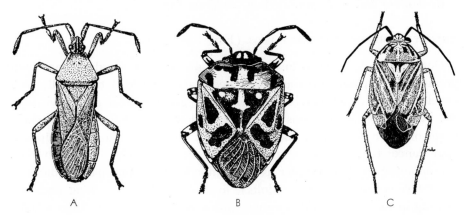

Fig. 4:9. Hemiptera. A, squash bug, Coreidae; B, harlequin bug, Pentatomidae; C, tarnished plant bug, Miridae. *A, B, courtesy USDA; C, courtesy Illinois Natural History Survey.*

Family Lygaeidae—lygaeid bugs, chinch bugs (Fig. 9:10)

Description: ⅛ to ⅗ in. long; beak and antennae are four-segmented; differ from plant bugs (Miridae) in having ocelli but lacking cuneus of forewings; differ from squash bugs (Coreidae) in having few veins in membranous portions of forewings; many species are conspicuously marked with spots or bands of red, white, or black.

Bionomics: most winter as adults in plant debris; eggs laid in or near the ground; five nymphal instars; swarms of nymphs may build up at certain times and move into cultivated crops; most species are plant feeders, but some are predaceous; big-eyed bugs are important predators of leafhoppers, aphids, and other small insects.

Examples: chinch bug, hairy chinch bug, western chinch bug, false chinch bug, large milkweed bug, small milkweed bug.

Family Cimicidae—bat, bed, and bird bugs (Fig. 17:1E)

Description: about ¼ in. long; flat, broadly oval body; wingless; head with conspicuous, protruding eyes; eggs are elongate and white, about ¹⁄₃₂ in. long.

Bionomics: active throughout the year in protected places; eggs glued a few at a time to surfaces of hiding places; five nymphal instars; hide during day in dark places; feed by sucking blood from birds and mammals; they may exist without feeding for a year or so under otherwise favorable conditions.

Examples: bed bug, poultry bug, swallow bug.

FAMILY MIRIDAE—THE PLANT BUGS (FIG. 4:9C)

Description: $\frac{1}{17}$ to $\frac{1}{4}$ in. long; elongate or oval; head distinct with prominent compound eyes and with ocelli absent; hemelytra usually well developed but sometimes brachypterous (a given species may have both short and long-winged forms); wings have a well-developed cuneus which is set off from the rest of the wing with a groove, producing a "hipped" appearance; they are active and run fast and fly freely when disturbed.

Bionomics: most overwinter as eggs imbedded in some part of the host plant (lygus bugs winter as adults); five nymphal instars, wing pads appearing in the third; mostly one generation per season (lygus bugs usually have two or three); females may mate within two to three days after emerging, start ovipositing seven to ten days later.

Examples: lygus bugs, alfalfa plant bug, rapid plant bug, suckfly, onion plant bug, meadow plant bug, apple red bug, tarnished plant bug, hollyhock plant bug, four-lined plant bug, cotton fleahopper.

Order Homoptera: cicadas, treehoppers, spittlebugs, leafhoppers, aphids, whiteflies, scale insects, and others

Mouthparts—piercing-sucking.

Wings—usually sloping over sides of body at rest, forewings uniform texture throughout; some forms wingless.

Metamorphosis—simple.

Additional feature—base of sucking beak extending between anterior coxae ("beak" arises at rear of underside of head).

FAMILY MEMBRACIDAE—TREEHOPPERS (FIG. 4:10A)

Description: $\frac{1}{5}$ to $\frac{2}{5}$ in. long; enlarged and prolonged prothorax projects forward over head and backward over abdomen; antennae minute, bristle-like; tarsi three-jointed; only two ocelli; colors and shapes often protective by mimicking plant parts, especially thorns.

Bionomics: winter as eggs inserted in bark of trees (some as nymphs or adults); nymphs are laterally flattened and usually have fringe of hairs or spines along eavelike back; often are minor pests of orchards, especially nursery stock because egg-laying punctures stunt the tips of the branches.

Examples: buffalo treehopper, two-marked treehopper, quince treehopper, three-cornered alfalfa hopper.

Family Cercopidae—spittlebugs, froghoppers (Fig. 10:18)

Description: ⅙ to ⅖ in. long; nymphs live in mass of white froth or spittle; antennae minute, bristle-like; adults mostly drab-colored, brown, gray or black; robust, almost as wide as long; hind tibia smooth with one to two heavy spines on sides and smaller spines at junction with tarsus.

Bionomics: winter as eggs or adults depending on species; nymphs appear in spring and early summer; one generation per season; spittle provides a moist environment for nymphs; feed on grasses and herbaceous plants.

Examples: rhubarb spittlebug, pine spittlebug, Saratoga spittlebug, dogwood spittlebug, meadow spittlebug, lined spittlebug.

Family Cicadellidae—leafhoppers (Fig. 4:10B)

Description: ⅛ to ⅜ in. long; slender insects with bristle-like antennae; hind tibia with double row of spines; forewings somewhat thickened and often colored; characteristic habit of running sideways.

Bionomics: usually overwinter as eggs or adults in grasses, weeds, or trash (rarely as nymphs); eggs inserted into plant tissues; five nymphal instars and one to six generations per season; usually develop two or

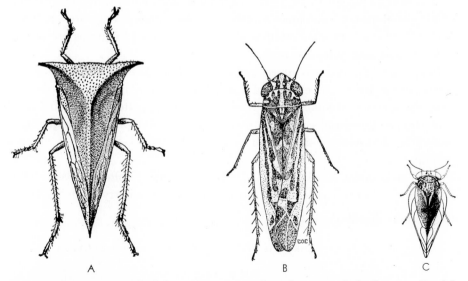

Fig. 4:10. Homoptera. A, buffalo treehopper, Membracidae; B, apple leafhopper, Cicadellidae; C, pear psylla, Psyllidae. A, *courtesy USDA; B, from* Insects and Mites of Western North America, *1958, by permission The Macmillan Company; C, courtesy Conn. Agr. Exp. Sta.*

more population peaks during season; four types of injury to crops: disease transmission (especially the "yellows type" plant virus diseases), toxicogenic effects, direct removal of plant materials, and miscellaneous (e.g., honeydew injuries and oviposition injuries).

Examples: geminate leafhopper, rose leafhopper, grape leafhoppers, six-spotted leafhopper, beet leafhopper, apple leafhopper, clover leafhopper, yellow-headed leafhopper, potato leafhopper, plum leafhopper, blunt-nosed cranberry leafhopper, and many other pest species.

FAMILY PSYLLIDAE—PSYLLIDS, JUMPING PLANTLICE (FIG. 4:10C)

Description: $\frac{1}{17}$ to $\frac{1}{5}$ in. long; adults look much like miniature cicadas; hind legs enlarged for jumping; antennae with nine or more segments; eggs are elongate and usually elevated on a short stalk; nymphs circular and flattened, with large wing pads and fringed margins.

Bionomics: winter as adults, sometimes as eggs; usually five nymphal instars; several generations per season; some species secrete a white, woolly wax covering; heavy infestations produce damaging amounts of honeydew.

Examples: potato (tomato) psyllid, boxwood psyllid, apple sucker, pear psylla, persimmon psylla.

FAMILY ALEYRODIDAE—WHITEFLIES (FIG. 15:9)

Description: $\frac{1}{25}$ to $\frac{1}{8}$ in. long; adult body and wings covered with fine, white, powdery wax; antennae usually seven-segmented; eggs are small and oval and attached to plants with a stalk; newly hatched nymphs are motile, but lose legs and antennae at first molt.

Bionomics: winter as nymphs; female lays 10 to 20 eggs in circle, or may scatter them; 100 to 200 eggs per female; first instar active but after the first molt, the nymph becomes a flat, scalelike creature, often with a fringe of waxy filaments; nymphs produce honeydew; last nymphal instar quiescent and often designated pupa; adult emerges through T-shaped slit in back of pupal case.

Examples: citrus blackfly; woolly whitefly, azalea whitefly, sweet-potato whitefly, rhododendron whitefly, citrus whitefly, strawberry whitefly, greenhouse whitefly, grape whitefly, iris whitefly.

FAMILY CHERMIDAE—BARK APHIDS, GALL APHIDS, AND PHYLLOXERAS (FIG. 4:11B)

Description: mostly about $\frac{1}{25}$ in. long; no cornicles or cauda (true aphid structures); reduced wing venation (fewer than true aphids); bark aphids and gall aphids have three to five antennal segments, phylloxeras have three; body of bark aphids often covered with waxy threads, phylloxeras with waxy powder.

Bionomics: gall aphids and bark aphids feed only on conifers, phylloxeras feed on other kinds of plants; all females are oviparous, none give birth to living young; gall-forming species alternate in their life history between two different conifers, forming galls only on primary host.

Examples: eastern spruce gall aphid, Cooley spruce gall aphid, pine bark aphid, pecan phylloxera, grape phylloxera.

FAMILY APHIDAE—APHIDS OR PLANTLICE (FIG. 4:11A)

Description: mostly $\frac{1}{25}$ to $\frac{1}{5}$ in. long; delicate insects; antennae usually well developed, usually six-segmented; adults wingless or with two pairs of membranous wings; some are covered with powdery or cottony wax; corni-cles (pairs of erect tubules on top of rear of abdomen) and cauda (pointed tip structure of abdomen) are structures peculiar to true aphids.

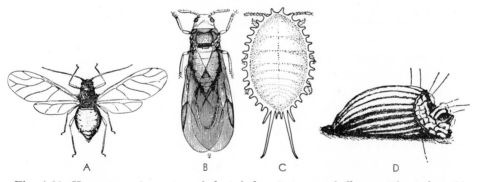

Fig. 4:11. Homoptera. A, turnip aphid, Aphidae; B, grape phylloxera, Chermidae; C, grape mealybug, Pseudococcidae; D, cottony-cushion scale, Coccidae. *A, B, D, courtesy USDA; C, original.*

Bionomics: usually overwinter as black, shiny eggs on a woody "primary" host plant (few exceptions winter as nymphs or adults); four nymphal instars and up to 20 or more generations per season; life cycles usually complicated, often involving "alternation" of host plants; both partheno-genetic and sexual forms usually occur each year; often abundant and in-jurious on all types of plants; tend to be specific feeders; important as vectors of many virus diseases of plants.

Examples: rosy apple aphid, woolly apple aphid, black cherry aphid, mealy plum aphid, green peach aphid, strawberry aphid, currant aphid, pea aphid, cabbage aphid, sugar-beet root aphid, potato aphid, clover aphid, English grain aphid, hop aphid, corn root aphid, snowball aphid, cotton aphid, spotted alfalfa aphid, corn leaf aphid, walnut aphid, rose aphid, apple grain aphid, greenbug, and many other economic pest species.

SUPERFAMILY COCCOIDEA—SCALE INSECTS, MEALYBUGS (FIG. 4:11C AND D)

Description: $\frac{1}{25}$ to $\frac{2}{5}$ in. long; active or stationary, naked with hard epidermis or waxy covering, or with definite round, oval, or elongate shell; antennae well developed or absent; some coated with powdery or cottony wax.

Bionomics: overwinter as eggs or partly grown nymphs; young born alive or hatch from eggs; young are motile "crawlers," after first molt, scaled species become sessile; male scales usually transform, after four nymphal instars, into delicate two-winged insects with two long anal filaments; female scales usually have two nymphal instars; generally not very host-specific; often present in enormous numbers and one of the most destructive types of pests; feed on stems, leaves, roots, and fruits of plants.

Examples:

1. **Pseudococcidae (mealybugs)**—Rhodes-grass scale, Mexican mealybug, long-tailed mealybug, pineapple mealybug, citrus mealybug, grape mealybug, ground mealybug (Fig. 4:11C).

2. **Coccidae (soft scales)**—Florida wax scale, brown soft scale, citricola scale, European fruit lecanium, terrapin scale, cottony peach scale, hemispherical scale, black scale, tuliptree scale (Fig. 4:11D).

3. **Diaspididae (armored scales)**—yellow scale, holly scale, black pine leaf scale, San Jose scale, grape scale, rose scale, Florida red scale, dictyospermum scale, Italian pear scale, fig scale, oystershell scale, olive scale (Fig. 13:23).

Order Neuroptera: lacewings, alderflies, dobsonflies, antlions, and others

Mouthparts—chewing.

Wings—two pairs large membranous wings with many cross veins and longitudinal veins, held rooflike over abdomen at rest.

Metamorphosis—complex.

Additional features—antennae usually long and many segmented; cerci absent.

FAMILY CHRYSOPIDAE—GREEN LACEWINGS (FIG. 4:12)

Description: adult $\frac{3}{5}$ to $\frac{4}{5}$ in. long; long, hairlike antennae; green, filmy wings; iridescent, red-gold eyes; small oval eggs are suspended by slender filaments about $\frac{1}{4}$ in. long; full grown larva $\frac{1}{4}$ to $\frac{2}{5}$ in. long; flattened, wedge-shaped body and well-developed legs; long sickle-like jaws are used to capture, puncture, and extract body juices from living prey; pupate in delicate, white cocoons about ⅛ in. in diameter.

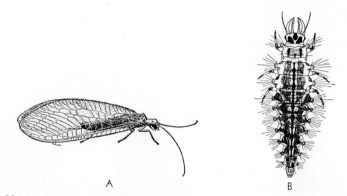

Fig. 4:12. Neuroptera. A, green lacewing adult; B, green lacewing larva. *A, courtesy Illinois Natural History Survey; B, courtesy Cornell Univ.*

Bionomics: winter as larvae in silken cocoons; adults appear in early spring; five to six generations per season; larvae (aphidlions) feed on 200 to 400 aphids or other soft-bodied creatures during their development; adults give off disagreeable odor when handled.

Examples: golden-eye lacewing, California green lacewing.

Order Coleoptera: beetles and weevils

Mouthparts—chewing.

Wings—forewings are elytra (hard, shell-like covers) which meet in a straight line over the abdomen when not in flight; hindwings membranous.

Metamorphosis—complex.

Additional features—prothorax large and mobile, mesothorax much reduced.

FAMILY CARABIDAE—GROUND BEETLES (FIG. 4:13A)

Description: ⅖ to 1⅖ in. long; elongate, flattened, often slender with long legs adapted for running; usually dark colors, shiny, sometimes metallic; a very common and familiar group.

Bionomics: usually winter as adults; eggs laid in soil; nocturnal; almost all are predaceous, equal to lady beetles in importance as destroyers of insect pests; mostly feed on caterpillars, slugs, other insect larvae and pupae.

Examples: seed-corn beetle, tule beetle, fiery hunter, stink beetle.

FAMILY ELATERIDAE—CLICK BEETLES, WIREWORMS (FIG. 4:13B)

Description: ¼ to 1⅘ in. long; elongate, flattened, short-legged beetles; usually dull-colored in browns, grays, and blacks; "click mechanism" is formed by long extension of first thoracic segment which fits into socket on underside of second segment; hind corners of pronotum usually pointed; larvae are elongate, cylindrical, usually hard bodied with smooth, shining, brown or yellowish integument (Fig. 8:18).

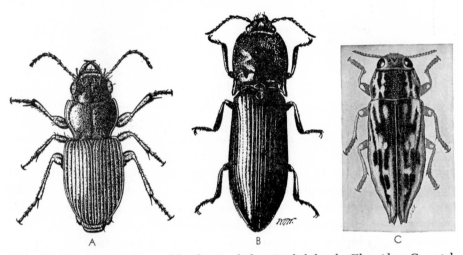

Fig. 4:13. Coleoptera. A, ground beetle, Carabidae; B, click beetle, Elateridae; C, metallic wood borer, Buprestidae. *A, courtesy Kan. State Univ.; B, courtesy USDA; C, courtesy J. N. Knull.*

Bionomics: overwinter as adults or larvae in soil; adults fly or crawl in spring and lay eggs in soil around roots of plants; larvae spend two to six seasons in soil, depending on species; larvae of economic species feed on seeds, roots, and crowns of plants, adults on flower buds; many noneconomic species live in rotten wood or are predaceous; many pupate in August, lie in soil cell as adults until spring.

Examples: Great Basin wireworm, Puget Sound wireworm, sugar-beet wireworm, dry-land wireworm, wheat wireworm, eyed click beetle, Gulf wireworm, tobacco wireworm, prairie grain wireworm, sand wireworm, eastern field wireworm.

FAMILY BUPRESTIDAE—FLATHEADED OR METALLIC WOOD BORERS (FIG. 4:13C)

Description: ⅕ to 1⅛ in. long; often metallic coppery, green, blue, or black; hard bodied and compactly built; antennae short, usually sawtoothed;

larvae are called flatheaded borers because of greatly enlarged and flattened thoracic segments.

Bionomics: usually winter as pupae; eggs laid in crevices in bark; larvae tunnel under bark and into wood; many species are injurious to trees and shrubs, shade trees, orchard trees, and cane berries.

Examples: bronze birch borer, two-lined chestnut borer, rose stem girdler, red-necked cane borer, sinuate pear tree borer, flatheaded apple tree borer, Australian-pine borer, flatheaded fir borer.

FAMILY DERMESTIDAE—DERMESTID BEETLES, SKIN BEETLES (FIG. 17:2)

Description: $\frac{1}{12}$ to $\frac{1}{2}$ in. long; small, oval, convex beetles with short, clubbed antennae; usually hairy or covered with scales; many are black or dull colored, others have checkered color patterns; larvae usually brown and covered with long hairs.

Bionomics: active the year round inside buildings; larvae feed on cereals and stored food products, woolens, feathers, furs, dried insects, and other dried animal products; adults usually feed on flower pollen.

Examples: carpet beetle, furniture carpet beetle, black carpet beetle, larder beetle, hide beetle, khapra beetle.

FAMILY CUCUJIDAE—FLAT BARK BEETLES, GRAIN BEETLES (FIG. 17:1A)

Description: $\frac{1}{10}$ to $\frac{3}{5}$ in. long; very flat and elongate; reddish, brownish, or yellowish; compound eyes small; antennae rather heavy and beadlike; larvae are flat or cylindrical.

Bionomics: stored-products pest species are active the year round in storage facilities; species that live under the dead bark of trees are predaceous or parasitic on wood-destroying insects.

Examples: square-necked grain beetle, rusty grain beetle, flat grain beetle, saw-toothed grain beetle.

FAMILY COCCINELLIDAE—LADY BEETLES (FIG. 4:14A)

Description: adult $\frac{1}{30}$ to $\frac{1}{3}$ in. long; oval and convex with the underside quite flat; often bright colored and spotted, although certain small species which are predaceous on scale insects and spider mites are wholly black; full grown larva $\frac{1}{17}$ to $\frac{3}{5}$ in. long; elongate, flattened and covered with tubercles, spines, or woolly wax secretions; often spotted or banded with bright colors (Fig. 12:10).

Bionomics: winter as adults, frequently in large masses, at elevations above the surrounding countryside, under plant debris; spindle-shaped eggs laid singly or in small clusters, attached to plants; mostly predaceous on aphids and other small soft-bodied insects and mites; only two exceptions in North America are injurious plant feeders, the Mexican bean beetle and the squash beetle.

Examples: two-spotted lady beetle, twice-stabbed lady beetle, squash beetle, Mexican bean beetle, convergent lady beetle, steel-blue lady beetle, black lady beetle, vedalia.

FAMILY BYTURIDAE—FRUITWORM BEETLES (FIG. 14:14)

Description: $\frac{1}{7}$ to $\frac{1}{4}$ in. long; body usually elongate oval, covered with short hairs, and brown, orange, or tan; mature fruitworm larvae are $\frac{1}{4}$ to $\frac{1}{3}$ in. long, light colored, with brown area on upper part of each segment.

Bionomics: winter as adults in pupal cells in soil; eggs laid on buds, flowers, or stems; one generation per season; *Byturus* larvae typically feed in wild or domestic bramble fruits, especially raspberry and loganberry; larvae of other genera feed in oak galls or other materials.

Examples: eastern raspberry fruitworm, western raspberry fruitworm.

FAMILY TENEBRIONIDAE—DARKLING BEETLES, FALSE WIREWORMS, FLOUR BEETLES (FIG. 16:13)

Description: $\frac{1}{8}$ to $1\frac{2}{5}$ in. long; large black, slow-moving, round-bodied, darkling beetles and small, flattened, red or brown flour beetles; false wireworm larvae of darkling beetles live in soil and resemble wireworms, very active when disturbed; larvae of flour beetles are small and live in grain or meal; darkling beetles have characteristic habit of pointing abdomen into the air and emitting an offensive vapor when disturbed.

Bionomics: darkling beetles usually winter as adults; flour beetles remain active the year round in stored grain and grain products.

Examples: false wireworms, yellow mealworm, red flour beetle, confused flour beetle, lesser mealworm, broad-horned flour beetle.

FAMILY SCARABAEIDAE—SCARABS, WHITE GRUBS, JUNE BEETLES (FIG. 4:14B)

Description: $\frac{1}{4}$ to $1\frac{2}{5}$ in. long; robust, dull to bright colored and metallic; antennae terminates in oval club composed of three to seven movable plates; white grub larva usually thick, wrinkled, light colored, C-shaped, and with swollen terminal portion of abdomen (Fig. 12:3).

Bionomics: usually winter as larvae or adults in the soil; pupate in cell or in ball of dung in soil; eggs are laid in or on food of larva; life cycle usually takes one to three years to complete; three larval instars, except rain beetles have seven to eleven; adults feed on plant foliage or pollen, fungi, or dung; larvae usually live in soil and feed on roots, dung, or decaying vegetable matter (Fig. 3:10).

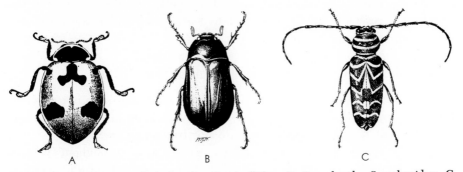

Fig. 4:14. Coleoptera. A, lady beetle, Coccinellidae; B, June beetle, Scarabaeidae; C, locust borer, Cerambycidae. *A from Essig,* Insects and Mites of Western North America, *1958, by permission The Macmillan Company; B and C from USDA.*

Examples: oriental beetle, green June beetle, southern masked chafer, sugarcane beetle, bumble flower beetle, carrot beetle, rose chafer, ten-lined June beetle, Japanese beetle, rain beetles.

FAMILY CERAMBYCIDAE—LONG-HORNED BEETLES, ROUNDHEADED WOOD BORERS (FIG. 4:14C)

Description: ⅕ to 2⅖ in. long; mostly large, slender beetles with very long antennae; larvae have small heads and long, almost cylindrical bodies.

Bionomics: winter as larvae; life cycle requires one to four years to complete; larvae tunnel through wood, adults feed on foliage, bark, pollen, or fungi.

Examples: grape trunk borer, old-house borer, locust borer, southern pine sawyer, raspberry cane borer, twig girdler, roundheaded apple tree borer, banded alder borer.

FAMILY CHRYSOMELIDAE—LEAF BEETLES AND FLEA BEETLES (FIG. 4:15A)

Description: 1/17 to ½ in. long; black, brown, iridescent blue, green, bronze, or purple, or with bright color patterns; circular to oval in shape; flea beetles have enlarged hind femora for jumping.

Bionomics: usually overwinter as adults in sheltered places in plant debris or soil; eggs laid in or on host plant, debris, or soil; adults usually feed on foliage, larvae either on foliage or roots (Fig. 9:16); pupate in soil or on plants.

Examples: asparagus beetle, tuber flea beetle, Colorado potato beetle, elm leaf beetle, striped cucumber beetle, northern corn rootworm, cranberry rootworm, alder flea beetle, corn flea beetle, tobacco flea beetle, hop flea beetle, rose leaf beetle, sweetpotato leaf beetle, and many other economic pest species.

FAMILY BRUCHIDAE—SEED BEETLES, BRUCHIDS (FIG. 4:15B)

Description: $\frac{1}{17}$ to $\frac{1}{5}$ in. long; oval, stout-bodied, elytra do not cover tip of abdomen; mottled black, gray, or brown with hairs and scales; clublike antennae; often called weevils, but are not true snout beetles.

Bionomics: usually winter as adults, may breed throughout year in storage facilities; usually four larval instars; mostly feed on seeds of leguminous plants, adults feed on pollen.

Examples: bean weevil, vetch bruchid, pea weevil, broadbean weevil, cowpea weevil.

FAMILY CURCULIONIDAE—SNOUT BEETLES OR WEEVILS (FIG. 4:15C)

Description: $\frac{1}{12}$ to $\frac{3}{4}$ in. long; mouth parts situated at end of snout of varying length which curves downward; antennae usually elbowed and ending in club; mostly dull gray, brown, or black; some are without hind wings and unable to fly; adults mostly diurnal in habit, walk slowly when disturbed, often "play dead"; larvae are legless, C-shaped, and white with brown heads (Fig. 11:10). This is the largest family of insects, containing thousands of species.

Bionomics: overwinter as larvae in soil or debris (sometimes as adults); eggs laid in punctures in plant made by "beak" of female or in soil; some species parthenogenetic; larvae usually feed on roots, adults usually notch or eat holes in foliage, fruits, seeds, or nuts.

Examples: strawberry root weevil, black vine weevil, strawberry crown borer, carrot weevil, clover root curculio, pea leaf weevil, alfalfa weevil, sweetclover weevil, clover leaf weevil, cabbage seedpod weevil, granary weevil, boll weevil, plum gouger, maize billbug, plum curculio, banana root borer, poplar-and-willow borer, pecan weevil, white-fringed beetles, rice water weevil, white-pine weevil, rose curculio, tobacco stalk borer, and many other economic pest species.

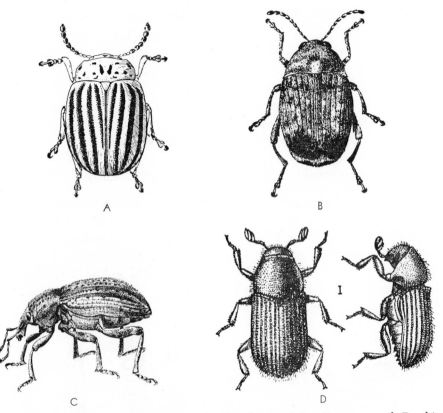

Fig. 4:15. Coleoptera. A, Colorado potato beetle, Chrysomelidae; B, pea weevil, Bruchidae; C, clover leaf weevil, Curculionidae; D, peach bark beetle, Scolytidae. *Courtesy USDA.*

FAMILY SCOLYTIDAE—BARK BEETLES (FIG. 4:15D)

Description: $\frac{1}{17}$ to $\frac{3}{8}$ in. long; usually robust, cylindrical with head partially concealed from above; antennae clubbed; usually brown or black; larvae usually white, legless and slightly curved.

Bionomics: winter as larvae or pupae, sometimes as adults; adults excavate gallery under bark and lay eggs; when eggs hatch, larvae tunnel away from brood gallery, forming pattern under bark characteristic for each species; most important group of forest insects, may girdle and kill trees.

Examples: lodgepole cone beetle, Douglas-fir beetle, Engelmann spruce beetle, western pine beetle, southern pine beetle, Black Hills beetle, red turpentine beetle, clover root borer, apple twig beetle, peach bark beetle, fir engraver, shot-hole borer, smaller European elm bark beetle (main vector of Dutch elm fungus disease).

Order Lepidoptera: butterflies and moths

Mouthparts—chewing in larvae; siphoning in adults.

Wings—two pairs of membranous wings covered with a layer of minute scales.

Metamorphosis—complex.

Additional features—legs relatively small; caterpillars (larvae) have cluster of lateral ocelli on each side of head (as contrasted to one on each side in the caterpillar-like larvae of some Hymenoptera).

FAMILY GRACILARIIDAE—LEAF BLOTCH MINERS (FIG. 4:16)

Description: wingspread ¼ to ⅗ in.; wings are narrow and pointed, often with hump near base of hindwing; moths rest with anterior part of body elevated, wing tips touching surface; larvae are flattened and with rudimentary legs.

Bionomics: usually winter as larvae in cocoons in soil or in plant debris; larvae usually form blotch mines in the upper surfaces of leaves, often folding or rolling the leaf.

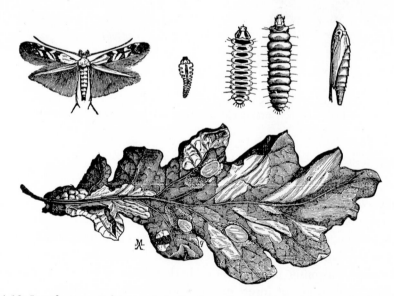

Fig. 4:16. Lepidoptera. Solitary oak leaf miner, Gracilariidae. Adult moth, three larval instars, pupa, and oak leaf showing mines of larvae. *From Comstock,* An Introduction to Entomology, *1940, by permission Cornell University Press.*

Examples: azalea leaf miner, privet leaf miner, boxelder leaf roller, lilac leaf miner, apple fruit miner, gregarious oak leaf miner, lantana leaf miner.

FAMILY TINEIDAE—CLOTHES MOTHS (FIG. 17:14)

Description: ⅓ to almost 1 in. wing expanse; straw-colored to brownish; mature larvae are about ⅓ in. long and white; spin silk webbing or protective cases.

Bionomics: moths lay minute white eggs on food of the larvae; larvae are scavengers or fungus-feeders, some feed on woolens.

Examples: European grain moth, fungus moth, casemaking clothes moth, webbing clothes moth, carpet moth.

FAMILY AEGERIIDE—CLEARWING MOTHS OR CROWN BORERS (FIG. 4:17A)

Description: ⅗ to 1⅕ in. wingspread; day-flying moths with narrow partially transparent (unscaled) wings; antennae long and enlarged toward the tips or else tapered at both ends; abdomen often with color bands and smooth appearance; striking resemblance to wasps; male has conspicuous anal tufts; larvae are ivory white without markings except yellow or brown thoracic shield and head.

Bionomics: overwinter as larvae in burrows in crowns or stems of host plants; moths are strong, swift fliers; larvae bore into stems, crowns, or roots of woody plants (Fig. 13:10).

Examples: western peach tree borer, strawberry crown moth, raspberry crown borer, currant borer, peach tree borer, squash vine borer, rhododendron borer, grape root borer.

FAMILY GELECHIIDAE—GELECHIID MOTHS (FIG. 4:17B)

Description: ½ to 1 in. wingspread; pale yellow to gray or brown, night-flying moths; caterpillars variable in color from white to pink to brown or even black; labial palps of moths long and curved upwards; forewings slender and often quite pointed at the apex (Fig. 11:13).

Bionomics: usually overwinter as larvae or pupae in silk-lined burrows or cocoons; eggs laid on host plant or stored vegetable materials; larvae usually feed in folded or spun leaves or shoots or in stems or seed heads, less commonly they are leaf miners; number of generations per season variable, one to six or more.

Examples: peach twig borer, strawberry crown miner, western strawberry leaf roller, palmerworm, juniper webworm, pine needle miner, potato tuberworm, eggplant leaf miner, tomato pinworm, pink bollworm, lesser bud moth, Angoumois grain moth, red-necked peanutworm.

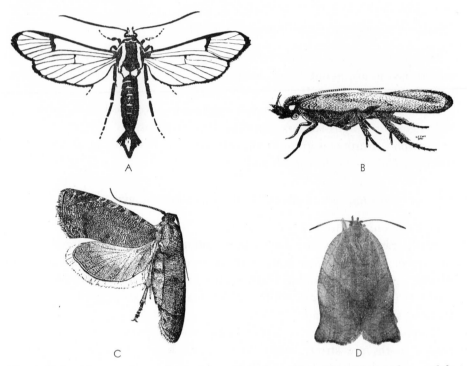

Fig. 4:17. Lepidoptera. A, peach tree borer adult, Aegeriidae; B, peach twig borer adult, Gelechiidae; C, oriental fruit moth, Olethreutidae; D, oblique-banded leaf roller adult, Tortricidae. *A, courtesy USDA; B, courtesy Calif. Agr. Exp. Sta.; C, courtesy Wood and Selkregg; D, courtesy Oregon State Univ.*

FAMILY OLETHREUTIDAE—FRUIT MOTHS, BUD MOTHS, FRUITWORMS
(FIG. 4:17C)

Description: ½ to 1 in. wingspread; dusk and night-flying moths; mostly brown or gray, variously mottled or banded (a number of species have short alternating light and dark markings on the leading edge of the front wings); caterpillars usually white to pinkish tan.

Bionomics: usually overwinter as mature larvae in cocoons under bark or in debris or other sheltered places; minute eggs usually laid singly on host plants; caterpillars feed on leaves and fruit, often webbing leaves and other materials together; usually two generations per season (Figs. 13:14 and 13:15).

Examples: codling moth, oriental fruit moth, cherry fruitworm, pea moth, black-headed fireworm, filbertworm, strawberry leaf roller, eye-spotted budmoth, clover head caterpillar, hickory shuckworm, pitch twig moth, grape berry moth, European pine shoot moth.

FAMILY TORTRICIDAE—LEAF ROLLERS (FIG. 4:17D)

Description: ½ to 1 in. wingspread; night-flying moths; often attractively striped or spotted in browns or grays ("X-shaped" patterns typical); resting adults often appear more or less bell-shaped; caterpillars usually greenish, active and drop on a silk strand when disturbed (Fig. 13:1).

Bionomics: overwinter as eggs on host plant or as young larvae in cocoons under bark or in debris; eggs laid in flat, overlapping masses; caterpillars roll or fold or tie leaves and other materials, securing these "nests" with silk.

Examples: fruit-tree leaf roller, omnivorous leaf tier, oblique-banded leaf roller, orange tortrix, ugly-nest caterpillar, red-banded leaf roller, spruce budworm, pecan bud moth.

SUPERFAMILY PYRALIDOIDEA—PYRALID MOTHS, PYRAUSTID MOTHS, GRASS MOTHS, WAX MOTHS, PHYCITID MOTHS (FIG. 4:18A,B,C)

Description: ⅖ to 1⅖ in. wing expanse; mostly small, dull-colored brown, gray, or silvery moths, sometimes with bands or markings; most are day-flying, grass moths are dusk and night flyers; large, conspicuous palps give a "snout" effect to pyralids, pyraustids, and grass moths; forewings are elongate or triangular.

Bionomics: usually winter as larvae or pupae in plant debris or soil, some are active the year round in buildings or greenhouses; pyraustid larvae bore in stems and fruits or web over foliage and stems; pyralid larvae feed on living and dead plant tissues, including stored grain; grass moths bore in crowns and roots of grasses or feed on grass foliage; wax moths feed on wax and debris in beehives; phycitid moths tunnel in stems, fruits, seeds, or flowers, or feed in stored products.

Examples:

1. **Pyralidae (pyralid moths)**—clover hayworm, meal moth.

2. **Pyraustidae (pyraustid moths)**—grape leaf folder, pickleworm, alfalfa webworm, beet webworm, celery leaf tier, sweetpotato leaf roller, European corn borer, purple-backed cabbageworm, garden webworm (Fig. 4:18A, Figs. 9:14 and 9:15).

3. **Crambidae (grass moths)**—rice stalk borer, corn root webworm, bluegrass webworm, cranberry girdler, southern cornstalk borer, southwestern corn borer, sugarcane borer (Fig. 4:18B).

4. **Galleriidae (wax moths)**—lesser wax moth, greater wax moth.

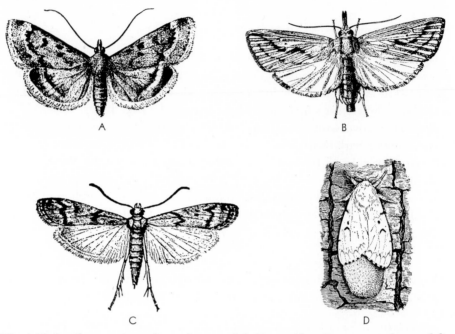

Fig. 4:18. Lepidoptera. A, garden webworm adult, Pyraustidae; B, sugarcane borer adult, Crambidae; C, Mediterranean flour moth, Phycitidae; D, Gypsy moth, Lymantriidae. *A, B, and C, courtesy USDA; D, courtesy Conn. Agr. Exp. Sta.*

5. **Phycitidae (phycitid moths)**—pecan nut casebearer, Zimmerman pine moth, almond moth, tobacco moth, raisin moth, Mediterranean flour moth, lima-bean pod borer, sugar-beet crown borer, leaf crumpler, cranberry fruitworm, navel orangeworm, Indian-meal moth, dried-fruit moth (Fig. 4:18C).

FAMILY ARCTIIDAE—TIGER MOTHS, WOOLLYBEARS (FIG. 4:19)

Description: 1⅖ to 2⅗ in. wing expanse; white, brown, or orange with conspicuous dark spots or bands; larvae usually hairy, woollybears especially; moths are mainly nocturnal, hold wings rooflike at rest.

Bionomics: winter as pupae in cocoons made largely from larval hairs; eggs laid in large clusters on plants; woollybears coil up when disturbed, other larval types live gregariously in large webs in deciduous trees.

Examples: yellow woollybear, salt-marsh caterpillar, hickory tussock moth, spotted tussock moth, fall webworm, banded woollybear, bella moth, silver-spotted tiger moth.

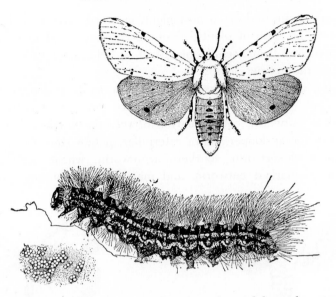

Fig. 4:19. Lepidoptera. Salt-marsh caterpillar, Arctiidae. Adult moth, caterpillar and eggs. *Courtesy USDA.*

Family Lymantriidae—tussock moths (Fig. 4:18D)

Description: wingless females about ½ in. long, winged females and males with ⅘ to 2 in. wingspread; moths hairy bodied; no ocelli; antennae are double comblike; larvae are hairy with characteristic tufts (tussocks) of hairs.

Bionomics: winter as eggs laid in large masses on cocoon or foliage or bark; larvae feed on foliage of orchard, shade, and forest trees.

Examples: white-marked tussock moth, Douglas-fir tussock moth, rusty tussock moth, brown-tail moth, gypsy moth, satin moth.

Family Noctuidae—owlet moths, millers, cutworms, armyworms, loopers, semiloopers (Fig. 8:11)

Description: wingspan generally 1 to 2 in.; with somber yellow, tan, gray, or brown colors, irregular patterns or markings on the forewings, hindwings typically pale; caterpillars naked or nearly so, with striped or mottled patterns; caterpillars usually have five pairs of prolegs, but semiloopers have only three or four pairs.

Bionomics: overwinter as caterpillars or pupae in soil or debris; moths are mostly night flyers, strongly attracted to lights; globular eggs laid singly or in masses on ground or on host plant; cutworms live in soil and cut off roots or feed on base of plants; climbing cutworms and green fruitworms feed on buds and fruits; semiloopers feed on field and forage crops; one to several generations per season.

Examples: green fruitworms, corn earworm, cabbage looper, red-backed cutworm, pale western cutworm, army cutworm, glassy cutworm, celery looper, black cutworm, cotton leafworm, velvetbean caterpillar, bean leaf skeletonizer, forage looper, zebra caterpillar, potato stem borer, fall armyworm, green cloverworm, southern armyworm, wheat head armyworm, armyworm, w-marked cutworm, and many other economic pest species.

A   B

Fig. 4:20. Lepidoptera. A, tobacco hornworm adult, Sphingidae; B, alfalfa caterpillar adult, Pieridae. *Courtesy USDA.*

Family Sphingidae—sphinx moths, hornworms (Fig. 4:20A)

Description: wingspread of 2 to 5 in.; heavy body tapered at both ends; forewings long, narrow and pointed; hindwings relatively small; antennae thickened in middle or toward the tip; large larvae are often green, usually possess conspicuous horn on top of posterior end of body; pupae often "jug-handled" by looped form of proboscis.

Bionomics: usually overwinter as pupae in soil or plant debris; moth resembles hummingbird when hovering in front of flower and feeding with proboscis extended; some are day flyers, most fly at dusk or night.

Examples: sweetpotato hornworm, Virginia-creeper sphinx, white-lined sphinx, walnut sphinx, tomato hornworm, tobacco hornworm.

Family Geometridae—geometrid moths, measuringworms, loopers (Fig. 4:21)

Description: generally 1 to 2 in. wingspan; some species have large-bodied, wingless females; wings broad, usually marked with wavy parallel bands; larvae are true loopers with only two well-developed pairs of prolegs.

Bionomics: most winter as eggs or as pupae; eggs laid in clusters of 100 to 400 upon plants; larvae have more pronounced looping movement than semiloopers (Noctuidae); adults are mainly nocturnal and attracted to lights.

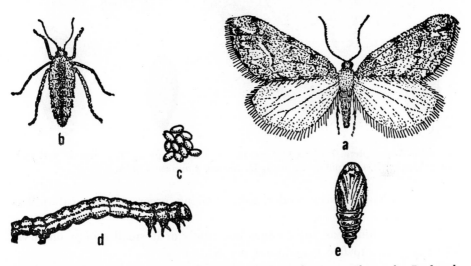

Fig. 4:21. Lepidoptera. Spring cankerworm, Geometridae. A, male moth; B, female moth, note that it is wingless; C, eggs; D, larva or cankerworm; E, pupa. *From Wellhouse,* How Insects Live, *1926, by permission W. H. Wellhouse.*

Examples: fall cankerworm, spring cankerworm, cranberry spanworm, elm spanworm, hemlock looper, grapevine looper, filament bearer.

FAMILY LASIOCAMPIDAE—TENT CATERPILLARS (FIG. 4:22)

Description: ¾ to 1½ in. wingspread; stout bodied and hairy; usually brown or gray with light bands across the forewings; caterpillar is often colorful with contrasting stripes and spots.

Bionomics: winter as tiny larvae within the egg shells; larvae are gregarious and usually live in large webs (tents); pupate in silken cocoons in sheltered places.

Examples: eastern tent caterpillar, forest tent caterpillar, western tent caterpillar, Great Basin tent caterpillar, lappet moth.

FAMILY PIERIDAE—WHITE AND SULFUR BUTTERFLIES (FIG. 4:20B)

Description: wing expanse 1 to 2⅖ in.; usually white or yellow with black marginal wing markings; chrysalids (naked pupae) long and narrow,

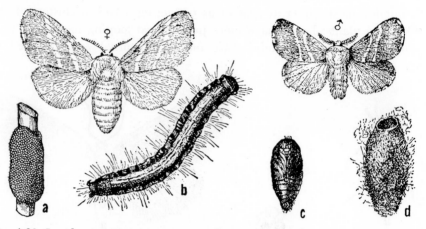

Fig. 4:22. Lepidoptera. Eastern tent caterpillar, Lasiocampidae. Top, female and male moth; A, eggs; B, caterpillar; C, pupa; D, cocoon. *Courtesy USDA.*

⅖ to ⅘ in. long; mostly slender, naked-looking, green or white caterpillars (Fig. 12:12).

Bionomics: winter as pupae; eggs laid singly or in small groups on larval host plant; two to five generations per season.

Examples: alfalfa caterpillar, clouded sulphur, pine butterfly, southern cabbageworm, imported cabbageworm.

Order Hymenoptera: sawflies, ichneumons, chalcids, ants, wasps, bees

Mouthparts—chewing in larvae; chewing or chewing-lapping in adults.

Wings—usually two pairs of membranous wings, the hind pair often attached to the fore pair with minute hooks.

Metamorphosis—complex.

Additional features—abdomen often with slender waist; female with ovipositor often specialized as a piercing, sawing, or stinging organ.

Family Tenthredinidae—sawflies (Fig. 4:23A)

Description: ⅛ to ½ in. long; robust body with head, thorax, and base of abdomen about equal in width; ovipositor sawlike for inserting eggs into plant tissues; larvae greatly resemble lepidopterous caterpillars but have six to eight pairs of prolegs without crochets.

Bionomics: usually winter as pupae in parchmentlike cocoons in plant debris; one to two generations per season; larvae usually are leaf feeders, some live in galls, and a few are leaf miners; some larvae, like the pear-slug, secrete a covering slime (Fig. 13:8).

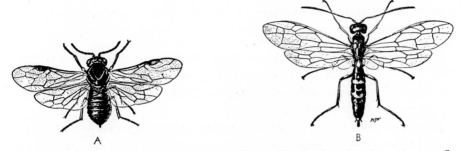

Fig. 4:23. Hymenoptera. A, cherry fruit sawfly, Tenthredinidae; B, wheat stem sawfly, Cephidae. *Courtesy USDA.*

Examples: curled rose sawfly, pear-slug, rose-slug, grape sawfly, birch leaf miner, cherry fruit sawfly, raspberry sawfly, imported currantworm, grass sawfly, larch sawfly.

FAMILY CEPHIDAE—STEM SAWFLIES (FIG. 4:23B)

Description: ⅓ to ⅗ in. long; body slender and compressed; larvae without prolegs, usually white, about ½ to 1 in. long when full grown.

Bionomics: usually winter as mature larvae in silk-lined burrows; one to two generations per season; larvae bore in the stems of grasses and berries.

Examples: wheat stem sawfly, black grain stem sawfly, willow shoot sawfly, currant stem girdler.

SUPERFAMILY ICHNEUMONOIDEA—BRACONIDS, ICHNEUMONS (FIG. 4:24A)

Description: braconids ¹⁄₂₀ to ½ in. long, ichneumons ⅙ to 1½ in. long; wasplike in appearance, but rarely able to sting; stigma (color spot) of forewing is large and conspicuous; mostly brown, red, or black with variable markings.

Bionomics: usually winter as larvae or pupae; eggs laid in, on, or near suitable host insect; ichneumons mainly parasitize caterpillars or pupae of moths and butterflies, braconids parasitize larvae or pupae of moths, butterflies, flies, wasps, or beetles and also aphids; four to five larval instars; larvae are external or internal parasites; adults are attracted to honeydew, nectar, and other sweets; important natural checks on pest insect populations, some have been successfully used in biological control programs.

Examples:

1. **Ichneumonidae**—ichneumon parasites.
2. **Braconidae**—braconid parasites.

SUPERFAMILY CHALCIDOIDEA—MINUTE EGG PARASITES, EULOPHIDS, ENCYRTIDS, PTEROMALIDS, JOINTWORMS, CHALCIDS (FIG. 4:24B,C)

Description: ⅛₅ to ½ in. long, majority about ⅛ in.; mostly dark colored, often metallic blue or green; often have unusual shapes, abdomen sometimes laterally compressed and triangular; hind coxae in some groups are greatly enlarged for jumping.

Bionomics: most winter as larvae or pupae, parasitic species in host corpse; three to five larval instars; one to eight or more generations per season; many are parasitic on Lepidoptera, Diptera, Coleoptera, or Homoptera; some are hyperparasites preying on primary parasites; a few bore into seeds or feed inside grass stems.

Fig. 4:24. Hymenoptera. A, *Apanteles thompsoni,* a parasite of European corn borer, Braconidae; B, wheat jointworm, Eurytomidae; C, *Aphelinus mali,* a parasite of woolly apple aphid, Eulophidae. *Courtesy USDA.*

Examples:
1. **Trichogrammatidae**—minute egg parasites.
2. **Eulophidae**—eulophid parasites.
3. **Encyrtidae**—parasites of aphids, scale insects, and other pests.
4. **Pteromalidae**—pteromalid parasites.
5. **Eurytomidae**—clover seed chalcid (Fig. 10:17), orchidfly, grape seed chalcid, wheat straw-worm, wheat jointworm (Fig. 8:1).
6. **Chalcididae**—chalcid parasites.

FAMILY FORMICIDAE—ANTS (FIG. 4:25A)

Description: workers ⅕₀ to ½ in. long; ants differ from termites in having a constricted abdomen, from other hymenoptera in having the constricted portion (pedicel) humped; antennae usually elbowed with first segment long; social insects, queens, males, and usually several types of workers and soldiers (Fig. 17:16).

Bionomics: colonies live through the winter; winged males and females produced at certain seasons; after mating, the female sheds her wings, finds a suitable nesting site, and starts a new colony; some feed on other animals (living or dead), some on plants, fungi, or honeydew and other sweets.

Examples: Texas leaf-cutting ant, black carpenter ant, Argentine ant, cornfield ant, little black ant, Pharaoh ant, red harvester ant, imported fire ant, pavement ant.

FAMILY APIDAE—BUMBLE BEES, CARPENTER BEES, HONEY BEES (FIG. 4:25B)

Description: ⅓ to 1 in. long; mostly robust, hairy, long-tongued bees; heavy-bodied, legless larvae.

Bionomics: winter as colonies or as fertilized queens; either social, solitary, or parasitic in habit; larvae live in cells on food supplied by adults; most important group of pollinating insects.

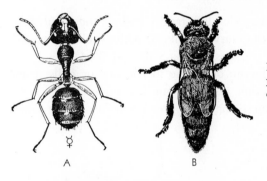

Fig. 4:25. Hymenoptera. A, black carpenter ant, Formicidae; B, honey bee queen, Apidae. *Courtesy USDA.*

Examples: honey bee, hairy flower bee, great carpenter bee, western bumble bee, yellow bumble bee.

Order Diptera: flies

Mouthparts—chewing or reduced in larvae; piercing-sucking, sponging, or vestigial in adults.

Wings—one pair of membranous forewings, hindwings modified as halteres.

Metamorphosis—complex.

Additional features—head, thorax, and abdomen quite distinct; compound eyes usually large.

FAMILY CULICIDAE—MOSQUITOES (FIGS. 4:26A AND 20:9)

Description: mostly about ¼ in. long; slender, long-legged flies; characteristically with scales along wing veins or margins; larvae are elongate with well-developed head and thorax, respiratory tube on next to last abdominal segment except in *Anopheles* which breathe through paired spiracular plates on posterior end of body.

Bionomics: mainly winter as adults in protected places, sometimes as eggs; adult females usually must feed at least once on the blood of a warm-blooded animal before their eggs will develop; larvae and pupae are aquatic; important as transmitters of diseases such as malaria, yellow fever, and filariasis to man; encephalitis, anthrax, and other diseases to domestic animals.

Examples: yellow-fever mosquito, salt-marsh mosquito, floodwater mosquito, western tree-hole mosquito, common malaria mosquito, northern house mosquito.

FAMILY CECIDOMYIIDAE—GALL MIDGES (FIG. 4:26B)

Description: ⅟₂₅ to ⅛ in. long; slender, fragile-bodied flies; antennae long and ringed with short bristles; larvae pinkish, white, yellow, or red; pupae are in silken or resinous cocoons (Figs. 8:13 and 8:14).

Bionomics: usually winter as larvae or pupae in cocoons or galls; some larvae feed on galls formed by other insects; some live under bark, in decaying vegetation, in dung, or fungi; some are predaceous on spider mites,

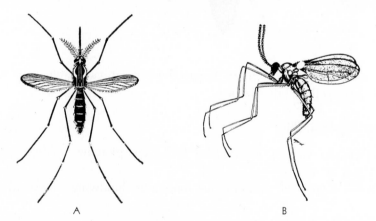

Fig. 4:26. Diptera. A, yellow-fever mosquito, Culicidae; B, *Aphidoletes meridionalis,* an aphid predator, Cecidomyiidae. *Courtesy USDA.*

aphids, scale insects, or bark beetle larvae; the destructive species live in plant tissues, rolled leaves, or galls which they cause in grasses, composites, and willows.

Examples: alfalfa gall midge, grape blossom midge, pear midge, sorghum midge, clover seed midge, rose midge, chrysanthemum gall midge, boxwood leaf miner, Hessian fly, wheat midge.

FAMILY TABANIDAE—HORSE FLIES, DEER FLIES (FIG. 4:27A)

Description: ⅓ to 1 in. long; robust with large, often bright-colored or iridescent eyes; modified piercing-sucking (actually cutting-sponging) mouth parts are short and beaklike; eggs are long and spindle shaped; larvae are long, hard bodied, tapered at both ends, and with a ring of tubercles around each segment.

Bionomics: usually overwinter in larval stage; eggs are laid directly in water or in masses on undersides of foliage overhanging water; larvae are predaceous on other insect larvae, snails, and earthworms in wet soil or mud; adult females suck the blood of domestic animals and man; certain species transmit tularemia and anthrax, and a type of filariasis.

Examples: black horse fly, striped horse fly, western horse fly.

FAMILY SYRPHIDAE—SYRPHID FLIES, FLOWER FLIES, HOVER FLIES (FIG. 4:27B)

Description: ⅛ to ⅗ in. long; adults usually brightly colored and resemble bees or wasps, some are hairy and look very much like honey bees or bumble bees; eggs of aphid-feeding species are long, white, with "pebbled" surface, and usually laid singly amongst aphid colonies; most larvae are wrinkled, maggot shaped, and green, brown, or white.

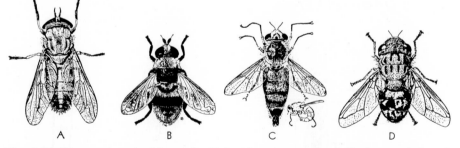

A   B   C   D

Fig. 4:27. Diptera. A, striped horse fly, Tabanidae; B, narcissus bulb fly, Syrphidae; C, horse bot fly, Gasterophilidae; D, sheep bot fly, Oestridae. *Courtesy USDA.*

Bionomics: usually winter as pupae in puparia in soil or plant debris; larvae are predaceous on aphids, live in the nests of social insects, live in decaying vegetable matter, live in liquid filth (rat-tailed maggots), or feed on growing plants.

Examples: lesser bulb fly, narcissus bulb fly, drone fly, and many species which are common and effective destroyers of aphids.

FAMILY TEPHRITIDAE—FRUIT FLIES (FIG. 4:30A)

Description: ⅐ to ⅕ in. long; colorful flies with "pictured" wings (bands of color on wings); wide heads with greenish eyes; body and legs quite hairy and bristly; larvae are typical, white, tapered maggots (Figs. 13:25 and 13:26).

Bionomics: overwinter as pupae within puparia in the soil; eggs inserted under skin of fruit by ovipositor; maggots live in fruit, berries, leaves, stems, or galls.

Examples: cherry fruit fly, currant fruit fly, walnut husk fly, Mediterranean fruit fly, melon fly, oriental fruit fly, apple maggot, sunflower maggot, papaya fruit fly, pepper maggot.

FAMILY PSILIDAE—RUST FLIES (FIG. 4:28)

Description: ⅛ to ²⁄₇ in. long; slender, shiny flies with relatively long antennae; basal ⅓ of wing has characteristic constriction.

Bionomics: winter as pupae in puparia in soil (sometimes as maggots in plant tissues); one to two generations per season; larvae feed in roots, underground stems, or galls of plants; one pest species feeds on carrot, celery, parsnip and parsley.

Example: carrot rust fly.

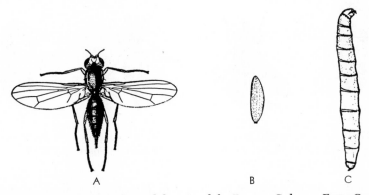

Fig. 4:28. Diptera. Carrot rust fly, Psilidae. A, adult; B, egg; C, larva. *From Crosby and Leonard, 1918,* Manual of Vegetable-Garden Insects, *by permission M. D. Leonard and E. E. Crosby.*

FAMILY AGROMYZIDAE—LEAF MINER FLIES (FIG. 4:29)

Description: ¹⁄₁₇ to ¹⁄₁₀ in. long; adults are robust, short bodied, and usually black (sometimes yellow); larvae are white or yellow and ⅛ to ⅕ in. long.

Bionomics: winter as pupae in puparia in soil or plant debris; adults insert their eggs singly into leaves or stems; larvae feed between upper and lower surfaces of leaves or in stems, causing linear, serpentine, or blotch mines.

Examples: corn blotch leaf miner, serpentine leaf miner, asparagus miner, chrysanthemum leaf miner, holly leaf miner.

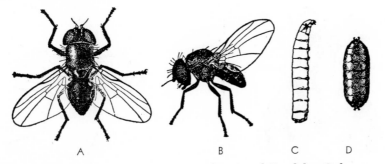

A   B   C   D

Fig. 4:29. Diptera. Asparagus miner, Agromyzidae. A and B, adults; C, larva or miner; D, pupa. *Courtesy USDA.*

FAMILY GASTEROPHILIDAE—HORSE BOTS (FIG. 4:27C)

Description: ⅗ to ¾ in. long; robust, hairy flies; spiny, grublike larvae are about ⅔ in. long when full grown.

Bionomics: winter as larvae (bots) in horse's stomach or intestine; eggs are attached to hairs; horse bot fly eggs hatch upon being removed by lips or tongue of host and, after burrowing through mouth membranes, attach to lining of digestive tract; when full grown, the larvae pass out with feces and pupate in ground.

Examples: horse bot fly, nose bot fly, throat bot fly.

FAMILY OESTRIDAE—BOT FLIES (FIG. 4:27D)

Description: about ½ in. long; robust, yellowish gray, and hairy; larvae are heavy bodied, black banded, and almost an inch long when mature.

Bionomics: winter as larvae in nasal passages, sinuses, or head cavities of host; female deposits larvae in the nostrils of host; larvae may complete development in one month during summer or may take up to 10 months when they overwinter in the host, leave nostrils and pupate in ground.

Example: sheep bot fly.

FAMILY HYPODERMATIDAE—WARBLE FLIES (FIG. 18:14)

Description: about ½ in. long; heavy-bodied, hairy flies; mature larva (warble) is robust and about 1 in. long.

Bionomics: winter as larvae in host tissues; eggs are glued singly or in rows on hairs; larvae penetrate skin and migrate in connective tissues of

A   B

Fig. 4:30. Diptera. A, apple maggot adult, Tephritidae; B, cabbage maggot adult, Anthomyiidae. *A, from Snodgrass; B, courtesy N.C. Agr. Exp. Sta.*

host, later form swellings under skin of back; in spring, mature larvae leave cysts through breathing holes and pupate in ground.

Examples: northern cattle grub, common cattle grub.

FAMILY TACHINIDAE—TACHINA FLIES (FIG. 4:31A)

Description: ⅛ to ⅗ in. long; highly variable, usually dark, bristly, often beelike in appearance; larvae are typical maggots; puparium usually brown.

Bionomics: winter as larvae or pupae; larvae or eggs placed in or on host insect, or on foliage to be consumed by host; usually a single fly develops from one host individual, often devouring most of the host tissues; mainly parasitize larvae of Lepidoptera, sawflies, and beetles.

Examples: red-tailed tachina, tussock moth tachina, and many other native or introduced species which are beneficial in controlling insect pests.

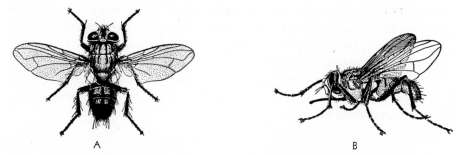

Fig. 4:31. A, *Compsilura concinnata*, parasite of satin moth, gypsy moth, brown-tail moth, and tent caterpillars, Tachinidae; B, stable fly, Muscidae. *Courtesy USDA.*

FAMILY CALLIPHORIDAE—BLOW FLIES (FIG. 18:16)

Description: ³⁄₁₆ to ½ in. long; metallic blue or green; larvae are typical white maggots.

Bionomics: usually winter as adults in protected places; eggs laid in decaying flesh or open wounds of wild or domesticated animals; larvae feed mainly on decaying flesh, screw-worm invades living tissues; many are of great benefit to man in consuming dead carcasses; some are injurious parasites of man and animals, causing myiasis.

Examples: screw-worm, black blow fly, greenbottle fly, secondary screw-worm, cluster fly.

FAMILY MUSCIDAE—HOUSE FLIES AND STABLE FLIES (FIGS. 4:31B AND 20:7)

Description: robust, short-bodied, bristly flies, ⅛ to ⅜ in. long; head and compound eyes large; compound eyes usually separated; some have sponging mouth parts (house fly) and some have piercing-sucking (horn fly); larvae are typical maggots; eggs are white to brown and spindle shaped.

Bionomics: mainly winter as maggots or pupae in breeding material; eggs are laid singly or in clusters near larval food; maggots breed in manure or decaying vegetable matter; house fly may have 10 to 20 generations per season; both males and females suck blood in hematophagous species.

Examples: house fly, stable fly, horn fly, oriental house fly.

FAMILY ANTHOMYIIDAE—THE ROOT MAGGOTS AND ALLIES (FIG. 4:30B)

Description: ⅛ to ¼ in. long; drab gray flies; larvae are typical, wedge-shaped, white maggots; resemble the Muscidae, to which they are closely related.

Bionomics: winter as pupae in puparia in soil (sometimes as maggots); eggs laid in soil or other breeding location; two to five generations per season; maggots feed on roots and seeds, mine in stems and leaves, or feed in decaying vegetable material and manure.

Examples: cabbage maggot, seed-corn maggot, onion maggot, spinach leaf miner, raspberry cane maggot, little house fly, latrine fly, carnation tip maggot, turnip maggot.

FAMILY HIPPOBOSCIDAE—LOUSE FLIES (FIG. 18:17)

Description: $\frac{1}{10}$ to $\frac{3}{8}$ in. long; flat brown, leathery bodies covered with short, spinelike hairs; both winged and wingless species; head, sunken into thorax, bears piercing-sucking mouth parts.

Bionomics: active the year round on their warm-blooded hosts; eggs hatch inside the mother and larvae develop in uterine pouch; at birth, full grown larvae glued to hair or feathers of hosts; larva forms puparium within few hours and emerges as adult a few weeks later.

Examples: sheep ked (sometimes erroneously called sheep-tick), pigeon fly.

Order Siphonaptera: fleas

Mouthparts—piercing-sucking in adult; chewing in larva.
Wings—wingless.
Metamorphosis—complex.
Additional features—body strongly flattened laterally and with many backward-projecting spines; long legs fitted for jumping; short antennae lie in grooves in head.

FAMILY PULICIDAE—PULICID FLEAS, COMMON FLEAS (FIG. 20:5)

Description: $\frac{1}{30}$ to $\frac{1}{5}$ in. long; eyes present or absent; eggs are rounded, smooth, and white to yellowish; larva is eyeless, legless, bristly, and elongate.

Bionomics: adults feed on blood of birds and mammals; eggs are laid singly and drop to ground or into nest of host; larvae feed on organic material on ground or in nest, pass through three instars; pupate in silken cocoon; the oriental rat flea transmits plague from rats to man; also flea-borne (murine) typhus.

Examples: dog flea, cat flea, human flea, oriental rat flea.

Selected References

Baker, E. W., and G. W. Wharton, *An Introduction to Acarology* (New York: Macmillan, 1952).

Baker, E. W., T. M. Evans, D. J. Gould, W. B. Hull, and H. L. Keegan, *A Manual of Parasitic Mites of Medical or Economic Importance* (Elizabeth, N. J.: Nat. Pest Control Assoc., Inc., 1956).

Beer, R. E., "A Revision of the Tarsonemidae of the Western Hemisphere (Order Acarina)," *Univ. Kansas Sci. Bul.*, 36(16):1091–387 (1954).

Borror, D. J., and D. M. DeLong, *An Introduction to the Study of Insects* (New York: Rinehart, 1954).

Brues, C. T., A. L. Melander, and F. M. Carpenter, *Classification of Insects*, Harvard Museum of Comp. Zool. Bul., Vol. 108, 1954.

Comstock, J. H., *An Introduction to Entomology* (Ithaca, N.Y.: Comstock, 1940).

Essig, E. O., *Insects and Mites of Western North America* (New York: Macmillan, 1958).

Jaques, H. E., *How to Know the Insects* (Dubuque, Iowa: Wm. C. Brown Co., 1947).

Keifer, H. H., "The Eriophyid Mites of California," *Bul. Calif. Insect Survey*, 2(1):1–123 (1952).

Pritchard, A. E., and E. W. Baker, *A Revision of the Spider Mite Family Tetranychidae*, Pac. Coast. Ent. Soc. Memoirs Series, Vol. 2, 1955.

Ross, H. H., *A Textbook of Entomology* (New York: Wiley, 1956).

Swain, R. B., *The Insect Guide* (New York: Doubleday, 1948).

Chapter 5 | PRINCIPLES OF INSECT CONTROL | *Carl Johansen*

Insects are the only animals giving man a real battle for supremacy. They have been upon this earth for some 250 million years and have developed special adaptations to live under many environmental conditions.

Man has been on the earth for a much shorter interval and is actually the "intruder." He is the most upsetting factor in the balance of nature. Development of crop agriculture led to concentrations of host plants which literally "spread the table" for pest insects. Domestication and large-scale production of livestock also provided ideal conditions for the multiplication of parasitic insects. Storage of foodstuffs led to other pest problems. Increases in human population were followed by increases in human lice, mosquitoes, and insect-borne diseases.

Present-day insect problems, created or aggravated by the concentrations of host plants and animals, are diverse and complex and without simple solutions. In order to cope effectively with pest populations, farmers and ranchers should follow a set of control principles and exploit fully the methods available for combating insects. In the following pages we shall discuss the principles and methods that have proved useful in man's war against his small but powerful foes.

Insect classification and life history

Knowledge of insect classification, growth and development, and life cycles is requisite to the conduct of control programs. Accurate determinations of insect species, keys to the published work of others, are valuable tools in developing control measures. Life cycle data are essential in the timing of controls. One of the most familiar principles of insect control is that of the "weakest link." Only through a thorough knowledge of a pest's life cycle can one hope to aim control measures effectively at its most vulnerable stage. Even closely related insect species usually vary in their life histories and reactions to control measures.

Introduced pests

Many of the most destructive insect pests in the United States were introduced from foreign countries. About 50 per cent have been accidentally transported; while "new" species from other continents are being discovered here each year. As we shall see in a later discussion, this forms the basis for almost all biological control and plant quarantine projects.

Crop values

The unit value of an agricultural crop is an important consideration. Control of pest insects is usually justifiable when the increase in marketable yield produced is worth more than the cost of the control. However, insect damage to pastures or range land may not be in terms of marketable value

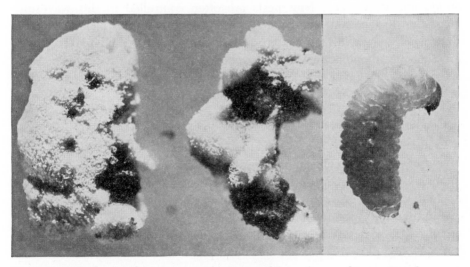

Fig. 5:1. Natural control of the sweetclover weevil by a fungus disease. Two larvae at left attacked by the fungus, *Beauveria bassiana* (Bals.); healthy larva at right. *Courtesy University of Minnesota.*

but may represent a considerable loss, for example, the interruption of the seeding cycle of grasses. In the case of low unit-value crops, such as certain forage crops, the feasibility of controlling pests is difficult to determine. Costly controls can be more logically applied to florist crops and fruit crops than to field crops and cereals.

Consumer pressure

Consumer demands also have an effect upon insect control. Certain fruits and vegetables may be rejected by the processor if one or more insects are found in samples taken from a truckload. Not even the slightest blemish or "sting" is allowed on certain top-grade fruits. This often forces the use of chemical controls, whether they represent the most biologically sound method or not.

Preventive control

Preventive control measures can be applied when one knows through experience that a certain pest or pests will develop to a damaging degree in a given area year after year. It is often true that early season applications are more efficient than later ones. Early treatments tend to control a pest species before it has reached its maximum rate of development and reproduction and before the crop foliage has grown difficult to penetrate with sprays and dusts. Tree fruit pests are often controlled in this way since consumer demand and unit value provide the impetus for making applications when only a few insects are present. In contrast, one should wait till a certain pest population level is reached before treating field crops. Some seasons may not favor the development of damaging numbers of the insect or natural enemies may keep it under control.

Community projects

Community projects are required in some pest control situations. Control of a virus disease by controlling its insect vector, control of pests of domestic animals and man, and control of insects which readily migrate from one area or crop to another are examples where the cooperative effort of everyone in a sizable locality may be essential. Supervised programs have been organized in some areas in which groups of growers or individual growers hire qualified persons to check fields and provide control recommendations.

New methods and materials

Development of many effective insecticides in recent years has changed the insect control picture in many ways. The numbers of applications previously required with the older kinds of insecticides made the cost of control often prohibitive. These older materials could only be afforded on high value fruit and vegetable crops. Now it is often feasible to treat field and range crops and even forests because modern insecticides can be used at extremely low dosages. For example 2 ounces of aldrin per acre will control range grasshoppers. The eradication of introduced pests has also become a more definite possibility. Development of new insecticide formulations and types of application equipment has gone hand in hand with the appearance of new insecticides.

Extension

The Agricultural Extension Service forms an important part of all pest control programs. No one can benefit from insect control research conducted by USDA or state agricultural experiment station personnel unless their findings are somehow brought to his attention. It is the job of extension

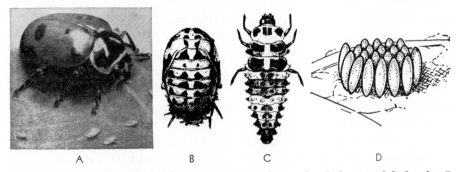

A   B   C   D

Fig. 5:2. Convergent lady beetle, a common predator of aphids. A, adult beetle; B, pupa; C, larva; D, eggs. *Courtesy USDA.*

personnel, particularly the county agent, to disseminate such information to the farmers. Fieldmen working for agricultural chemical companies, processors, or groups of growers also perform a vital function in carrying control recommendations to the individual farmer.

Causes of insect outbreaks

Outbreaks or epidemics of insect pests are usually caused by one or more of the following:

1. Large-scale culture of a single crop or stock animal by man.
2. Introduction of a pest into a favorable new area without its natural enemies.
3. Favorable weather conditions for rapid development and multiplication of a pest; which conditions may also be unfavorable to natural enemies.
4. Use of insecticides which kill the natural enemies of a pest, exert other effects favorable to a pest, or reduce the competing species of a pest while allowing it to multiply unmolested.

In the discussion of kinds of insect controls, you will see that these factors are being counteracted in various ways.

NATURAL CONTROL

Natural control is the reduction of insect populations by the forces of nature uncontrolled by man. Three types of factors are usually considered under this category: climatic, topographic, and natural enemies.

Climatic factors

Weather conditions, especially temperature, affect insects directly and may govern the number of pest generations in a given season. Moisture and temperature influence the condition of the host plant and thereby indirectly affect the plant-feeding insect. The seasonal development of phytophagous insects is closely correlated with the development of their host plants. Unusual weather conditions may change this adjustment so that either greater or less damage to crops may occur. For example, less damage will be done during a cool spring which retards development of the cherry fruit fly so that very few are present to infest the fruit before harvest time.

The suitability to insects of a given locality is partly determined by climate. Direct killing of insects may result from extreme low temperatures during winter. Winter-killing is modified by the amount and kind of protection available to the insect and the inherent resistance to cold of the hibernating stage. The fact that many insects are killed in the laboratory when subjected to temperatures just below the freezing point does not prove that they will be killed by similar air temperatures in nature. Insects usually seek a sheltered place for overwintering—under bark, in the crowns of weeds and grasses, under plant debris, or in the ground. Snow cover also provides considerable protection to hibernating insects, insulating them against extreme low temperatures.

Topographic factors

Major topographic factors such as mountain ranges and large water bodies act as barriers to the spread of insects. An indication of the effectiveness of these barriers may be seen in the slow spread of certain introduced pests across the United States. The European corn borer, first discovered in Massachusetts about 1907, didn't reach Colorado until 1953. Although the alfalfa weevil was introduced into Utah about 1904, it didn't reach the state of Washington until 1955.

Major topographic features also affect the climate of an area, thereby limiting the distribution of certain insects. For example, the pea moth is an established pest only near large bodies of water. Apparently this pest requires the temperate and humid conditions of such areas. One often sees striking examples of insects which occur on one side of a mountain

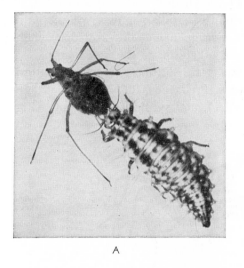

A

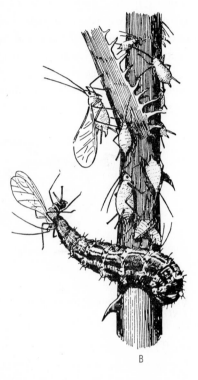

B

Fig. 5:3. Two efficient predators of aphids. A, lacewing larva feeding on aphids; B, syrphid maggot feeding on aphids. *A, courtesy USDA; B, from Snodgrass.*

range and not on the other. The moist, windward side will encourage a quite different fauna from that found on the dry, leeward or "rain shadow" side.

Soil type is a major factor affecting the suitability of an area to a pest. Certain wireworms live only in heavy, poorly-drained soils; others live only in light, sandy soils. Soil type also influences plant distribution which in turn affects the distribution of plant-feeding insects and mites.

Natural enemies

Birds, small mammals, reptiles, fishes, disease organisms, and predaceous insects are natural enemies which help reduce insect pest populations. More than 100 species of birds have been observed to feed upon scale insects, woodboring insect larvae, caterpillars, grasshoppers, and other types of pest species. Moles, shrews, skunks, and ground squirrels feed upon soil-inhabiting insects. Lizards, snakes, salamanders, and toads also destroy insects. Many fresh-water fish feed on the nymphs or larvae of aquatic insects.

Fungus, bacterial, and virus disease organisms often reduce insect epidemics to low populations (Fig. 5:1). Polyhedral and granular types of viruses are especially effective against tent caterpillars, pine sawflies, alfalfa caterpillars, and cabbage caterpillars. Certain nematodes also destroy insects, sometimes by transmitting disease organisms to the insect host.

Predaceous insects and parasitic insects are the most important natural enemies which destroy injurious species. Predaceous insects such as lady beetles (Fig. 5:2), lacewings (Fig. 5:3A), and syrphid fly maggots (Fig.

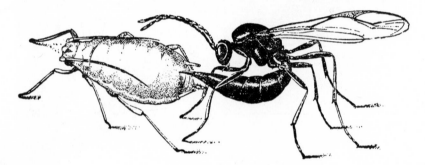

Fig. 5:4. A minute parasitic wasp, *Aphidius testaceipes,* laying egg in an aphid. *Courtesy USDA.*

5:3B), are effective aphid destroyers. Small parasitic wasps belonging to the genera *Aphidius, Aphelinus,* and *Praon* lay their eggs within the bodies of aphids and the resulting larvae kill the hosts (Fig. 5:4). Typhlodromid mites feed upon the phytophagous spider mites, rust mites, and cyclamen mite. Braconid and ichneumonid wasps and tachinid flies are important parasites of caterpillars and various stages of other insects.

BIOLOGICAL CONTROL

Biological control is the reduction of insect populations by means of living organisms encouraged by man. The essential difference between this control method and natural control is merely that in biological control natural enemies are encouraged and disseminated by man.

The basis for most biological control work lies in the fact that half of the major injurious insects in the United States were introduced from

foreign countries. Usually, when foreign insects are accidentally transported into this country, they arrive without the parasites and predators
which attack them in their native land. Furthermore, native American
parasites tend to be specific and not adapted to attack an introduced species.

Almost all biological control programs involve searching for parasites and
predators of an introduced pest in the native land of the pest. Therefore,
most projects are developed by central governments. The United States
maintains biological control laboratories in various foreign countries. Teams
are composed of several units: "foreign explorers," who look for potential

Fig. 5:5. Mass culturing of the braconid wasp, *Macrocentrus ancylivorus* Roh., a parasite
of the oriental fruit moth. Stacked trays of potatoes infested with potato tuberworms
which serve as host for culture of the parasite. *Courtesy University of California.*

control agents; "quarantine," where parasites or predators are checked to
make sure they will be entirely beneficial; "insectary production," for increasing the numbers of the control agents (Fig. 5:5); and "release and
recovery," to establish the parasites or predators in the United States. Other
countries conduct biological control projects in a similar manner.

Advantages of biological control

Only a limited number of introduced pests have been successfully exter-
minated with chemicals. It would seem wiser in many instances to attempt
a biological control program which might reduce pest populations below

the level which causes economic damage. Biological control has the tremendous advantage that, if successful, it becomes self-sustaining and integrated into the normal environment of the control area.

If pest populations are reduced to the point where economic damage is negligible, the control program is a success. Biological controls tend to be particularly useful on low unit-value crops where complete control may not be required or where chemicals are not recommended. Pests of field and forage crops, forests, and range may be economically controlled by biological methods; chemical controls against such pests may be impractical.

A biological control destined to be fully effective will be easily and quickly established. If an imported parasite or predator is not established within three years of careful releases under good conditions for its development, the program may be justifiably discontinued.

Problems of biological control

One of the greatest underlying problems in this type of work is the enormous size of insect populations. Even though thousands of an imported parasite may be released, it takes time for the parasite to reproduce sufficiently to bring the pest under control. A farmer often feels that he cannot wait for the natural enemy to do the job; he needs a marketable crop each year.

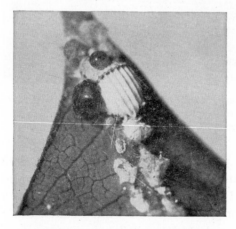

Fig. 5:6. Vedalia, a lady beetle which was successfully introduced into California from Australia to control the cottony-cushion scale on citrus. The adult lady beetle feeding on cottony-cushion scale. *Courtesy F. E. Skinner.*

When a parasite has become well established in a new area it may control 90 per cent of the injurious species. However, this degree of control has not often been obtained and even the most successful campaigns are likely to result in fluctuating populations of the pest. Such results are not good enough, especially for the grower who raises a high value crop for human consumption. The consumer demands a "perfect," unblemished product. Naturally, the farmer usually resorts to chemical control measures and the biological control agent is likely to be killed in the process. The ironic feature of such cases (and they have been numerous) is that often the chemical control is unsatisfactory or will cause greater problems to develop.

Other technical difficulties involve such items as determination of which parasites or predators to introduce, whether to use more than one parasitic species at a time, how to eliminate secondary parasites that prey on the beneficial form, and whether a program of continuous liberations may be feasible.

Combination of chemical and biological controls

Recent developments in the area of combining chemical and biological or natural controls are of considerable interest. Some of the most promising methods of developing compatible combinations are through the use of systemic insecticides, oil sprays, disease pathogens, stomach poison insecticides, selective chemicals, and "spot" treatments of localized infestations within fields.

Biological agents

Many types of animals have been utilized as biological control agents: top minnows, toads, birds, mites, spiders, snails, and insects. Most of the successful cases to date have involved the use of parasitic or predaceous insects. Ninety-five imported species were established in the United States during the 60-year period ending in 1956 (81 parasites and 14 predators). A greater number, 390 imported species, did not become established during this same time. Some 20 pests have been cited as successfully controlled in the United States by this method (Fig. 5:6).

Use of disease organisms, "microbial control," has developed into a more important part of biological control in comparatively recent years. Nematodes, protozoans, bacteria, fungi, and viruses have been tested experimentally. Only certain bacterial spores, the causal agents of milky diseases in the Japanese beetle, have been marketed commercially as insecticidal materials. Certain other bacterial disease organisms are being produced by chemical or biological companies for large-scale experimental work at the present time (Fig. 5:7). Two types of virus diseases, polyhedrosis and granulosis, have shown considerable promise experimentally in controlling insect pests.

Microbial controls have a number of interesting advantages: there is no chemical residue problem; they are usually quite specific and are not a

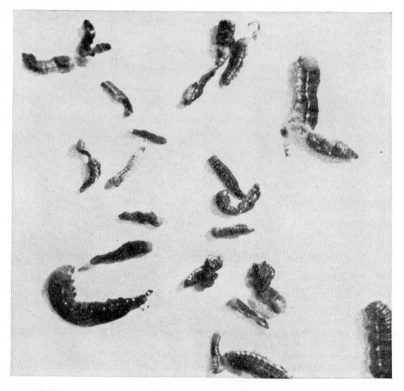

Fig. 5:7. Alfalfa caterpillars, *Colias eurytheme* Bdv., killed with a bacterial agent, *Bacillus thuringiensis* Berliner. *Courtesy University of California.*

hazard to beneficial insects or to man; commercial preparations could be made quite inexpensively and low dosages would suffice in control work; they are compatible with insecticidal chemicals and quite versatile; and, insects have not developed resistance to microbial organisms to date. Disadvantages of this method include: timing of applications is very critical because of dependence on weather conditions and lack of residual action in many cases; specificity is a disadvantage where several major pests must be controlled on a single crop; some types of microorganisms are difficult to produce in quantity and cheaply; and fungi, especially, require high atmospheric moisture for successful development.

Weeds

The biological control of weeds is a related topic. Since this method involves the introduction of insects to attack weeds, the same branch of the USDA investigates both the biological control of insects and of weeds. The outstanding success in the United States has been the use of certain leaf beetles, *Chrysolina quadrigemina* Suffr. and *C. hyperici* (Forst.), to control the Klamath weed throughout most of the West. These beetles have completely eradicated Klamath weed from thousands of acres of range land (Fig. 5:8). *C. quadrigemina* has been the most effective of the two Klamath weed beetles. Its life cycle and habits are better synchronized with the development of the host weed than are those of *C. hyperici*.

CULTURAL CONTROL

Cultural control is the reduction of insect populations by the utilization of agricultural practices. It has also been defined as "making environments unfavorable for pests"; of course, this definition would also apply to other types of control methods.

The method, more or less associated with agricultural production, usually

Fig. 5:8. Biological control of Klamath weed by the leaf beetle *Chrysolina quadrigemina* in Humboldt County, California. Foreground shows flowering weed; background weed destroyed by the beetles. *Courtesy USDA and University of California.*

involves certain changes in the normal farming practices rather than the addition of special procedures. It sometimes consists of avoidance of factors which favor an increase of injurious insects.

Knowledge of the life history or bionomics of a pest species is essential to the effective use of cultural control methods. The principle of the "weakest link" or most vulnerable part of the life cycle usually applies. The environment is changed by altering farming practices at the correct time so as to kill the pests or to slow down their multiplication. In this way, the method is aimed more at prevention than at cure. If the environment is unfavorable, the pest may not reach a population level which will cause serious damage.

Cultural controls are often used when chemical or biological methods have not yet been devised for an injurious species. Cleanup of the sources of infestation and changes in the planting or harvesting time are particularly important when no effective method of killing the pest is known. However, these methods are also used in combination with other controls.

Sometimes cultural control practices are inconvenient to the farmer and are quickly dropped after other methods have been developed. At other times, the fact that insect control was the primary reason for establishing certain practices may be forgotten with the passage of time. Methods such

Fig. 5:9. Rows of resistant and susceptible varieties of wheat planted in a heavy Hessian fly area. The good row is W38 from which the resistant gene in Dual, a soft winter wheat variety resistant to Hessian fly, was obtained. *Courtesy Purdue University.*

as certain crop rotations may become so well established that they are simply conducted as standard practices.

Since cultural methods are usually economical, they are especially useful against pests of low unit-value crops. Practices which reduce the chances of buildup of pest populations may hold them below the level which will cause economic damage. Such methods are particularly applicable to field crops and forests.

Rotation

Certain kinds of crop rotations may aid in the control of pests. Insects which are effectively reduced by rotations usually have a long life cycle, limited host range, and are relatively immobile in some stage of their development. Changing crops in a rotation system isolates such pests from their food supply. Long-cycle insects such as wireworms and white grubs are good examples.

Planting row crops following sod is a poor type of rotation. Wireworms, cutworms, or webworms are concentrated on the row crop in this way and may cause serious damage. Planting two similar crops in succession also tends to increase insect problems.

Rotations are usually more effectively applied to field crops than truck crops because of the larger size of plantings and because isolation of the relatively immobile stage of an insect is more complete.

Location

Careful choice of crops to be planted adjacent to each other may help reduce insect damage. Similar crops may be attacked by the same pests or one crop may attract a pest which later moves on to the adjacent field.

Mixed crops may also deter the infestation of an injurious insect. Plantings containing mixtures of two or more species of forest trees have been particularly effective in preventing damage by certain forest pests.

Trap crop

Small plantings of a susceptible or preferred crop may be established near a major crop to act as a "trap." After the pest insect has been attracted to the trap crop, it is usually treated with insecticides, plowed under, or both.

Tillage

The use of tillage operations to reduce populations of soil-inhabiting insects may work in several ways: change physical condition of soil; bury a stage of the pest; expose a stage of the insect; mechanically damage some stage of the insect; eliminate host plants of the pest; and hasten growth or increase vigor of the crop.

Clean culture

Removal of crop residues, disposal of volunteer plants, and burning of chaff stacks are measures commonly applied against vegetable and field crop insects. This method is especially useful for control of caterpillars or beetles which hibernate in plant debris.

Timing

Changes in planting time or harvesting time are used to keep the infesting stage of a pest separated from the susceptible stage of the host. Timing is effective as a control measure when the crop concerned may be infested or injured only during a brief period, or when the infesting stage in the life of the insect is very brief.

Resistant plant varieties

The sources of resistance to insects in crops have been classified as nonpreference, antibiosis, and tolerance. Insect preference for a certain host plant is related to color, light reflection, physical structure of the surface, and chemical stimuli such as taste and odor. A resistant variety may have the quality of **nonpreference** by lacking one or more of the preferred factors or characteristics of the host plant (Fig. 5:9).

Antibiosis is defined as an adverse effect of the plant upon the insect. This may be caused either by the deleterious effect of a specific chemical or the lack of a specific nutrient requirement.

Tolerance is the term applied to the general vigor of certain plants which may be able to withstand the attack of pests such as sucking insects. Tolerance also includes the ability to repair tissues and recover from an attack.

Management

Most cultural control methods could be described as management. However, cultural procedures which aid in the control of livestock pests are especially referred to as management control. Such practices as destruction of breeding places of pests, cleanup of pens, barns, and shelters, and isolation of infested animals exemplify the methods used.

MECHANICAL AND PHYSICAL CONTROL

Mechanical control is the reduction of insect populations by means of devices which affect them directly or which radically alter their physical environment. These methods are often hard to distinguish from cultural methods. However, mechanical controls involve special physical measures rather than normal farm practices. They tend to require considerable time and labor and often are impractical on a large scale.

Hand-picking, shingling, and trapping are familiar mechanical methods of insect control. Screens, barriers, sticky bands, and shading devices represent other mechanical methods; while hopper-dozers, drags, and entoleters (Fig. 5:10) are special items of equipment for collecting or smashing pests.

Physical controls include the use of electricity, sound waves, infrared rays, X-rays, or light to kill insects, reduce their reproductive capacity, or attract them to killing mechanisms. Probably the commonest physical

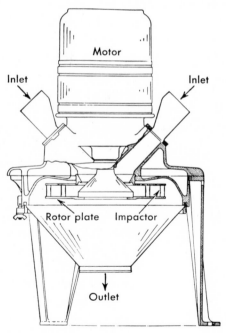

Fig. 5:10. An entoleter or centrifugal force machine employed in flour mills to kill stored grain insects by smashing them. *Courtesy USDA.*

methods are those which employ heat or cold. Cold storage of farm produce will usually eliminate further insect activity and damage during the storage period even though the pests may not be killed. Both heat and cold have been used to reduce insect populations in grain elevators. No insect can survive temperatures of 140 to 150° F. for very long. Soaking flower bulbs in hot water is a standard method of controlling certain pests.

LEGAL CONTROL

Legal control is the lawful regulation of areas to eradicate, prevent, or control infestation or reduce damage by insects. This mainly involves the use of quarantines and pest control procedures. Federal and state officials often work with local, community, or county legally established districts, as in mosquito or grasshopper control projects.

Plant and animal quarantines

Fundamental prerequisites of plant quarantines are: (1) the pest must offer actual or expected threat to large interests; (2) no substitute action, less disruptive of normal trade, is available; (3) the objectives must be reasonably possible to attain; and (4) the economic gains from pest control must outweigh the cost of administration and the interference with normal trade activity.

Some of the problems of plant quarantine work are: (1) high speed transportation and increased travel; (2) lack of information about potential pests in foreign countries with whom we trade; and (3) incomplete knowledge of the biology of the pest. One aspect of the third problem is that insects sometimes cause serious damage in a new place. In their native land they may be of minor concern because of natural enemies present, weather conditions, and agricultural methods of the area. However, when they are accidentally introduced into a favorable new area, considerable injury may result.

Plant quarantines are mainly based on the **Plant Quarantine Act of 1912,** the **Mexican Border Act of 1942,** and various state regulations. Federal plant quarantines are administered by the Plant Quarantine Division of the Agricultural Research Service, employing 350 to 400 inspectors at some 75 ports of entry. A number of **domestic quarantines** (within the United States and its territories) have been established. Some of the more important are directed against the following: infestations in Hawaiian fruits and vegetables, gypsy and brown-tail moths, Japanese beetle, pink bollworm, infestations in Puerto Rican fruits and vegetables, Mexican fruit fly, and white-fringed beetles. **Foreign quarantines** (directed against materials from other countries) include: sugarcane, sweetpotato and yams, nursery stock, corn and related plants, rice, fruits (Fig. 5:11) and vegetables, and cut flowers.

Fig. 5:11. Map of the citrus blackfly campaign, an example of control and quarantine work. *Courtesy USDA.*

Quarantines for protection against infectious diseases of domestic animals are administered by the Animal Inspection and Quarantine Division of Agricultural Research Service. Foreign animal quarantines are based on laws enacted in 1890 and 1926; domestic quarantines on laws of 1903, 1905 and 1928.

Eradication and control

Some provision for the eradication of introduced pests was made under the Plant Quarantine Act of 1912. Later, this activity was more specifically established by the **Incipient and Emergency Outbreak Resolution of 1938** and by a section of the **Department of Agriculture Organic Act of 1944.** An amendment in 1957 to the Organic Act provides for the large-scale control by the Plant Pest Control Division, in cooperation with states, of the spread of newly introduced pests, such as imported fire ant, khapra beetle, soybean cyst nematode, witch-weed, and spotted alfalfa aphid.

Control and eradication of arthropod-borne diseases of domestic animals are provided for in the Department of Agriculture Organic Acts of 1944 and 1956, based on earlier laws of 1884 and 1903. The Animal Disease

Eradication Division of ARS is currently conducting campaigns against cattle tick fever, screw-worm myiasis, bluetongue of sheep, and other maladies. A special act for the development of an eradication program for cattle grubs was passed in 1948. The Entomology Research and Animal Disease and Parasite Research Divisions work on this problem.

Successful eradication campaigns have been conducted against the Mediterranean fruit fly in 1929–30 and 1956–57, the parlatoria date scale, the citrus blackfly, and the white garden snail. The Hall scale is believed to have been eradicated from the United States; the cattle tick control program is now confined to occasional reinfestations in Texas and California; and, the screw-worm has apparently (1959) been eradicated from the southeastern states. An active program to eradicate infestations of the gypsy moth is currently being conducted (Fig. 5:12).

Export certification, terminal inspection, and movement of plant pests

Export certification of domestic plant materials according to the sanitary requirements of the foreign country to which they are being exported was originally included under the Plant Quarantine Act of 1912. Now, such activities are provided for in the Department of Agriculture Organic Act of 1944. Prevention of the export of diseased cattle was specifically included in the act establishing the Bureau of Animal Industry in 1884. Export certification of domestic animals is based on laws enacted in 1890 and 1903, and more recent amendments.

Inspection of plants and plant products moving interstate was established by the **Terminal Inspection Act of 1915.** Such inspections are conducted by state officials at designated mail terminals. Importation or interstate movement of any living pest organism that is injurious to cultivated plants is prohibited by the **Federal Plant Pest Act of 1957** which replaced the **Insect Pest Act of 1905.** Movement of living insect pests for scientific purposes can only be conducted by permit obtained according to the provisions of this act. Eradication of insects which may be introduced by intercontinental airplane travel is also covered by the Plant Pest Act.

Although tourists are likely to be provoked by inspection activities at state or national boundaries, they undergo only minor inconveniences when one considers the millions of dollars that quarantine and eradication programs have saved the United States over the years. Even if a serious pest is only prevented or retarded for a few years, the monetary savings to a specific industry, such as citrus growing, may be considerable. Some of the recent trends for increasing the effectiveness of plant quarantine work are preshipment inspection and treatment of airplanes and ships in foreign

Fig. 5:12. Map of the gypsy moth campaign, an example of control and eradication work. *Courtesy USDA.*

countries, a special training center for quarantine workers at the Port of New York, plant quarantine courses offered in several colleges, training of foreign nationals at the **Plant Quarantine Training Center,** and more effective education of tourists concerning quarantine activities.

CHEMICAL CONTROL

Chemical control is the reduction of insect populations or prevention of insect injury by the use of materials to poison them, attract them to other devices, or repel them from specified areas. This topic is discussed in Chapters 6 and 7.

Selected References

Anon., *Cooperative Plant Pest Control Programs*, Plant Pest Control Div., ARS, USDA, Washington, D. C., 1960.

Camp, A. F., "Modern Quarantine Problems," *Ann. Rev. Ent.*, 1:367–78 (1956).

Clausen, C. P., "Biological Control of Insects," *Ann. Rev. Ent.*, 3:291–310 (1958).

Huffaker, C. B., "Fundamentals of Biological Control of Weeds," *Hilgardia*, 27:101–57 (1957).

Isely, D., *Methods of Insect Control* (Minneapolis: Burgess, 1941), Parts I and II.

Painter, R. H., *Insect Resistance in Crop Plants* (New York: Macmillan, 1951).

————, "Resistance of Plants to Insects," *Ann. Rev. Ent.*, 3:267–90 (1958).

Perry, C. C., *Gypsy Moth Appraisal Program and Proposed Plan to Prevent Spread of the Moths*, USDA Tech. Bull. 1124, 1955.

Popham, W. L., and D. G. Hall, "Insect Eradication Programs," *Ann. Rev. Ent.*, 3:335–54 (1958).

Ripper, W. E., "Effect of Pesticides on Balance of Arthropod Populations," *Ann. Rev. Ent.*, 1:403–38 (1956).

Smith, H. S., *The Efficacy and Economic Effects of Plant Quarantines in California*, Calif. Agr. Exp. Sta. Bull. 553, 1933.

Smith, R. F., and W. W. Allen, "Insect Control and the Balance of Nature," *Sci. Am.*, 190(6):38–42 (1954).

Solomon, M. E., "Dynamics of Insect Populations," *Ann. Rev. Ent.*, 2:121–42 (1957).

Steinhaus, E. A., "Microbial Control—the Emergence of an Idea," *Hilgardia*, 26:107–60 (1956).

————, *Principles of Insect Pathology* (New York: McGraw-Hill, 1949).

Stern, V. M., R. F. Smith, R. van den Bosch, and K. S. Hagen, "The Integrated Control Concept," *Hilgardia*, 29:81–101 (1959).

Sweetman, H. L., *The Principles of Biological Control* (Dubuque: Wm. C. Brown Co., 1958).

Thompson, W. R., "The Fundamental Theory of Natural and Biological Control," *Ann. Rev. Ent.*, 1:379–402 (1956).

Uvarov, B. P., "Insects and Climate," *Trans. Ent. Soc. London*, 79:1–247 (1931).

Wellington, W. G., "The Synoptic Approach to Studies of Insects and Climate," *Ann. Rev. Ent.*, 2:143–62 (1957).

Chapter 6 | CHEMICAL CONTROL | *W. Don Fronk*

Recent discoveries of new synthetic insecticides have sparked exciting advances and major breakthroughs in the control of insect enemies. Chemicals have subdued pests that once caused national calamities—widespread crop destruction, wholesale death of domestic animals, and epidemics of insect-borne human diseases. Because modern insecticides are both effective and reliable, we in America are resorting to them more and more for the solution of our many insect problems.

Pesticide production and sales are in the ranks of big business in the United States. In 1939 there was 40 million dollars worth of sales. By 1956 this had reached 260 million and the value is estimated to reach one billion dollars by 1975. Insecticides account for about 36 per cent of this figure, the remainder being made up of fungicides, herbicides, and several other classes of pesticides.

Insecticides were in use before man learned to write. Homer, in about 1000 B.C., spoke of "pest-averting" sulfur. Cato, about 200 B.C., advised boiling a mixture of bitumen (mineral pitch or asphalt) in such a way that the fumes would blow through grape leaves and thus rid them of insects. Hellebore was used by the Romans for control of human lice.

The toxic nature of arsenic was known to the Greek physician Dioscorides (40–90 A.D.) and the Chinese were using arsenic sulfide to control garden pests before 900 A.D. Arsenic was not used by the western world until 1669 when it was suggested for use in honey as an ant bait. Marco Polo, in writing of his travels, told of using oil for control of camel mange in 1300. By 1690 tobacco was being used for control of pear lace bug on pear trees. Pyrethrum, an insecticide of wide use at the present time, was known and used by the Persians before 1800.

The modern use of insecticides dates from 1867 when Paris green was first used for Colorado potato beetle control. Until 1939 most insecticides were inorganic chemicals plus a few insecticides derived from plants, but the discovery of the insecticidal nature of DDT in 1939 revolutionized our concept of insecticides and of insect control. Since this date, so many new discoveries and insecticides have been revealed that it is hardly possible to make a completely up-to-date summary. In 1941–42 English and French investigators discovered the value of benzene hexachloride. During this same period, the Germans advanced the field of phosphorous insecticides which led to the development of parathion, TEPP, malathion, demeton, and many more. Other families of chemicals are now being investigated for possible insecticidal activity. Insecticides have been found among the urethanes, sulfones, sulfonates, carbamates, and other classes of compounds by American chemists and entomologists.

INSECTICIDE FORMULATIONS

Insecticides are seldom used full strength but are formulated in ways to dilute, extend, and make them easier to apply. The most common formulations are dusts, granules, insecticide-fertilizer mixtures, wettable powders, solutions, emulsifiable concentrates, aerosols, and fumigants.

Dusts

Insecticides which are to be used dry are mixed with or impregnated on organic materials such as walnut shell flour or pulverized minerals such as talc, pyrophyllite, bentonite, and attapulgite. The finished dust may be from 0.1 to 25 per cent active material. Ground to a fine size, most dust particles will pass through a 325 mesh screen and range in size from 1 to 40 microns. In general the toxicity of an insecticide increases as the particle size decreases. Because some insecticidal compounds are inactivated by alkali, the potential reaction of the diluent is an important factor in the manufacture of a dust. Also important in formulation are the catalytically active sites on dust particles, which, to assure insecticide stability, must be deactivated.

Granular formulations

Granular formulations are much like dusts except for larger particle size. The range of particle size in a granular product is designated by a two-figured mesh classification. For example, $3\%_0$ means that virtually all of the granules will pass through a standard 30 mesh sieve (30 openings per linear inch) while only a negligible quantity will pass through a standard 60 mesh sieve. Some common granule sizes are $^{16}/_{30}$, $^{20}/_{40}$, $^{24}/_{48}$, and $^{30}/_{60}$. Granular insecticides are usually used as dressings on or in the soil and may be applied with fertilizer spreaders or special granule applicators.

Insecticide-fertilizer mixtures

Insecticide-fertilizer mixtures may be formulated by adding granular insecticide to commercial fertilizers or by spraying insecticide directly onto the fertilizer. Such mixtures are applied at the regular fertilizing time to provide both plant nutrients and control of soil insects.

Wettable powders

Wettable powders have the appearance of dusts but are meant to be diluted and suspended in water and used as sprays. To make an insecticidal dust act in this manner a dispersing and wetting agent is added to the formulation. They are more concentrated than dusts as they may contain as high as 75 per cent toxicant.

Solutions

Not many of the present synthetic organic insecticides are soluble in water but most are soluble in organic solvents. Some materials are dissolved in an organic solvent and used directly for insect control. Seldom are such solutions used on plants because of phytotoxic reactions, but they are used in the household, in barns and buildings, and for spraying on the surface of water to control mosquitoes and other aquatic insects.

Emulsifiable concentrates

The most common and versatile formulation is the emulsifiable concentrate. This formulation consists of the insecticide, a solvent for the insecticide, and an emulsifying agent. Mixing the concentrate with water forms an emulsion of the oil-in-water type. The solvent used may evaporate quickly after spraying leaving a deposit of toxicant after the water has evaporated.

The use of an **emulsifying agent** serves several purposes: (1) it makes possible the diluting of a water-insoluble chemical with water, (2) it reduces the surface tension of the spray thus allowing it to spread and wet the treated surface, and (3) it helps the spray make better contact with the insect cuticle. An oil-soluble emulsifier is most generally used. The types of insecticide emulsifiers include: alkaline soaps, organic amines, sulfates of long-chain alcohols, sulfonated aliphatic esters and amides, mixed aliphatic-aromatic sulfonates, nonionic types (ethers, alcohols and esters of polyhydric alcohols and long-chain fatty acids), and natural materials such as proteins and gums.

Emulsions are not stable and tend to separate into their component parts. This action is termed "breaking." To some extent this can be controlled by the amount of agitation and amount of emulsifier in the mixture. A fairly quick breaking mixture is preferred for plant spraying since this results in heavier deposits of toxicant by limiting run-off. However, quick breaking mixtures do not wet nor spread as well as the slower breaking mixtures.

An emulsifiable concentrate left standing will sometimes separate into its various parts due to the differences in specific gravity of the components. Simply shaking the container will suffice to return these to the proper form.

Insecticidal aerosols

Aerosols are minute particles suspended in air such as fog or mist. Insecticides may likewise be suspended in air as minute particles in which diameters range from 0.1 to 50 microns. The dispersion of insecticide into aerosol form may be accomplished by burning, vaporizing with heat, atomizing mechanically, or releasing through a small hole an insecticide that has been dissolved in a liquefied gas. In the latter method, the released gas evaporates rapidly and leaves small particles of the insecticide floating in air. The popular household "aerosol bomb" operates in this manner.

Fumigants

Insecticides used in the gaseous form are known as fumigants. With few exceptions, these are used where the gas can be confined, i.e., in buildings, storage bins, ship holds, and even in soil. Fumigants are most often formulated as liquids under pressure and are held in cans or tanks. When the liquid is released in open air, it changes back to a gas. Quite often fumigants are mixtures of two or more gases. In some cases, the gas is made at the location to be fumigated. Hydrogen cyanide is produced, for example, by dropping calcium cyanide into earthenware crocks filled with sulphuric acid.

Miscellaneous formulations

Special formulations may be found for specific uses. Boluses (large pills) and capsules are used with a balling gun to introduce insecticides into the stomachs of animals. Insecticides may be mixed in shampoos intended for use on house pets. Waxes for use on floors may contain an insecticide.

Poison baits consist of toxicants combined with a foodstuff attractive to the insect pest.

COMPATIBILITY OF AGRICULTURAL CHEMICALS

When certain chemicals are brought together they will react to form a compound which differs from either parent. This simple fact has been ignored at times by applicators of agricultural chemicals with regrettable results. Before combining chemicals in a single spray mixture, one should know how or if they will react. This information may be gained from a compatibility chart (Table 6:1).

There are several forms of incompatibility: (1) **chemical incompatibility,** in which the various chemicals react to form different compounds (usually this arises from use of synthetic organic compounds with an alkaline material); (2) **phytotoxic incompatibility,** in which there may be no chemical reaction, but the mixture causes injury to plants whereas the component parts used separately cause no injury; (3) **physical incompatibility,** in which the chemicals being used change their physical form to one that is unstable and hazardous for application.

FACTORS INFLUENCING THE EFFECTIVENESS OF INSECTICIDES

The route by which the chemical enters the insect affects its toxicity. Through the cuticle we find the following order of toxicity DDT > lindane > chlordane; through the mouth lindane > DDT > chlordane; and through the spiracle chlordane > lindane > DDT. The cuticle is impermeable to strongly dissociating chemicals, but is not a barrier to lipophilic substances. It is for this reason that adding an oil to a spray mixture often increases its toxicity. Insecticides taken through the mouth are absorbed in the midgut. Some chemicals are repellent to insects and are avoided while eating or if eaten they may be regurgitated. Some poisons either are not absorbed in the gut or are inactivated there. Water is unable to penetrate the tracheal system because of its high surface tension. The addition of a material to lower the surface tension allows the spray to enter. Insecticides which have a rapid effect probably enter largely through the tracheae or the cuticle.

The developmental stage of an insect influences its susceptibility to in-

Compatibility of Spray Chemicals

C Caution
X Incompatible

	INSECTICIDES									
	BHC, Lindane	Chlorobenzilate, Kelthane	DDT, TDE, perthane, methoxychlor	Demeton, malathion, parathion, schradan	Diazinon	Dieldrin	EPN, Metacide	Guthion	Lead arsenate	Oil
INSECTICIDES										
BHC, Lindane									C	
Chlorobenzilate, Kelthane										X
DDT, TDE, perthane, methoxychlor										C
Demeton, malathion, parathion, schradan										C
Diazinon										
Dieldrin										C
EPN, Metacide										
Guthion										
Lead arsenate	C									
Oil		X	C	C		C				
Ovex, Genite 923, Mitox, Fenson										
Phosdrin										
Phostex										
Sevin										X
Sulphenone				C						
Tedion				C						
TEPP									C	X
Toxaphene										X
Trithion										X
FUNGICIDES										
Bordeaux	X	C	C	X	X	C	X	X		
Captan				C		C				X
Copper (fixed)	X	C		C	X	C		C		C
Cyprex		C	C		C				C	C
Ferbam, Maneb, Zineb, Ziram										
Glyodin										X
Karathane				C	X				X	X
Lime-sulfur	X	C	C	C	X	C	C	X	C	C
Mercurials				C				C		C
Phygon XL									C	X
Sodium polysulfide	X	C	C	C	X	C	C	X	X	C
Sulfur (wettable)								C		C
OTHERS										
2,4-D, NAA										
2,4,5-TP										
Solubor				C						X
Zinc sulfate	C	X	C	C	C	C	C	C		X
Urea										X

Table 6:1. Compatability of insecticides, fungicides, and several

Ovex, Genite 923, Mitox, Fenson	Phosdrin	Phostex	Sevin	Sulphenone	Tedion	TEPP	Toxaphene	Trithion	Bordeaux	Captan	Copper (fixed)	Cyprex	Ferbam, Maneb, Zineb, Ziram	Glyodin	Karathane	Lime-sulfur	Mercurials	Phygon XL	Sodium polysulfide	Sulfur (wettable)	2,4-D, NAA	2,4,5-TP	Solubor	Zinc sulfate	Urea
									X		X					X			X					C	
									C		C	C				C			C					X	
									C			C				C			C					C	
			C	C					X	C	C				C	C	C		C				C	C	
									X		X	C			X	X			X					C	
									C	C	C					C			C					C	
									X							C			C					C	
									X		C					X	C		X	C				C	
					C							C				X	C	C	X						
		X				X	X	X	X	C	C				X	X	C	C	X	C			X	X	X
										C		C							C						
									C	C	C														
									C	C															
									X	X	C	C				C			C	C	C				
										C														C	
									C	C	C														
									X	C						C	X		X			C		C	
									C			C	C			X			X	C			C	C	
																C		C							
	C	C	X		C	X	C			X		C	C	X	X	X	X	X	X	X	X	X			
C									X		C	C				X	C		X	C				X	
	C	C	X	C	C	C				C		C	C	C		X	C	C	C	X					
C	C		C		C				C	C	C		C			C	C	C	C						C
			C		C			C	C		C	C				C	C		C			C	C		
			C					C	X		C					C			C					C	X
					C			C	X		C					X			X	C				C	X
		C				X	X		X	X	X	C	C	C	X		X	X			X	X	C	X	C
								C	X	C	C	C	C			X		C	X	C				C	C
C			C						X		C	C				X	C		X					C	C
			C				X	X	X	X	C	C	C		X		X	X		X	X	C	X	C
			C					C	X	C	X				C		C			C			C	X	C
									X								X			X	C				
					C				X								X			X					
							C						C				C			C	C				
				C		C	C			X			C			C	X	C	C	X	X				
								C								X	C	C	C	C	C				

other classes of agricultural chemicals. *Courtesy Wash. Agr. Exp. Sta.*

secticides. In general, larvae and nymphs are easier to kill than pupae and adults, and the early instars are often more susceptible than the later ones. Eggs are usually most susceptible just before hatching.

Environmental conditions may alter the effectiveness of insecticides. The rate at which the insecticide is absorbed into the insect body and the rate at which the insect detoxifies the insecticide inside its body is proportional to rise in temperature. Thus the most effective temperature conditions for a successful kill are a high temperature to get the poison inside the insect followed by low temperatures which slow the rate of detoxification. Some chemicals (DDT, methoxychlor, and TDE) are an exception to this rule in that they are most effective at continual relatively low temperatures. Usually the quick-acting poisons are more effective at higher temperatures and the slow-acting poisons at lower temperatures.

Low relative humidities have a deleterious drying effect on the fine mists produced in concentrate spraying. Rains wash off water-soluble sprays, but most insecticides now in use do not fall into this category. Wind and rain cause the "weathering" of the less tenacious portions of spray deposits, and sunlight, though slower in action, causes breakdown for as long as residues remain. Air currents are of importance, as winds of greater than 6 mph. carry spray and dust away from the point of application resulting in uneven distribution. Air currents may seriously interfere with the airplane application of insecticides and in cases where there are strong rising currents it becomes difficult to get a good deposit on the ground.

The condition of the plant may influence the effectiveness of an insecticide. Plants such as cabbage, cauliflower, and many others have waxy leaves, and spray material tends to run off the leaf and drip on the ground. The addition of a wetting agent to the spray will help to correct this condition. Heavy foliage or dense fur may prevent an insecticide penetrating deeply into the area to be treated. Again the addition of a wetting agent will give some help as will increasing the pressure at which the application is made. Growers should realize that after application of insecticides the new foliage of rapidly growing plants lacks a surface residue of toxicant. An apple tree may double its foliage area in two weeks. Some cucurbit plants may grow five inches in a day.

MODE OF ACTION OF INSECTICIDES

By mode of action of an insecticide, we mean the way in which the chemical acts upon the system of an insect to cause its death. Though much research has been done on this subject, there is yet much to be learned before we know exactly how insecticides kill. Attempts to determine a single basic mode of action are fraught with difficulties, for the reason that life processes are numerous, complex, and interdependent. Lethal action of an insecticide is probably due to multiple effects involving the impairment of several life processes.

Realizing the inadequacies of present knowledge, we may for the sake of convenience classify insecticides into five groups: physical poisons, protoplasmic poisons, respiratory poisons, nerve poisons, and poisons of a more general action. **Physical poisons** kill by some physical action such as excluding air—for example, mineral oils—or by abrasive or sorptive actions resulting in loss of water—for example, certain dusts such as silica aerogel. **Protoplasmic poisons,** such as the arsenicals, kill by precipitating protein. **Respiratory poisons,** such as hydrogen cyanide, inactivate respiratory enzymes. Although acting in different ways, many important insecticides like parathion, pyrethrin, and DDT may be classed together as **nerve poisons.**

The discovery of organic phosphorus insecticides has stimulated much research on the physiology of the insect nervous system. This system is high in **acetylcholine** (abbreviated ACh), a chemical that is known to be involved in the synaptic transmission of nerve impulses in mammals. For the normal functioning of ACh, it must be removed from the synaptic region immediately after the nerve impulse is mediated. The removal is accomplished by an enzyme called **cholinesterase** (ChE). Though the exact nature and function of chemical mediators of the nerve impulse in insects are yet to be discovered, it is known that ChE is important in the insect nervous process.

Organic phosphorus insecticides are active inhibitors of cholinesterase enzymes in both mammals and insects. The inhibition in insects results in facilitation of nerve impulses and increased excitation which induce the production of a **neuroactive substance** by the central nervous system. In the large amounts produced, this natural substance becomes a toxicant and disrupts normal nerve functions. The organic phosphorus insecticides and DDT apparently have a common factor in their mode of action. Although DDT itself does not inhibit cholinesterase, it initiates high nervous excitation and causes the release of excessive amounts of the same neuroactive substance.

SYNERGISTS FOR INSECTICIDES

Some chemicals have the property of greatly increasing toxicity of certain insecticides. When the increased toxicity is markedly greater than the sum of the two used separately, it is termed a synergistic action. This is like saying 2 plus 2 equals 10. For example, chemical A may kill 30 per cent of the flies sprayed and chemical B 10 per cent. Should these two be mixed and applied together you might expect at best a 40 per cent kill. However, if synergism takes place, the kill may be as high as 90 per cent or even more. Most synergists have been used with pyrethrum or allethrin. First discovered by United States workers in 1938, insecticide synergists now include such materials as **sesamine, piperonyl cyclonene, sulfoxide,** and **MGK 264.** Synergistic action is important because it provides a means for a more effective insecticide and it reduces the cost of control.

HAZARDS OF INSECTICIDES

To most people the only danger that comes to mind in the use of insecticides is accidental poisoning. However, there are many other dangers and anyone using insecticides should have some knowledge of their existence and possible means of evasion.

Accidental poisoning can and does occur with insecticides. Depending on the nature of the insecticide, all or part of the following precautions should be followed to reduce this hazard: (1) wear a face mask to avoid inhalation of poison; (2) wear dustproof goggles and protective clothing; (3) change clothing as soon as insecticidal treatment is completed; (4) wash off immediately any insecticide that is spilled on the body with plenty of fresh, clean water; (5) bathe as soon as possible after spraying or dusting; (6) avoid remaining in any drift of the spray or dust; (7) destroy all empty containers; (8) store all insecticides where children, irresponsible persons, or livestock cannot get to them; (9) call a doctor immediately if any poison symptoms appear in a person who is using or has recently used insecticides; (10) read all instructions carefully on the label and follow completely.

Because the hazards of using insecticides are closely related to their mammalian toxicities, the latter are important considerations for both health officials and agriculturalists. Most information on mammalian toxicities is obtained by conducting tests on small mammals such as white mice, white rats, and rabbits. Chemicals are administered to experimental animals in several ways to provide information on acute oral toxicity, acute dermal toxicity, inhalation toxicity, and subacute or chronic feeding toxicity.

Results of acute oral and dermal toxicities are usually given in terms of LD_{50}, a designation for the dose lethal to 50 per cent of the test animals. The LD_{50} is expressed in milligrams of toxicant per kilogram of body weight of the test animal and abbreviated to mg./kg. For example, the acute oral LD_{50} of DDT for rats is 250 mg./kg. If one were to feed this amount of toxicant to each test rat of a large group, one could expect around 50 per cent to die and 50 per cent to survive. Having a list of LD_{50}'s available gives us a handy way of comparing the toxicities of insecticides. The acute oral LD_{50}'s for rats in mg./kg. of some common insecticides are: methoxychlor 6000, malathion 1500, DDT 250, lindane 125, dieldrin 100, parathion 3. The lower the figure the greater the toxicity.

From the above data we can calculate that dieldrin is 15 times more toxic than malathion and that parathion is approximately 33 times more toxic than dieldrin. In spite of wide differences in toxic properties, insecticides do not have hazards proportionately different. There are several reasons for the lack of direct relationship. First the rates at which they are employed to control insects may vary. For example, less dieldrin would be applied to an acre of cantaloupe to control cucumber beetles than methoxychlor. Second, the residual characteristics of insecticides vary. Parathion breaks down more quickly on foliage than dieldrin. Third, recommendations and precautions for use vary. Malathion may be applied to livestock for controlling a number of pests, whereas, parathion is never recommended for direct application to livestock. We also take more precautions, such as wearing a face mask, in applying parathion than in applying malathion.

Acute dermal toxicity figures are usually larger than those of oral toxicity as it takes a greater amount of insecticide placed on the skin to cause death than an ingested amount.

Inhalation toxicities are often expressed as LC_{50}'s (lethal concentration) and chronic toxicities as parts per million (ppm) of the daily diet for a specified number of days.

Residues on crops and in meat present a problem of chronic poisoning. DDT may be excreted in milk. The government is aware of this danger and there are laws, both state and federal, forbidding residues in cow's and goat's milk.

Insecticides, if improperly used, may upset the insect balance in such a manner that greater insect damage results from treatment than from no treatment at all. Some chemicals are very destructive to predators and parasites of insect pests without being particularly effective against the pest. The results are that the pest increases greatly in number. Walnut trees sprayed with DDT for codling moth have been defoliated by the resulting increase in aphids. Insecticides may also kill pollinating insects with a resulting poor fruit or seed set.

Wildlife may be adversely affected by unwise applications of insecticides. Chemicals used in recommended manner usually have little effect, but there have been cases where fish and birds have been killed.

Insecticides may have a deleterious effect on plants, either directly by affecting growth of the plant or indirectly by tainting the edible part. Certain chemicals used on stored grain for insect control may lower or destroy seed germination. Others leave a visible residue and lower the quality of the grain. Insecticides may accumulate to such an extent in the soil that it becomes impossible to grow plants.

In treating buildings with flammable fumigants, one risks the danger of explosion and burning. Application of insecticides may involve the user in a legal battle should excessive drift occur, or excessive residues remain on forage or food. Many states as well as the federal government have laws pertaining to use of pesticides.

Lastly, using insecticides may lead to the development of resistance in insects. This is not a new discovery since it was noted many years ago that scale insects became resistant to lime-sulfur sprays and HCN fumigation, and codling moth to arsenical sprays. Resistance to the newer insecticides has been discovered in 137 species of insects and mites, such as the house fly, certain mosquitoes, the cabbage butterfly, the boll weevil, and the two-spotted spider mite. Resistance becomes apparent when rigorous chemical control of a population of insects results in the selection of the naturally resistant forms, which produce offspring of similar resistance.

CLASSES OF INSECTICIDES

Insecticides may be classified in several ways. One of the most widely used systems, until the new synthetics came into the picture, was based on the mode of entry into the insect—stomach, contact, and fumigant poisons. **Stomach poisons** are materials which are ingested by the insect and which kill primarily by action on or absorption from the digestive system. Usually they are limited to the control of chewing insects. **Contact poisons** are absorbed through the body wall and must come in direct contact with the insect to kill. They are usually required against sucking insects. **Fumigant poisons** enter the tracheal system in the form of a gas. Insects, such as stored grain pests, living within an enclosure, are readily killed with fumigants. Soil insects may also be controlled with fumigants.

Classification by mode of entry breaks down with the newer insecticides since many of them enter the insect body in more than one way. To avoid this overlapping, classification now is usually based on the chemical nature of the insecticide. The major divisions are inorganic and organic. The organic insecticides are further divided into oils, botanicals, and synthetic. Oils are petroleum products used primarily against fruit-tree insects. Botanicals are of plant origin and include such insecticides as rotenone, pyrethrum, sabadilla, and ryania. The synthetic organic compounds are by far the most important and include about 100 of the more recently discovered insecticides such as DDT, benzene hexachloride, chlordane, and parathion.

INORGANICS

Though inorganic insecticides have largely been replaced by the more efficient organics, some still find a place in American agriculture. Lead arsenate is commonly used in the form of **acid lead arsenate** ($PbHAsO_4$) and less so as **basic lead arsenate,** which is a mixture of $Pb_4(PbOH)$ $(AsO_4)_3 \cdot H_2O$ and $Pb_5(PbOH)_2(AsO_4)_4$. Acid lead arsenate is used primarily in fruit orchards, on forest and shade trees, and on shrubs to control chewing insects. Though not as toxic to insects, basic lead arsenate is safer to use on plants in foggy costal regions than is the more soluble acid lead arsenate.

Sodium fluoride (NaF) was once a common insecticide used in cockroach and ant bait. A related compound, **sodium fluosilicate** (Na_2SiF_6), is used in baits for ants, cockroaches, and grasshoppers. **Cryolite** (Na_3AlF_6), which is mined in Greenland as well as manufactured in the United States, has proven effective against a number of truck-crop insects, and is used on plants which are generally sensitive to chemical injury. It has also been used in the past in the Pacific Northwest on apples for codling moth control.

Sulfur is the only element which has been found valuable as an insecticide. Finely ground sulfur has been widely applied as a dust for control of mites and of certain fungi. The addition of a wetting agent to sulfur makes possible the use of sulfur as a spray. Boiling together sulfur and freshly slaked or hydrated lime produces a mixture of compounds known as **liquid lime-sulfur.** The active material in the mixture is probably the calcium polysulfides (CaS_4, CaS_5, and others). This material has been used as a fungicide, and on fruit trees against scales, aphids, and mites. Liquid lime-sulfur may be mixed with a stabilizer and evaporated to dryness to form **dry lime-sulfur.** In general the dry lime-sulfur is less effective than the liquid form but is much easier to handle.

In 1882, to discourage school children from stealing grapes, a vineyardist daubed a mixture of lime and copper sulfate over his vines nearest the road. That year many grape vineyards were destroyed by downy mildew of grape but it was noticed the grapes treated to prevent thievery showed no symptoms of the disease. An investigation of this response led to the discovery of **Bordeaux mixture.** The strength of Bordeaux is usually indicated by a series of three figures (6–10–100, for example) the first of which designates the number of pounds of copper sulfate, the second the pounds of lime, and the last the number of gallons of water. Bordeaux is used mostly as a fungicide but has been recommended a number of times as an insect repellent against such insects as flea beetles, cucumber beetles, and leafhoppers.

There are many other inorganic compounds which are now or have been employed as insecticides. **Sodium selenate,** Na_2SeO_4, applied in the soil acts as a systemic and is used primarily to control aphids and mites on greenhouse ornamentals. Cabbage maggots are controlled with **mercurous chloride** (calomel), Hg_2Cl_2, solution. **Phosphorus** has been used in cockroach bait and **thallous sulfate,** Tl_2SO_4, in ant bait for control of ants which will not take arsenical baits.

OILS

Oils in their natural state are highly phytotoxic but when used in an emulsion may, under certain conditions, be safely applied to plants. Mineral oil is a heterogeneous mixture of saturated and unsaturated chain and cyclic hydrocarbons. Certain fractions of this mixture are much more useful as insecticides than others. To designate the quality of oil, data commonly supplied on the label are viscosity, boiling or distillation range, and sulfonation rating (purity or degree of refinement).

Viscosity is usually stated in terms of the time in seconds for 60 cc. to flow through a standard orifice. In general oils of low viscosity are safer to use than are those of higher viscosity; however, the viscosity rating may be misleading since oil from different parts of the country having the same viscosity rating may react quite differently when sprayed on foliage.

Boiling or **distillation range** is a more important character of oil, and is an indirect indication of volatility. Phytotoxicity increases with increase in distillation range. However, it is also true that the heavier spray oil fractions have a greater effectiveness against insects than do the lighter oils. In both cases this probably has to do with the period of time the oils remain in contact with the plant or animal surface. The lighter oils, being more volatile soon escape into the air while the heavier oils remain in contact with the surface for a longer time.

Oils are composed of both saturated and unsaturated hydrocarbons. The unsaturated hydrocarbons are unstable and readily form compounds which are toxic to plants. Consequently the less the amount of unsaturated hydrocarbons present in an oil, the safer that oil is for use on plants. The usual testing procedure of determining the amount of unsaturated hydrocarbons present is by means of the sulfonation test. The oil to be tested is reacted with strong sulfuric acid and the unsaturated hydrocarbons which react with the acid sink to the bottom. The unreacted part, the **unsulfonated residue** (U.R.), is measured in percentage and is used as a measure of purity. Dormant oils have a U.R. rating of 50 to 90 per cent and the more highly refined summer oils a rating of 90 to 96 per cent.

Oils are employed in a number of ways. They may be used as solvents or carriers for insecticides. Diesel fuel is often used as a carrier for insecticide in airplane application. Oil may also serve to carry DDT over water being treated for mosquito control.

Oils by themselves are insecticidal and based on time of usage are classified as either summer or dormant oils. **Summer oils,** which are highly refined and less phytotoxic, are applied to trees in foliage. For example, citrus trees may be treated with summer oils to control mites and scale insects. The **dormant oils,** which are less refined, are applied when no foliage is present. To increase plant safety as well as insecticidal action, new types of oils have been developed which are called **superior** (or **supreme**) **spray oils.** From the time buds show green up to the time leaves are one half inch long, apple trees may be given a delayed dormant spray with these oils to control aphids, scale insects, and mites.

Oil is not applied full strength to trees but diluted with water and applied as an emulsion containing around 1 to 4 or more per cent oil. Several types of agricultural spray oil stocks are formulated. One type, called **emulsible oils,** contains 95 to 99 per cent oil plus emulsifier. Some formulations of these produce an emulsion instantly when poured into a tank of water, while others require preliminary agitation with a small amount of water. The former are often referred to as **miscible oils** and the latter as emulsible oils.

A second type of spray oil stock is the **concentrated emulsion.** These are preformed emulsions in a concentrated state and contain about 83 per cent oil plus emulsifier and water. They have the appearance of a whitish paste, some being flowable, others being thick like mayonnaise.

A third type, **tank-mix oils,** have the oil, the emulsifier, and the water added separately to the spray tank. Violent agitation forms the emulsion. Such an emulsion is termed "quick breaking" because it separates quickly into its component parts upon coming in contact with the plant surface.

The use of oils has several advantages. They are relatively cheap, have a good spreading capacity, are easy to mix, and quite safe to animal life. An important consideration is the fact that insects have not developed any resistance to them. On the other hand they also possess certain disadvantages, such as low toxicity to insects, instability in storage, phytotoxicity, and injury to rubber hose and parts.

BOTANICALS

The botanical insecticides, derived from plants, are the most romantic group of insecticides. These chemicals have been and are still used as fish poisons and as arrow-tip poisons. The source of pyrethrum was kept secret for many years while it was being sold as a powder for louse control. The story of tobacco, the source of nicotine, is filled with many adventures.

Plant products have several uses in insect control. Some act as attractants such as geraniol and eugenol; some as repellents such as citronella and oil of cedar; and some as solvents or extenders such as cottonseed oil, walnut-shell flour, and soybean flour. Their most important role, however, is as insect toxicants. Chief among these are nicotine, sabadilla, ryania, pyrethrum, and rotenone.

Nicotine ($C_{10}H_{14}N_2$)

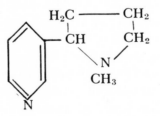

Nicotine was first used as a decoction in 1690 against the pear lace bug in France. This same form was used in the 1700's against soft bodied sucking insects and the plum curculio. Tobacco smoke was directed onto plants by 1773 for control of aphids and other insects. In 1828 the chemical nature of nicotine was discovered and named, and the structure was established in 1893. The most commonly used form today, **nicotine sulfate,** was patented in 1908.

Nicotine comes chiefly from two plants, *Nicotiana tabacum,* the common tobacco plant, and *N. rustica,* which is grown primarily for its high nicotine alkaloid content. The nicotine content of this last plant varies from 2 to 20 per cent depending on the climate and condition of the soil. However, in the United States, *N. tabacum* is the only commercial source of nicotine. Nicotine is taken from leaves and stems of waste tobacco by steam distillation or by solvent extraction. The stems and leaves vary from 0.5 per cent to 3 per cent nicotine. Tobacco contains 11 other alkaloids, but only two of these, anabasine and nornicotine, have received much attention as insecticides.

Pure nicotine is a colorless liquid soluble in water and in most organic solvents. It darkens and becomes viscous on exposure to air. It is an organic base which reacts with acids producing salts which are usually water soluble.

Nicotine is highly toxic to a great number of insects. Evidence indicates that it acts on the ganglia of the insect central nervous system, possibly at the synapses. It is toxic when ingested, absorbed through the body wall, or taken in through the tracheae. Its mammalian toxicity is very high. It causes headache and vomiting followed by respiratory failure due to paralysis of the breathing muscles. It can be absorbed through the skin in lethal amounts. Nicotine has a very low phytotoxicity and is used on many plants where it is economically feasible.

Nicotine is formulated in several ways. The oldest method was to soak waste tobacco in water and use the liquid as a spray. Today we have standardized materials containing known amounts of the active material. The chief form is nicotine sulfate which is relatively safe to handle and readily dissolves in water to make a useful spray. Nicotine may also be used as a dust in the form of finely ground crude tobacco, but the usual formulation consists of nicotine sulfate absorbed on active (bentonite) or inactive (gypsum) carrier. The active carriers change the nicotine sulfate into free nicotine in the presence of moisture. When used as a fumigant dried tobacco may be burned and the smoke directed among the infested plants. Extracts may be vaporized by heat or they may be absorbed on a combustible material which, when burned releases the nicotine. Nicotine may also serve as a stomach poison by fixing or stabilizing it as a salt. Nicotine may be incorporated into aerosol formulations and dispensed to form a space fumigant.

The uses of nicotine are varied, for they are applied to both plants and animals. As a dip solution nicotine has effectively controlled external parasites of animals. The greatest current use is in the control of insects attacking plants. Gardeners often resort to liquid nicotine sulfate which is effective against soft bodied, sucking insects. Frequently soap or other alkali is added to the spray solution which acts to free nicotine from its salt. Nicotine dusts are used in much the same manner as sprays. Fumigation with nicotine is practiced in some greenhouses. It is particularly effective in treating a small house where more expensive and elaborate equipment is unavailable. A common fumigating canister is the Nico-Fume Pressure Fumigator.

Nicotine leaves no harmful residue on plants, but it has the disadvantage of being highly toxic to mammals and great care should be exercised in its use.

Pyrethrum derives its toxicity from four esters, pyrethrin I and pyrethrin II and cinerin I and cinerin II.

Pyrethrin I $(C_{21}H_{30}O_3)$

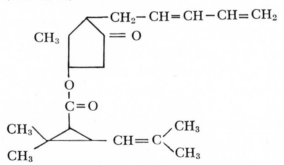

The structural formulas of the other three compounds, are similar to that of pyrethrin I.

The insecticidal activity of pyrethrum was discovered in Iran (then called Persia) around 1800. Great secrecy surrounded the source of the material which was called Persian Powder and was sold at extravagant prices for louse and flea control. The discovery of the source of the powder was made by an Armenian merchant who had been traveling in the Caucasus Mountains. Another version of the story is that the secret was given to Russian soldiers by prisoners of war during the Russo-Persian war in 1827 or the Russo-Turkish War of 1828–29. The original powder came from the daisy *Chrysanthemum coccineum* and *C. carneum*. In 1840 it was found *C. cinerariaefolium,* produced in Dalmatia, had a higher insecticidal activity and this species of daisy soon replaced the previous sources.

Pyrethrum was introduced into the United States about 1858 and found wide application. From 1876 to about 1914 an attempt was made to grow pyrethrum commercially in California. The flower has also been experimentally grown around Fort Collins, Colorado. Because neither of these two ventures was a commercial success, the United States still imports all of its pyrethrum.

In 1924 the chemical nature of pyrethrum was discovered by two United States chemists. From knowledge of the chemical formula, it became possible in 1949 to produce synthetically a closely related compound having nearly the same toxic activity as pyrethrum. The new compound is called **allethrin.**

Currently most pyrethrum comes from the flower *Chrysanthemum cinerariaefolium,* which is a white, daisy-like flower with a yellow center growing 18 to 24 inches high (Fig. 6:1). Pyrethrum flowers were imported at first from Dalmatia and Japan. Since World War II most of the United States import has come from British East Africa and the Congo. In 1956

Fig. 6:1. The flower from which the insecticide pyrethrum is made. *Courtesy Chas. Hurd Associates.*

the United States imported approximately eight million pounds of pyrethrum flowers or its equivalent in extract.

The insecticide is produced by grinding the flowers and mixing this with a dust diluent or, more commonly, by extracting the active materials with solvents and formulating the extracts into sprays and dusts. The active materials are esters which are rapidly hydrolized by alkali and decomposed by sunlight.

Pyrethrum is toxic to most insects with which it comes in contact. Because the material acts rapidly as a nerve poison, affected insects fall quickly to the ground or floor. Such action is termed "knockdown," and pyrethrum is characterized by its rapid knockdown. Insects knocked down do not necessarily die; some will recover if allowed to do so. Pyrethrum lacks persistence in the field due to its breakdown by sunlight and thus leaves no harmful residue. It acts almost entirely as a contact poison.

Pyrethrum is relatively harmless to mammals by ingestion, though it is poisonous if injected into the blood stream, and the dust may cause allergic reactions in some people. It is harmless to plants. Two disadvantages of pyrethrum are that it breaks down rather rapidly and is relatively expensive.

Pyrethrum is formulated in the form of dusts, sprays, and aerosols. Usually a synergist such as sulfoxide or piperonyl butoxide is added to increase toxicity and also to reduce the amount of pyrethrum necessary for a satisfactory kill.

A material with such low mammalian toxicity would obviously find many uses. It can be applied to edible plants shortly before harvest since it leaves no harmful residue. It is effective against a wide range of insects and is one of the insecticides preferred by the backyard gardener. Pyrethrum has been used on livestock as a toxicant for external parasites and as an insect repellent. One of its greatest uses is in household sprays. It possesses rapid knockdown and is perfectly safe for spraying in the home. Pyrethrum mixed with stored grain protects the grain from insect injury.

Rotenone $(C_{23}H_{22}O_6)$

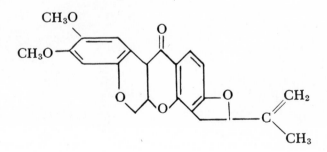

Long ago natives in the tropics of Africa, Asia and South America discovered that certain plants when placed in water would stupify fish causing them to rise to the surface and to be easy to capture. Extracts of these same plants are used today by fish managers to remove rough fish from ponds, lakes, and streams so that the waters may be restocked with desirable fish. We now know that these fish poison plants contain a toxic compound, rotenone, and five other related rotenoids.

As early as 1848 rotenone was used as an insecticide on crops in British Malaya. The Chinese may have employed it even before this time. Extracts of rotenone-bearing plants were patented in England in 1911. The chemical nature of rotenone was determined in 1932.

Rotenone is found in 68 species of leguminous plants. The important commercial ones are two species of *Derris* which grow in the Far East and contain 5 to 9 per cent rotenone, and several species of *Lonchocarpus* which grow in the Amazon Valley of South America and contain 8 to 11 per cent rotenone. The devil's shoestring (*Tephrosia*) of the eastern United States contains some rotenone but has never come into commercial production.

To obtain rotenone only the roots of the plants are utilized. These are dried, powdered and either mixed with a diluent powder to be used as a dust or extracted and the extract used in making sprays or dusts.

Pure rotenone is white, crystalline, and insoluble in water but soluble in many organic solvents. It is rapidly oxidized in the presence of light or alkali.

Rotenone is a selective insecticide being very effective against some insects and inactive against others. It is believed to kill insects by inhibiting the utilization of oxygen by the body cells or by depriving the tissues of oxygen through a depressant action on nerve and muscle concerned with tracheal breathing. Rotenone acts as both a stomach and contact poison.

Although rotenone may be used with relative safety on most mammals, swine are highly susceptible to rotenone poisoning. In New Guinea fresh roots containing rotenone have been used several times to commit suicide. Continued exposure to rotenone dust may lead to toxic symptoms. It causes no phytotoxicity.

The usual formulations of rotenone are dusts, which must be mixed with nonalkaline carriers to prevent breakdown, wettable powders, emulsifiable concentrates, and aerosols.

Rotenone finds many applications. It is widely used in the horticultural field on vegetables and ornamentals. Until the discovery of the animal systemic insecticides, it was the best material for control of cattle grubs. It has also been used for control of external pests of livestock.

The material has several advantages, such as safety to both mammals and plants, but it also has disadvantages, such as breakdown in storage, slow action, and low toxicity to some insects.

There are several other botanical insecticides of minor importance. **Sabadilla** comes from the seeds of a lily grown in Venezuela. It has been used against human lice and for control of Homoptera and Hemiptera. **Ryania** is obtained from stems and roots of *Ryania speciosa*, family Flacourtiaceae. It is less toxic to mammals than rotenone, more stable, and possesses a longer residual action. It has been used primarily against the European corn borer, codling moth, and some other lepidopterous insects. **Hellebore**, which comes from a lily, was in wide use many years ago for control of pests of vegetables, fruit, and livestock. It is rarely used today.

SYNTHETIC ORGANIC INSECTICIDES

The synthetic organics completely dominate the insecticide field today. Although several synthetic organic insecticides were known previous to World War II, not until the discovery of DDT did interest in the field become widespread. Following the release of DDT, many companies became active in searching for new insecticides. Among these were chemical companies, perfume and drug importers, rubber companies, pine products companies, and many more. Former waste products were carefully examined to see if some chemical reaction might convert them to insect toxicants. Many formulating companies entered the field, and the same chemical became available under a multitude of different names. Today this flurry of activity has leveled off because of economic competition and the enactment of laws to protect the consumer.

Although the majority of synthetic organic insecticides now in use were developed after 1947, several were marketed prior to this time. Dinitrocresol was sold as an insecticide in Germany as early as 1892, and by 1932 several thiocyanates were commercially available in the United States.

The development of the organic phosphate insecticides began in Germany. During World War II, certain German chemists searched for synthetic compounds to replace insecticides which had become unavailable in Germany because of war conditions. Several organic phosphate compounds proved highly toxic to insects. From these chemicals came a number of effective and practical insecticides, such as parathion, TEPP, schradan, and demeton.

Rapid developments in the field of synthetic organic insecticides makes an up-to-date classification difficult. One generally applicable has the following headings: (1) chlorinated hydrocarbons, (2) phosphorus-containing compounds, (3) sulfur-containing compounds, (4) nitrophenols and derivatives, (5) thiocyanates, (6) fumigants, (7) repellents (regardless of structure), and (8) miscellaneous compounds. Because of their group importance, we have chosen to discuss the chlorinated hydrocarbons and phosphorus-containing compounds at some length. We shall briefly consider fumigants and repellents and a special group of compounds known as specific miticides. The latter are chemicals, often related chemically to insecticides, which are markedly toxic to mites but not to insects. Most of the currently used specific miticides are relatives of DDT and are sulfur-containing compounds. In addition, insect attractants will be mentioned as they are becoming increasingly important in the detection and control of serious pests.

Chlorinated hydrocarbons

These insecticides have molecules made up of chlorine, hydrogen, carbon, and occasionally oxygen.

DDT—($C_{14}H_9Cl_5$)

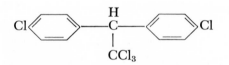

In 1932 chemists of the **Geigy** Company in Switzerland began a search for an improved moth-proofing compound. Seven years later **Dr. Paul Müller** found a material that showed great promise. The company was given a patent on it by the Swiss government on March 7, 1940 and later it became known as DDT.

DDT soon proved itself as an agricultural insecticide by stopping an outbreak of the Colorado potato beetle during 1941 in Switzerland. At the same time it was found highly effective in controlling fleas, lice, mosquitoes, and flies. In 1942 samples of the compound were sent to the British branch of Geigy Company and 200 pounds to the United States. Production of DDT in the United States began after a pilot plant was established at Norwood, Ohio, in May 1943. All of these developments were kept secret at the time.

The first wide use of DDT came in 1944, when typhus broke out among the civilian population of Naples. Mass delousing with the new insecticide was started and within three weeks the typhus outbreak was brought under control. Never before during a war had an epidemic of typhus been halted.

In World War I, 25 per cent of the Serbian soldiers perished from typhus, and Russia lost several millions to this disease.

In Naples 1,300,000 civilians were treated with DDT during January, 1944. It became more and more difficult to keep secret such mass medication and such spectacular control of a dreaded disease. On August 2, 1944, the British government disclosed the identity of the chemical. The world recognized the major advance made in medical science through the development of DDT, and in 1948 Dr. Müller (Fig. 6:2) was awarded the Nobel Prize for medicine.

DDT is made by the condensation of chloral and monochlorobenzene in the presence of sulfuric acid. In its pure state it is a crystalline powder with a melting point of 108°C. The crude form is a waxy solid with a melting point near 89°C. It is insoluble in water, but soluble in most organic solvents. DDT is broken down by alkali and by organic bases; otherwise it is stable and inert. It is not attacked by ordinary acids.

DDT is effective against a great number of insect pests. However, it has little toxicity to most Orthoptera, the boll weevil, Mexican bean beetle, and most aphids.

Fig. 6:2. Dr. Paul Müller, discoverer of insecticidal properties of DDT. *Courtesy Geigy Chemical Corporation.*

Fig. 6:3. George Buntin, discoverer of toxaphene. *Courtesy Hercules Powder Co.*

DDT is a relatively safe insecticide. Human deaths attributed to DDT have always included a solvent, and in all probability it was the solvent which caused the death and not the DDT. This chemical has been widely used in insect control and no increase in illness of workers using it has been detected. Also, workers exposed to DDT in its manufacture have shown no ill effects. DDT is known to be stored up to certain levels in the fatty tissues of animals and to be excreted in the milk of dairy cows. For the latter reason DDT is not applied to dairy herds nor in dairy barns.

Although DDT is safe to use on most plants, the crude form causes phytotoxic symptoms on cucurbits, tomatoes, and several other plants. Pure DDT (mp 108°C.) does not cause this reaction. One surprising effect of DDT is that at very low concentrations it stimulates growth in potatoes and cabbage much like plant hormones do. And in fact, symptoms of plant injury by DDT are often "hormone-like" in nature.

DDT is formulated in several ways: a 5 per cent kerosene solution; emulsifiable concentrates usually containing 2 lbs. of DDT per gallon; dusts containing from 1 to 10 per cent DDT; wettable powders containing from 25 to 50 per cent DDT; aerosol bombs; and granular DDT.

DDT is the most familiar and the most widely used insecticide. It has been applied for control of insects on livestock, in the home, on fruits, vegetables, field crops, fiber crops, and for many other purposes.

There are several advantages and a few disadvantages in using DDT. It is effective against a wide range of insects, but several species have developed resistance to it. It acts as both a contact and stomach poison and is stable under most conditions. Its residual action is usually an advantage, but may also be a disadvantage when it gets into food products. DDT has the disadvantage of killing some beneficial predators and parasites and encouraging certain pest species, especially the spider mites.

Methoxychlor, another development of the Geigy Company, is closely related to DDT. In general, it is useful against the same insect pests as DDT except it is more effective against plum curculio and the Mexican bean beetle and less effective against the European corn borer and corn earworm. It is only $\frac{1}{25}$ to $\frac{1}{50}$ as toxic to mammals as DDT and accumulates less in the fat and is excreted less into the milk. It is usually safer to apply on plants than DDT. Two other valuable insecticides related chemically to DDT are **perthane** and **TDE.**

Toxaphene ($C_{10}H_{10}Cl_8$), an American development, was discovered by George Buntin (Fig. 6:3) of Hercules Powder Company. It is a yellow, waxy solid, insoluble in water, but soluble in many organic solvents. It is broken down by strong alkali and sunlight. It is effective against a large number of insects and is about four times more toxic to mammals than DDT. It has low chronic toxicity, and accumulations in fat dissipate rather quickly in the living animal. It is safe on most plants, but is highly toxic to cucurbits. It is formulated much like DDT. It has been used against grasshoppers, cutworms, webworms, cotton insects, and legume insects.

Benzene hexachloride ($C_6H_6Cl_6$) was first synthesized by Michael Faraday in 1825. BHC, as benzene hexachloride is commonly called, was found (independently) to be an active insecticide by scientists in France and in Great Britain in 1941 and 1942.

BHC occurs in at least six isomers, each one of which exhibits distinctly different biological activity. The beta and epsilon isomers are virtually nontoxic to insects, alpha, delta, and eta isomers slightly to moderately active, and the gamma isomer highly active. Their toxicities to plants and mammals also differ. The purified form of BHC (99 per cent gamma isomer) is known as **lindane.**

Raw BHC is white to brown in color and has a strong musty odor. Lindane is white to colorless and lacks an odor. Both are stable compounds but are broken down by alkali.

BHC and lindane are effective against a great number of insects. They act as stomach, contact, and fumigant poisons. BHC is more toxic to insects than DDT. Lindane is 1,000 times more toxic to insects than crude BHC. BHC may cause injury to some plants and has caused deformation and polyploidy in some plant roots. Lindane is safer than BHC on plants.

One serious drawback of BHC is its production of taint or off-flavor in treated plants. BHC applied to the soil for wireworm control has completely ruined potato crops. Peaches sprayed with BHC for curculio control have no off-flavors as fresh fruit, but a definite musty flavor as canned fruit. BHC used on cotton may accumulate in sufficient quantities in the soil to give an off-flavor to peanuts grown in rotation. Lindane largely overcomes this disadvantage.

Aldrin ($C_{12}H_8Cl_6$), **dieldrin** ($C_{12}H_8Cl_6O$), **chlordane** ($C_{10}H_6Cl_8$), **heptachlor** ($C_{10}H_5Cl_7$), and **endrin** (isomer of dieldrin) are chemically related (cyclodienes) and were developed in the United States. Aldrin, dieldrin, and endrin are stable in alkalis. All are insoluble in water and soluble in most organic solvents. They are more toxic to mammals than DDT, and endrin is highly toxic, falling within the range of toxicity found among the more toxic phosphorus compounds. Most are persistent insecticides and effective against a wide range of insects. Endrin is particularly effective against lepidopterous larvae, such as cutworms and webworms. All of these insecticides have been used in the soil with success.

Organic phosphorus insecticides

These synthetic insecticides contain phosphorus in their molecules and act either as surface-active poisons or systemically, i.e., they are absorbed by plants rendering the sap toxic to insects or they are taken in by animals rendering the blood toxic. Examples of nonsystemic or only slightly systemic compounds are parathion, TEPP malathion, and Diazinon. Systemic compounds include demeton, schradan, phorate, Phosdrin, Dylox, and Ruelene.

The discovery of the insecticidal value of this chemical group was made by Dr. Gerhard Schrader (Fig. 6:4) in Germany during World War II. He was instrumental in the development of TEPP, parathion, demeton, schradan, and several other phosphate insecticides.

Parathion ($C_{10}H_{14}NO_5PS$)

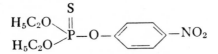

Pure parathion is a pale yellow liquid, but in its usual crude form it is a brown liquid with an odor of garlic. It is slightly soluble in water and rapidly hydrolyzes in alkali solution. It is highly toxic to both insects and mammals. Symptoms of parathion poisoning are headache, nausea, and

Fig. 6:4. Dr. Gerhard Schrader in his laboratory at Wuppertal, Germany. *Courtesy Bayer Company.*

constriction of pupils. People handling these dangerous chemicals should be familiar with the symptoms and upon any indication of their occurrence, they should call a doctor. Atropine is an antidote.

Because of its general effect on the nervous system, parathion is effective against a great many insects and mites. It is noncumulative in mammals, but highly toxic. It is safe for use on most plants, except for a few varieties of plums and pear and on McIntosh apples.

It is widely used in production of fruit, vegetables, ornamentals, and field crops. Its high mammalian toxicity precludes its application on livestock, in the household, or where it will come in contact with man.

Methylparathion has characteristics and uses similar to parathion.

TEPP or tetraethyl pyrophosphate ($C_8H_{20}O_7P_2$), a phosphorus insecticide discovered in Germany, is a colorless, odorless, hygroscopic liquid that is miscible with water and most organic solvents. It is rapidly hydrolyzed to biologically inactive materials by water and thus leaves no harmful residue.

It is effective as a contact insecticide against a great many insects. It is also highly toxic to warm-blooded animals, being one of the most toxic of all the insecticides in current use. TEPP is relatively safe for application to most plants and is often used to clean up insect infestations on vegetable or fruit crops shortly before harvest.

Demeton ($C_8H_{19}O_3PS_2$), better known by its trade name of Systox, is a colorless, viscous liquid with a slight but characteristic odor. It is slightly soluble in water and soluble in most organic solvents. Though demeton acts as a contact poison and has some fumigant action, its systemic property is most important. It is about equal to parathion in mammalian toxicity. McIntosh apple is about the only plant which shows phytotoxic symptoms following demeton application; but if overdosed, practically all plants show severe toxic symptoms.

Demeton is used either as a spray on foliage where the material enters the sap stream through the leaves or as an application to the ground where the material is taken up by the roots. Treatment may also be made by soaking or by applying a coat of demeton in activated charcoal to seeds, though a derivative of this insecticide, **Di-Syston**, is more frequently applied as a seed systemic. Demeton is particularly valuable where injurious insects must be controlled and beneficial forms protected. For example, in controlling destructive insects in seed crops, it is necessary to remove the sucking insects from the field without injuring the pollinating insects. Demeton, in general, is not effective against chewing insects.

Malathion ($C_{10}H_{19}O_6PS_2$) developed in the United States, is a yellow to dark brown liquid. Agricultural grades have a rather strong odor but premium grades have practically no odor. It is only slightly soluble in water, but is miscible with most organic solvents.

Malathion is effective against a large number of insects. In general, its phytotoxicity is low, but it has caused injury to McIntosh apples, Bartlett pears, and to some ferns. Unlike most phosphorus compounds, malathion has very low mammalian toxicity, much lower than that of DDT. It is used in many of the same situations as parathion, and in addition may be used where low mammalian toxicity is desirable such as application to livestock, in dairy barns, and on ornamental plants around homes.

There are many more synthetic insecticides that have been found helpful in man's battle to control insect enemies. Every year new compounds are added to the already long list of recommended insecticides. Some of these not specifically mentioned in this chapter will be referred to in the host Chapters 8 to 20 and short descriptions of them may be found in the Glossary.

FUMIGANTS

Fumigants afford a practical solution for insect control within an enclosure. To be a good fumigant, a chemical should possess certain qualities. It should be volatile and penetrate deeply into stored products. The gas should be toxic to insects and mites, but should not be corrosive or interfere with seed quality if used on stored grain. The gas must desorb from treated products so that no toxic residue remains. Two serious hazards of fumigation are the flammability of certain gasses and the danger of accidental poisoning of man.

Hydrogen cyanide (HCN) is a colorless gas with an almond odor. It is toxic to all insects and is highly toxic to man with dangerous amounts entering quickly through the lungs and even through the skin. It is not toxic to plants at recommended dosages, although it may injure plants bearing copper residues from previous spraying. Mills, warehouses, greenhouses, and other buildings and citrus trees under gas-proof tarpaulins are often treated with HCN. It is nonflammable but is rather difficult to remove from treated materials.

Carbon disulfide (CS_2) is a colorless to yellow liquid with an unpleasant odor. It is highly flammable and is usually diluted with four parts of carbon tetrachloride to reduce this hazard. Carbon disulfide is highly absorptive and penetrating and has been used in buildings and in the soil. Besides its high flammability it also has the disadvantage of reacting with many surfaces, leaving yellow stains.

Methyl bromide (CH_3Br) has in recent years become a widely used fumigant. It is a colorless gas with a faintly sweetish odor. It is stable and nonflammable, has high insect toxicity, and some acaricidal properties. It has very high penetrating properties and is rapidly desorbed from treated materials. It is quite safe for use on dormant plants. Methyl bromide is used in the fumigation of plant products imported into this country. It is useful in mills, warehouses, and granaries. Methyl bromide is highly volatile and needs special equipment for application.

Ethylene dichloride ($C_2H_4Cl_2$) is a sweet smelling, noncorrosive liquid. Because it is flammable, it is usually mixed with carbon tetrachloride. This mixture is used mainly for fumigation of stored products, but has also been used in emulsion form to control the peach tree borer. It has relatively low mammalian toxicity.

Carbon tetrachloride (CCl_4) is much less toxic to insects than the usual insect fumigants. It is neither flammable nor explosive and is mixed with other fumigants to reduce the hazards of fire and explosion.

Paradichlorobenzene ($C_6H_4Cl_2$) and **naphthalene** ($C_{10}H_8$) are solids which slowly give off gas. They have been used as soil fumigants, and are popular in the form of moth balls or flakes for clothes moth control.

Dichloropropene ($C_3H_4Cl_2$) and **dichloropropane** ($C_3H_5Cl_2$) mixture (**D-D mixture**) is a common soil fumigant. The mixture is toxic to nematodes as well as to all soil insects. Because this fumigant is phytotoxic and may cause off-flavor in potatoes, the soil must be treated well in advance of planting date.

SPECIFIC MITICIDES

Although some insecticides, such as parathion and malathion, are effective miticides, the majority of insecticides have little activity against phytophagous mites. To control this serious group of crop pests special chemicals, known as specific miticides, have been developed. They are relatively noninsecticidal but show a high degree of toxicity to mites.

Ovex ($C_{12}H_8Cl_2O_3S$)

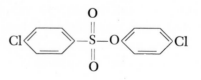

Ovex, developed in the United States and an example of a sulfur-containing miticide, is a white to tan flaky solid that is commonly formulated as a 50 per cent wettable powder. It is highly toxic to mite eggs and has high residual ovicidal action. It is frequently used in early season, preventive control of spider mites on fruit trees. Other useful miticides for early season treatment include **Genite, Fenson,** and **Mitox.**

Kelthane is a miticide closely related to DDT and is formulated as an 18.5 per cent emulsifiable concentrate or wettable powder. It gives high initial kill and long residual activity against most species of plant mites. It is generally applied when mites appear in threatening numbers during the summer. Other effective miticides with long residual include **Chlorobenzilate** and **Tedion.**

Aramite has been widely used as a miticide on fruits, vegetables, and ornamentals. On the basis of laboratory tests with rats and dogs, it is suspected of being a carcenogen and can only be used where no detectable residues will remain on foodstuffs. In its pure form it is a colorless liquid. It is formulated as a 15 per cent wettable powder.

INSECT REPELLENTS

Insect repellents are much more important in the protection of man and animals from insect attack than in the protection of plants. Bordeaux mixture which acts as a fungicide also has a repelling effect on some plant-feeding insects and has been used in potato fields for that purpose. Inactive dusts have been used on cucurbits to repel cucumber beetles.

Pyrethrum in low concentrations repels blood-sucking insects. This characteristic has been exploited in cattle sprays. Other repellents suitable for application to livestock include **butoxy polypropylene glycol** and **dibutyl succinate.**

During World War II United States troops applied **dimethyl phthalate** to repel anopheles mosquitoes, the vectors of malaria. The chemical also repels other blood-sucking insects, ticks, and chiggers. **Diethyl toluamide,** a recent discovery of the USDA, is one of the best all-purpose insect repellents so far developed. It protects the wearer against mosquitoes, chiggers, ticks, fleas, and biting flies. Its resistance to rubbing gives it a long-lasting quality and it can be applied safely to skin and most fabrics.

Several other repellents are commercially available including ethyl hexanediol, butyl ethyl propanediol, dimethyl carbate, Indalone, and MGK Repellent 11.

INSECT ATTRACTANTS

In applied entomology insect attractants have been developed for several purposes: to sample local populations; to lure insects into traps or to poisons for control of injurious populations; to offset repellent properties of certain sprays; and to lure insects away from crops. Substances that have been used for these purposes include geraniol, eugenol, sugar, molasses, yeast extract, certain fatty acids, protein hydrolysates, Q-Lure, siglure, medlure, and trimedlure.

Selected References

Bailey, S. F., and L. M. Smith, *Handbook of Agricultural Pest Control* (Industry Publications, Inc., 1951).

Brown, A. W. A., *Insect Control by Chemicals* (New York: Wiley, 1951).

Dethier, V. G., *Chemical Insect Attractants and Repellents* (Blakiston, 1947).

Frear, D. E. H., *Chemistry of Insecticides, Fungicides, and Herbicides* (Princeton: Van Nostrand, 1948).

Entoma: A Directory of Insect and Plant Pest Control, Entomological Soc. of America (issued each year).

Martin, H., *Guide to the Chemicals used in Crop Protection,* Canada Dept. of Agr., 1957.

Metcalf, R. L., *Organic Insecticides* (New York: Interscience, 1955).

Shepard, H. H., *The Chemistry and Action of Insecticides* (New York: McGraw-Hill, 1951).

Chapter 7 | INSECTICIDE APPLICATION EQUIPMENT | *W. Don Fronk*

Recent advances in chemical control of insects have come not only from the discovery of more effective insecticides but also from the development of new and better machines for applying these chemicals. Early farm sprayers, such as those invented by John Bean in 1883 (Fig. 7:1), were small, hand-operated tanks which had to be carried about the field being treated. Somewhat later, bigger tanks were placed on wheels with larger but still hand-operated pumps. In 1887 the first traction sprayer was designed, and in 1894 sprayers powered by steam engines were invented. The first complete power sprayer operated by a gasoline engine was not marketed until around 1900. In 1911 the Bean Spray Pump Company perfected the modern pressure regulator and in 1914 the Friend Sprayer Company introduced the spray gun.

Although improvements came gradually, we today have available a multitude of types and sizes of sprayers and dusters which provide the means for almost any practical application of insecticide. Insect problems, ranging from unwanted insects in the home to insects infesting thousands of acres of range or forest, are neither too small nor too big that we can not find some piece of equipment suitable for applying a chemical to help solve them. Yet in spite of this variety, improvements are still needed in both ground and aerial equipment and we can expect to see further changes and advances in the future.

In this chapter we shall present a short summary of the common types of sprayers, dusters, and granule applicators. Special application equipment will be discussed in appropriate host chapters. Only brief mention will be made of the operation and function of the various parts of sprayers and dusters, as this subject more properly belongs to the field of agricultural engineering.

An accepted classification of application equipment is presented in the outline below and general characteristics of sprayers and dusters are given in Table 7:1.

Sprayers

Hand sprayers
  Household—intermittent and continuous sprayers
  Compressed air sprayers
  Knapsack sprayers
  Hand spray pumps, bucket, barrel, and slide type
  Wheelbarrow sprayers
Household electric sprayers
Traction sprayers
Power sprayers
  Hydraulic
    Estate-type sprayers
    Multipurpose sprayers
    Low-pressure, low-volume sprayers
    High-pressure, high-volume sprayers
    Self-propelled, high-clearance sprayers
    Stationary sprayers
  Hydro-pneumatic sprayers
  Blower sprayers, air-blast and concentrate
  Aerosol generators
  Aircraft sprayers, fixed-wing and helicopter

Dusters

Hand dusters
  Plunger dusters
  Bellows dusters
  Crank dusters
  Knapsack dusters
Traction or wheelbarrow dusters
Power dusters
  Row and field crop dusters
  Radial, vertical, and single-outlet fruit dusters
  Self-propelled, high-clearance dusters

Granule Applicators

Row crop attachments
Trailer-type granule applicators

SPRAYERS

The household **intermittent and continuous sprayers** are used in homes to control insects such as house flies, mosquitoes, ants, clothes moths, and cockroaches. One type of nozzle produces a fine mist to put a space spray into the air, another type produces a coarse spray for residual deposits. **Electric household sprayers** are often used by professional pest control operators to control insect pests in restaurants and hotels (Fig. 7:2).

The **compressed air sprayer** has many applications. Gardeners use them to apply sprays to lawns, shrubs, fruit trees, and vegetables. They can be

Fig. 7:1. John Bean with sprayer he invented in 1883 and started manufacturing in 1884. *Courtesy John Bean Division, Lansing, Mich.*

Table 7:1 | Performance of Common Types of Sprayers and Dusters

Type	Equipment	Insecticide Application Equipment			General Use
		Concentration of Toxicant Applied	Method of Propulsion	Liquid Pressure	
Hand-powered sprayers	Nozzle extension rods	Low (0.01–0.5%)	Liquid pressure	Low (25–250 p.s.i.)	Home gardens and small plantings
Hydraulic sprayers (conventional)	Piston pump Horizontal or vertical booms hand guns	Low (0.01–0.5%)	Liquid pressure (20–85 g.p.m.)	Moderate to high (200–800 p.s.i.)	Diverse uses (most common type)
Low-gallonage sprayers	Gear or roller pump horizontal boom	Moderate to high (1–5%)	Liquid pressure (1–25 g.p.m.)	Usually low (15–125 p.s.i.)	Weedicides, row, and field crops
Air-blast sprayers	Centrifugal pump usually radial nozzle arrangement	Low to moderate (1–4X, or 0.01–2%)	Liquid pressure plus air blast[a] (20–100 g.p.m., up to 200)	Usually low (50–70 or more p.s.i., up to 200)	Widely used on tree fruit
Concentrate sprayers (mist blowers)	Gear or piston pump airstream injection nozzle arrangements	Low to very high (5–12X, or 0.05–100%)	Air blast[b] (3–15 g.p.m. liquid output, up to 30)	Usually moderate (150–400 p.s.i.)	Use developing on tree fruit and shade trees
Hand-powered dusters	Single or multiple fishtail extensions	Moderate to very high (0.5–15%)	Air blast		Home gardens and small plantings
Engine-powered dusters	Horizontal, vertical, radial, or single outlet fishtail arrangements	Moderate to very high (0.5–15%)	Air blast		Row and field crops (some fruit)
Aircraft dusters	Special venturi discharge devices	Moderate to very high (0.5–15%)	Air blast		Row and field crops (some fruit)
Aircraft sprayers	Gear or centrifugal pump horizontal boom under wing	Moderate to very high (10–20X, or 0.1–10%)	Liquid pressure plus air blast (2.75–12 g.p.m.)	Low (25–70 p.s.i.)	Row and field crops (some fruit)

[a] High volume 20,000–100,000 cu. ft./min., moderate velocity 10–100 m.p.h. air blast.
[b] Moderate volume 4,000–30,000 cu. ft./min., high velocity 90–180 m.p.h. air blast.

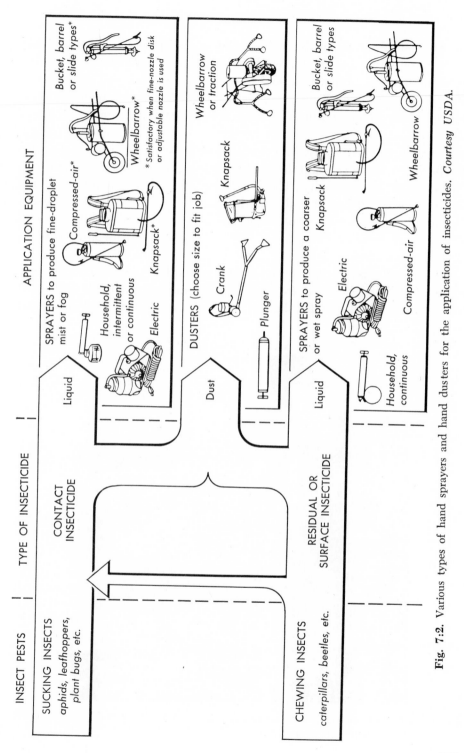

Fig. 7:2. Various types of hand sprayers and hand dusters for the application of insecticides. *Courtesy USDA.*

used to control insects in the home, in barns, and in poultry houses. They are used by public health workers for applying residual deposits of insecticides in homes and other buildings to control mosquitoes and other insects of medical importance. Tanks range from 1½ to 5 gal. and should be filled not to exceed ⅔ to ¾ full of spray materials, leaving an air space above the liquid.

Knapsack sprayers, carried on the back of the operator, have tanks with a capacity of 4 to 6 gal. and develop maximum pressures of 80 to 180 p.s.i. (pounds per square inch). The handle of the pump extends over the shoulder or at hip height and must be operated by hand while spraying. Because these sprayers develop higher pressures and have greater capacity than most compressed air sprayers they are better suited for large gardens or truck farms (Fig. 7:3).

Bucket and barrel type sprayers are useful for small plantings. The bucket type may be used for spraying ornamental plantings and small trees and the barrel type for slightly larger jobs such as small orchards and

Fig. 7:3. Knapsack sprayer being used to apply insecticide to a vegetable garden. *From D. B. Smith & Company, Utica, N. Y.*

vegetable gardens. These sprayers are equipped with plunger type pumps and an air chamber to maintain constant pressure. Pressure up to 250 p.s.i. may be developed by these sprayers.

Slide or trombone sprayers, like the bucket sprayers, are used mostly on ornamental plantings and small trees. Pressure is provided by a telescoping type pump which has a nozzle on the discharge end. The spray is usually carried in a bucket.

Wheelbarrow sprayers may be either hand or engine operated. To be most efficiently used, the hand-operated type requires two men, one to pump and one to spray. The wheelbarrow sprayers are the largest hand-operated units and may be used for spraying trees, orchards, greenhouses, and vegetable gardens. The tanks in these sprayers range in capacity from 5 to 20 gal. They may be equipped with pressure gauge and agitator. The pumps develop up to 200 p.s.i. pressure.

Traction sprayers are small, row-crop machines that derive power for the pump from the supporting traction wheels. These sprayers have tanks of around 25 gal. capacity, a 4- to 6-nozzle boom, and develop maximum pressures of around 150 p.s.i.

POWER SPRAYERS

A common sprayer on American farms today is the **multipurpose hydraulic** type (Fig. 7:4). As the name suggests, these sprayers are used for many purposes—spraying a wide variety of crops for insects and weeds, spraying livestock and farm buildings, washing machinery, and even fighting fires. They have reciprocating piston or plunger-type pumps, which develop pressures ranging from 30 to 400 or more p.s.i. They deliver from 3 to 8 gal. of spray per minute and tanks vary in size from 50 to 200 gal. Both skid and wheel mounted types are available.

The **estate-type sprayer** is a small wheel mounted sprayer popularly used on golf greens, estates, large gardens, and greenhouses. Tank sizes range from 15 to 50 gal., and pumps develop up to 300 lbs. pressure and discharge at rates of 1½ to 3 gal. per minute.

Low-pressure, low-volume sprayers are inexpensive machines commonly used to control weeds and field crop insects (Fig. 7:5). They operate at pressures of 15 to 125 lbs. and deliver 1 to 25 gal. per minute. They are available as kits for mounting on tractors or as wheel-mounted sprayers. A rotary-type pump is usually supplied for direct mounting on the tractor power-take-off shaft.

Fig. 7:4. Multipurpose hydraulic sprayers for general farm use. A, employing boom to apply insecticide for insect control; B, employing spray gun for cleaning farm equipment. A, *courtesy F. E. Meyers & Bro. Co., Ashland, Ohio; B, courtesy Oliver Corp., South Bend, Ind.*

Fig. 7:5. A low-pressure, low-volume tractor mounted sprayer. *Courtesy Farm Equipment Institute.*

High-pressure, high-volume sprayers are large sprayers developed to take care of the needs of fruit growers and truck farmers (Fig. 7:6). They have plunger-type pumps that deliver from 8 to 85 g.p.m. at maximum pressures of 400 to 1,000 p.s.i. and have tanks up to 600 gal. capacity. Booms are of various designs to fit the requirements of treating vegetable and fruit crops. For many vegetable crops, the nozzles are suspended and arranged to cover the plants on the top, sides, and underside of foliage. For tree fruits the sprayer may be equipped with hand guns or with an automatic spray head.

The **self-propelled, high-clearance sprayers** (Fig. 11:6) have been developed to treat crops that grow tall, such as corn and cotton. They are usually equipped with low-pressure, low-volume pumps and with booms that are adjustable for either high or low growing crops.

A **stationary spray plant** is found almost exclusively in orchards. It is composed of a spiderweb of pipes throughout the orchard and connected to a tank and pump housed in a shed. Hose lines are attached to outlets in the orchard and the hoses are dragged about the trees while spraying. Systems such as these may be used in hilly country where tractors and heavy equipment are unable to go. Spraying may be done when the ground is too wet for a tractor. This system works best where temperatures do not go so low as to freeze pipes laid on the ground or buried shallow. Pumps usually develop 600 to 1,000+ p.s.i., and tanks are about 500 to 600 gal. capacity.

Hydropneumatic sprayers are low-pressure, low-volume machines mounted on skids or wheels. Spray liquid is carried in a pressure-tight tank and does not pass through a pump. A compressor forces air into the tank and the liquid is in turn forced out through the nozzles. Tank size is usually less than 300 gal. and maximum working pressures range from 75 to 100 p.s.i.

Blower sprayers are a recent development, though the idea goes back to the twenties. The principle of the sprayer is that an air blast carries the insecticide and replaces most of the water of high-pressure high-volume sprayers. A series of nozzles or a shear plate directs spray under low pressure into an airstream that carries the atomized liquid to the surface to be treated (Fig. 7:7). Blower sprayers are rated in terms of air capacity in cubic feet per minute and velocity in miles per hour. Low-volume blower sprayers deliver 250 up to 30,000 cubic feet of air per minute at velocities around 150 m.p.h., high-volume sprayers deliver 20,000 to 100,000 c.f.m. at velocities up to 100 m.p.h. Many insecticides such as DDT may be used in blower sprayers at two to five times the concentration normally employed

Fig. 7:6. High-pressure, high-volume sprayer being used on a truck farm. *Courtesy Oliver Corp., South Bend, Ind.*

Fig. 7:7. A blower or air carrier sprayer applying concentrate spray to an orchard. *Courtesy Hardie Mfg. Division, Wilkes-Barre, Pa.*

with spray guns. These machines save both time and materials and can cut the cost of orchard spraying 75 per cent. They are also efficient for treating shade trees.

Aerosol generators or **fog machines** disperse insecticide into the air in the form of small particles ranging in diameter from 0.1 to 50 microns. They are used to control mosquitoes and flies in recreational parks, resort areas, and in communities.

A major advance in insect control has been made by the adaptation and use of **aircraft** to apply insecticides. Airplane application has several advantages—quick coverage of large acreages, no mechanical damage to crops, treatment of inaccessible areas such as forests, rangeland, and swamps, and treatment of fields after rains when ground is soft. In the United States agricultural aircraft number more than 7,000. Over half of these are modified Stearmans and N3N's, and all but a small percentage are modified trainers and pleasure aircraft. Several companies are now building specially designed agricultural airplanes (Fig. 7:8).

Few farmers, themselves, use aircraft for treating crops. Most agricul-

Fig. 7:8. A specially designed agricultural aircraft, the Grumman Ag-Cat. *Courtesy Grumman Aircraft Engineering Corp., Bethpage, L. I., N. Y.*

tural airplanes are the tools of professional aerial applicators who serve the farmer in protecting crops from diseases, weeds, and insects.

SPRAYER PARTS

To operate a power sprayer properly, make repairs, and replace parts, one should know and understand the functions of the units that make up the sprayer: power source, pump, air chamber on some models, tank, agitator, pressure regulator, valves, pressure gauge, screens and strainers, distribution system, and nozzles (Fig. 7:9).

The **power source** is either a gasoline engine or the power-take-off shaft of the tractor. The engines most commonly used develop 1 to 3 h.p. and are air cooled. On larger machines an engine developing 30 h.p. or even as much as 65 h.p. may be required.

The **pump** is one of the most important parts of the sprayer. Gear, roller impeller, piston, and plunger are the most commonly utilized types (Fig. 7:10). The piston and plunger pumps develop pressure by pushing directly on the liquid in a cylinder. Gear and roller impeller develop pressure by passing the liquid through teeth or rollers which pick up the liquid and force it through an outlet.

Piston pumps deliver 2 to 8 g.p.m. and develop pressures up to 400 p.s.i. The plunger type is used at 7 to 70 g.p.m. and develops pressures up to 1,000 p.s.i. Gear and some impeller pumps will, when new, develop pressures up to 300 to 400 p.s.i. However, after a short time, wear reduces the pressure to 50 to 100 p.s.i. with a maximum output of around 20 to 30 g.p.m.

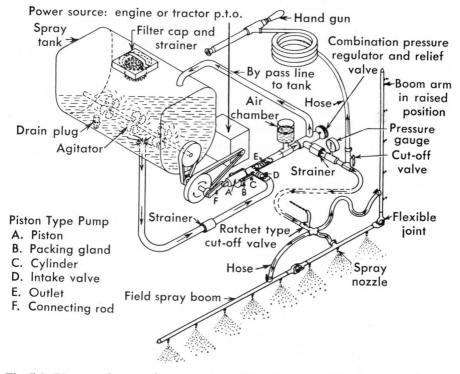

Fig. 7:9. Diagram of a typical power sprayer. *From* Sprayer and Duster Manual *by permission National Sprayer & Duster Association.*

Tanks vary in size from 50 to 600 gal. or larger on power operated sprayers. The tank may be either of wood or metal. They are usually equipped with a large opening and strainer at top to enable cleaning and inspection. A plug in the bottom enables one to drain the tank. The spray liquid is kept mixed in the tank by means of a mechanical **agitator** or by hydraulic action.

With piston and plunger pumps, an **air chamber** is connected on the discharge line to level out the pulsations of the pump. Such an arrangement prevents spurts of liquid from the discharge end.

A **pressure gauge** is located on the discharge side of the pump or on the air tank to enable the operator to select the pressure he wishes. The pressure is regulated by means of a **pressure regulator.** These are commonly of the plunger type. If the pressure in the line exceeds the tension selected on the spring of the plunger, a ball-valve will lift and by-pass the excess liquid back into the tank. This regulator not only allows the operator to select his pressure, but also acts as a safety valve and keeps the liquid in circulation while the discharge end is closed.

Strainers are located in the opening of the tank and in the suction line between the tank and the pump. They remove any foreign matter which might lodge in the pump, line valves, or nozzles. The strainers should be in such a position that they can be easily removed and cleaned.

From the pump, the liquid is carried through **pipes** and **hoses** to the nozzles. Improper pipe or hose size can cause a decrease in pressure, since pressure loss varies with the square of the velocity of flow. The hose should be made to withstand about three times the regular spraying pressure.

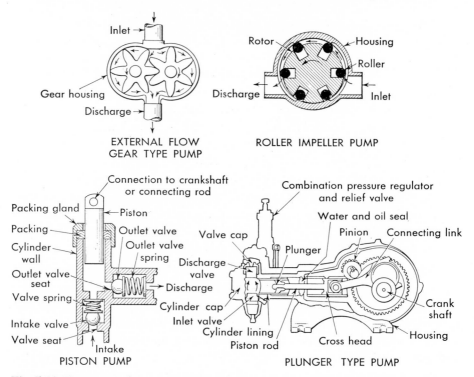

Fig. 7:10. Four types of sprayer pumps. *From* Sprayer and Duster Manual *by permission National Sprayer & Duster Association.*

The liquid spray emerges from a nozzle or nozzles on a hand **spray gun** or from several nozzles on a **spray boom.** Booms are usually adjustable to various heights to compensate for height of the plants. Most booms are about 21 feet long.

The **nozzle** is a vital part of a sprayer as it breaks up the liquid stream and spreads it out into the proper sized spray droplets. The nozzle and the pressure determine the degree of atomization and the amount of liquid discharged. Nozzles are manufactured so as to give differences in rate of discharge, angle of spray, and pattern of spray. Nozzles are designed for either high or low pressure and for producing a fan-shaped, solid cone, or hollow cone spray pattern, and for spray angles ranging from a straight stream to 100°.

High-pressure nozzles are composed of a body, strainer, whirl plate, gasket, disc, and cap (Fig. 7:11). The body encloses all the parts except the cap. The whirl plate twists the liquid about at high velocity before it is discharged through the disc. This whirling motion contributes to breaking the liquid into droplets, and the resulting swirling action of the spray moves foliage and provides better coverage of all surfaces. The whirl plate may be a disc with holes cut into it at angles, a screw type, or a cylinder with slits cut at an angle through it. A hole in the center of the whirl produces a solid cone. All nozzles have a number which represents the diameter of the opening in the disc in $\frac{1}{64}$ of an inch. Size 2 to 4 are usually used for row crops and size 10 on large capacity hand or orchard guns. The largest size available is 20. The gasket prevents leakage and the cap holds the disc in place. Many nozzles have a small strainer located just above the nozzle itself.

High-pressure nozzles may well be used at low pressures, but the weed-spraying nozzle is commonly employed on low-pressure sprayers. These nozzles usually produce a fan-shaped spray pattern. The weed-spraying nozzle is composed of a body, strainer assembly, cap, and orifice tip. The liquid passes through the strainer and is broken up in passing through the hole in the tip. By selecting tips of a certain size and with a certain shaped opening, the operator can determine spray pattern and discharge rate.

Sprayer care

Any sprayer will last longer and perform more satisfactorily if it is properly cared for and maintained. The manufacturers instruction manual should be studied and followed in every detail. Proper lubrication is very important and care should be taken to check each lubrication site. With a new sprayer, it is wise to start it slowly and, using water only, check for any leaks, and proper operation of valves, pump, motor, and gauge. After each

Fig. 7:11. Parts of a high pressure nozzle. *Courtesy John Bean Division.*

use, the sprayer should be drained and flushed with clean water. All nozzles and strainers should be removed and thoroughly cleaned. Before placing in storage for a period of time, add 2 to 5 gal. of oil to the tank and fill with clean water. Pump this out until tank is dry. This will leave a thin coat of oil throughout the system. Be sure there is no water left in any part of the system during freezing weather.

If the sprayer has been used for weed spraying, it is necessary to pay special attention to cleaning before it can be used for other spraying jobs.

Sprayer calibration

In order to spray the correct amount of material per acre, it is necessary to calibrate the sprayer. The number of gallons per acre that a unit discharges is dependent upon: speed of the sprayer over the ground, the operating pressure, the spacing of the nozzles on the boom, and the size of nozzles used. In an average situation for row crops, speeds of around 4 m.p.h., pressures between 50 to 100 p.s.i., nozzle spacings of 12 to 20 in., and nozzle sizes of 2 to 7 are practical ranges for operating the sprayer.

In order to select a suitable nozzle for a particular spray job, an operator may use the following formula to determine the desirable nozzle size in gallons per minute.

$$\frac{\text{gals. per acre desired } X \text{ nozzle spacing (inches) } X \text{ m.p.h. } X \text{ ft. per mile}}{\text{sq. ft. per acre } X \text{ minutes per hour } X \text{ inches per foot}} = \text{g.p.m.}$$

The constants in this formula may be combined so the formula will read:

$$\frac{\text{gal. per acre } X \text{ nozzle spacing (inches) } X \text{ m.p.h.}}{5,940} = \text{g.p.m.}$$

From a dealer's chart it is possible to determine the nozzle size necessary and the pressure at which it must be used.

After nozzles have been installed, the final calibration is made. The sprayer is filled with clear water and the pump started and the desired pressure regulated. The sprayer is then driven at the desired speed over the land to be sprayed. The spray from one nozzle is collected for one minute and measured. This is converted to gallons per minute and substituted into the above formula and the formula solved for gallons per acre.

Another method of calibration is as follows:

1. Measure off 80 rods.
2. Starting with a full tank, drive at desired rate of speed with sprayer operating the 80 rods.
3. Measure the amount of water required to refill the tank.
4. Multiply the number of gallons used by 33 and divide by the width of the boom. This will give the amount of spray used in gallons per acre.

There is available today a plastic or glass measuring device which fastens under one nozzle and catches the spray discharged while driving over a measured distance. The device is marked on the side to indicate the number of gallons per acre being discharged by the sprayer.

DUSTERS

Dusters are not as mechanically complicated as sprayers and are lighter in weight than comparable sprayers. Like sprayers, dusters may be either hand operated or powered by a motor. The hand dusters may be a simple **plunger or bellows** type used chiefly about the house or in a small garden. **Crank dusters** (Fig. 7:12) are practical for treating small acreages of row crops, such as tobacco, cotton, and vegetables. The dust is held in a hopper and discharged through an adjustable feeding device. The dust is kept stirred up in the hopper by means of a mechanical agitator. A fan is operated by a hand crank through a series of high speed gears. The blast of air picks up the dust and carries it out through the nozzles. **Knapsack dusters** are bellows-type dusters operated by means of a handle. Each pump of the handle produces a spot application of dust. In some areas vegetable growers use lightweight, back-pack, power dusters (Fig. 7:13).

Power row crop dusters (Fig. 7:14) are commonly used in the South to treat peanuts, cotton, and tobacco. Power dusters are composed of a source of power, hopper, agitator, metering device, fan, discharge tubes, boom and nozzles (Fig. 7:15). The **hopper** usually holds 2 to 4 cubic feet

Fig. 7:12. Crank duster used for treating row crops. *Courtesy D. B. Smith & Co.*

of dust. The **agitator** inside the hopper keeps the dust fluffed up so that it will flow evenly through the metering device. The **metering device** can be regulated so that 5 to 50 lbs. of dust may be delivered per acre. Common **fans** are centrifugal ones which operate at 2,200 to 3,400 r.p.m. and deliver 500 to 1,000 cubic feet of air per minute at velocities ranging from 50 to

Fig. 7:13. Treating a field of tomatoes with insecticide dispensed from a back-pack power duster. *Courtesy Powerpak Equipment Co., Vista, Calif.*

Fig. 7:14. A power row-crop duster in operation. *Courtesy John Bean Division.*

100 m.p.h. The dust is carried through wire-reinforced rubber hose or flexible metal **tubes** to the nozzles. The **nozzles**, scoop-shaped metal pieces attached to the tubes, serve to direct the stream of dust. A metal **boom**,

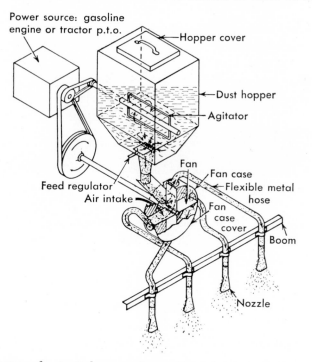

Fig. 7:15. Diagram of a typical power duster. *From* Sprayer and Duster Manual *by permission National Sprayer & Duster Association.*

commonly 18 to 20 feet long, supports the tubes and nozzles. The **power** for the duster may come from a separate engine (from 1½ h.p. up to 6 h.p.) or it may operate from the power-take-off of a tractor (Fig. 7:16). Large fruit dusters may require engines of 15 to 25 h.p. or more.

As with sprayers, the operator should be thoroughly familiar with the manufacturers operational manual. The recommended fan speed should never be exceeded. All designated spots should be carefully lubricated. After each dusting, the excess dust should be removed from the hopper as it will tend to cake if left standing too long. The duster should always be stored in a dry place.

Fig. 7:16. An orchard duster mounted on tractor. *Courtesy John Bean Division.*

To calibrate a duster, it is necessary to measure off a known area and measure the amount of dust delivered. More or less dust can be applied by adjusting the metering device.

GRANULE APPLICATORS

Granule applicators are a relatively new development designed to provide a means of accurately and uniformly dispersing granular formulations of insecticides. Because granular formulations have been found useful for controlling certain pests of row crops, much emphasis has been given to the development of row-crop applicators which attach to planters (Fig. 7:17), to high-clearance tractors, and to several other farm machines. Granular row-crop applicators are convenient tools for applying insecticides in-the-row for control of soil pests of corn, sugar beets, and several other crops.

Trailer-type granule applicators (Fig. 9:6) are also available. These machines are quite versatile as they can apply granules broadcast or in bands. They are equipped with metering devices for regulating the dosage. They may be calibrated by catching the granules in a trough as the machine is pulled over a measured distance.

Fig. 7:17. Row crop granule applicator attached to corn planter. The two higher hoppers contain granular insecticide which is directed into the rows by two malleable tubes leading from each hopper. Press wheels follow application of granules and compact the drill row. *Courtesy Gandy Co., Owatonna, Minn.*

Selected References

Akesson, N. B., and W. A. Harvey, *Chemical Weed Control Equipment*, Calif. Agr. Exp. Sta. Circ. 389, 1948.

Anonymous, *Farm Power Sprayers*, Pacific Northwest Cooperative Extension Bul. 23, 1958.

Brown, A. W. A., *Insect Control by Chemicals* (New York: Wiley, 1951).

Hough, Walter S., and A. F. Mason, *Spraying, Dusting and Fumigating of Plants* (New York: Macmillan, 1951).

Ingerson, Howard, "One Acre to Seventy a Day," *Amer. Fruit Grower,* 79(3):10, 11, 48 (1959).

Chapter 8 | INSECT PESTS OF SMALL
GRAINS | Robert E. Pfadt

The pests

Many insects—well over 100 destructive species—find fields of small grains favorable places to room and board. Fortunately, only a few of these are major pests.

The most destructive insect pest of wheat in the United States is the **Hessian fly,** a mosquito-like midge introduced from Europe (Fig. 8:13). Its larvae feed on juices of wheat stems and occasionally on the stems of barley and rye. This insect damages wheat over a wide region from the Atlantic coast to the Great Plains and from the Canadian provinces to Georgia and South Carolina. Humid Pacific Coast areas likewise suffer its attack.

Nearly as important as the Hessian fly is the **greenbug** (Fig. 8:16), an aphid which destroys many acres of oats, barley, and wheat. It ranges over the entire United States and much of Canada. Additional destructive aphids of small grains include the **corn leaf aphid, apple grain aphid,** and **English grain aphid.** The **chinch bug** (Fig. 9:10), a serious pest of corn and sorghums, damages small grains too, building up highly destructive populations in the central and eastern United States.

Grasshoppers (Fig. 8:7), particularly the **migratory grasshopper,** injured small grains in North America as long ago as early pioneer days. Today, they are especially bad pests in the more arid regions west of the Mississippi River. A western insect, the **Mormon cricket,** periodically damages small grains. The **armyworm** (Fig. 8:11), widely injurious throughout the United States and Canada, is a dangerous pest of small grains, other cereals, and grasses. Soon after aggregations of flying adults settle in grain fields and deposit their eggs, hordes of larvae hatch and begin to devour the crop.

Several insects bore in the stems of wheat (Fig. 8:1). The most serious are the **wheat stem sawfly** (Fig. 4:23B), the **wheat jointworm,** and the **wheat straw-worm.** The sawfly injures crops in the northern Great Plains states and in the Great Plains provinces, the jointworm in wheat-growing states east of the Mississippi River, and the straw-worm in almost all wheat-growing states and provinces. Of somewhat less importance are the **wheat stem maggot,** the **European wheat stem sawfly,** the **black grain stem sawfly, lesser cornstalk borer,** and the **stalk borer.**

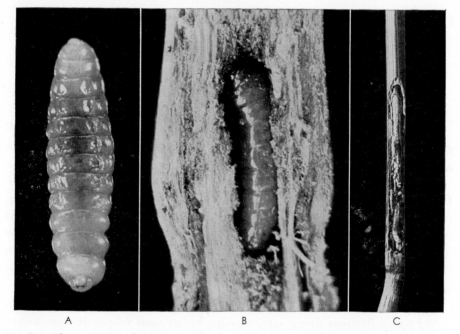

A   B   C

Fig. 8:1. Three species of insects that bore in the stems of wheat. A, wheat jointworm; B, wheat straw-worm within stem of wheat; C, wheat stem maggot and damage to wheat stem. *A and B courtesy USDA; C courtesy Kan. Agr. Exp. Sta.*

A number of important insect enemies of small grains lurk in the soil. They include wireworms, false wireworms, white grubs, and cutworms. **Wireworms** (Fig. 8:18) are most severe in the northern Great Plains states, the Pacific Northwest, and in western provinces; **false wireworms** in arid western states; **white grubs** in Kansas and Oklahoma; and cutworms throughout the United States and Canada. The **pale western cutworm** (Fig. 8:2) and **army cutworm** periodically destroy large acreages of small grains.

Several species of mites attack wheat. Two of the most destructive are the **brown wheat mite** which causes injury in the West, often during droughts, and the **wheat curl mite** which transmits the virus of wheat streak mosaic.

The injury

Insects injure small grains in the field from the time the seed is planted until the grain is harvested. Both wireworms and false wireworms feed on the planted seed. In dry soil they may even destroy a crop before rains stimulate germination and growth. After the grain germinates, these pests devour the tender sprouts just as they push out of the seeds.

Wireworms also kill seedlings by boring into and shredding the underground portion of stems. Wireworms and white grubs feed on roots and sever them from the plant. Cutworms, white grubs, and false wireworms cut off young plants near soil level (Fig. 8:3). In addition, the wounds left by soil pests allow rot pathogens to enter the plant.

Grasshoppers, Mormon crickets, and armyworms may devour young plants completely; they may strip the leaves from older plants, feed on maturing heads, or cut through the stems below the heads.

By extracting juices from the stem for food, larvae of Hessian flies retard or kill seedlings and reduce the yields of older plants. Weakened stems of older plants are likely to cause the crop to lodge. Wheat stem sawfly, wheat jointworm, and wheat straw-worm bore within culms and obstruct the flow of sap. This damage reduces the number and weight of kernels. Boring insects also cause grain to lodge.

Insects such as the chinch bug and various aphids impoverish plants by sucking juices from leaves or stems. Moreover, by injecting toxic saliva they produce fatal necroses. Small grain pests may transmit serious plant diseases, such as wheat streak mosaic by the wheat curl mite, striate by the painted leafhopper, and barley yellow dwarf by several species of aphids.

Barley yellow dwarf, a new and widespread virus disease of cereals characterized by leaves rapidly turning light green and yellow beginning at the tips, is causing much concern in the United States. Transmission of the disease is solely by aphids. Six species have been incriminated, the English grain aphid, apple grain aphid, corn leaf aphid, greenbug, rose grass aphid, and bluegrass aphid. Recent research has demonstrated that three different strains of the virus are present and that they are usually carried by different species of aphids. Vector specificity, however, is not absolute, for in some cases one aphid species may transmit the strain usually carried by another.

In 1959 yellow dwarf losses of spring oats ranged up to more than one-third of the crop in the north-central and north-western states and in 1960 losses ranged from 10 to 50 per cent in infected fields in the northeastern states. Amount of injury depends on the stage at which the plants become infected. Young plants are frequently killed, older plants are stunted. When

Fig. 8:2. The pale western cutworm, a serious small grain pest in western North America. *Courtesy University of Nebraska.*

infection occurs in late stages of development, only the flag leaf exhibits signs of yellowing or reddening. As with other virus diseases, yield of grain shows greatest reduction when plants become infected early in their growth.

Cultural control

Growers of small grains rely heavily on cultural methods to control insect pests. The methods fall into six broad categories: promotion of vigorous plants and stands; rotations; clean culture; tillage; timing of planting or harvesting; and early maturing and resistant varieties.

Vigorous stands more easily withstand the attacks of Hessian flies, greenbugs and other aphids, wheat jointworms, and wireworms. Against these pests, the method owes its effectiveness to the ability of strong plants to tolerate injury better than weak ones. It also operates successfully against chinch bugs, but somewhat differently. These insects prefer thin stands; they seldom congregate in heavy stands as damp, shady places are unfavorable habitats. Clover grown with the grain provides an even less favorable chinch bug environment.

Rotation of small grains with alfalfa, sweetclover, soybeans, flax, mustard, and other plants reduces the population of false wireworms, white grubs, brown wheat mites, and wheat stem sawflies. Control mainly results from substitution of a plant upon which the insect starves or refuses to oviposit. Rotation methods need not be regularly applied; growers may need only to plant substitute crops when danger of an outbreak looms. For example, sow sorghums in place of wheat when grasshopper populations are increasing.

Crop grasshoppers relish wheat, but practically refuse sorghums as food. To control wheat straw-worms, plant wheat at a distance of 65 yards or more from stubble or straw since the spring form of the adult is flightless and cannot travel very far to infest young wheat.

Survival of large, injurious populations of insect pests depends on sufficient food remaining available through their entire period of growth and reproduction. When **clean culture** destroys food, pest populations fall to insignificant levels. Insect pests of small grains maintain themselves chiefly on volunteer grain or in stubble from time of harvest until the next crop appears. Plowing under stubble and volunteer grain aids greatly in keeping pest populations down. Also helpful is the destruction of weeds on which pests may feed. Clean culture aids in the control of Hessian flies, greenbugs, wheat curl mites, false wireworms, wheat straw-worms, stem sawflies, and grasshoppers.

Tillage methods may bury egg, larval, or pupal stages so deeply in the soil that the insects die before they can emerge. Deep plowing is effective against the egg stage of grasshoppers and the larval and pupal stages of Hessian flies, wheat jointworms, wheat straw-worms, stem sawflies, and others. Shallow tillage may destroy pests by crushing the insects or by throwing them to the surface where they are exposed to enemies and unfavorable weather.

In some areas cultural control methods that require plowing expose soil to dangers of water and wind erosion. When faced with this problem, use

Fig. 8:3. Destruction of young wheat plants by pale western cutworms begins at the edges or on the knolls of fields and may continue until all plants are killed. *Courtesy University of Wyoming.*

Fig. 8:4. Airplane spraying wheat field to control an infestation of insect pests. *Courtesy American Cyanamid.*

the cultural method only when severe infestations threaten heavy losses. Plowing may also interfere temporarily with growing red clover or alfalfa in grain; however, growers may plant other crops like soybeans and cowpeas after grain harvest.

Timing of planting or harvesting may control small grain enemies. In fall, Hessian flies infest early planted wheat, but live too briefly as adults to infest late planted wheat. Entomologists have determined for various regions the dates on which to plant wheat to escape Hessian fly damage. These periods usually coincide with planting times that agronomists have found result in highest yields.

By harvesting early before stems fall to the ground, we can reduce wheat stem sawfly losses. Because larvae actively girdle stems in August, the longer we delay harvest during this month the greater is our loss from lodging.

The planting of **resistant varieties** is one of the more promising methods of insect pest control. Varieties of hard winter wheat such as Pawnee and Ponca and soft winter wheat such as Dual and Todd are resistant to Hessian flies. The spring wheats Rescue and Chinook, though only fair agronomically, are resistant to wheat stem sawfly. There are several small grain varieties resistant to greenbugs and to chinch bugs.

Some varieties may escape injury by maturing early. Kansas growers have reduced infestations of wheat straw-worm by growing such varieties as Pawnee and Triumph which mature earlier than varieties formerly grown, such as Turkey and Blackhull.

Chemical control

Cultural methods do not adequately control all pests of small grains and sometimes they fail even against pests upon which they are usually successful. In either case we may be able to resort to a chemical method. Insecticides are effective against some enemies of small grains but are worthless against others. Although the new systemic insecticides may prove effective, the usual chemical treatments do not control important pests like the Hessian fly, the wheat stem sawfly, the wheat jointworm, and the wheat straw-worm. Surface-active insecticides do control, however, many serious pests such as grasshoppers, cutworms, wireworms, white grubs, aphids, and mites.

Chemicals commonly used to control insect pests of small grains belong to two families of synthetic insecticides—the chlorinated hydrocarbons and the organic phosphates. Aldrin, dieldrin, and heptachlor have been widely used to control grasshoppers; lindane, aldrin, and dieldrin to control wireworms; DDT, aldrin, and heptachlor to control white grubs; endrin, TDE, dieldrin, DDT, and toxaphene to control cutworms; and parathion, malathion, and methyl parathion to control aphids and mites. Poison bran baits which contain organic insecticides such as dieldrin or heptachlor, or inorganic insecticides such as paris green or sodium fluosilicate, are sometimes useful.

Growers should follow several precautions in applying insecticides to small grains. Use recommended amounts since exceeding suggested dosages wastes chemicals and may injure seeds or plants. Treat seed that is plump and has high germination, because insecticides may injure poor seed. If you use diesel oil as diluent for insecticides applied by airplane, never put on more than 1 gallon per acre nor apply it when temperature is above 75°F. as burning of foliage may result. Also diesel oil used on small grains after the boot stage may render the flowers sterile.

For personal safety follow all precautions printed on the label of insecticide containers, particularly when using the organic phosphates.

Control equipment

Small-grain growers commonly apply insecticides with low pressure boom-type sprayers; less often with dusters. Power for this equipment can come from the power take-off of a tractor or from a small gasoline engine. Trucks or tractors pull the equipment over the fields. Because large acreages of small grains frequently need immediate treatment to stop the ravages of pests, growers often hire aerial applicators to treat the fields. Airplanes are rapid and have an advantage in that they do not run down growing or maturing crops (Fig. 8:4).

Though we still recommend bran baits to control grasshoppers, Mormon crickets, and cutworms, this method is fast giving way to sprays and dusts which perform more reliably against these insects. For scattering wet bait, growers often use mechanical spreaders (Fig. 8:5). They may adapt end-gate seeders for this purpose. Some spread the bait by hand from the back end of a truck. Airplanes are best adapted to apply dry bran baits or steam-rolled wheat baits.

Growers use seed or soil treatments to control small grain pests that live in the soil. Seed treatment is more economical and more widely practiced. Frequently, growers use an insecticide-fungicide mixture so that the treatment combats plant diseases as well as insect pests. It is first necessary to pass seed through a fanning mill to get rid of trash and light seed that would unnecessarily dilute the chemical. Insecticides may be applied as dust, slurry (a thin paste formed by addition of a little water to wettable pow-

Fig. 8:5. A power bait spreader used in grasshopper control.

der), or liquid. Patented machines apply these materials efficiently. Since seed treaters are fairly expensive, growers generally have custom operators clean and treat their seed. Less efficient methods of treatment include mixing grain and dust with a shovel, mixing them in the drill box, or treating seed with a home-made machine.

REPRESENTATIVE SMALL GRAIN INSECTS

For detailed study we have chosen the following serious pests of small grains: grasshoppers, armyworm, Hessian fly, greenbug, and wireworms.

Migratory grasshopper *Melanoplus bilituratus* (Walker)

Differential grasshopper *Melanoplus differentialis* (Thomas)

Two-striped grasshopper *Melanoplus bivittatus* (Say)

Red-legged grasshopper *Melanoplus femurrubrum* (De Geer)

Clear-winged grasshopper *Camnula pellucida* (Scudder)

Big-headed grasshopper *Aulocara elliotti* (Thomas)
[Orthoptera:Acrididae]

Although grasshoppers cause injury over all of the United States and much of Canada, they reach greatest numbers and do the severest damage in areas with average annual precipitation of 10 to 30 inches (Fig. 8:6).

Around 600 native species of grasshoppers inhabit the two countries. Five species are responsible for 90 per cent of the total grasshopper damage to cultivated crops, while more than 25 species injure range and pasture lands. Grasshoppers especially relish small grains, but readily devour other crops such as corn, alfalfa, clover, soybeans, and flax. Indeed few cultivated crops are immune from grasshopper injury and do not need protection during an outbreak.

Although grasshopper injury consists primarily of the defoliation or destruction of the plant, it may occur in other ways. Grasshoppers may feed on particular parts of plants and cause injury which far exceeds estimates based on the number of the attacking pests alone. For example, by feeding on the stems of grain, they sever the heads; or by feeding on the ripening

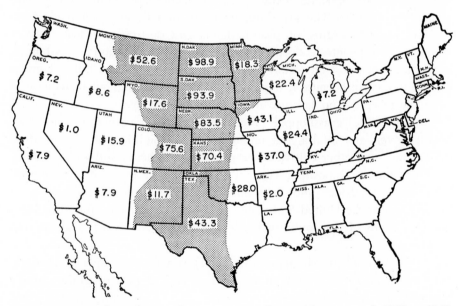

Fig. 8:6. Estimated grasshopper damage to crops during 25-year period, 1925 to 1949, by state. Heaviest losses took place in areas with average annual rainfall of 10 to 30 inches (shaded region on map). *Courtesy USDA.*

kernels they cause extensive shattering. In corn, their feeding on the silks prevents fertilization and filling of the ears. The preference of grasshoppers for the blooms of plants causes considerable loss of legume and vegetable seed crops. Furthermore, we know that grasshoppers can transmit diseases deadly to potatoes, beans, and tobacco.

Injury to range and pasture vegetation parallels somewhat closely the injury to crops. The main damage is the defoliation or destruction of the plant. Heavy infestations of 25 to 75 grasshoppers per square yard may completely destroy all vegetation in an area. This overgrazing leaves the soil exposed to erosion by wind and water. Some of the worst "dust bowls" have followed grasshopper outbreaks. Grasshoppers may also prevent re-seeding of ranges by cutting grass stems below the head before the seed is mature or by feeding on the head itself.

Of all the injurious species of grasshoppers in North America, the migratory grasshopper is the most serious (Fig. 8:7F). This pest ranges from Nova Scotia south to Florida, west to the Pacific Coast, and on into Mexico. It prefers light, well-drained soils. In the North this species has one generation annually, but in central states it may have two generations, and in southern Arizona three. It is particularly destructive to small grains and alfalfa. In winter-wheat growing areas the seedling plants of fall-seeded, small grains are especially attractive to first-generation adults and second-generation nymphs. The grasshoppers move into these green fields from stubble, weedy margins, or pasture lands and destroy row after row of plants as they penetrate deeper into the field. The migratory grasshopper is also a serious pest on weedy ranges and pastures. It is a difficult grasshopper to control because it deposits its egg pods throughout fields as well as in the margins and because it migrates extensively.

The differential grasshopper (Fig. 8:7D) is a serious pest of corn, soybeans, clover, and alfalfa, but under outbreak conditions it also destroys small grains and other cultivated crops. It prefers heavy soil and relatively rank vegetation. Depositing eggs in the crowns of grass, it concentrates them along roadsides and field margins. The species ranges widely in Mexico and in the United States, but it is only occasionally found in large numbers north of the southern borders of Minnesota, North Dakota, and Montana.

The two-striped grasshopper (Fig. 8:7B) is a common species throughout Canada and the United States. It is a serious pest of grains, forage legumes, and pastures.

The red-legged grasshopper (Fig. 8:7A) preferring low, comparatively moist ground, inhabits field margins, roadsides, pastures, and meadows. It is especially destructive to clovers and alfalfa. The species ranges from central Mexico, through all of the United States, to the interior of Canada. A subspecies, the southern red-legged grasshopper, *Melanoplus femur-rubrum propinquus* Scudder, is the most abundant grasshopper in the southeastern states.

Fig. 8:7. Six species of injurious grasshoppers (not to scale). A, red-legged grasshopper; B, two-striped grasshopper; C, clear-winged grasshopper; D, differential grasshopper; E, big-headed grasshopper; F, migratory grasshopper. *D, courtesy Shell Chemical Company; others courtesy University of Wyoming.*

The clear-winged grasshopper (Fig. 8:7C) inhabits the northern states and the Canadian provinces from the Atlantic to the Pacific coasts. Its favorite haunts are mountain meadows, pastures, and roadsides. It is chiefly injurious to range and pasture grasses, but during outbreaks it also severely damages small grains.

The big-headed grasshopper (Fig. 8:7E) is a grassland species occurring widely in western North America from the Canadian provinces south into Mexico. It is primarily a pest of rangeland grasses, but occasionally damages small grains.

Description. The migratory grasshopper, as do most other grasshoppers, deposits its eggs in the ground in clusters. A gluelike secretion holds the eggs together and also binds soil particles around the eggs. The eggs thus become enclosed in a small case called an egg pod (Fig. 8:8). Pods of different species are of different sizes and shapes and contain different numbers of eggs. The egg pod of the migratory grasshopper is about an inch long and contains an average of 20 cream colored eggs, each egg being about 4 mm. long.

Newly hatched nymphs are pale yellow, but soon turn dull yellow with dark brown markings. They are approximately 4 mm. long and have somewhat the same appearance as adult grasshoppers except for smaller size and lack of wings. Adults are approximately 1 in. long and are light brown with dark markings.

The differential grasshopper is a large species of the genus *Melanoplus;* adult males are about 1¼ in. and females about 1½ in. long. They are usually bright yellow with dark markings, though a small number in a population are melanistic. Dark chevrons on the hind femur are distinguishing marks.

The two-striped grasshopper, another large species of *Melanoplus,* is about the same size as the differential. The general color is greenish yellow or olive. Two light yellow stripes, from which this grasshopper gets its common name, run down the back from the head to the wing tips. The yellow, outside face of the hind femur has a conspicuous black dorsal band.

The red-legged grasshopper, a medium sized species of *Melanoplus,* is about ¾ in. long. The ventral surface of the body is bright yellow, the rest of the body is reddish brown. The species derives its name from the red hind tibia.

The clear-winged grasshopper is a medium sized grasshopper; males are about ¾ in. long and females about 1 in. long. Body and front wing vary in color from yellow to brown and are marked with large, dark-brown spots.

The big-headed grasshopper is also a medium sized grasshopper; males are about ¾ in. long and females about 1 in. long. General body color is grayish brown. The hind tibia is colored deep blue. This species is called the big-headed grasshopper because the head appears large compared with the size of the body.

Life history. Most species of economic grasshoppers have a single generation annually and overwinter as eggs in the soil. The migratory grasshopper, however, completes as many as two generations a year in Kansas and three generations a year in southern Arizona. Another exception is the southern red-legged grasshopper which has two and sometimes a partial third generation in Florida. Both species have the usual single generation each year in northern areas.

The eggs of grasshoppers, stimulated by warming soils and spring rains, hatch over a period of four to six weeks. Ordinarily, the various species hatch at different times. For example, the migratory and the two-striped grasshoppers hatch two to three weeks earlier than the differential and red-legged grasshoppers. In addition to the built-in time clock of grasshoppers, the earliness or lateness of the season may vary the time of hatching by as much as two months.

After emerging the young nymphs feed on nearby green vegetation. Grasshoppers are selective in their choice of food plants. Unless forced by hunger, they do not eat just anything green as commonly supposed. All six species of grasshoppers considered here seem to relish small grains, but they may differ in their preferences for other plants.

Nymphal development proceeds at a rapid rate when the weather is warm and not too wet. Grasshoppers go through four to six nymphal instars in 35 to 50 days to become full-fledged adults. After mating and passing through a preovipositional period of about two weeks, the female grass-hopper produces her first cluster of eggs. She deposits them in the soil, the sites varying with the species. A female differential or two-striped grass-hopper usually oviposits in sod or weedy ground bordering the crop upon which they are feeding. The female migratory grasshopper may deposit eggs over an entire field of grain stubble, alfalfa, or weedy idle land or rangeland. Female clear-winged grasshoppers may come long distances to congregate and lay eggs in sod, forming so-called egg beds. The big-headed grasshopper deposits eggs in bare spaces between range vegetation.

The number of eggs in a cluster vary with the species. The pods of the big-headed grasshopper contain around six to ten eggs, those of the migra-tory and clear-winged 15 to 25, those of the red-legged 25 to 30, while those of the two-striped and differential contain as many as 50 to 100. The grass-hoppers which lay fewer eggs per pod usually produce more pods. Under ideal conditions, a long-lived female may lay up to 300 eggs.

Populations of grasshoppers in both the nymphal and adult stages do much moving and shifting about from field borders into fields and from one field into another. Mass flights of the migratory grasshopper may cover distances as great as 575 miles during a single season. The most spectacular and most injurious migrations of this species for over half a century befell the Northern Great Plains States and Provinces in the summers of 1938, 1939, and 1940. Flights started on clear days usually between 11:00 A.M. and 1:00 P.M. when temperatures approached 80°F. and winds came in gentle gusts. Flying with the wind, grasshoppers attained speeds of 10 or more m.p.h. As evening drew near the swarms drifted slowly to the ground,

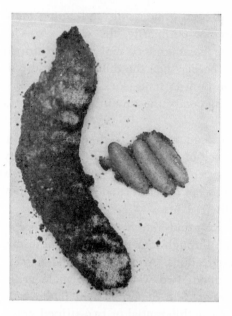

Fig. 8:8. Egg pod and eggs of the migratory grasshopper. *Courtesy University of Wyoming.*

infesting and destroying crops and range vegetation. When conditions again became favorable for flight, the hordes took to the air and moved on.

Few individual grasshoppers live long enough to realize their full reproductive potential because of the many natural enemies that constantly prey upon them. Some enemies attack the nymphs and adults; others prey upon the eggs. Robber flies, sphecid wasps, spiders, rodents, and birds feed upon the nymphs and adults while the maggots of flesh flies, tachinid flies, and tangle-veined flies parasitize these stages internally. Rodents and the larvae of bee flies, blister beetles, and ground beetles feed upon the eggs; the larva of *Scelio*, a small wasp, parasitizes the egg. Other predators, parasites, and many diseases also attack grasshoppers.

Although predators and parasites help to keep grasshopper populations down, and may terminate serious infestations, many entomologists believe outbreaks are due not to any relaxation of enemies, but rather to favorable weather and an abundant supply of food during the nymphal and adult stages. Populations reach outbreak levels when the density of adult grasshoppers becomes 25 or more per square yard. In severe outbreaks numbers may reach as high as 80 or more per square yard.

Control. Good grasshopper control depends upon the employment of both cultural and chemical methods. Though recently discovered chemicals like chlordane, toxaphene, aldrin, heptachlor, and dieldrin make the protection of crops, pasture, and range much easier and more certain than formerly, they have by no means replaced cultural methods, which still play an important role in grasshopper control.

Cultural methods include (1) elimination of weedy habitats, (2) planting resistant crops, (3) tilling land infested with eggs, and (4) timing of seeding.

(1) Favorable habitats for the migratory, two-striped, differential, and red-legged grasshoppers are weedy field margins, fence rows, and roadsides. From these areas grasshoppers, during periods of moderate densities, work into the crop and cause material damage. Worst of all, these habitats and weedy idle land harbor the nucleus of an outbreak. We can eliminate weedy habitats by tillage, use of weedicides, and by planting perennial grasses.

(2) During bad grasshopper years, we can cut losses by reducing the acreage of susceptible small grains and substituting resistant sorghums such as sorgo and kafir. Grasshoppers rarely feed upon sorghums over 8 inches high.

(3) The migratory grasshopper deposits many eggs throughout fields of small grains both before and after harvest. Plowing with a mold-board plow to a depth of 5 to 6 inches, followed by packing, will cover up the eggs so that few nymphs can reach the surface. Either fall plowing or spring plowing before eggs hatch is effective. In regions where there is danger of soil blowing only spring plowing is advisable. Plow under egg-infested stubble land, planned for summer fallow, before eggs hatch in spring. Then maintain clean fallow through the summer to destroy host plants of grasshoppers such as volunteer wheat and various weeds and to keep the soil loose and unfavorable for egg laying.

Another method providing effective control is spring tillage that destroys all weed and volunteer growth just before or soon after grasshoppers begin to hatch. Most newly hatched grasshoppers starve to death before finding their way out of a field with no green food. The one-way disk, properly adjusted, is the most effective farm implement for this purpose.

(4) Seeding spring small grains early is a recommended practice, as it gives the plants a chance to grow strong before grasshoppers hatch. Older plants can withstand a longer period of grasshopper feeding than younger plants. This practice allows the grower more time to obtain and to apply insecticides successfully. Furthermore, the sooner a grower plants and then harvests a crop, the less chance there is of migrating grasshoppers entering and destroying the grain.

Controlling grasshoppers with the newer insecticides is remarkably successful, provided growers discover infestations and apply treatment in time.

Within three days after application 90 per cent of the grasshoppers die; most of the survivors succumb soon afterward. Recommended insecticides with dosage ranges of actual toxicant to be applied per acre have been the following:

Aldrin	2 to 4 oz.
Diazinon	½ lb.
Dibrom	¾ lb.
Dieldrin	½ to 2 oz.
Heptachlor	2 to 4 oz.
Chlordane	¾ to 1½ lbs.
Malathion	1 lb.
Toxaphene	1 to 1½ lbs.

These are most effectively applied as broadcast sprays with low-gallonage sprayers, but they can be applied as dusts if dosages are increased by 50 per cent. Timing the treatment when grasshoppers are young, have not laid eggs, and are still confined mainly to the margins of fields, fence rows, roadsides, stubble fields, and idle land makes the job both cheaper and more effective. Unless grasshoppers migrate into the treated area, control may last for several years.

If grasshoppers hatch in spring-seeded small grain, prompt treatment with an insecticide will prevent serious damage. When fields are soft, airplane application is necessary. In the fall of the year migrating nymphal and adult grasshoppers often menace fall-seeded small grains. These grasshoppers should be killed before the new wheat emerges. In protecting newly sprouted wheat, baits may be more effective since the plants at this time have little leaf surface to hold lethal concentrations of the insecticidal sprays.

In the West large tracts of grassland are subject to periodical outbreaks of range grasshoppers. Economical control has been obtained through application of 2 oz. of aldrin in 1 gal. of diesel fuel per acre by airplane (Fig. 8:9). The operation is precisely timed so that no egg laying takes place before treatment. Control lasts for periods exceeding five years. Since residues of insecticide accumulate in cattle that feed on treated range, grazing restrictions must be carefully followed.

Each year scientists in the Entomology Research Division screen and field test new insecticides for their efficiency against grasshoppers. These studies show promise for the eventual discovery of chemicals that will not only control grasshoppers effectively, but also do away with residue problems.

Fig. 8:9. A converted bomber spraying range to control heavy infestation of grasshoppers. *Courtesy Denver Post.*

Because grasshoppers are a national menace and migrate without regard to state boundaries, the federal government maintains an organization of grasshopper specialists to aid the states and individual farmers and ranchers in controlling these pests. A central office collects, analyzes, and publishes reports from fieldmen, who are entomologists that at one time were called "grasshopper supervisors." Almost every state in the bad grasshopper areas of the West has a grasshopper fieldman. His duties include making surveys of grasshopper adults in summer, eggs in fall, and nymphs in spring so that farmers and ranchers may learn of impending dangers and organize control. Because of the migratory nature of grasshoppers community action is vital for successful control of these insects.

Armyworm

Pseudaletia unipuncta (Haworth) [Lepidoptera:Noctuidae]

The armyworm, a widely distributed and injurious cutworm, lives in most regions of the world. In North America it destroys grass and grain crops over a wide area. Records of its destructiveness go back as far as colonial times; in 1743 a ravaging outbreak took place in the area now known as the North Atlantic States. Since then it has plagued farmers at irregular intervals. Recent outbreaks have occurred in the years 1937–39 and in 1953 and 1954.

An attack by armyworms is notable for its suddenness and severity. Aggregations of the adult moths, flying or wind carried, alight in green fields of grain at night to deposit hundreds of eggs. Upon hatching the larvae usually go unnoticed until the serious condition of the crop calls attention to their presence (Fig. 8:10). They may be so numerous as to completely devour a crop before a grower can apply control measures. As food becomes exhausted, the larvae assume a gregarious marching habit and crawl away to fresh fields.

Fig. 8:10. Laying back wheat plants exposes heavy infestation of armyworms attacking the crop. Note at lower right how leaves are being consumed. *Courtesy USDA.*

Since armyworms prefer grasses as food they are particularly destructive to small grains, corn, and forage grasses. They may occasionally injure broad-leaved crops such as alfalfa, clover, sugar beets, and tobacco. In attacking grains, they eat the succulent leaves first. Then as plants become stripped of foliage, they feed on other parts. In headed small grains, they may feed on awns and tender kernels and frequently will cut through the stem a short distance below the head.

Losses resulting from attack of armyworms reach astonishing proportions during outbreak years. In Kentucky during the 1953 outbreak, armyworms consumed around ten million dollars worth of crops and pastures on an estimated 1,085,000 acres. In Minnesota during 1954 armyworms caused a crop loss amounting to twelve million dollars (Table 8:1).

Table 8:1 | Crop Losses from Armyworm in Minnesota in 1954 and Savings Resulting from Control

	Estimated Loss		Estimated Savings	
Crop	*Bushels*	*Dollar Value*	*Bushels*	*Dollar Value*
Oats	7,255,000	$4,570,650	15,495,000	$ 9,761,850
Barley	3,466,000	3,569,980	7,963,000	8,201,890
Wheat	963,000	2,070,450	4,697,000	10,098,550
Corn	1,296,000	1,788,480	8,228,000	11,354,640

Description. Female moths lay eggs in clusters of 25 to over 100 in the folded blades or under the leaf sheaths of grasses and grains. The eggs are minute, greenish-white, and globular. Young armyworms are pale green. The full-grown armyworm is a conspicuously striped, yellow to brownish-green cutworm about 1½ to 2 in. long. The adult moths are pale-brown to grayish-brown with a wingspread of about 1½ in. In the center of each front wing is a characteristic white spot (Fig. 8:11).

Life history. In northern states and in Canada the armyworm has two generations annually. Partly grown larvae pass the winter hidden in the soil or under ground litter in succulent stands of grass. When spring arrives the larvae resume feeding and developing. First generation adults appear in May and June. Before ovipositing, females feed for seven to ten days on sweet substances like honeydew and nectar or on decaying fruit. They lay their eggs at night in clusters of 25 to 134 on grass or grains, usually in folded blades or under leaf sheaths. An individual female may produce as many as 2,000 eggs.

After six to ten days of incubation the eggs hatch into small caterpillars which soon begin to feed on the leaf surface down to the parenchyma leaving the lower leaf surface a transparent membrane. Older larvae feed from the edge of the leaf and devour all leaf tissues. Their usual feeding time is at dusk, but in cloudy weather they may eat during day light hours. During the day they ordinarily hide in the crowns of plants or under surface litter.

The armyworm has six larval instars and requires three to four weeks to complete larval development. The last or sixth instar is the longest, about

Fig. 8:11. Life stages of the armyworm. A, adult moths; B, eggs; C, larva; D, pupa. A, B, courtesy Can. Dept. Agr.; C, courtesy USDA; D, courtesy University of Nebraska.

seven days. This instar consumes more than 80 per cent of all foliage eaten during the entire larval period.

Full-grown larvae pupate in earthern cells under litter or 2 to 3 in. down in the soil. The pupal period lasts from 12 to 15 days. Following pupation, in August and September, the second generation adults emerge and oviposit on lush grass. The eggs hatch and the larvae develop partially before winter sets in.

The farther south in the United States the armyworm resides, the more generations it has each year. In the central states it has three to four generations annually, while in the South it has five or more generations and all stages may be present and developing throughout the winter.

Hymenopterous and dipterous parasites and various diseases take their toll of armyworms. The most efficient natural enemy appears to be the small wasp, *Apanteles militaris* (Walsh) which normally keeps the armyworm in check. Outbreaks of the armyworm follow years of drought which are detrimental to populations of *A. militaris*.

The source of armyworm infestations is still somewhat uncertain. A locality may raise its own armyworms when conditions are favorable or it may be invaded by flying moths which originate in other areas.

Control. An essential requirement for effective and profitable control is the early discovery of infestations. Shrewd growers regularly inspect crops for armyworms as well as for other insect pests. Armyworms hide under ground litter and in plant crowns during the day. A danger sign is feeding injury to foliage—chunks eaten out of the leaves or entire leaves almost completely eaten away. Armyworms prefer low, wet areas covered by rank stands of grain. These areas are the first to harbor the pests and deserve careful examination.

Insecticides in the form of sprays, dusts, or baits readily control armyworms. Recent tests have shown that dieldrin at 0.25 lb., endrin at 0.2 lb., and toxaphene at 2 lb. of the actual toxicant per acre are among the most effective insecticides for controlling armyworms and for preventing reinfestation of a crop. Application may be by ground or aerial equipment.

Chlorinated hydrocarbon insecticides applied to maturing small grains usually leave toxic residues on the straw at harvest time, but do not contaminate the grain. To keep residues at a minimum, follow label directions. Do not feed contaminated straw to livestock.

Armyworms may also be controlled successfully with bran baits. Spread baits in the evening when the armyworms begin to feed. Spread them by hand, by grain seeder, or by grasshopper bait spreader. Apply about 40 pounds of wet bait to an acre.

If armyworms begin to migrate, one can protect clean fields by surrounding the infested area with a deep furrow or ditch. In plowing throw the soil toward the armyworms. Armyworms march into the furrow, but are unable to get up the steep side. A log dragged back and forth in the furrow will either crush the armyworms or pulverize the soil to make the barrier more impassible. Sometimes traps are built in the furrows by digging post holes about 18 inches deep and 20 feet apart. The armyworms which have fallen into the holes can be destroyed by sprinkling kerosene or diesel fuel over them.

Hessian fly

Phytophaga destructor (Say) [Diptera:Cecidomyiidae]

The Hessian fly is the most destructive insect enemy of wheat in the United States. Widespread outbreaks of this pest occur at irregular intervals and last from one to as many as six years. Local outbreaks cause considerable crop losses nearly every year.

The Hessian fly is an introduced insect, supposedly a stowaway from Europe in straw used for bedding Hessian troops during the Revolutionary War. Regardless of how it arrived here, the Hessian fly probably crossed the Atlantic some time in the latter half of the eighteenth century. It now occurs widely in the United States and Canada, though it inflicts serious injury over a somewhat smaller area.

The Hessian fly has two main broods. One attacks winter wheat in fall and the other attacks both winter and spring wheat in spring. The larvae alone cause injury by extracting juice and altering the stem tissues. The number of larvae infesting a plant determines amount of injury. The presence of one or two larvae on a plant may not be serious, but during severe outbreaks numbers may average 20 or 30 per plant and run as high as 80 on some individual plants.

Wheat infested before jointing takes on a characteristic stunted appearance. The leaves of an infested plant are shorter, broader, more erect, and darker green than the leaves of an uninfested plant. Larvae may kill individual tillers or the entire plant. The leaves turn yellow and finally brown. Infested plants that do survive injury in fall are more susceptible to winter killing and to diseases. Hessian flies pave the way for invasion of fungi which cause crown and basal stem rot of wheat.

Wheat infested after jointing suffers a different kind of injury. The larvae attack the stems above joints, causing damage that interferes with the transfer of food to the developing heads. Infested culms yield 25 to 30 per cent less grain by weight than uninfested. Plants with larvae-weakened stems tend to fall down or lodge (Fig. 8:12). Lodged grain is lost grain because binders or combines cannot pick it up.

In the United States losses due to Hessian flies have gradually lessened as resistant varieties of wheat have become available for various sections of the country. In 1915 before any resistant varieties were grown, an outbreak of Hessian flies brought about a loss of wheat amounting to 100

Fig. 8:12. Lodging of winter wheat resulting from infestation by spring generation of Hessian fly. *Courtesy Kan. Agr. Exp. Sta.*

million dollars. In 1945, the last year of general distribution of susceptible varieties the loss amounted to 37 million dollars. At present, damage to small grains, mostly winter wheat, averages around 16 million dollars a year. In Kansas the growing of fly-resistant Pawnee since 1945 and Ponca since 1951 has greatly reduced the Hessian fly populations in this state.

In addition to wheat, Hessian flies also injure barley, rye, emmer, and spelt. The fly does not develop readily in rye and has never been found in oats.

Fig. 8:13. A, female Hessian fly; B, eggs on wheat leaf. *A, courtesy Kan. Agr. Exp. Sta.; B, courtesy USDA.*

Description. The eggs, laid in the grooves of the upper surface of wheat leaves, are about 0.5 mm. long and visible to the unaided eye. Their surface is a glossy red, which deepens with age. The newly hatched larvae are about the same size and hue as the eggs, but the color changes to white within a few days. Full-grown larvae are glistening white. A translucent green stripe runs down the middle of the back where the stomach contents show through the integument. The puparium or "flaxseed" is dark brown and about 3 to 5 mm. long. Adults are mosquito-like in form, black, and about 2.5 mm. long. The abdomen of the female appears red due to the eggs showing through the body wall (Figs. 8:13 and 8:14).

Life history. In the winter-wheat areas of the United States the Hessian fly has two principle broods annually, one in spring and one in fall. The species passes the winter as larvae protected in puparia on stubble, volunteer wheat, and early-seeded winter wheat. When warm, wet, spring weather arrives the larvae enter the pupal stage for two to three weeks.

The flies emerge in March in southern states and in April or May in northern states. Emergence usually takes place early in the morning and mating occurs soon afterwards, often in less than an hour. Adults do no feeding, as far as known. Females may begin laying eggs within 15 minutes after mating. They prefer to deposit eggs on young wheat plants, usually in the grooves on the upper surface of the leaves. Egg capacity varies with the size of each female and ranges from 30 to 485. Oviposition is completed in a short time, as females do not usually live longer than two or three days. Eggs hatch in three to 12 days.

The newly emerged larvae migrate down the leaves to feeding positions underneath the leaf sheaths next to the stems. In young tillers they migrate down close to the crowns, but on leaves of older plants, they stop just above the joints. The larvae take from 12 to 25 hours to crawl to their feeding positions and many die before completing the migration. They feed on plant juices which they obtain by cupping their mouth parts against the stem and sucking intermittently. The period of growth varies from two to six weeks depending on temperature. When full grown, the larva contracts from the old larval skin which hardens and becomes the puparium. The puparium is usually referred to as the "flaxseed" because of its resemblance to the seed of flax. Within flaxseeds, larvae remain dormant during summer.

From the last days of August in the North to November in the South, the adults emerge from the flaxseeds and produce the eggs of the fall brood. Females lay eggs on volunteer wheat and early-planted winter wheat. Larvae hatching from these eggs migrate down the leaves to the crowns. There they develop to the flaxseed stage and pass the winter.

Not all flaxseeds of either the spring or fall generation become adult flies during a single emergence period. Some remain dormant and emerge later with subsequent generations. For this reason we term the group of individuals of approximately the same age and present at approximately the same time in a wheat field a "brood" rather than a "generation."

In addition to the two main broods, favorable rainfall and temperature may foster supplementary broods. One supplementary brood may follow the spring brood, one may occur in summer, and one may follow the fall brood.

In California, in the Pacific Northwest, and in the northern spring wheat regions, the seasonal history of the Hessian fly varies from that described for the winter-wheat areas of the United States. Differences in climate induce these variations. Active stages of the fly synchronize with the humid, moderately warm periods of the year. Dry, hot weather forces the species to estivate and, if prolonged, causes mortality among the flaxseeds. This combination of factors also prevents the Hessian fly from doing serious injury in the arid sections of the West and Southwest.

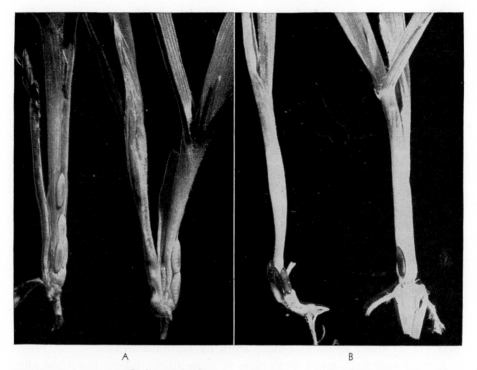

Fig. 8:14. A, Hessian fly larvae feeding on stems of young wheat; B, puparia or "flax-seeds" on tillers of seedling wheat. *Courtesy Kan. Agr. Exp. Sta.*

Investigations on resistant varieties of wheat have disclosed the existence of races of Hessian fly. The wheat varieties Dawson and Wabash are resistant to California flies, but are susceptible to Indiana flies. Within the state of Kansas two populations appear to exist, one in the soft-wheat belt and another in the hard-wheat belt.

Thirty-five species of parasites attack the Hessian fly and play a part in controlling populations of this pest.

Control. Cultural control methods may either prevent infestation of wheat by Hessian flies or lessen the effect of attack. An important cultural method is the timing of seeding in the fall. Wheat sown late enough will escape the egg laying of the fall brood of flies. Entomologists and agronomists have worked out average safe dates for planting wheat to avoid Hessian fly. These dates are approximate and vary from year to year depending on weather. In some states the agricultural college each fall notifies growers of the safe time for seeding.

One should sow wheat as soon as possible after the safe date to allow the plant to make sufficient growth before winter sets in. In California adults and larvae are active only from February to May so that early, rather than late, planting reduces injury.

For certain regions plant breeders have developed varieties of wheat that have both desirable agronomic characteristics and resistance to the Hessian fly. Pawnee, one of the leading varieties of wheat grown in the United States, is resistant and is recommended for Kansas, Nebraska, Oklahoma, and Colorado. Actually, its value in reducing Hessian fly damage is due to both resistance and tolerance. Pawnee expresses resistance by low infestation rate, by depressing the development of fly larvae, and by causing undersized flaxseeds. It expresses tolerance by sustaining slight injury and yielding well, even though infested.

The variety Ponca carries more resistance than Pawnee and is recommended for eastern Kansas and for most of Oklahoma. Big Club 43 and Poso 48, adapted to certain parts of California and Utah, are resistant varieties. Dual, Todd, and Monon, soft winter wheat varieties grown in the East and Midwest, are resistant. Mida and Marquillo, spring wheats adapted to the North Central States, are moderately resistant. Certain varieties like Cheyenne have no resistance, but express some degree of tolerance. Plant breeders continue to develop new varieties so that we may expect other areas to benefit from fly resistant wheat.

A third cultural control method is to plow under infested stubble after harvest and to follow with harrowing or rolling of the soil so that flies cannot emerge. This method is feasible for most of the winter-wheat areas west of the Mississippi River, but not for areas where grass or clover is grown with the wheat or where heavy winds blow the soil. Destroying all volunteer wheat as soon as it sprouts prevents the increase of flies during the summer and saves moisture and soil fertility. In the spring-wheat region of the North Central States, plowing infested stubble and packing the soil before the spring emergence of adults in May reduce danger of infestation.

Wherever annual rotation of wheat with other crops fits into agricultural practices, it aids in reducing fly infestation of wheat. Furthermore, the farther away we plant wheat from infested stubble, the more we reduce the danger of infestation even though adults can fly or be carried by wind at least five miles.

Recommended cropping practices—such as good seed bed preparation, fertilization, and planting healthy, strong seed—aid in control by promoting vigorous plants able to tolerate and outgrow light infestations of Hessian fly.

Best results from these cultural methods come when all wheat growers in a community practice them.

A chemical method for controlling the Hessian fly has recently become available. It consists of applying 10 per cent granular phorate, a systemic insecticide, evenly in the furrow at time of planting at the rate of 10 lbs. per acre. Because of cost this method would not appear as practical as the cultural practices outlined above.

Greenbug

Toxoptera graminum (Rondani) [Homoptera:Aphidae]

The greenbug is a widely distributed aphid—not a bug—in North and South America, Europe, Africa, and Asia. It is a serious pest of oats, barley, and wheat in this country, particularly in the central states from Texas to North Dakota and Minnesota. Infestations may also extend into Manitoba and Saskatchewan. Heavy numbers of greenbugs cause total destruction of both winter and spring grains.

Damaging infestations develop in two ways. First, in southern states as in Texas and Oklahoma, small isolated aggregations of greenbugs may begin to increase and to kill out circular areas of wheat a few feet in diameter. As the grain dies the aphids move out to healthy wheat in increasing numbers until eventually the dead areas of wheat join. **Greenbug spots** have a characteristic appearance. The inner area consists of brown, dead plants surrounded by a circle of bright yellow plants. Immediately outside of this circle the grain is green.

Secondly, infestations may develop as an invasion of an entire field by swarms of migrating greenbugs. If this happens, all plants become injured and die at about the same time.

Light or moderate infestations of greenbugs do not cause total destruction, but do cause measurable reduction in yield. In fall, greenbugs may thin stands and prevent tillering of winter small grains; in winter and in early spring, they may cause greenbug spots; and in spring, they may stunt the heads by feeding inside the boot leaf (Fig. 8:15).

Greenbugs directly injure plants by injecting saliva and by sucking up juices. Powerful enzymes in the saliva alter the cells and their contents and eventually kill the living tissues. Leaf injury is evident as yellow spots with necrotic centers. Greenbugs may also act as vectors of plant diseases, for they are able to transmit the viruses of sugarcane mosaic and of barley yellow dwarf.

The first report of greenbugs in North America came from Virginia in 1882. Since then the country has suffered 21 outbreaks. One of the most severe centered in Texas and Oklahoma in 1942. Losses in these states

Fig. 8:15. Greenbug injury to wheat. Normal head on left; others stunted by feeding of greenbugs when heads were within the boot. *Courtesy Kan. Agr. Exp. Sta.*

totaled more than 61 million bushels of grain valued at 38 million dollars. Besides destroying grain, greenbugs reduce the pasture value of small grains.

Although the greenbug is primarily a pest of oats, barley, and wheat, it also feeds on other small grains, and on corn, rice, sorghum, and forage grasses.

Description. Greenbug eggs are pale yellow when first laid, but become shiny black by the end of the third day (Fig. 8:16C). They are kidney shaped and about 0.8 mm. long. Dark green nymphs hatch from eggs and develop, after molting four times, into stem-mothers. The latter are wingless, yellow to green in color, and without the darker green dorsal stripe of the summer adult forms.

Summer forms of the greenbug are either wingless females, the **apterous summer viviparae** (Fig. 8:16B); or winged females, the **alate viviparae**

(Fig. 8:16A). They are pale yellowish to bluish green with a darker green dorsal stripe and 2 mm. long. They give birth to pale green living young about 0.8 mm. long.

Egg-laying females, the **oviparae,** are wingless and similar to summer apterous viviparae in general color and measurements. Males are winged and colored like summer females, but are only about 1.3 mm. long.

Life history. In southern states greenbugs reproduce continuously throughout the year; while in the North eggs laid in the fall carry the species through the winter. During mild winters they may continue to breed slowly in states as far north as Kansas and Indiana. But farther north as in Minnesota, early cold weather may stop all activity, even before they can lay eggs. Infestations in this area would therefore have to start from invasions by migrating greenbugs.

Among species of aphids the greenbug has one of the simpler life histories. In early spring small green nymphs hatch from eggs and develop on native grasses into stem-mothers. These are wingless females that give birth parthenogenetically to living young. The latter are the first generation of summer forms. They develop into wingless females called apterous summer viviparae, which also give birth parthenogenetically to living young. This form reproduces its kind through the summer and also gives rise to the other summer form, the winged females or alate viviparae.

Winged females migrate from the native grasses to small grains and other host plants and produce additional generations of both winged and wingless females. When small grains mature, winged aphids develop in large numbers and migrate to green food plants, while the wingless aphids perish. There may be twenty generations of the summer forms produced during one season.

The final summer generation gives birth in early fall to a bisexual generation. The male is winged but the female is wingless. After mating the female deposits from one to ten eggs in the folds of dead or dying leaves of native grasses. As the dead leaves fall to the ground, the eggs become buried in ground litter. In the South, summer forms reproduce continuously throughout the year giving rise to thirty or more generations; here eggs are rarely produced.

All forms of the greenbug pass through four nymphal instars before adulthood. The summer females usually start reproducing from 6 to 16 days after birth and may continue for as long as 45 days. Individual females bear from one to ten young each day. Although a single aphid may produce as many as 93 young, the average number is 25 to 30. Greenbugs repro-

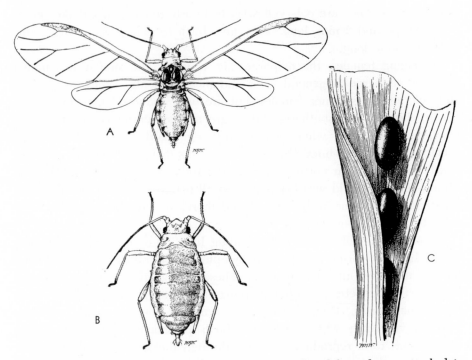

Fig. 8:16. Greenbug stages. Winged and wingless female adults and eggs attached to grass leaf. *Courtesy USDA.*

duce and develop optimumly at temperatures between 55° and 65°F. When temperatures go below 50°F. they crawl down the plant and seek shelter under the mat of dead leaves at the base.

Outbreaks of greenbugs in the South correlate well with a succession of favorable weather conditions. The summer previous to an outbreak is cool and has excessive rain. Such weather delays harvest and causes the grain to lodge and shatter. The enormous volunteer grain crop that springs up provides a favorable habitat for greenbugs. This condition followed by a mild winter and a cool, dry, backward spring favors the production of huge numbers of aphids, but retards their natural enemies.

Natural enemies are important in checking populations of greenbugs. A small wasp, *Aphidius testaceipes* (Cress.), is one of the most efficient parasites. Female wasps deposit eggs within the bodies of aphids. The eggs hatch into larvae that feed on the internal organs of the hosts and kill them. The convergent lady beetle and other species of lady beetles are efficient predators in both their larval and adult stages.

Control. Both cultural and chemical methods are used to control greenbugs. Three cultural practices are feasible. One is to grow vigorous plants which, under attack of greenbugs, are injured less and yield more than weak plants. Agronomic practices that foster strong, healthy plants include preparing friable, firm seedbeds, planting good seed of suitable varieties, fertilizing where needed, regulating adequate soil moisture, and rotating crops systematically. Greenbugs injure fall-sown barley, oats, and wheat more severely when they follow grain sorghum in rotation than when they follow soybeans, corn, or wheat. Providing more nitrogen for small grains, either by applying fertilizer or by rotating with legumes, reduces greenbugs and greenbug injury. The second cultural practice is to grow resistant varieties of grain, such as Dicktoo barley in Kansas and Kearney barley in the Texas Panhandle.

The third practice is to destroy volunteer grains by disking or plowing. Volunteer grains provide shelter and food during the summer months for large numbers of greenbugs and constitute an important link in the chain of events that lead to outbreaks. Preventing growth of volunteer small grain is particularly advisable in Texas and Oklahoma, where serious outbreaks may originate and sweep northward.

When cultural and natural controls cannot cope with injurious populations, growers can effectively protect their crops with insecticides. For best results, use them at the first signs of injury—usually in February and March in the South up to as late as June and July in the North.

Parathion or methyl parathion applied at the rate of 4 oz. of toxicant per acre provides adequate control. Temperature at time of application and for at least three hours afterwards should be 50°F. or above. These insecticides are ordinarily applied as sprays by ground power-equipment or by airplane. Dusts are effective in calm weather. Since parathion and methyl parathion are highly toxic to man and livestock, take special precautions in using them. Read the container label carefully and follow all directions strictly.

Prairie grain wireworm *Ctenicera aeripennis destructor* (Brown)

Great Basin wireworm *Ctenicera pruinina* (Horn)

Corn wireworm *Melanotus communis* Gyllenhal

Wheat wireworm *Agriotes mancus* (Say)

[Coleoptera:Elateridae]

Wireworms, the larval stage of click beetles, comprise a large family in the order Coleoptera. Approximately 700 native species inhabit the United States and Canada. In the larval stage most of these feed on the roots and underground stems of grasses and forbs. A few live in decaying wood and may prey on small arthropods. Several species are important pests of small grains, corn, cotton, tobacco, potatoes, and many other crops.

The most serious wireworm injury to small grains occurs in the northern wheat-growing areas of North America. Several species are responsible for the losses. In the northern Great Plains States and in the western provinces of Canada, the prairie grain wireworm is the principal pest. This species prefers well-drained, light and medium soils of the open prairies, but also inhabits irrigated sandy soil.

In the Pacific Northwest and in British Columbia the Great Basin wireworm is the prominent soil pest of dry-land small grains. It lives only in regions that normally receive precipitation of 15 or fewer inches annually. In Canada's western provinces, *Hypolithus nocturnus* Esch. follows closely the prairie grain wireworm in importance. Widely distributed over open prairies and in parklands, it is more abundant in areas of heavy soil, particularly in meadows and in fields recently broken from sod. In Alberta it is also a pest in irrigated fields.

Although wireworm damage to small grains is not as great in the central and southern wheat growing areas of the United States, several species of wireworms do sometimes cause injury there. The wheat wireworm, an

Fig. 8:17. Wireworm damage to wheat in foreground. Seed of wheat in background was treated with insecticide for control of wireworms. *Courtesy Chipman Chemical Co.*

important pest of corn and potatoes, may also injure wheat. It occurs in northeastern and midwestern states and in eastern provinces. It prefers poorly drained soil planted to meadows or sod crops. The corn wireworms, *Melanotus communis* Gyll. and others of the genus, are widely distributed in North America and may at times injure wheat. A minor wireworm pest of wheat widely distributed in the United States and Canada is *Aeolus mellillus* (Say). Many other species infest fields of small grains and more or less suppress yields.

To learn about wireworms and their control in small grains, we shall consider in some detail the life history and control of the prairie grain wireworm. Larvae of this species feed underground on the seeds and the young seedling plants of wheat and other small grains in the spring of the year. After the plants have stooled out, wireworms no longer cause severe damage, but often by this time they have ruined entire stands.

Wireworms attack the crop as soon as the seeds are planted. In feeding they hollow out the kernels of grain leaving only the husks. After unharmed seeds have sprouted, wireworms bore through leaf sheaths into the stems of young plants. This feeding destroys the growing point and kills the central shoot. After several days the leaves and roots also die. Stems injured by wireworms are not cut off, but have a characteristic shredded appearance at the point of injury. The marks of wireworm attack in fields are bare areas of various sizes, general thinning of stand (Fig. 8:17), and reduced yields. Wireworm wounds may also allow disease organisms to enter plants and cause rots.

Fields most seriously affected by wireworms are those planted the first year after being summer-fallowed or after being in grass for several years. Wireworm control in these fields increases yields from one to 12 bushels of wheat per acre, with an average increase of about five bushels under favorable moisture conditions.

Description. The prairie grain wireworm deposits eggs in clusters in the soil. They are minute, nearly round, and pearly white. Young wireworms are creamy white, but change to a shiny yellow as they grow older. Full-grown larvae reach a length of about 1 inch. They transform to fragile white pupae. The adults are dark brown to nearly black beetles ¼ to ½ in. long (Fig. 8:18).

Life history. The life cycle of the prairie grain wireworm takes a minimum of four years to complete and may require as many as nine years, most of this time in the larval stage. Adult beetles emerge from hibernation in the soil during April and mate immediately. The females then seek protection in the soil or under stones until their eggs are well developed in May. Males stay on the soil surface wandering about until they succumb to old age or high July temperatures.

Adults do little feeding; indeed, females can develop normal numbers of eggs without eating any food. Although both sexes bear well-developed wings, males do little flying and females likely none at all. They crawl about freely but rarely move for very long in any one direction. From late May till late July, female beetles make frequent journeys into the soil to various depths up to 6 inches to lay clusters of eggs.

Individual females develop up to 400 eggs but probably deposit only half that number. After approximately one month of incubation, the eggs hatch into small, creamy-white wireworms. The latter burrow immediately

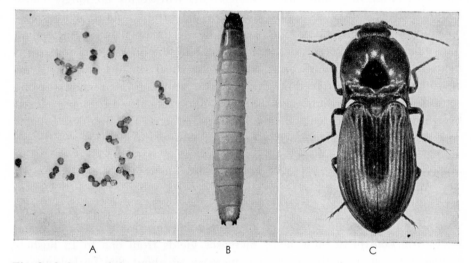

A   B   C

Fig. 8:18. Stages of the prairie grain wireworm. A, eggs; B, larva; C, adult. A, *courtesy Can. Dept. Agr.; B, C, courtesy Ralph Bird.*

up or down seeking food and favorable soil temperature and moisture. Wireworms prefer moist soil and temperatures between 70° and 85°F. Heat and dryness in summer and cold in winter drive wireworms down to lower levels in the soil and suppress their activity. During the winter larvae hibernate at depths of 6 to 10 inches.

Young wireworms require living vegetation for food. Roots and underground stems of grasses and grains—but not of forbs—furnish favorable and adequate diets. At this stage of development many young wireworms perish from starvation. Older wireworms, not so restricted as to diet, are able to survive even on humus in the soil. Feeding is heaviest in spring and fall when soil environment is optimum.

Three to eight years after hatching, the wireworms reach full growth. This stage occurs in July after the larvae have molted from 10 to 24 times. They burrow upwards to within 2 inches of the surface—if the soil is firm and moist—where they pupate in small cells. After a few days they molt to fragile white pupae. Within a month the pupae transform to adult beetles which remain in their cells until the following spring.

Predators seldom bother wireworms in their underground hiding places. Ground beetle larvae prey on them and they may cannabalize each other. Bacterial and fungus diseases of larvae, however, are widespread and are probably important factors in natural control. Birds feed on the adults.

Control. Since the twenties cultural methods have been somewhat successful for controlling wireworms in fields of small grains. More recently chemical control with lindane, aldrin, dieldrin, or heptachlor has provided greater and surer protection. Insecticides are most economically applied by dressing the seeds with powders or slurries. Automatic seed-treating machines cover each seed uniformly and thoroughly with the insecticide and sometimes also a fungicide such as organic mercury to control smut. In the slurry treatment the dressing may include a methyl cellulose solution to stick the chemicals to the seed. The actual amount of lindane dressing to apply per bushel of seed varies with the strength of the dressing and the rate of seeding. Recommended rates for applying aldrin, dieldrin, or heptachlor, are 2 to 4 oz. of the actual toxicant per 100 lbs. of seed.

If growers do not have seed-treating machines and custom treaters are unavailable, they may apply the insecticidal powders directly to the seed. One method is to sprinkle the required dosage over the seeds as they are poured into the drill box.

In treating seed, follow these precautions: (1) Use recommended dosages as printed on container label—overdoses may injure seeds and young plants. (2) Do not treat seed with lindane more than one or two weeks before seeding or lower germination may result. (3) Do not feed treated seed to livestock or mix with clean grain. (4) Do not touch or breathe dusts, particularly when they contain mercury.

Cultural control consists of cultivating and seeding practices that make the environment unsuitable for wireworms or hasten the growth of plants. Sow seed moderately early when the soil has first become thoroughly warm and only when there is enough moisture at seed depth to ensure rapid germination. If moisture is insufficient wait for rain. In dry soil, wireworms injure a larger number of seeds because lacking moisture they eat only the softer part of each grain. Sow seed as shallow as 1.5 to 2 inches when moisture is adequate. Use a press drill or follow immediately with a heavy packer. When planting untreated seed, heavier than normal seeding is advisable. This practice provides an overabundance of wireworm food and allows survival of sufficient numbers of seed and young plants to provide a good stand. Using plump vigorous seed with high germination rate helps for the same reason.

Clean summer fallow will starve the newly hatched larvae but does not harm older wireworms. Shallow tillage during the pupal period in late July and early August crushes the soft pupae or throws them to the surface where they perish. Deep plowing and cultivating are inadvisable at any time, as these practices provide highly favorable soil environments for the wireworms.

Selected References

Anon., *The Wheat Jointworm: How to Fight It*, USDA Leaflet 380, 1954.

Arnason, A. P., and W. B. Fox, *Wireworm Control in the Prairie Provinces*, Can. Dept. Agr. Processed Publ. 111, 1948.

Cartwright, W. B., and E. T. Jones, *The Hessian Fly and How Losses from it Can Be Avoided*, Farmers' Bul. 1627, 1953.

Dahms, R. G., *Preventing Greenbug Outbreaks*, USDA Leaflet 309, 1951.

Davis, E. G., J. A. Callenbach, and J. A. Munro, *The Wheat Stem Sawfly and its Control*, USDA EC-14, 1950.

Lane, M. C., *The Great Basin Wireworm in the Pacific Northwest*, USDA Farmers' Bul. 1657, 1931.

Mitchener, A. V., *Field Crop Insects and their Control in the Prairie Provinces*, Line Elevators Farm Service Bul. 8, 1956.

Painter, R. H., H. R. Bryson, and D. A. Wilbur, *Insects that Attack Wheat in Kansas*, Kan. Agr. Exp. Sta. Bul. 367, 1954.

Parker, J. R., *Grasshoppers: A New Look at an Ancient Enemy*, USDA Farmers' Bul. 2064, 1957.

Phillips, W. J., and F. W. Poos, *The Wheat Strawworm and its Control*, USDA Farmers' Bul. 1323, 1953.

Putnam, L. G., and R. H. Handford, *Control of Grasshoppers in the Prairie Provinces*, Can. Dept. Agr. Publ. 1036, 1958.

Walkden, H. H., *Cutworms, Armyworms, and Related Species Attacking Cereal and Forage Crops in the Central Great Plains*, USDA Circ. 849, 1950.

Walton, W. R., and C. M. Packard, *The Armyworm and its Control*, USDA Farmers' Bul. 1850, 1951.

Chapter 9 | INSECT PESTS OF
CORN | *Robert E. Pfadt*

Corn has the highest value of any crop produced in the United States. It is raised in every state of the Union, occupies approximately 85,000,000 acres or a fifth of the total crop land, is grown on two-thirds of all farms, and is valued at almost five billion dollars annually. A recent estimate indicates that field insects cause an average yearly damage to this agricultural giant of $900,000,000. Over 25 major destructive species and many more minor ones are responsible. Some of these pests are readily visible as they feed on the leaves, stems, or silks, but the majority hide and feed inside the stalk and roots, in the ears, in the whorl, or underground.

The pests

A national survey has revealed that there are seven pests that can be placed in the category "most destructive." They are the European corn borer, corn earworm, fall armyworm, corn leaf aphid, southwestern corn borer, rice weevil, and soil insects (a complex of species).

The **European corn borer,** a minor foreign pest that was accidentally introduced near Boston around 1910, has become the single most injurious insect enemy of corn in America (Figs. 9:14 and 9:15). It now occurs in 39 states and is spreading farther south and west every year. Next in line is a native species, the **corn earworm** (Fig. 9:12). Although it ranks second among pests of the total corn crop, it is the number one enemy of sweet corn and is a serious pest of cotton, tomatoes, and tobacco as well. The **fall armyworm,** a close relative of the corn earworm, is an important pest of corn, particularly in the northeastern and southern states.

About the time that the European corn borer was spreading into the Corn Belt, another foreign pest, the **southwestern corn borer** (Fig. 9:2), was expanding its range in the Southwest having originally invaded this area from Mexico. Today this insect is causing grave concern because of its rapid migration eastward from Oklahoma and Arkansas.

The **rice weevil,** called the "corn weevil" by many southern farmers, attacks growing corn in the South shortly after the roasting-ear stage (Fig. 16:10). At harvest this insect is brought into storage where it continues to breed and to do damage as a stored grain pest. The **corn leaf aphid,** a widely distributed insect, causes reduction in pollen shedding and partial to complete barrenness.

In North America over thirty kinds of **soil insects** (Fig. 9:1) are enemies of the corn crop. This diversity of species does not exist in any one field nor in any one area, but when corn in a field is beset with soil insects, the

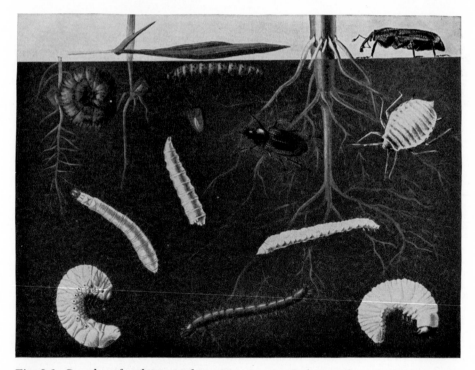

Fig. 9:1. Complex of soil insects destructive to corn. Left to right, top row: cutworm, sod webworm, billbug; Middle: flea beetle larva, seed-corn maggot, seed-corn beetle, corn rootworm, corn root aphid; Bottom row: white grub, wireworm, grape colaspis. Figures not to scale. *Courtesy Illinois Natural History Survey.*

damage often originates from the activities of a complex of species. Highly destructive soil insects include corn rootworms, cutworms, wireworms, billbugs, webworms, and the seed-corn maggot.

In addition to the above major pests, there are insects of great regional importance such as grasshoppers, chinch bugs, sap beetles, and spider mites. **Grasshoppers** have caused great destruction of the corn crop west of the Mississippi River. One of the chief species involved in these depredations has been the **differential grasshopper,** which in many places has rightly earned the name of "corn hopper" (Fig. 8:7D).

In the East and South, **sap beetles,** *Carpophilus* spp., are destructive pests of the ear of sweet corn, being both primary and secondary invaders (Fig. 9:3). The **two-spotted spider mite** is a serious pest of corn in the West. And the **chinch bug,** a widely distributed native insect, causes much damage during outbreak years in the Midwest and Southwest (Fig. 9:10).

The injury

Insects begin attacking corn as soon as the seed enters the ground and never let up through the entire period of plant growth to maturity. An old Indian rule for planting corn goes:

> One for the bug,
> One for the crow,
> One to rot,
> And two to grow.

Insects injure corn seed severely when cool, wet weather delays germination. By eating into and hollowing out the seed, wireworms, seed-corn maggots, seed-corn beetles, thief ants, and the larvae of pale-striped flea beetles, seriously reduce stands.

Soil pests like rootworms, white grubs, wireworms, corn root aphids, and other root feeders, stunt plant growth and reduce yields. Corn plants injured by rootworms frequently fall over or lodge during hard rains.

Young corn plants bear the brunt of much insect injury. Heavy feeding on leaves by armyworms, grasshoppers, or flea beetles retards growth and reduces yields. Cutworms kill plants by cutting them off at or below ground level. Corn earworms, fall armyworms, European corn borers, southern cornstalk borers, and southwestern corn borers enter the whorl and feed on the tender, folded leaves and often destroy the central bud. When injured leaves unfold they appear ragged. Growers refer to this injury as "budworm damage." Wireworms feed not only on the roots of young corn plants but also on underground stems and may tunnel upward within them killing the central shoot. Chinch bugs, which pierce leaves and stems and suck the sap, cause young plants to wilt and die.

Fig. 9:2. Corn stalk cut to expose the southwestern corn borer and its tunnel. *Courtesy Kan. Agr. Exp. Sta.*

As corn plants become older and stronger, they can better withstand the feeding injuries of various insect pests. Yet even during the later stages of corn growth, insects, especially those attacking the silks and ears and those tunneling the stalks, cause serious damage. Insects which relish corn silks often prevent pollination and cause poorly filled ears and nubbins. Corn earworms work their way into the developing ear through the tip and feed on the soft kernels and contaminate the ear with excreta. Fall armyworms likewise damage corn ears, but they differ from corn earworms in that they burrow into the ear at various places. Entrance into an ear through the side or butt end destroys the value of sweet corn for human consumption.

Corn leaf aphids may infest the leaves, tassel, and ears in such great numbers that they seriously interfere with pollen production and cause plants to be barren or to produce only nubbins. Data indicate that barrenness is not due merely to suppression of pollination but to a physiological effect of the aphid upon the corn plant. According to recent research, even light infestations may reduce yields by as much as 10 per cent through decreased size and weight of ears.

A   B

Fig. 9:3. A, larvae of dusky sap beetle feeding on ear of canning sweet corn; B, sap beetle damage to sweet corn. *Courtesy University of Maryland.*

Borers tunneling within the stalk cause injury in several ways. In young corn they stunt the plants which subsequently yield less. In older plants they do not greatly affect yield, but they weaken stalks mechanically so that the plants break over in strong winds. Close to harvest time, the southwestern corn borer girdles the inside of the stalk about 3 to 4 inches above soil surface. This injury results in the lodging of about 75 per cent of the attacked stalks (Fig. 9:4). Borers, particularly the European corn borer, enter and weaken the shanks causing ears to break off and fall to the ground. The lodging of plants and the breaking off of ears during picking makes harvesting slow and difficult. Corn on the ground, which often falls prey to rodents, birds, and molds, forces growers to salvage by pasturing the field with livestock or by picking it off the ground. European corn borer and corn earworm often feed on the caps of the kernels of dent corn resulting in a serious cleaning problem in seed corn.

In southern states stored grain insects such as the rice weevil and Angoumois grain moth infest and destroy mature grain standing in the field. The Angoumois grain moth also infests corn in the field in areas as far north as southern Indiana, particularly popcorn and hominy corn causing serious losses. At harvest these pests are carried into storage where they continue their destruction.

Besides directly injuring corn, insects aid in the spread and development of corn diseases. Corn seeds wounded by soil insects are highly susceptible to attack by soil fungi, the most common cause of seed rots and seedling diseases. By tunneling into the ear or boring into the stalk insects open pathways for the entrance of ear rot and stalk rot fungi. They then facilitate infection by wounding host tissues.

Fig. 9:4. Lodged corn plants resulting from the girdling of southwestern corn borers. *Courtesy Kan. Agr. Exp. Sta.*

Flea beetles and corn rootworms transmit bacterial wilt, known also as Stewart's disease, which is especially destructive to sweet corn. Flea beetles carry the bacteria within their bodies during winter and are ready to transmit the disease as soon as they come out of hibernation in spring.

Insects also spread several of the virus diseases of corn. The leafhopper, *Dalbulus maidis* (DeL. & W.), transmits the virus of corn stunt; the melon aphid, the virus of southern celery mosaic, which likewise infects corn, and the corn planthopper, the virus of corn mosaic.

Cultural control

Cultural and chemical methods are the chief means of controlling corn pests, though entomologists have employed biological methods against the European corn borer by introducing parasites of this pest from foreign countries.

We may divide cultural methods into seven categories: (1) promotion of vigorous plants and stands; (2) rotation; (3) clean culture; (4) tillage; (5) sanitation; (6) modification in the timing or method of planting or harvesting; and (7) resistant varieties.

(1) Vigorous corn plants tolerate the feeding of insects better than weak ones and may overcome or outgrow injury. Growers produce vigorous plants by carrying out good agronomic practices. This cultural method is useful against such injurious pests as corn earworm, southern cornstalk borer, corn rootworms, wireworms, corn root aphid, and corn leaf aphid. Since chinch bugs prefer thinner or poorer parts of grain fields, growing heavy stands helps to control these pests.

(2) One of the most effective ways of avoiding some insect troubles is the proper rotation of corn with other crops. Allowing corn to occupy ground for only one or two years in rotation prevents large build-ups of pests favored by this crop. Species against which rotation works include rootworms, wireworms, white grubs, corn root aphid, and billbugs.

Planting immune crops on newly broken sod land instead of corn often averts serious damage from cutworms, wireworms, billbugs, and white grubs. Also planting immune crops when a corn pest is unusually abundant is desirable. Various legumes, and sometimes small grains or vegetables, make good substitute crops.

(3) Clean culture or the elimination of weeds and volunteer plants stifles the development of insect populations by doing away with plants upon which the insects feed or upon which females lay their eggs. This method is useful in controlling the fall armyworm, flea beetles, southern corn rootworm, corn root aphid, grasshoppers, and the stalk borer.

(4) With tillage operations we can control insect pests in several ways. First, we can bury insects in dormant stages so deep that they are unable to emerge from the soil. This measure has been recommended for controlling the European corn borer, the southwestern corn borer, the southern cornstalk borer, and grasshoppers.

Second, we can bring dormant stages to the surface and expose them to inclement weather and enemies. Insects controllable by this method include southwestern corn borer, southern cornstalk borer, webworms, bill-bugs, and grasshoppers.

Third, just before planting we can break up the nests of thief ants and cornfield ants and scatter corn root aphids. The operation reduces the numbers of these pests and gives the corn a chance to outgrow them.

(5) Sanitation—cleaning up of corn refuse and stubble in fields, feed lots, and other places on the farm—cuts down the numbers of surviving individuals of European corn borer, southern cornstalk borer, and southwestern corn borer. Sanitation also helps in controlling field infestations of rice weevil. Since field infestations are started by weevils which have migrated from nearby infested stored grain, a clean up of bins and cribs helps control this pest.

(6) Modifying the time or method of planting or harvesting is sometimes useful in controlling insect pests of corn. We can avoid some insect troubles by planting early, some by planting late, and still others by planting at the normal time. What we do depends on what kinds of pests are prevalent and how serious they are. Planting early sometimes helps to reduce injury by the southwestern corn borer, lesser cornstalk borer, southern corn rootworm in the South, corn leaf aphid, and chinch bug. Planting late and shallow to get a quick germination lessens damage to seed by pests in-

Fig. 9:5. European corn borer injury to leaves of corn plant. A, resistant hybrid; B, susceptible hybrid. *Courtesy USDA.*

Fig. 9:6. Granular insecticide being applied for control of European corn borer. *Courtesy Gandy Company.*

habiting the soil. This practice is useful against wireworms, seed-corn maggot, seed-corn beetle, and flea beetles. Planting at the usual time for a given locality is best where both European corn borer and corn earworm are troublesome.

Harvesting early before the southwestern corn borer starts girdling within the stem prevents lodging losses due to this insect. Seeding more thickly than normal to obtain a good stand is sometimes helpful in reducing the damage of the southern corn rootworm in the lowlands of the South.

(7) We can prevent or reduce the injury of a few insect pests by planting resistant or tolerant varieties adapted to the locality. Insects partially controllable by this method include the European corn borer (Fig. 9:5), corn earworm, rice weevil, and chinch bug.

Chemical control

As cultural methods may not be sufficiently effective, corn, particularly sweet corn, needs the protection provided by insecticides. Growers use the chlorinated hydrocarbons more than any other group of insecticides in controlling corn pests. When corn crop residues are not to be used as feed for dairy animals or animals being finished for slaughter, growers may apply

DDT as it is especially good against the corn earworm and European corn borer. They also use DDT to control cutworms, armyworms, corn flea beetles, Japanese beetles, and corn rootworm adults.

Other chlorinated hydrocarbons applied in large amounts include aldrin and heptachlor for control of corn rootworms, wireworms, cutworms, and white grubs; dieldrin for control of chinch bugs, grasshoppers, seed-corn maggot, and seed-corn beetle; and toxaphene for control of cutworms and webworms, and in lesser amounts TDE, chlordane, and lindane against several corn pests. Endrin's usage is increasing as this insecticide is especially effective against cutworms and other lepidopterous larvae.

Phosphate insecticides, such as malathion and parathion, have been useful in controlling two-spotted spider mite and corn leaf aphid.

Control equipment

Corn growers use both regular and special equipment in applying insecticides. For preplanting applications or applications when corn is young, ordinary ground sprayers and granule applicators (Fig. 9:6) are adequate, but after corn has grown tall, high clearance machines (Fig. 9:7) or airplanes are necessary. Growers may hire airplane applicators to apply insecticides at any stage of corn development.

Fig. 9:7. Treating sweet corn with a high-clearance sprayer. *Courtesy Farm Equipment Institute.*

Fig. 9:8. Row crop granular applicator attached to planter for in-row placement of insecticide at the time seed is planted. The higher placed hoppers hold the insecticide. *Courtesy Noble Manufacturing Company.*

To control soil insects, we may apply insecticides either broadcast or in bands along the rows. Broadcast treatment, the application of insecticide evenly over the entire field with immediate disking into the soil, protects the main root mass of surface planted corn. Broadcast treatments may be made with sprays, granules, or insecticide-fertilizer mixtures or solutions. For effective protection of listed corn, band treatment is necessary because the seed is planted in a deep furrow. Growers also employ the band treatment method on surface planted corn.

Proper placement of insecticides in the row has been achieved with a variety of devices. Planter or lister mounted spray or granule applicators disperse the insecticide in a band behind the planter shoes and in front of the covering disks or press wheels (Fig. 9:8). Another way has been to combine insecticides with starter fertilizers and to apply the mixture with a split-boot attachment that puts the material to one side of and below the seed—a position that permits good use of fertilizer but one possibly less efficient for insecticides. For this reason an additional attachment is often employed for separate application of the insecticidal sprays or granules. Applying liquid starter fertilizer-insecticide solutions with special attachments is still another method that growers use to place insecticide in the soil.

Coating seeds with insecticide, such as dieldrin, effectively controls some soil insects like the seed-corn maggot and seed-corn beetle. Seed-treating machines are the most efficient devices for applying chemicals to seed, but more often growers mix insecticidal dusts with corn seed in the planter box.

REPRESENTATIVE CORN PESTS

For our detailed study of important corn pests, we have chosen the chinch bug, the corn earworm, the European corn borer, and the three species of corn rootworms.

Chinch bug

Blissus leucopterus (Say) [Hemiptera:Lygaeidae]

The chinch bug, a widely distributed and native insect of North America, injures small grains, sorghum, and corn primarily in the Midwest and Southwest United States. The states most seriously affected are Illinois, Indiana, Iowa, Kansas, Missouri, Ohio, Nebraska, Oklahoma, and Texas. The first report of its being an injurious pest came in 1785 when it destroyed much of the wheat in North Carolina. Since that time chinch bugs have appeared recurrently in destructive numbers, usually during periods of drouth. One of the worst outbreaks took place in 1874 when grain crops suffered an estimated loss of 100 million dollars. In 1934, another year of serious infestation, the chinch bug caused an estimated loss of $27,500,000 to the corn crop and $28,000,000 to wheat, barley, rye, and oats. In some areas, as in Oklahoma, chinch bugs are present in more or less injurious numbers every year.

The kind of crop attacked and the extent of injury may vary depending on the generation of chinch bug doing the damage. Normally two generations develop in the Midwest and three in the Southwest. The first generation is injurious to small grains, but as these crops mature the bugs migrate to corn and sorghums. All generations injure the latter crops, though damage by the first generation is the most severe because the plants are young and tender at the time of attack.

Chinch bugs destroy plants principally by withdrawing enormous quantities of plant juices (Fig. 9:9). Young plants are highly susceptible, sustaining severe, often fatal, injury within a few days. Older and tougher plants are better able to withstand attack, but they too become weak and stunted, yield less, and frequently lodge. Fifty-five bugs per square foot cause severe injury to small grains, while 500 are usually necessary for serious injury to corn. Part of the injury to plants results from exudation of sap through the wounds produced by the feeding chinch bugs. Wounds also facilitate the entrance of pathogenic organisms. Chinch bugs do not

Fig. 9:9. A mass of chinch bugs sucking the sap from the stalk and leaves of a corn plant. *Courtesy USDA.*

seem to inject toxic substances into plants, as there is little evidence of cell injury in tissues directly pierced, but stylet sheath secretion may clog conductive tissue of the plant resulting in a yellowing or reddening of the affected region.

In addition to the destruction of small grains, corn, and sorghum, chinch bugs injure other members of the grass family, both cultivated and native.

Description. Eggs are laid on host plants behind the lower leaf sheaths, on roots, or in ground nearby. Eggs are 0.8 mm. long, white at first but gradually become reddish. Newly hatched nymphs are pale yellow, but they soon become red except for the first two abdominal segments, legs, and antennae, which remain pale yellow. Although the second, third, and fourth nymphal instars become darker red after each molt, they retain the pale yellow band on the fore part of the abdomen. The fifth and final nymphal instar is a black and gray nymph with a conspicuous white spot on the back between the wing pads. The adult chinch bug is black with conspicuous white forewings. Each of the latter has a black triangular spot at the middle of the outer margin. The adult is about ⅙ in. long (Fig. 9:10).

Life history. Chinch bugs overwinter as adults sheltered principally in tufts of bunch and clump-forming grasses. Some may hibernate under leaves or litter at the borders of woodlands, under hedges, in fence rows or in fields of sorghum stubble. They remain inactive during the winter unless spells of abnormally warm weather induce them to stir. Migration from winter quarters usually begins in early spring after one or two sunny days when temperatures rise to 70°F. or higher. The bugs, preferring the thinner parts of fields, fly to small grains. When cool weather delays migration, they may fly directly to corn or sorghum. Soon after reaching the fields of grain the bugs mate. Females then begin to lay eggs, placing them behind the lower leaf sheaths, on roots, or in ground close to the host plant. They deposit eggs at the rate of 15 to 20 a day over a period of two to three weeks.

Nymphs hatch from the eggs in one to two weeks and begin to feed on the small grain crop piercing stems and leaves and sucking up plant juices. The bugs pass through five nymphal instars in about 30 to 40 days. When small grains mature before the adult stage of the insect is reached, the bugs must migrate on foot to green food in order to survive. During afternoons of sunny days hordes of young bugs march into fields of corn, sorghum, or other succulent grasses. In the Southwest, where chinch bugs become adult before small grains mature, migration is by flight.

When chinch bugs reach the adult stage, they do much flying about and dispersing. Eventually they settle down and the females start laying eggs on corn or sorghum plants. These eggs hatch into the bugs of the second generation, which become adult in late summer or early fall. From August through October adults gradually leave the grain fields and fly to their wintering quarters. In the Southwest a third generation develops before the bugs enter hibernation.

Size of chinch bug populations and hence severity of injury are largely determined by weather. During dry years in the Midwest infestations build up gradually to a peak. When rainfall becomes normal again, populations drop off. Rainfall may affect chinch bugs in several ways. Heavy rains during the hatching period beat the young nymphs into the mud killing them, while splashing mud covers the eggs and prevents them from hatching. The white fungus disease caused by *Beauveria globulifera* (Speg.) spreads rapidly among chinch bugs during periods of warm, damp weather.

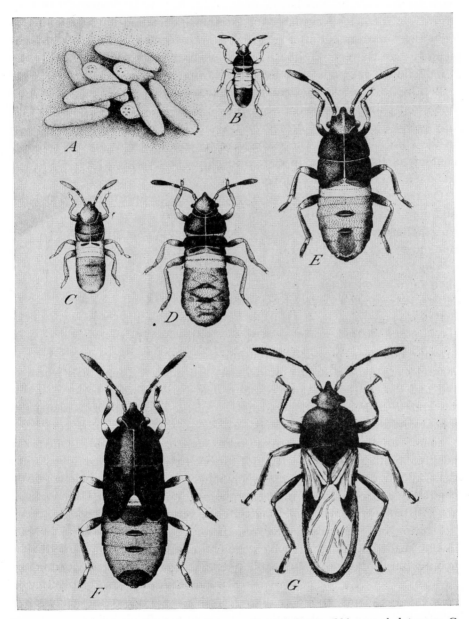

Fig. 9:10. Stages of the chinch bug. A, eggs; B to F first to fifth nymphal instars; G, adult. *Courtesy USDA.*

In the Southwest, weather affects chinch bugs differently. There, rainfall must be adequate, 2.5 inches or more, from July 10 to August 20 to keep green, succulent food available for the third-generation bugs. If rainfall is light, sorghums dry out after ripening and no second growth develops. Lack of food then prevents the third-generation bugs from maturing and causes a reduction of the population for the following year.

Besides adverse weather, natural enemies destroy chinch bugs. The most important is the white fungus, but chinch bugs have another enemy in the tiny wasp, *Eumicrosoma beneficum* Gahan. The female wasp lays her egg in the chinch bug egg. The wasp larva hatches and feeds on the internal contents of the host egg. In certain localities the wasp parasitizes from 30 to 50 per cent of chinch bug eggs.

Control. Cultural practices, erection of barriers against migrating nymphs, and application of insecticides comprise the methods for controlling chinch bugs. There are several cultural practices that are helpful. Growers can minimize chinch bug injury by reducing either the acreage of small grains or the acreage of corn and sorghum, whichever are the least important in their farming operation. This practice limits the size of chinch bug populations by removing essential food from a part of the life cycle.

Growing nongrass crops like legumes, flax, rape, or buckwheat cuts losses, because chinch bugs rarely feed on any plant outside the grass family. If growing nongrass crops does not fit into the agriculture of a region, farmers may elect to plant resistant grains. Oats are more resistant than wheat or rye, and these latter are more resistant than barley. Spring barley is highly susceptible to injury and should not be planted when there is danger of a heavy infestation of chinch bugs.

Some varieties of corn are resistant, such as Hays Golden, a variety adapted to the Southwest. Hybrid corn varieties suffer less injury than their inbred parents, while open-pollinated varieties vary widely in susceptibility and resistance. Among sorghums, most sorgo and Kafir varieties are resistant, while most milo and feterita varieties are susceptible.

Planting legumes among small grains and corn aids in control by producing shade and dampness which chinch bugs avoid. For the same reason, good cultural practices that stimulate dense, vigorous stands reduce injury. In areas where European corn borer is not a problem, early planting of corn gets the plants past the most susceptible stage before the chinch bugs attack. Early planting of sorghum is likewise beneficial, but in some areas this practice may lead to poorer stands and lower yields.

For many years growers in the Midwest erected barriers to prevent migrating nymphs from entering fields of corn. Barriers have been of various sorts such as dusty trenches, creosoted dirt-ridges, and creosoted paper fences to the simplest and currently recommended barrier of dieldrin. To construct the latter barrier, apply dieldrin at ½ lb. per acre as a spray to the ground in strips 4 rods wide between adjoining fields of small grains and of corn. Bugs crossing the strip contact the insecticide and die. To stop nymphs from skirting the ends, apply a strip of dieldrin 2 rods wide and 8 to 10 rods long at right angles to both ends of the main barrier. Dieldrin barriers last from 7 to 14 days and may have to be renewed during heavy migrations or after rain. Construct barriers when small grains begin to mature and dry and before migration starts. In the Southwest barriers are not successful, because bugs reach the flying stage before small grains mature.

Spraying chinch bugs already infesting a crop with 4 oz. of dieldrin or 2 lbs. of toxaphene per acre provides effective but more costly control and imposes feeding restrictions on the stover.

Corn earworm

Heliothis zea (Boddie) [Lepidoptera:Noctuidae]

The corn earworm, a native insect with wide distribution, is the most serious insect pest of sweet corn in North America. It ranges from southern Canada through the rest of North America to as far south as Montevideo, Uruguay. It also inhabits the Hawaiian Islands, apparently having been introduced from North America.

The favored host plant of the corn earworm is sweet corn, but it feeds on and damages field corn and tomatoes too. Further, it is an important pest of cotton, tobacco, various legumes, and vegetables in the South. Depending on the crop it attacks, the corn earworm may be called the cotton bollworm or tomato fruitworm.

The corn earworm damages corn in several ways. Larvae, which hatch from eggs laid on the leaves and stalks of young early corn, migrate to the whorl and feed on the tender, folded leaves. When the damaged leaves unfold they appear ragged. Growers refer to this as ragworm or budworm injury. Usually budworm injury does not reduce yields greatly, but occasionally it may stunt the plant which then produces little grain.

Earworms do their greatest damage when the ears begin to silk. Larvae desert all other parts of the plant to feed on the silks and the moths prefer to lay their eggs on them. The larvae work their way through the mass of silk to the tip of the ear where they feed on the kernels (Fig. 9:11). Occasionally young or partially grown larvae make side entry into the ears. Sweet-corn growers lose heavily because the damaged portion must be

Fig. 9:11. Nearly full-grown earworm devouring silks and soft kernels of corn. Note the dark brown frass. *Courtesy USDA.*

clipped from the ears. Trimming of ears not only takes time but also reduces quality and lowers value of the corn.

In field corn or seed corn, the larvae burrow under the kernels when they begin to harden and feed on the softer germ. Later during husking and handling, the injured kernels drop from the ear.

Corn earworms indirectly damage corn by opening entrances for molds and insect pests such as grain beetles, sap beetles, and weevils. Ears with thick growths of mold are unsafe to use for livestock feed, especially for horses.

In the United States, agriculturalists have estimated corn losses of 75 to 140 million dollars annually due to corn earworms.

Description. Corn earworm eggs have the appearance of tiny, flattened spheres. They are prominently ribbed and approximately 1.2 mm. in diameter. When deposited they are light yellow but they soon darken and at hatching time they are dusky brown. Newly hatched larvae are about 1.5 mm. long, nearly white with shiny black heads and legs. They grow rapidly and become variously colored ranging from pink, green, or yellow to almost black. Many are conspicuously striped. Often down the side there is a pale stripe edged above with a dark one, while down the middle of the back there is a dark stripe divided by a narrow white line. Full-grown larvae are robust and 1½ to 2 in. long. Pupae are about ¾ in. long, first green in color and later brown. Moths are about ¾ in. long with a wingspread of 1½ in. They vary in color from dusty yellow, olive green, or gray to dark reddish brown (Fig. 9:12).

Life history. The corn earworm passes the winter in the pupal stage protected in the soil. In Canada and in the northern part of the United States, pupae are unable to survive the winter. Infestations in these areas arise from moths flying in from southern overwintering grounds. Entomologists have found that pupae do not usually survive north of a line running from central Virginia through St. Louis, Missouri to Topeka, Kansas. On the Pacific Coast, they may survive as far north as southern Washington.

The corn earworm has several generations annually in all but the most northern part of its range. In mild climates like southern Florida, moths remain active the year round and produce as many as seven generations annually. In the Corn Belt there are usually two or three generations a year.

Moths emerge from overwintering pupae in spring at a time when early corn is in the seedling stage. Female moths lay the eggs of the first generation on young corn, vetch, alfalfa, and on other available host plants.

Duration of life stages and of complete life cycles of the several generations varies with prevailing temperatures and available host plants. Incubation of eggs takes from two to eight days. Upon hatching, young larvae feed on the empty egg shells. Soon afterwards they begin feeding on plant tissues. Molting five times, they develop to full-grown larvae in two to four weeks. Those inhabiting corn ears gnaw their way through the husks and drop to the ground where they bore into the soil to depths of 1 to 9 inches and construct cells. In order that the moth may reach the surface easily, they construct a smooth passageway to within ½ inch of the surface. Then they return to their cells where they transform to pupae. In summer the pupal period lasts from two to three weeks. Under favorable conditions a life cycle may be completed in thirty days.

Emerging moths mate and the females, as young as a day old, begin to lay eggs. They deposit eggs singly but usually place many on an individual plant before seeking another host.

The moths are strong fliers and may fly far from the fields in which they developed as larvae. Thus they infest other areas and invade the North. They are most active in the evening and feed heavily on the nectar of flowers. Females live about 12 days and each may deposit from 350 to 3,000 eggs. Fecundity as well as rate of larval growth and size of the insect depend upon what species of plant the larva feeds. Moths reared from larvae fed on corn ears are larger and produce twice as many eggs as

A   B

C   D

Fig. 9:12. Life stages of the corn earworm. A, eggs; B, larvae; C, pupa; D, adult. *A, C, D, courtesy USDA; B, courtesy Kan. Agr. Exp. Sta.*

those reared on any other host. Less favorable host plants include cotton, soybeans, lima beans, alfalfa, and tomato.

Although females may lay many eggs on the silks of a single ear, few larvae survive to full growth in an individual ear because of their canni-balistic habits. Whenever two earworms come together they fight until one or both are fatally injured.

Earworms are present in damaging numbers every year, but in some years populations are unusually heavy and the damage correspondingly greater. Favorable weather and a favorable succession of host plants foster outbreaks of corn earworms. Natural limiting factors include cannibalism of larvae, predators, parasites, and disease. The wasp, *Trichogramma minutum* Riley, parasitizes the egg, while a fly, *Winthemia quadripustulata* (Fabr.), parasitizes the larvae. A bug, *Orius insidiosus* (Say), feeds on corn earworm eggs. At least 21 species of birds feed on the larvae and moles feed on the pupae. Wet weather promotes disease among the larvae and wet soil among the pupae.

Control. The methods growers use to control corn earworms vary depending on whether they grow sweet corn, seed corn, or field corn and on whether they farm in the North or in the South. Application of insecticides is currently practiced only on sweet corn.

For control of earworms in field corn or seed corn, cultural methods are relied on to reduce injury. Damage is lessened if one employs good agronomic practices such as fertilizing, rotating crops, and planting adapted varieties. Corn planted at the usual time for an area sustains less injury than either early or late planted corn. In the South, corn earworms infest both early and late planted corn more heavily. In the North, the European corn borer more seriously attacks the early corn and the corn earworm the late corn.

Planting resistant varieties of corn is an economical way of reducing injury. Plant breeders have found that resistance in corn is associated with tighter husks, harder kernels, less attractiveness for oviposition, and lower food value for larvae. Southern dent corns, evolved in regions where corn earworms are a constant feature of the environment, show the highest type of resistance. Resistant varieties of field corn include Dixie 18, Dixie 11, Georgia 281, Louisiana 521, Texas 30, and Texas 11W.

Variations in susceptibility and resistance are also present among varieties of sweet corn. In stands untreated with insecticides some sweet corn varieties may have as high as 90 per cent marketable ears, while others may have as low as 10 per cent or less. Country Gentlemen and related types are among the more resistant varieties. Plant breeders are working constantly on transferring earworm resistance to new and better varieties.

Growers of sweet corn rely chiefly on insecticides to control earworms. They apply DDT with high-clearance sprayers, dusters, or airplanes. A common spray recommendation for ground application suggests applying 2 lbs. of actual DDT per acre in 20 to 25 gal. of water at pressures of 100 to 200 lbs. p.s.i. Four flat fan nozzles per row are adjusted so that the spray hits the ears.

Some growers add white mineral oil to the spray at a rate of 1¾ gal. per acre. Mineral oils should be applied to corn with caution for several reasons: certain oils cause injury to the ears; mineral oils may cause foliage and ear injury during hot dry weather; and some varieties of corn are highly susceptible to oil injury.

Since other insect pests of sweet corn may need to be controlled, such as sap beetles which are not too well arrested by DDT, a malathion-DDT combination is often applied.

Several applications are necessary for satisfactory control. In the South where the problem is severe, growers may apply as many as seventeen treatments at daily intervals making two of the treatments before silks first appear. They may even make earlier applications when whorls are heavily infested. Growers in the North may get by with as few as two treatments in nonoutbreak years. They make the first treatment about the time that 20 per cent of the silks are out and the second treatment four days later.

Growers may also control corn earworms with insecticidal dusts. Many use high-clearance dusters or airplanes to apply 5 or 10 per cent DDT dust at the rate of 30 to 40 pounds per acre. A slower but more effective method of applying DDT dust is with a puff-type duster or a round stencil brush. In using a puff-type duster, direct the dust onto the silks of each ear. In using a stencil brush insert bristles into the DDT dust, which is conveniently carried along in a pail, then plunge bristles into silk channel.

In areas where control of corn earworms and other insects in the whorl is needed, granular DDT is a convenient and effective formulation to apply. By employing the inexpensive granule applicators on the whorl stage corn, growers of multiple plantings are able to release the high-clearance machines for treatment of maturing fields.

Since treated corn plants carry residues of DDT, federal law restricts feeding of the stover to livestock. The insecticide Sevin at 1.5 to 2 lbs. per acre appears promising for corn earworm control and has fewer limitations in the feeding of treated plants to livestock.

European corn borer

Ostrinia nubilalis (Hübner) [Lepidoptera:Pyraustidae]

The European corn borer, the most destructive pest of corn in America, is an introduced insect having been discovered in 1917 on sweet corn near Boston. The borer is believed to have entered this country about eight years earlier in broom-corn imported from Italy or Hungary. Entomologists quickly recognized the serious threat that this pest presented to the corn industry and attempted to prevent its spread. In spite of stringent foreign and domestic quarantines and the application of other control measures, the borer invaded new areas. It has since extended its range from the

Atlantic to the Rocky Mountain states and from Canada to the southern states.

During its early period of expansion, the European corn borer had but one generation each year. In the thirties a second generation began to appear in some areas and as time passed, the capacity of the insect to produce more than one generation annually became widespread. Now in North America the second generation constitutes an important part of European corn borer populations.

First-generation borers greatly affect yields since they attack corn plants in an early stage of development. The borers begin feeding in the whorl on the leaf surface but later they bore into the stalk where their tunneling destroys food channels. The latter injury is a major cause of reduction in

A   B

Fig. 9:13. European corn borer damage. A, ears attacked directly, nubbins and light chaffy ears; normal ear on right from an uninfested field; B, stalk rot developing around borer tunnels; note borer in left stalk. *Courtesy University of Minnesota.*

yield as it weakens the plant and starves the ears. The tunneling of second-generation borers in older plants does not affect yields greatly but it does mechanically weaken the plants so that much stalk breaking and ear dropping occur. Borings in the shanks lead to chaffy ears and nubbins, while invasions of the cob may make sweet corn unsalable (Fig. 9:13).

A serious secondary effect is the opening of the stalk and ears to both saprophytic and pathogenic fungi and bacteria and their distribution inside the plant. Rots developing in individual plants may cause greater weakening of the stalks and more dropping of ears than do the borers themselves. A survey in Minnesota revealed that 80 to 90 per cent of borer tunnels were infected with rots. Thus, damage often attributed to borers may be due in part to damage caused by stalk- and ear-rotting fungi.

Annual losses due to European corn borer vary with the intensity of infestations. In the United States losses have averaged annually over eighty million dollars to field corn and over three million dollars to sweet corn during the period 1942 to 1951.

The European corn borer infests over 200 kinds of plants. Besides corn, it attacks sorghums, soybeans, millet, buckwheat, oats, barley, potatoes, beans, and many large stemmed flowers and weeds.

Description. Adult females of the European corn borer lay their eggs on the underside of corn leaves usually in clusters of 14 to 20. The eggs overlap one another like fish scales. Individual clusters measure ⅛ to ³⁄₁₆ in. wide and ¼ to ⅜ in. long (Fig. 9:15A and B). The egg is nearly flat and about 1 mm. in diameter. It is white when first laid but later turns yellow, and just before hatching the black head of the larva shows through the shell.

The newly hatched larva, approximately 1.5 mm. long, has a black head and a pale yellow body bearing several rows of brown or black spots. The full-grown larva is about one inch long, gray to light brown or pink, and

Fig. 9:14. Adult moths of the European corn borer. The female, larger and lighter, is near an egg mass. The male is smaller and darker. *Courtesy Illinois Natural History Survey.*

faintly spotted on the dorsal surface (Fig. 9:15C). The underside of the body is cream colored and unmarked.

The pupa is about ½ to ¾ in. long and light to dark reddish brown (Fig. 9:15D). The adult female is a moth with a robust body and a wing spread of about 1¼ in. Its general color varies from a pale yellow to light brown. The male moth is slightly smaller, more slender bodied, and darker than the female (Fig. 9:14).

Life history. The European corn borer passes the winter as a full-grown larva inside its tunnel in stubble, in a stalk, or in an ear of corn, in a weed, or in other protective plant material. In May or June before changing to the pupal stage within the plant, the borer cuts a circular exit hole for the escape of the future moth. It then closes the hole with a thin webbing of silk, returns to the tunnel, and usually spins a flimsy cocoon before it pupates. After the pupal stage, which lasts from 10 to 15 days, the moths appear in late spring and early summer. Within 24 hours after emergence, mating takes place. This usually occurs at dusk, a period when European corn borer moths are most active. During the day they remain hidden under the leaves of corn or in weeds growing in and around the fields. Three days after mating the females begin to lay eggs. In the evening they fly from plant to plant frequently selecting the tallest upon which to lay their eggs. On the under surface of the leaves, they usually deposit eggs in clusters of 14 to 20, but may deposit as few as one or as many as 162. During their lifetime of six to 24 days individual females may lay up to 1900 eggs, though the average is about 400.

The eggs hatch in three to twelve days depending on temperature. The young larvae wander for awhile on the leaf and feed slightly on the surface. Soon they migrate down into the growing whorl where they live as young larvae. The borers have five or six instars and become full grown in about 25 to 35 days.

The part of the plant upon which borers feed is influenced by their age and generation and also by the stage of the corn plant. Hatching when corn is in the whorl stage, first-generation larvae feed in the whorl on the leaf surface. Later, as third and fourth instar larvae, they feed heavily on the sheath, midrib, and around the collar. The fifth and sixth instars bore extensively in the stalk. Larvae of the second generation, hatching when corn plants are at their maximum height, feed on plant tissues near the leaf axil where pollen grains often accumulate or they seek shelter and feed in between the husks and around the silk of the ear. They begin to bore into the stalks at an earlier age than do first-generation larvae and they tunnel extensively in stalk, shanks, and ears. Many larvae that hatch do not survive. The highest survival occurs when eggs hatch at the time corn is in the early green tassel stage to the midsilk stage.

In midsummer as first-generation larvae become full grown, some enter a state of diapause and eventually overwinter, others pupate and emerge

Fig. 9:15. Stages in the life of the European corn borer. A, fresh egg mass; B, egg mass in "black head" stage; C, larva; D, pupa. *A, courtesy Iowa State University; B and C, courtesy USDA; D, courtesy University of Minnesota.*

as moths in August. The latter, the first-generation adults, produce the eggs that hatch into second-generation larvae. The larvae which become full grown before cold weather sets in are able to hibernate and survive through the winter. The development of all stages is influenced by seasonal temperatures and may be either advanced or retarded depending on the earliness or lateness of the growing season.

Recent laboratory studies have indicated that the induction of diapause is controlled mainly by temperature and photoperiod acting upon the last larval instar. At 65°F. and 9½ to 14 hours of light per day, 95 per cent of the larvae entered diapause. Both greater and lesser amounts of light reduced the number entering diapause. Larvae kept at a temperature of 75°F. could not be induced to diapause at any photoperiod.

Biological control. As the European corn borer was introduced from abroad, it had few parasites and predators to contend with in its new home. In 1919 entomologists began searching for its natural enemies in Europe and in the Orient. They imported 24 species and of these 21 were released over the borer infested areas of this country. Four of the parasites have succeeded in reducing infestations. The most abundant and most widely effective is *Lydella stabulans grisescens* R.-D., a fly that looks much like the common house fly. Live maggots, deposited by female flies in vicinity of host larvae, penetrate the bodies of the pests, feed internally, and cause their death. The other three parasites are small wasps which also attack the borer stage. Further aid from biological control may be gained by promising research now in progress on diseases of borers.

Cultural control. Corn growers can reduce the amount of borer injury by employing several cultural methods: (1) selecting resistant or tolerant varieties, (2) correctly timing the planting, and (3) destruction of over-wintering borers by plowing and by sanitation.

(1) Plant breeders have developed inbred lines of field corn with a good degree of resistance to the borer. These are used to produce hybrids with even greater resistance through the cumulative effect of an undetermined number of resistant factors. In hybrids that contain three resistant lines, 50 per cent fewer borers survive than in hybrids made up of three susceptible lines. Certain hybrids tolerate borer infestation, for they produce high yields in spite of being infested. They stand up well and retain their ears permitting efficient mechanical harvesting. As yet few commercial hybrids incorporate high degrees of resistance.

(2) Planting corn at the time that gives best yields for an area keeps the injurious effects of borers at a minimum. Planting early results in a heavier infestation of first-generation borers, which reduce yields; while planting late, results in increased infestations of second-generation borers which cause stalk breakage and ear dropping. Planting late, in itself, may reduce yields and increase moisture content at harvest.

(3) Entomologists have found that plowing under of corn stubble and residues reduces the number of hibernating larvae by as much as 99 per cent. Preferably plowing is done in fall, but may be done in spring before the moths emerge. Borers are able to crawl to the surface but finding no plant fragments for shelter, they succumb to adverse weather and predators. Buried moths cannot make their way to the soil surface.

In actual practice, control of the European corn borer by plowing and sanitation methods has been disappointing. In Ontario where the government enforced cleanup practices, the population of this insect did not differ from that in Michigan just across the Detroit River where these practices were not enforced.

Chemical control. As cultural methods alone do not afford sufficient protection of field corn from heavy infestations of European corn borer, chemical methods have been developed and are now recommended. DDT has been the most widely used insecticide, though other chemicals such as endrin are increasing in usage.

Proper timing of applications is a critical factor in achieving adequate control and differs with the area in which corn is grown. Various procedures have been devised to determine correct timing. For control of first-generation borers, one method consists of determining the number of plants showing feeding injury in the whorl. When 75 out of 100 plants in a field show the characteristic holes in leaves, it is time to apply insecticide. A heavily infested field or a valuable seed crop may require a second treatment seven days later.

When heavy populations of first-generation moths develop and reproduce, a treatment to control second-generation borers may be necessary in order to prevent stalk breaking and ear dropping. The level of infestation requiring treatment is approximately 100 egg masses or more per 100 plants and the suggested time for applying the treatment is when eggs begin to hatch.

Growers treat field corn with insecticidal granules, sprays, or dusts. Against first-generation borers granules are most efficient, because they roll down into the whorl of growing leaves where the young borers congregate. Dust is the least efficient formulation. Commonly applied rates of DDT have been: granules, 1 lb. of active toxicant per acre, sprays 1.5 lb. active per acre, and dusts, 2 lbs. active per acre. Other insecticides that have been recommended are endrin, EPN, and toxaphene.

Insecticidal control of borers attacking sweet corn is essential to obtain marketable ears. The rates and methods of applying DDT are the same as for field corn, but the number of treatments are usually increased. Against borers of either first- or second-generations adequate control may require up to four applications spaced at intervals of five days. It is advisable to begin treating when eggs start to hatch.

Northern corn rootworm *Diabrotica longicornis* (Say)

Western corn rootworm *Diabrotica virgifera* LeConte

Southern corn rootworm *Diabrotica undecimpunctata howardi* Barber

[Coleoptera:Chrysomelidae]

Three species of beetles, whose larval stages are called corn rootworms, are major pests of corn. The economic importance of each species varies in different regions of the United States. The northern corn rootworm is most serious in Corn Belt states, the western corn rootworm in Colorado, Kansas, and Nebraska, and the southern corn rootworm in the South and Midwest. In Canada the southern corn rootworm is widely distributed in eastern provinces while the northern corn rootworm is found mainly in southwestern Ontario.

Rootworms damage corn by feeding on and tunneling inside the roots. The injury reduces the amount of food available to the plant for growth and ear development and consequently lowers yield. Tests have indicated yield reductions of 10 to 30 per cent where corn was picked by hand and weighed.

A   B

Fig. 9:16. Eggs (A) and larva (B) of the northern corn rootworm. *A, courtesy University of Nebraska; B, courtesy Illinois Natural History Survey.*

Rootworms may completely destroy both the main roots and the brace roots touching the soil. Affected plants readily lodge during wind and rain storms and are difficult to harvest. In addition to direct injury, rootworms transmit bacterial wilt or Stewart's disease of corn and make wounds which allow the entry of rot organisms.

The southern corn rootworm not only bores into roots but also enters the stalk just above the roots. Here it eats out the crown of young plants and kills the bud. In the South this species often destroys 25 per cent of the stand when plants are 6 to 18 inches high.

Although the larvae cause most of the injury to corn, the adults feed upon every part of the plant above ground. Most serious is their feeding on newly emerging silks prior to pollination. This injury can result in sparsely filled ears.

Description. The egg of the northern corn rootworm is oval, 0.5 mm. long, pale yellow, and sculptured with hexagonal pits. The larva is a slender, white or pale yellow grub which grows to a length of $\frac{4}{10}$ in. (Fig. 9:16). The pupa is white and fragile. The adult beetle is $\frac{1}{6}$ to $\frac{1}{4}$ in. long and is uniform green to yellowish green in color (Fig. 9:17A).

The egg, larva, and pupa of the western and southern corn rootworm are similar in general appearance to the same stages of the northern corn rootworm. The adults, however, are easily distinguishable as the western species is yellowish green with three dark stripes or a large dark area on the elytra and the southern species is yellowish green with eleven black spots on the elytra (Fig. 9:17B,C,D).

Life history. The northern and the western corn rootworm have similar life histories. There is a single generation annually and the species over-winter in the egg stage. Eggs hatch in May and June and the larvae move about in the soil till they find the roots of corn upon which they feed. Without corn, they usually die of starvation, as few other plants can serve adequately as food.

Rootworms become full grown during July and pupate in cells in the soil. The adult beetles emerge in late July and August. In corn fields they feed principally upon corn pollen and silks, but if they leave corn fields they consume the pollen of many different kinds of plants. The beetles are active insects and fly away rapidly when disturbed. They often congregate

| A | B | C | D |

Fig. 9:17. Adult stage of northern corn rootworm (A), southern corn rootworm (B), and western corn rootworm (C and D). *Courtesy Iowa State University.*

in large numbers in the whorls, in axils of leaves, on tassels, or on ears. After mating the females lay clusters of eggs in the soil at depths of ½ to 2 inches usually among the brace roots of corn plants. The main period of egg laying extends from late July through September.

Control. Growers use both cultural and chemical methods to control rootworms. Cultural practices useful against the northern and the western corn rootworms include crop rotation and application of nitrogen fertilizers. A general rule for rotation is to grow corn for one or two years then to follow with a legume or small grain crop for two years. An exception to the rule is rotating corn with oats, since this practice will allow rootworms to multiply and injure corn.

In the North, rotation is ineffective against the southern corn rootworm because the adults migrate in from the South and lay eggs after the corn is up and because the species has two generations a year.

Applying extra nitrogen helps overcome the injury of rootworms. Whether the beneficial effect results from the remaining roots being able to supply the plants requirement or whether the additional nitrogen stimulates regeneration of roots is still unknown. If corn is under irrigation, timely application of water also helps plants to surmount rootworm injury.

In the South, growers use four cultural practices to control the southern corn rootworm. They plow and disk early, at least thirty days before planting corn, which kills many rootworms and discourages further egg laying. They plant early when rootworms are least active. They plant heavier than normal to ensure a good stand. And finally they carry out recommended agronomic practices to obtain sturdy plants which tolerate injury better.

Applying insecticides, aldrin or heptachlor, to the soil before or at time of planting effectively controls all species of rootworms. Growers have a choice of either broadcasting the insecticide over the field or applying it in the rows. In the broadcast method one applies sprays, dusts, granules, or insecticide-fertilizer mixtures uniformly over the field before planting and immediately disks the material into the top 3 or 4 inches of soil. Delaying the disking operation only four hours reduces control by 50 per cent. Rates of actual toxicant recommended for this method have been 1 lb. of aldrin or heptachlor per acre.

A recent advance in broadcast treatment is airplane application of the insecticide in winter. At this time of year the treatment does not require immediate disking of the soil.

An additional method of applying insecticides broadcast and one becoming quite popular is to dispense them in fertilizer solutions. For this method, specially formulated emulsifiable concentrates are added to liquid fertilizers. The broadcast method is effective in protecting surface planted corn but less effective in protecting listed corn.

In row treatment one applies, when seeding, a narrow band of spray or granules. The insecticide flows through tubes and emerges behind the planter shoes and in front of the covering disks or press wheels. The insecticide thus comes to lie in the soil near the seed. Rates of actual toxicant found to be effective are ½ lb. of aldrin or heptachlor per acre.

By employing a starter-fertilizer attachment at planting time, one may also row-treat with insecticide-fertilizer mixtures. The same insecticides and rates of actual toxicant as in row treatments above are effective.

Recommended rates of broadcast and row applications failed to control numerous heavy populations of the western corn rootworm in Nebraska in 1960. Although the causes of failure have not been definitely determined, entomologists have suggested doubling recommended rates in the problem areas until more is known.

For successful control of complexes of soil insects that may attack corn, growers should increase application rates of aldrin or heptachlor to 1 lb. in the row and 1½ to 3 lbs. broadcast.

Selected References

Anon., *Chinch Bugs: How to Control Them*, USDA Leaflet 364, 1958.

Anon., *The Corn Earworm in Sweet Corn: How to Control It*, USDA Leaflet 411, 1957.

Anon., *The European Corn Borer and Its Control*, USDA Farmers' Bul. 2084, 1955.

Anon., *The Southern Corn Rootworm: How to Control It*, USDA Leaflet 391, 1961.

Anon., *The Southern Cornstalk Borer*, USDA Leaflet 363, 1954.

Bigger, J. H., and R. A. Blanchard, *Insecticidal Control of Underground Insects of Corn. A Report of a Five-Year Study*, Ill. Agr. Exp. Sta. Bul. 641, 1959.

Blanchard, R. A., *Hibernation of the Corn Earworm in the Central and Northeastern Parts of the United States*, USDA Tech. Bul. 838, 1942.

———, and W. A. Douglas, *The Corn Earworm as an Enemy of Field Corn in the Eastern States*, USDA Farmers' Bul. 1651, 1953.

Davis, John J., *The Corn Root Aphid and Methods of Controlling It*, USDA Farmers' Bul. 891, 1949.

Dicke, F. F., and M. T. Jenkins, *Susceptibility of Certain Strains of Field Corn in Hybrid Combinations to Damage by Corn Earworms*, USDA Tech. Bul. 898, 1945.

Douglas, W. A., and R. C. Eckhardt, *Dent Corn Inbreds and Hybrids Resistant to the Corn Earworm in the South*, USDA Tech. Bul. 1160, 1957.

Eden, W. G., and H. Yates, *Corn Earworm Control*, Ala. Agr. Exp. Sta. Bul. 326, 1960.

Everett, T. R., H. C. Chiang, and E. T. Hibbs, *Some Factors Influencing Populations of European Corn Borer Pyrausta nubilalis (Hbn.) in the North Central States*, Minn. Agr. Exp. Sta. Tech. Bul. 229, 1958.

Gunderson, H., and J. H. Lilly, *Control Corn Rootworms*, Iowa Agr. Exp. Sta. Ser. Pamphlet 178, 1953.

Hansen, H. L., and C. K. Dorsey, *Southern Corn Rootworm Control in West Virginia*, W. Va. Agr. Sta. Cir. 102, 1957.

Huber, L. L., C. R. Neiswander, and R. M. Salter, *The European Corn Borer and Its Environment*, Ohio Agr. Exp. Sta. Bul. 429, 1928.

Kelsheimer, E. G., N. C. Hayslip, and J. W. Wilson, *Control of Budworms, Earworms and Other Insects Attacking Sweet Corn and Green Corn in Florida*, Fla. Agr. Exp. Sta. Bul. 466, 1950.

Kirk, V. M., *Corn Insects in South Carolina*, So. Car. Agr. Exp. Sta. Bul. 478, 1960.

Lunginbill, Philip, *Habits and Control of the Fall Armyworm*, USDA Bul. 1990, 1950.

Lunginbill, Philip, Sr., and T. R. Chamberlin, *Control of Common White Grubs in Cereal and Forage Crops*, USDA Farmers' Bul. 1798, 1953.

Miller, L. A., and A. G. Dustan, *Control of the Seed-Corn Maggot*, Can. Dept. Agr. Publ. 912, 1954.

Packard, C. M., P. Lunginbill, Sr., and C. Benton, *How to Fight the Chinch Bug*, USDA Farmers' Bul. 1780, 1951.

Patch, L. H., J. R. Holbert, and R. T. Everly, *Strains of Field Corn Resistant to the Survival of the European Corn Borer*, USDA Tech. Bul. 823, 1942.

Robert, Alice L., *Bacterial Wilt and Stewarts Leaf Blight of Corn*, USDA Farmers' Bul. 2092, 1955.

Rolston, L. H., *The Southwestern Corn Borer in Arkansas*, Ark. Agr. Exp. Sta. Bul. 553, 1955.

——, C. R. Neiswander, K. D. Arbuthnot, and G. T. York, *Parasites of the European Corn Borer in Ohio*, Ohio Agr. Exp. Sta. Res. Bul. 819, 1958.

Satterthwait, A. F., *How to Control Billbugs Destructive to Cereal and Forage Crops*, USDA Farmers' Bul. 1003, 1932.

Stirrett, G. M., "A Field Study of the Flight, Oviposition, and Establishment Periods in the Life Cycle of the European Corn Borer, *Pyrausta nubilalis* Hbn., and Physical Factors Affecting Them," *Sci. Agr.*, 18(7–12): 355, 462, 536, 568, and 656 (1938).

Wilbur, D. A., H. R. Bryson, and R. H. Painter, *Southwestern Corn Borer in Kansas*, Kan. Agri. Exp. Sta. Bul. 339, 1950.

Wressell, H. B., *Insects Attacking Corn in Eastern Canada*, Canada Dept. of Agr. Publ. 945, 1955.

Chapter 10 | INSECTS OF

LEGUMES | *B. Austin Haws*

Cultivated leguminous plants may be grouped for convenience into three categories: (1) forage and pasture plants such as alfalfa, clovers, and vetches; (2) food plants such as peas, beans, and peanuts; and (3) miscellaneous plants that yield medicines, dyes, oil, insecticides, and timber. In this chapter we shall be concerned mainly with the insect pests of forage and pasture legumes. Pests of the second group will be discussed in the chapter on vegetable insects.

Hundreds of different insect species live in a legume crop such as alfalfa. Some entomologists have classified more than 500 different insect species from individual alfalfa fields, and undoubtedly there are other insects in alfalfa yet to be found and identified. Fortunately, the majority are not injurious species. Many insects found on legumes are just "visitors" such as certain flies. These insects may be "neutral" in their relationship with the plants. They may just rest on the plants or they may feed on nectar, pollen, or other substances associated with the crop.

The pests

There are two main types of insect pest problems on forage legumes. One problem concerns insects affecting the production of forage and hay, the other those influencing production of seed. Many of the insects, however, are pests of both hay and seed crops.

Because of the large number of insects associated with legumes, we shall discuss only a few representative pests, their injury, and control. Some of these are pests of nearly all kinds of legumes, while others may restrict their feeding and damage to one particular kind.

Among the important insect pests of forage legumes are the **alfalfa weevil, lygus bugs, clover seed chalcid,** and **meadow spittlebug.** These four insects will be discussed in detail later in this chapter. Some of the other major injurious species belong to the following six groups: plant bugs, leaf-hoppers, aphids, grasshoppers, weevils and other beetles, and various lepidopterous larvae.

One of the most abundant insect groups to be found in many legume crops are those insects belonging to the family Miridae, commonly called plant bugs, such as, the **tarnished plant bug, alfalfa plant bug,** and **rapid plant bug.** Insects in this family commonly feed on many plant hosts and are likely to be found on all the major forage legumes (Fig. 10:16). They are universally destructive pests of both hay and seed crops.

Leafhoppers (Fig. 10:1) represent a group of pests that frequently are overlooked in legume fields but are often present in tremendous numbers. In the eastern United States, west to Colorado and Wyoming, the **potato leafhopper** inflicts a unique injury upon its hosts—alfalfa and various clovers. It feeds upon the vascular tissues of the plants, which results in a spotting or stippling and eventually in a pink or reddish discoloration beginning at the rib of the leaves. In severe attacks, the foliage may wilt and exhibit a condition commonly known as **yellows.** These small wedge-shaped, pale green insects do not appear to hibernate or overwinter in the north but breed continuously throughout the winter in the Gulf States and migrate northward early in spring.

The **clover leafhopper** is commonly found on clovers and sometimes on alfalfa. There are many other species of leafhoppers, and they are well known for the plant pathogens they transmit as well as for their toxic effects on plants.

Aphids are one of the most common pests of clovers and alfalfa in the United States. The **pea aphid** is often found in tremendous numbers and can be present in large numbers without apparent injury to the plants (Fig. 10:2). Heavy infestations, however, cause the plants to wilt, become stunted, and discolored. Severe infestations have been known to destroy new seedings and even old stands of alfalfa.

The **spotted alfalfa aphid** was first introduced into United States in 1954 in New Mexico. Its spread through at least 31 states and into Mexico has been phenomenal. This aphid is smaller than the pea aphid, is yellowish-green with four to six rows of small black spots and little spines on its back, and has spotted wings. It has been most abundant on alfalfa, but it also infests bur clover, sweetclover, sour clover, and berseem. Fortunately, cul-tural practices—such as early planting of seed, mowing or pasturing alfalfa, and maintaining vigorous alfalfa stands—have been useful in reducing its depredation. Several resistant alfalfas including Moapa and Lahontan have

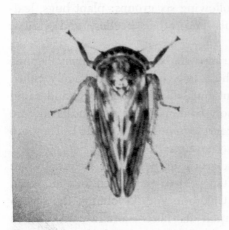

Fig. 10:1. A leafhopper, an insect found abundantly in legume forage crops. Species shown here is *Aceratagallia arida* Oman.

Fig. 10:2. The pea aphid, *Macrosiphum pisi* (Harr.), a common insect in fields of alfalfa and other legumes. Note female on left giving birth to young aphid.

been developed. Natural enemies such as lady beetles, collops adults, lacewing fly larvae, syrphid fly larvae, hemipterous insects, and predaceous mites have been of some value in reducing spotted alfalfa aphid populations. Several species of parasites and predators have been introduced with varying degrees of success, and a few diseases have been reported to kill large percentages of the aphid population in certain areas.

The **clover aphid** is a common pest of red clover and alsike clover and is responsible for serious reductions in growth; its excretions of honeydew cause the seeds to stick together in clumps.

Grasshoppers probably do more damage to alfalfa than any other insect. They are present in all parts of the country and are represented by many different species. Four of the major species of grasshoppers which damage alfalfa are the **differential grasshopper, migratory grasshopper, red-legged grasshopper,** and **two-striped grasshopper.**

A large number of weevils are important pests of legumes. One of the larger weevils commonly reported from many areas of the country is the **clover leaf weevil,** *Hypera punctata* (F.), which has been present for many years in United States, but is a native of Europe. These brown snout beetles, which are about ¼ in. long, have distinct stripes on their wings. Usually there is one generation a year, but a second generation develops under some circumstances. Both the larvae and the adults feed on the foliage of clovers and alfalfa.

Three of the important insects that injure the roots of legume crops are: clover root curculio, *Sitona hispidula* (F.); clover root borer, *Hylastinus obscurus* (Marsh.); and the alfalfa snout beetle, *Brachyrhinus ligustici* (L.). Adults of the **clover root curculio** feed on leaf edges but are of relatively minor importance. The larvae, however, feed on tender roots and chew large cavities in the main roots of the plant. This weevil is an important pest of red, sweet, and alsike clovers and of alfalfa in many areas of United States and southern Canada.

Clover root borer is recognized as a major pest of red clover. Most of the life cycle of the clover root borer is spent in the roots of red clover (Fig. 10:3). The adults are cylindrical, black or dark brown beetles about $\frac{1}{10}$ in. long. This insect is distributed in the northern part of United States and eastern Canada.

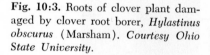

Fig. 10:3. Roots of clover plant damaged by clover root borer, *Hylastinus obscurus* (Marsham). *Courtesy Ohio State University.*

The **alfalfa snout beetle,** which injures roots of alfalfa and red clover, has a two-year cycle and spends most of its larval stage in the soil.

The **sweetclover weevil,** *Sitona cylindricollis* (Fahr.), is a gray or brownish weevil, about $\frac{1}{4}$ in. long with a short snout. It is one of the major pests of sweetclover in many areas of United States and Canada. Details of this

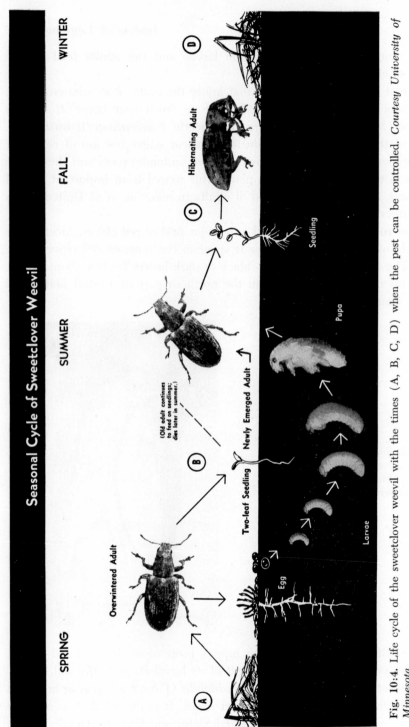

Fig. 10:4. Life cycle of the sweetclover weevil with the times (A, B, C, D) when the pest can be controlled. *Courtesy University of Minnesota.*

insect's life history are illustrated in Fig. 10:4. Larval feeding on the roots is reported to have a negligible effect on the plants, but the adults often completely destroy new seedlings and may defoliate larger plants.

One of the common weevils found on red clover and on other species of clovers and alfalfa is the **lesser clover leaf weevil,** *Hypera nigrirostris* (F.). These beetles are about ⅛ in. long, and the younger beetles are various shades of green with light stripes on the wings. Adults feed mostly on leaves, but the larvae feed on the stems, buds, and florets. Larval feeding deforms the clover heads.

The **clover seed weevil,** *Miccotrogus picirostris* (F.), is frequently a pest of alsike clover. The adult is a small gray snout beetle about ¹⁄₁₆ in. long. Damage by this weevil is mostly by the larvae developing inside the seed pods. Adults may also injure the plant stem by their feeding.

The **clover head weevil,** *Hypera meles* (Fabr.), lives in the heads of clovers and has been reported damaging alfalfa. This species appears to be spreading from the East into previously uninfested areas of western United States. The adults of this weevil and of the alfalfa weevil look much alike.

The **vetch bruchid,** *Bruchus brachialis* (Fahr.), is a pest known mostly in the Atlantic and seaboard states, New Jersey south to Georgia. It is important only in seed production. The larvae are found in seed pods and feed on the developing seed.

Several species of adult **blister beetles** feed on florets or other plant parts and are considered periodic pests of forage legumes. The adults may be black, gray with black spots, or colored with black and yellow stripes, and are usually about ½ to ¾ in. long.

Among the important lepidopterous pests of legumes, the **alfalfa caterpillar** is the worst insect pest of hay in some states. Periodically several species of armyworms—the **fall armyworm, western yellow-striped armyworm** (Fig. 10:5), and **beet armyworm**—infest legumes. Cutworms and armyworms often feed at night and hide under the surface litter or in the soil during the daytime. Because of this behavior, fields may be severely injured before these pests are discovered. The **army cutworm** is a serious pest early in the spring and may keep alfalfa from growing for a month or longer.

Occasionally, webworms—the **garden webworm,** and the **alfalfa webworm**—plague clover or alfalfa. These are yellowish green caterpillars with conspicuous black spots and about 1 in. long when full grown. Large numbers may completely defoliate a crop and leave considerable webbing on the plants. A **leafroller,** *Sparganothis xanthoides* Walker, damages birds-

Fig. 10:5. The western yellow-striped armyworm, a general feeder that is sometimes a pest of alfalfa and other legumes. *Courtesy William P. Nye, USDA.*

foot trefoil and prevents pollination and seed setting by webbing the terminal floral parts.

White, red, mammoth, and alsike clovers are sometimes attacked by the **clover head caterpillar.** These small hairy caterpillars, about ¼ in. long, feed on the developing seeds or at the base of the florets. The larvae may attack the leaves of plants when heads are not present.

An important dipterous pest is the **clover seed midge** which is widely distributed in England, Europe, New Zealand, and North America. The larvae, which are approximately ⅟₁₆ in. long and colored deep red or orange, destroy the ovaries of developing seeds in red clover. Infested heads can be recognized by the uneven bloom.

Other pests of legumes include thrips, stink bugs, harvester ants, and spider mites.

The injury

Insects injure legumes by feeding on or in seeds, seedlings, leaves, roots, and stems, and by ovipositing in plants, by secreting honeydew or spittle, and by causing or transmitting plant diseases.

Seed injury. Insects, such as the clover seed chalcid, may attack legume seeds as they develop in the field (Fig. 10:17). Female chalcids insert their ovipositor through the pods and deposit eggs in the soft, developing seeds.

The resulting larvae destroy the seeds by feeding on the internal contents.

Insects with chewing mouthparts may devour seeds and pods. For example, various lepidopterous larvae—such as the western yellow-striped armyworm (Fig. 10:5), weevil adults, grasshoppers, field crickets, or blister beetles—may climb up legume plants and eat the florets (Fig. 10:6) or newly developing seed pods. After the seed is planted in the soil, wireworms and other soil pests may feed on and destroy the seed.

Lygus bugs, plant bugs, stink bugs, and similar insects with piercing-sucking mouthparts, feed on developing seeds and leave them shriveled and nonviable.

Fig. 10:6. Blossom of sweetclover attacked by sweetclover weevil. Blossom at left has been chewed by adult weevil as contrasted with normal blossom (right). *Courtesy University of Minnesota.*

The clover seed midge is a fly that lays eggs in young clover heads and whose larvae may destroy the developing seed. Clover head weevils and clover seed weevils also attack florets and seeds of clovers.

Some of the tortricid larvae (Lepidoptera) tie leaves, flowers, or stems of legumes together and feed or pupate in the "bundle" they have made (Fig. 10:7). These webbed bunches of flowers appear to interfere with pollination and seed development.

Seedling injury. New seedlings are often attacked by insects as soon as the tiny plants emerge from the soil. Various kinds of chewing insects such as grasshoppers, flea beetles, or weevils may consume the small plants when they are only an inch or so tall (Fig. 10:8), or insects such as aphids with piercing-sucking mouthparts (Fig. 10:2) may kill or debilitate new seedlings by injections of toxins or agents of disease or by removal of plant fluids.

Leaf injury. Insects may injure plant leaves various ways. Some weevils, grasshoppers, crickets, or various beetles chew notches (Fig. 10:10), or they may consume entire leaves. Some weevil larvae, such as alfalfa weevil, do not chew sections out of the leaves, but they eat the surface cells and skeletonize the leaves. Leaf miners, which are larvae of small flies, bore between the bottom and top layers of leaf surfaces and leave winding trails in the leaf. Feeding by mites mottles the leaves (Fig. 10:9) and eventually turns them brown and dry. Leafhopper feeding may also discolor leaves.

Some insects, such as the spotted alfalfa aphid, excrete large amounts of honeydew which covers the leaves and makes hay difficult to harvest. Plants stick together, and the honeydew may cause machines to slow down or break because of gumming up of parts. A secondary problem of the aphids' excretion is the growth of a fungus in the honeydew which may cover the alfalfa. The fungus degrades or ruins the hay.

Root injury. Insects, such as the clover root borer, may bore holes in legume roots or feed on nitrogen nodules attached to the roots (Fig. 10:3). This injury may kill or damage plants directly, or may weaken the plants by permitting secondary infections of plant diseases. Some aphids attack the roots of legumes.

Stem injury. Injury to plant stems may include consumption of stems by chewing insects, or a change in the structure, appearance, growth, and development due to toxins or agents of disease left when insects with piercing-sucking mouthparts feed on the plants, such as results from lygus injury.

Plant breeders should be aware of changes in plant growth due to insect feeding so as not to draw wrong conclusions about plant characteristics being compared in studies of plant varieties.

Oviposition of insect eggs and development of immature insects inside

Fig. 10:7. Tortricid moth larva tying alfalfa blossoms and leaves into bunches. *Courtesy William P. Nye, USDA.*

the stems is also a source of insect injury to plants (Figs. 10:15A and 10:18A). A few larvae and adults, such as the stem borers, tunnel in the stems of clovers and alfalfa.

Beneficial insects on legumes

Pollinating insects must cross-pollinate legume crops if profitable seed yields are to be realized (Figs. 10:11 and 10:12). In the cross-pollinating of crops such as alfalfa and red clover, various bees take the pollen from the flowers of one plant and transfer it to the flowers of another plant. Wind or rain or artificial pollinating devices are not effective agents of cross-pollination in these plants.

In addition to the pollinating insects, other beneficial species in legume fields are the predators and parasites of pest species. Both groups should be protected when you plan chemical control programs. Insecticides applied to legume crops often kill beneficial as well as harmful insects. Large quantities of powerful insecticides have been sometimes applied to legume fields before the insects present were identified. Occasionally some of the most plentiful species killed were beneficial insects that were not injuring the crops but feeding on injurious pests in the field.

Seed producers in certain parts of the country have organized supervised pest control programs and hired professional entomologists to keep a constant lookout for beneficial and injurious insects in the growers' fields. The entomologist watches the development of both the injurious and beneficial insects. When chemical control is necessary, he sees that selective insecticides are applied at the proper times to destroy the pests but give protection to the beneficial insects. This practice of integrating chemical control with protection of beneficial insects seems likely to be more generally adopted.

Cultural control

Manipulation of crops or insect environment to kill insects directly or indirectly or to create unfavorable conditions for insect reproduction is an important and often the most economical way of combating legume pests. Cultural methods are cheapest because a pest may be controlled by using ordinary farm machinery and by simply adjusting the timing of the farm work that has to be done anyhow—for example, planting, irrigating, harvesting, cleaning plant residues from fields, plowing, or cultivating the land.

Crop management for control of insect pests of legumes includes selection of varieties known to grow vigorously in one's particular area and, if possible, insect resistant varieties. Sometimes seed can be planted so that the crop emerges when the injurious pests are absent, dormant, or fewest in numbers, or at a time of year when the insect pest is confined to a particular host. Lygus and some other plant bugs may be partially controlled by cutting hay crops when eggs deposited in the stems of the plants will be destroyed or young nymphs in the crops will be exposed to high temperatures and drought.

Crops may be substituted to avoid damage from a particular pest; for example, in areas where sweetclover weevil destroys sweetclover other legumes may be planted. In areas where the clover root borers have become abundant, grain crops or other plants not attacked by the weevils might be rotated with the legumes. Management of the crop by regulation of the pounds of seed sown per acre has been shown to influence differences in insect populations by producing sparse or dense stands which are favorable or unfavorable environments for different insects. There are some indications that improper use of fertilizers and irrigation water have created environments favorable for certain destructive pests and unfavorable for beneficial insects.

Fig. 10:8. Legume seedling in two-leaf stage injured by chewing insect, right; normal seedling, left. *Courtesy University of Minnesota.*

Usual farm operations that can be employed to control insects include plowing or cultivating legume crops at a particular time to remove top or root growth and thus eliminate the food supply of the insect or to bury adult or immature insects or plant materials in which insects are developing. The practice of cultivating seed fields by disking or harrowing is reported to benefit alfalfa seed production. Such a practice may destroy aphids, nymphs, or larvae that might easily be killed by the exposure to heat or dust. Plowing under chaff or plant residues that remain after crops have been harvested for seed will kill many seed chalcids that would ordinarily survive to reinfest future crops. The common practice of summer fallowing removes the source of food for many soil pests, and the cultivation of such fallow to control weeds often dries the upper portions of the soil and kills

Fig. 10:9. Spider mite damage to alfalfa. Note the yellow spotting of the leaves. *Courtesy William P. Nye, USDA.*

Fig. 10:10. Typical notches in leaves made by sweetclover weevil. *Courtesy University of Minnesota.*

many insects. Ordinary practices of removing volunteer plants and weeds from fence rows or waste areas surrounding farm land often helps control insects that overwinter there. For example, populations of leafhoppers and some stink bugs frequently increase on weeds in waste land before the major crops are invaded by these insects.

Natural and biological control

The actions of parasites, predators, or pathogens are major factors in the regulation of legume pest populations. Some entomologists have speculated that these natural agents of control keep the plant-feeding insects from overwhelming the rest of the world. Attempts to introduce natural enemies of insect pests to help control them have been successful in several instances. The alfalfa weevil is sometimes held to subeconomic levels by an introduced parasite, *Bathyplectes curculionis* (Thoms.), which lays its eggs in the alfalfa weevil larva and eventually kills it.

Under certain environmental conditions insect populations may be greatly reduced by diseases. It is now possible to purchase some of these disease agents for control of certain pests, especially lepidopterous larvae.

Studies of the interrelationships between beneficial and injurious insects in alfalfa have suggested that biological control has many advantages. In contrast to certain chemical control practices, which only temporarily suppress insect populations, biological control programs provide a more enduring regulation of the population density.

There is evidence that as a consequence of some chemical control programs on legume crops, we are now faced with problems of resistant insects, outbreaks of insects other than those against which the original control program was directed, flarebacks of the primary pests to levels even more

Fig. 10:11. Honey bee tripping alfalfa blossom. *Courtesy William P. Nye, USDA.*

detrimental than their original populations, and residues on the crops that were treated. Some of these problems appear to be associated with the use of nonselective chemicals.

It is becoming increasingly clear that chemical control on legume crops needs to be viewed as complementary to natural and biological control. For example, it has been shown that Systox can be used for effective control of the spotted alfalfa aphid but that this insecticide is relatively nontoxic to many native predators of the aphid such as lady beetles, nabids, syrphids, and others.

Some entomologists suggest that when there is sufficient knowledge of the pest's parasites, predators, and diseases and of the selective action of insecticides, more permanent results from natural and biological control can be expected without the detrimental side effects of chemical control. Unfortunately there is not yet enough known about the pests of many crops to formulate completely satisfactory integrated control programs. There is an urgent need for more information and for an awareness by growers of the presence and importance of beneficial insects and the advantages of avoiding their mass destruction.

Chemical control

There are several suggestions that can help one solve insect problems on legume crops. First, learn which insect pests are injuring the crop. There are so many kinds of insects in clovers and alfalfa that the mere presence of insects does not necessarily mean an insecticide is needed.

A standard device for helping one decide what kinds and how many insects are in a legume crop is an insect net with a 15-inch diameter hoop and a 26-inch handle (Fig. 10:13). It is becoming common practice for growers to own an insect net and use it regularly to sample the insects in their crops. Many growers prepare a reference insect collection of their own to help identify the major pests and beneficial insects, or get assistance from entomologists in their area in identifying the insects. County agricultural agents or entomologists representing the state experiment stations, state departments of agriculture, or commercial insecticide companies are usually available for consultation.

Once an insect is correctly identified, it is easy to get the information that is available about the insect and recommended procedures for its control. For example, Fig. 10:4 shows in part the kind of information you might expect to find in literature about insect pests—a description, their life history, their seasonal cycle as related to crop development, injury to plants,

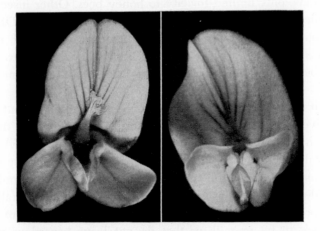

Fig. 10:12. Tripped alfalfa blossom (left)and untripped alfalfa blossom (right). *Courtesy William P. Nye, USDA.*

and results of insecticide tests. Find out if possible how many insects are necessary to cause economic losses to the crop and to merit expenditure of money for control.

In applying insecticides to legumes, consider not only the effect upon the pests to be controlled but also the effect upon the beneficial species. It is possible by selecting insecticides and by applying these at certain times or certain periods of plant growth to decimate the pests and yet cause little harm to beneficial species. In this way the grower receives benefit from both chemical control and natural or biological control. This sort of a program has been given the designation "integrated control."

Apply only the kinds and amounts of insecticides needed to take care of specific insect problems. Avoid the indiscriminate application of insecticides to legumes on a routine basis. Such use of insecticides is usually uneconomical and may even increase insect problems.

On seed crops the application of only those chemicals proved to be least toxic to insect pollinators and at times when the pollinators are not in the field cannot be overemphasized. Pollination of legumes by insects is essential for profitable production of seed. The relative toxicity of most of the better known insecticides to insect pollinators, particularly honey bees, has been studied. These tests indicate that dieldrin, aldrin, chlordane, heptachlor, and lindane tend to have a hazardous residual toxicity to bees, but that some of the organic phosphates—including TEPP, Trithion, Dibrom, Phostex, phosphamidon, Delnav, and Phosdrin—can be applied with relative safety to crops in bloom when the bees are not in the fields. Certain systemic insecticides—such as Thimet, demeton (Systox), and schradan—have only limited toxicity to honey bees. Other insecticides that can be applied safely while bees are not foraging are DDT, TDE, methoxychlor, Perthane, toxaphene, Thiodan, and endrin. A few of the organic phosphates, such as schradan and ethion, showed such low toxicity to bees that it has been suggested they can be applied safely to legume crops anytime.

Control of insects on hay crops is an acute problem at present because of many unsolved insecticide residue problems. The majority of the so-called chlorinated hydrocarbon insecticides have the disadvantage of being stored in the animal fat and of being excreted in milk. Most of these chlorinated hydrocarbons have a zero tolerance on hay crops. About the only selection of insecticides available for use in controlling insects on alfalfa hay are methoxychlor and some of the phosphate insecticides which are known not to accumulate in fat or milk or that do not leave hazardous residues on the plants.

A variety of insecticides have received clearance for use on legume seed crops. Because of the importance of pollinating insects, different insecticides are recommended for seed crops prior to bloom and during the blooming period. Insecticides being recommended for the prebloom period on seed crop include: dieldrin for control of alfalfa weevil adults and larvae, lygus bugs, leafhoppers, and thrips; malathion for alfalfa weevil larvae, pea

Fig. 10:13. Sweeping alfalfa with an insect net to estimate relative numbers of pests infesting the crop.

aphids, and grasshoppers; toxaphene for lygus bugs, leafhoppers, thrips, and yellow-striped armyworm; parathion for pea aphid, spotted alfalfa aphid, and tortricid moths; demeton for pea aphids; and Di-Syston as a seed treatment for spotted alfalfa aphids. Phorate (Thimet) is also recommended as a seed treatment for controlling spotted alfalfa aphid. Aldrin and chlordane are recommended for control of Mormon crickets.

Included in the insecticides that may be applied during the blooming period are: DDT, toxaphene, TEPP, sulfur, Systox, Dylox, and Aramite. These should be applied when bees are not in the field. During the blooming period toxaphene is recommended for control of lygus bugs, armyworms, grasshoppers, stink bugs, webworms; Systox for spotted alfalfa aphids; Dylox for leafrollers, armyworms, webworms, and stink bugs; and DDT for alfalfa weevil, lygus bugs, leafhoppers, thrips, pea aphids, and western yellow-striped armyworm.

Parathion, Systox, and Phosdrin are considered particularly hazardous for the applicator. Special permits are required before they can be applied in some states. Straw of seed crops treated with insecticides (excepting insecticides registered for use on hay crops) should not be fed to livestock.

Control equipment

Low-pressure boom sprayers are commonly used in applying insecticides on legumes (Fig. 10:14). These sprayers are especially effective for control of adult alfalfa weevil in stubble or in fields where there is short vegetative growth and the growth has not become too dense. It is sometimes difficult to get a thorough coverage of vegetation and to cover the undersides of the leaves with low-pressure, boom-type sprayers. Fan-type nozzles spaced to give thorough ground coverage are often used on booms 20 to 40 feet long. In general, application of 15 to 30 gal. of liquid per acre has proved more satisfactory on lush legume crops than lesser amounts.

In certain areas dusters are preferred for applying insecticides to legume crops. Dusts often penetrate dense foliage more effectively than sprays and may give more complete coverage on the undersides of the leaves. Dusters sometimes cost less than spray rigs, do not require water supply, and carry less weight than sprayers. Generally, there is less possibility of phytotoxicity from dusts than from sprays.

Sprays often give better pest control than dusts and require less insecticide for equal effectiveness. Sprays generally do not wash off the plants as rapidly as dusts, can often be applied more evenly, and are less hazardous to man, animals, other crops, or pollinators than dusts. Experience has

Fig. 10:14. A low pressure sprayer with boom commonly used to apply insecticides to forage legumes. *Courtesy William P. Nye, USDA.*

shown that sprays do a better, cheaper job that dusts, but often the decision as to which equipment to use must be based on local conditions and individual situations. One of the disadvantages of ground equipment is the wheel tracks made by the equipment in crops that have been broadcast or drilled.

Aircraft are available for applying sprays, dusts, granulated insecticides, or treated seeds. In open areas where the land has a flat or rolling contour, insecticides are easily applied by plane. Use of a plane makes it unnecessary to remodel ditches, make roads, or endure the washboardy rides through irrigated fields.

Effective control of certain legume pests—such as meadow spittlebug, spotted alfalfa aphid, and the clover root borer—have been obtained by application of granulated insecticides. Special ground equipment is available for applying these materials in rows or broadcast over the ground, or they can be applied by aircraft. Granulated insecticides are sometimes applied as a mixture with fertilizers by use of fertilizer spreaders or mixed with seed and applied with seed drills. Granular insecticides have advantages for control of certain insects because they fall through dense foliage and come to lie on the ground where many forage crop pests spend considerable time.

REPRESENTATIVE LEGUME PESTS

In this section we shall discuss four important legume pests: alfalfa weevil, lygus bug, clover seed chalcid, and meadow spittlebug.

Alfalfa weevil

Hypera postica (Gyllenhal) [Coleoptera:Curculionidae]

Alfalfa weevils were probably imported from southern Europe sometime in 1900. They were reported first in Utah in 1904 and gradually infested the other western states (Oregon, Washington, California, Montana, Idaho, Nevada, Arizona, Wyoming, Colorado, New Mexico) and the western parts of North Dakota, South Dakota, and Nebraska. The weevil appears to have jumped, somehow, across the midwestern, central, and southern states to the East Coast. Alfalfa weevils were collected in Maryland in 1951, and they have spread rapidly through some of the eastern states (Massachusetts, Rhode Island, Connecticut, New York, New Jersey, Delaware, Pennsylvania, Virginia, West Virginia, North and South Carolina, and Georgia).

The larvae are responsible for the major damage attributable to the alfalfa weevil. They mainly injure the first crop, but may also injure the second crop (Fig. 10:15E). Young larvae feed in the stems for awhile, then move to the leaf buds at the tops of the plants. They chew cavities in the young alfalfa buds and later feed on the leaves. Their feeding skeletonizes the leaves so that an infested alfalfa field may appear to be frosted, grayish, or whitish in appearance. The injury to buds and leaves stunts plant growth, reduces yields and quality of hay, and may make fields unfit for seed production.

Studies have shown that when there is an average of 0.5 overwintering weevil per square foot in an alfalfa field, very little damage may be expected the following year. When there is an average of 0.5 to 1.5 per square foot there may be some damage, but when the average is 1.5 to 2.5, damage may certainly be expected if the weather is favorable.

Alfalfa is usually the only crop severely injured by the alfalfa weevil, but vetch, alsike, birdsfoot trefoil, red clover, bur clover, crimson clover, white clover, yellow and white sweetclover, cabbage, potato, and raspberry are also fed upon.

Description. Adult weevils are about $\frac{3}{16}$ in. long and vary in color during their life (Fig. 10:15D). They are light brown with a broad, dark brown stripe extending from the front of the head posteriorly along the middle of the back approximately two-thirds or three-fourths the length of the body when they first emerge. As they grow old they become gray or brownish black. Eggs are white when first laid, but after a short time they turn black (Fig. 10:15A). The larva is yellow, about 1 mm. long, with shiny black head when first hatched. The full-grown larva (Fig. 10:15B) is legless, about $\frac{3}{8}$ in. long, and green with a brown head and a white stripe down the middle of the back. The larvae tend to curl and bring the tip of the head and the abdomen together when held in the hand. The pupae are white and are encased in small cocoons spun by the larvae (Fig. 10:15C).

Life history. Adult weevils overwinter in plant debris in or at the edges of fields or in alfalfa crowns. Some females mature during their first summer and lay eggs which may overwinter. Most females do not become sexually mature and lay eggs until the following spring. Estimates of the number of eggs laid by individual females range from 400 to 1,000 during a season. Eggs may be laid in dry litter or dead alfalfa stems in the early spring, but later they are usually placed in cavities chewed by the females in the growing alfalfa stems. The eggs hatch in four days to three weeks, depending on the weather. Eggs laid in the fall may not hatch for more than 170 days.

Each larva molts three times and takes about 25 days to one month to complete development. A round, white, netlike cocoon is spun by the

Fig. 10:15. The alfalfa weevil. A, eggs; B, larva; C, pupa in cocoon; D, adult laying eggs; E, alfalfa damaged by weevil at right; insecticide controlled weevils in plot at left. *Courtesy William P. Nye, USDA.*

larva preceding pupation. Though the cocoon is attached to the alfalfa leaves, it often falls to the ground where the pupa remains for varying periods of time depending on environmental conditions. The pupal stage lasts about ten days to two weeks. After the adults emerge they feed on alfalfa the rest of the summer. In fall they enter hibernation.

Usually there is only one generation of weevils a year, but there is some variation in the time of year the eggs, larvae, and adults are most abundant and in the rate they develop in different areas. Some investigators believe that there are at least two generations a year in certain areas.

Control. Early cutting of both the first and second hay crops is one method of cultural control that has proved fairly effective in reducing weevil populations. If the hay is removed from the fields soon after it is cut and if the ground is hot and dry, many eggs and larvae are killed. Cultivation and dragging fields after the hay is removed is an effective cultural control.

Recommendations for insecticidal control of alfalfa weevil differ between the East and West. In the West control is aimed mostly at the overwintering adults to prevent egg laying and thus development of larvae. In spring before new growth exceeds two inches, 4 oz. of heptachlor or dieldrin per acre are applied to the soil and stubble. As adults emerge or enter the field, they are killed by the residual deposit. For larval control on hay crops in the West, spraying parathion at 4 oz. or methoxychlor at 1 to 1½ lbs. per acre in May or June is recommended. Methoxychlor must be applied at least seven days before harvest and parathion at least 15 days before. For control of alfalfa weevil infesting seed crops in the West, one may apply insecticides when flower buds appear. DDT at 1½ to 2 lbs. or dieldrin at ¼ lb. per acre is recommended.

Recommendations for the East include either 1 lb. of malathion or 1½ lbs. of methoxychlor applied when plants are 10 to 15 in. tall (about April). These recommendations are aimed at controlling the larvae. Two applications may be necessary. The second treatment should not be applied later than one week before harvest. If harvest infestation is severe, one should treat stubble as soon as the crop is removed. One may control adult weevils in the East and Southeast by applying 1 lb. of dieldrin or heptachlor in the fall after the last cutting or in late winter before growth starts.

Granulated insecticides have been effective in controlling weevils in some areas.

Generally migration of weevils is unimportant in reinfesting established stands of alfalfa so that control is an individual field problem. Under certain conditions, however, large numbers of weevils are reported to leave fields in a summer flight, distributing in many directions.

An effective weevil parasite, *Bathyplectes curculionis* (Thomson), was introduced into weevil-infested areas of Utah from Europe just preceding World War I. The parasite deposits an egg inside the weevil larvae, but does not kill its host until after the weevil spins its cocoon. In areas where the parasite is established, 80 or 90 per cent or more of the larvae may be parasitized. Yet the parasite cannot be relied upon for complete control of the weevil.

Lygus bugs

Legume bug *Lygus hesperus* **Knight**

Pale legume bug *Lygus elisus* **Van Duzee**

Tarnished plant bug *Lygus lineolaris* (Palisot de Beauvois)
[Hemiptera:Miridae]

Lygus bugs have been called the most devastating insect pest of the alfalfa seed crop. Their importance as alfalfa pests was first discovered in Utah in 1932, but since that time many investigators in different areas have confirmed and added to the original observations which indicated that plant growth, buds, flowers, and seed development are all seriously affected by lygus feeding. Various lygus species feed on a large number of host plants and have proved to be serious pests of the seeds of other plants besides legumes.

In the alfalfa seed producing areas of Arizona and California, three main species of lygus have been present: the legume bug (the most common species), pale legume bug, and tarnished plant bug. In Utah the legume bug and the pale legume bug are the two predominant species in alfalfa. The tarnished plant bug is the common eastern species of lygus and has been the most common species found in northern Minnesota. Our discussion of lygus will concern particularly the legume bug and pale legume bug.

Both adult and immature lygus severely injure forage crops and seeds, but the nymphs are more serious pests than the adults. The piercing-sucking mouthparts of lygus enter and leave plants without much immediate, obvious damage, but later plants develop short internodes, become stemy, produce many branches and an unusual number of short racemes (Fig. 10:16C).

When lygus bugs feed on alfalfa buds, the buds turn white and die in two to five days. If lygus are sufficiently numerous in the field, blooming may be completely prevented. If plants in bloom are attacked, lygus feeding may result in flower dropping, or if the immature seeds are fed upon, the seeds may shrivel, become discolored, and fail to germinate when planted. Hay production may also be adversely affected by lygus feeding, and the quality of the forage lowered. After lygus are removed from plants or if the plants are clipped, the new growth is normal, indicating that injury is local.

Feeding activity of lygus bugs appears to be as great or even greater at night than during the day. Often during the extremely hot periods of the day the young nymphs will hide under vegetation. They can be seen feeding on the terminal portions of the plant during the cooler parts of the day and in the evening.

Description. Adult lygus (Fig. 10:16B) are about ¼ in. long, have four wings that lie more or less flat over the back, and are marked by a distinct "V" on the back just in front of the wings. Lygus may be light green, various shades of brown, or almost black. The eggs, which are inserted into plant tissues, are slightly curved and approximately 1 mm. long.

The nymphs have black spots of various sizes and numbers on their backs as may be seen in Fig. 10:16A. They sometimes look similar to aphids, but lygus nymphs usually run about rapidly in contrast to the relatively slow movement of aphids. Also lygus have antennae relatively short compared with their body, while aphid antennae are longer. Lygus nymphs are usually a green or yellowish-green color. When the nymphs

Fig. 10:16. Lygus bugs and injury. A, nymph; B, adult; C, Lygus-damaged racemes of alfalfa (left) and normal plant (right). *Courtesy William P. Nye, USDA.*

first hatch they are approximately 1.5 mm. long, delicate, and not easily seen among a group of insects collected in an insect net.

Life history. The life cycle of lygus bugs includes three stages: egg, nymph, and adult. In areas where adults hibernate during winter, the adults become active the first warm days of spring. They mate soon after they emerge, and the females begin immediately to lay eggs. Egg laying continues throughout the summer and fall. Studies in Utah have indicated that lygus bugs lay most eggs from April through July and that egg production decreases rapidly during the months of August and September. The majority of eggs are laid in the apical three inches of alfalfa stems; however, eggs have been found in various plant locations and structures. Eggs are inserted full length into plant tissues with egg caps approximately level with the outside surface.

The length of the egg and nymphal stages varies considerably depending on environmental conditions. In the West, the incubation period for eggs has been found to be from 11 to 19 days with an average of about 15 days. Lygus nymphs pass through five nymphal instars and require from 13 to 31 days, with an average of 21 days, to complete development and reach the adult stage. Newly emerged females begin to lay eggs in approximately ten days.

Undoubtedly, there is much variation in the life cycle among the different species of lygus. There are probably four or five generations of lygus a year in certain areas, but the number of generations may vary in different parts of the country.

Though in summer adult lygus fly from adverse to more favorable conditions, a number of natural factors aid in their control. Wet winter seasons with little or no snow cover and alternating mild and low temperatures result in poor survival of hibernating lygus adults. Oviposition, incubation of eggs, and nymphal development are retarded by wet cold spring weather, and these conditions are often fatal to large numbers of lygus nymphs. Lygus nymphs are extremely sensitive to heat and often are unable to survive short walks in the hot soil between plants on warm summer days.

Control. On alfalfa hay or seed, control of lygus is usually aimed at the young nymphs that hatch about the time the plants start to bud. Though a few overwintering lygus adults may be present in the field early in the season and application of insecticide could destroy some of these, the treatment would not protect the crop from the large number of bugs that fly in later.

At present there is a limited choice in methods of controlling lygus bugs on hay crops. Cutting the hay a little early when the alfalfa is in the bud stage will destroy large numbers of eggs and immature lygus. If hay crops become heavily infested with lygus and must be sprayed to save the crop, one of the following insecticides has been recommended for application in the bud stage: malathion, 1 lb. active ingredient per acre applied at least seven days before harvest; Phosdrin, ½ lb. active ingredient per acre applied at least one day before harvest (also recommended for control of aphids, alfalfa weevil larvae, and alfalfa loopers); Dylox, ½ lb. active ingredient per acre (also recommended for control of armyworm but not effective on aphids). Dylox appears to be relatively nontoxic to some beneficial insects, but has moderate human toxicity and precautions suggested on the label should be observed. Dylox should not be applied within two days of the time the crop is to be cut.

For controlling lygus on alfalfa seed crops, timing the application of insecticides with the bud stage or early bloom in order to kill the newly hatching nymphs is a general guide used in many areas of the country. It is common in some seed producing areas to use the number of lygus present as a guide in applying insecticides. Growers may use a 15-inch diameter insect net, sweep their fields in several areas, and keep a constant watch on lygus populations. In the early part of the season if populations average one or more lygus per sweep, they apply one or a combination of the following insecticides (amounts in active ingredient per acre): 2 lbs. DDT, ¼ lb. dieldrin, or 1 lb. malathion. These chemicals are applied as a spray or dust as soon as or before the buds appear but not when the crop is blooming. If it is necessary to control lygus three or four weeks after the bud treatment when plants are blooming, 2 to 3 lbs. of toxaphene applied as a dust or 1½ lbs. applied as a spray is recommended. Recommendations from California suggest that this second insecticide application may be delayed until there is an average of 12 lygus per sweep, presumably because most nymphs would have been destroyed previously. These entomologists also recommend that in tabulating lygus population counts, each nymph be counted as two lygus because of the more serious injury they cause.

If spotted alfalfa aphids or mites are serious problems as well as lygus, demeton may be added to the toxaphene treatment, 2 to 3 oz. of active ingredient per acre. Do not feed plants treated with toxaphene to poultry, dairy animals, or animals being finished for slaughter.

It has been noted in recent years that lygus bugs have developed resistance to certain insecticides. These problems are now being studied.

Lygus bugs have natural enemies, such as nabids and lacewing larvae, that reduce their numbers. Damsel bugs (*Nabis* spp.), big-eyed bugs (*Geocoris* spp.), lady beetles, and ants have been observed feeding on lygus nymphs. Lygus eggs are also sometimes parasitized by a chalcid egg parasite.

Clover seed chalcid

Bruchophagus gibbus (Boheman) [Hymenoptera:Eurytomidae]

The clover seed chalcid (Fig. 10:17) is commonly regarded as the most important unsolved alfalfa seed pest problem at the present time. New seed producing areas, such as California, find this pest an increasingly destructive one. It is difficult to indicate accurately what the losses due to alfalfa seed chalcid are, but observations have shown that from 2 to 85 per cent of the produced alfalfa seed may be infested. Seed losses are commonly estimated to range between 10 and 15 per cent.

The classification of chalcids infesting different legume seeds is in doubt at present. Some reports indicate that two or three different species of chalcids may infest clovers, alfalfa, and birdsfoot trefoil. As yet entomologists in the United States have been unable to separate taxonomically all of the chalcids infesting alfalfa and red clover. This problem of classification is currently being studied.

The clover seed chalcid appears to be present nearly everywhere alfalfa seed or red clover is grown. It has been reported from Germany, Turkey, Chile, Siberia, and in the major seed producing areas of the United States. There is some indication that this chalcid may be a native of the United States. At least 15 kinds of plants are reported to be hosts for clover seed chalcids.

The female chalcid inserts eggs into newly developing seeds by means of a short ovipositor. Seeds are destroyed when the larvae feed on the internal contents.

Description. The adult clover seed chalcid is black, about 2 mm. long, and has two pairs of membranous colorless wings (Fig. 10:17A). Parts of the legs are yellowish-brown. Female chalcids are slightly larger than males, but their antennae are shorter with joints more closely united; the abdomen of the female is more pointed than that of the male. The eggs are so small that a microscope is needed to see them. One end of the egg is slightly pointed and the other end drawn out into a long tube two or three times longer than the main body of the egg. Mature larvae are white with a brown pair of mandibles. The larvae develop into pupae about 2 mm. long.

Life history. The seasonal history of the seed chalcid varies greatly at different locations and from year to year. In the mountain West chalcids overwinter as larvae inside alfalfa seed. Infested seed may be found in volunteer plants along roadsides surrounding alfalfa fields, in chaff stacks, or scattered on the ground in alfalfa fields where seed pods have been knocked off plants or blown out of the combines during harvest. It is not uncommon to have large numbers of these overwintered chalcids emerge from clean seed stored over winter. Infested seeds are about the same size and weight as normal seeds, so that often both are bagged together. Persons handling the seed sometimes get the mistaken idea that the chalcids are infesting or attacking the dried seed in the bags.

As temperatures increase in spring, the larvae inside the seeds pupate and develop into adults. When development is complete, the adult escapes by chewing a hole through the seed coat. Changes in temperature influence the growth and activity of immature and adult seed chalcids so that emergence dates of adults in spring may vary considerably. Some studies in the West have indicated that males emerge before females in spring and that they are more numerous than females all season.

Chalcids mate almost immediately after they emerge and females lay eggs within a few hours if they can find seeds in the right stage of development. If suitable seed for oviposition cannot be found, the females apparently will fly several miles to find seed in which to oviposit. Seeds whose contents are semifluid or jelly-like seem to be most suitable for oviposition. The females usually deposit only one egg per seed. The eggs hatch in about three to 12 days, depending on the temperature, and the larvae feed on the contents of the seed until larval growth is complete.

If temperature and moisture conditions remain favorable, the larvae may change immediately into the pupal stage, and new adult chalcids emerge from the seeds five to 40 days later. If temperatures become low, the larvae may remain inside the seed until more favorable conditions for development return. Under excessively dry conditions the larvae may go into a resting state and remain in dry seeds for one or even two years. The number of generations produced per year varies from almost continuous generations in favorable areas to only two generations a year in some of the colder areas of the United States. The average feeding period for larvae under conditions in northeastern Utah was 10 to 15 days. Larvae developing from eggs laid the same day in pods on the same alfalfa stem pupated and emerged as adults within ten days to two weeks after they completed their feeding, while others of these same larvae hibernated over winter and emerged as adults the following May.

Control. Reports of studies on commercial and experimental fields show there has been little success in use of insecticides to control clover seed

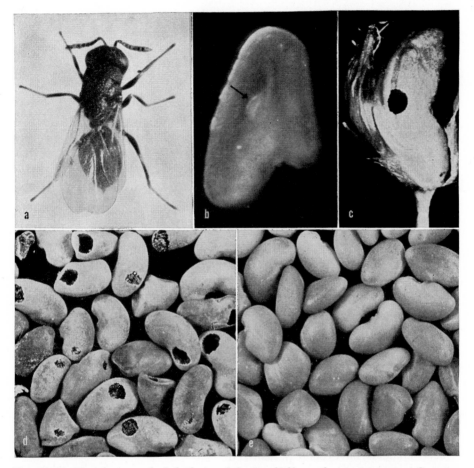

Fig. 10:17. The clover seed chalcid. A, adult; B, alfalfa seed containing egg; C, emergence hole; D, chalcid damaged alfalfa seed; E, noninfested seed. *Courtesy William P. Nye, USDA.*

chalcid. None of the insecticides tested, including some systemic insecticides, has been reported to reduce chalcid injury enough to make chemical control economically justifiable. Deposition of the eggs inside seeds, the constant sources of reinfestation, development of continuous generations of chalcids, and the presence of insect pollinators that are necessary for seed setting in the field when chalcid adults need to be destroyed have all complicated chemical control of chalcids. Since new insecticides and methods are being tested, it is possible that a chemical control for chalcid may be developed at any time.

Studies of seed chalcid life history and behavior have resulted in several recommendations for reducing chalcid damage:

1. Grow only either first or second crop seed in the same area. If both first and second crop seed are grown in the same seed area, a continuous supply of favorable host plants will be available for the breeding and increase of chalcids. Practical difficulties of obtaining the necessary cooperation of all seed growers in an area to establish such a practice and also to furnish the pollinators necessary to set seed in a large area all at the same time are obvious.
2. Grow only one seed chalcid host plant in an area. Destroy or prevent the development of volunteer host plants.
3. Manage the seed crops so there is a uniform ripening of the seed.
4. Feed badly infested seed crops as hay (if not contaminated by insecticides) and remove these crops from the fields as soon as possible.
5. If seed is threshed in a stationary location, eliminate the chaff stacks containing infested seed before the chalcids emerge in the spring. Do not feed chaff contaminated with insecticide to livestock.
6. Reclean harvested seed and destroy the infested seeds.
7. Cultivate fields to bury infested seeds which have fallen to the ground during harvest or have been scattered over the fields by the combine harvesters. There is some evidence that burying infested seed to a depth of 2 to 2½ inches will destroy a large percentage of the chalcids.

Ten species of parasites belonging to the superfamily Chalcidoidea are known to attack the larvae or pupae of the clover seed chalcid in the United States. Some studies have shown that often 90 per cent or more of seed chalcids have been parasitized.

The chalcid problem is being investigated by a number of different agencies. One project is a search for plant materials resistant to chalcid infestation. None of the varieties studied thus far is free from chalcid attack, but differences of chalcid infestation suggest that it may be possible to find plant materials with more resistance.

Meadow spittlebug

Philaenus leucophthalmus (Linnaeus) [Homoptera:Cercopidae]

The meadow spittlebug (Fig. 10:18) is present in Europe, North America, and Canada and is the most important species of spittlebug in the eastern United States.

It is frequently a serious pest of legumes (especially alfalfa and red clover) in the northeastern and north central states. Infestations of meadow spittlebugs can be readily recognized by the white, frothy masses of spittle on the plants. Plants may look as though soapy water had been thrown on them.

Most of the injury to plants by meadow spittlebug results from nymphal feeding. The nymphs have piercing-sucking mouthparts through which they suck juices from the plants. Their feeding on alfalfa results in stunted plants, reduced yields of forage and seed, wilting, difficulty in curing the hay because of dampness from the spittle masses, and rosetting of the terminal plant growth. Plant blossoms and seeds may also be injured. The alfalfa plant internodes are shortened and the plants are dwarfed; but, unlike the yellows that result from the feeding of potato leafhoppers, spittlebug-infested plants remain green. Clover is stunted by spittlebug feeding, but the rosetting of terminal growth is not as marked.

Control of spittlebugs in New York when there were two to 26 nymphs per square foot resulted in hay increases up to 59 per cent in certain meadow mixtures. Infestations of less than an average of six nymphs per stem have appeared to have little effect on alfalfa or red clover hay yields. No carry-over effect of spittlebug injury has been observed on later cuttings.

The meadow spittlebug commonly attacks meadow plants, weeds, and garden plants. It will survive on nearly any succulent foliage on which it becomes established, including shrubs, trees, and herbaceous species. The amount of damage seems less than might be expected from the tremendous numbers of spittlebug adults that are often seen on a crop.

Description. Adult spittlebugs are ¼ to ½ in. long and about ⅛ inch wide. They may be brown or gray with colors arranged in various designs; the adults have a short, bluntly angular head and prominent eyes located on the sides of the head. They are shaped much like leafhoppers, but the two can be readily told apart by the differences in their hind legs. Spittle bugs are sometimes called "froghoppers," because of their shape which slightly resembles that of tiny frogs.

The nymphs (Fig. 10:18B) are found in masses of spittle located various places up and down the stems of the plants they feed on. The first instar nymphs are orange and as development proceeds they gradually assume a green color becoming entirely green in the last nymphal instar. Spittle, a fluid voided from the anus, is a substance possibly secreted by glands. The air bubbles are formed by manipulation of the abdominal segments which forces air through the ventral "air canal" and into the spittle.

Life history. Meadow spittlebugs have one generation annually. In the fall the females lay eggs on grain stubble, alfalfa stubble, and on stems of many other plants, usually less than 4 inches above ground level (Fig.

Fig. 10:18. The meadow spittlebug. A, eggs on stalk; B, nymph; C, adult; D, spittle on legume plant. *A, B, C, Courtesy Ohio State University; D, Courtesy Lloyd L. Stitt.*

10:18A). One to 30 eggs per mass may be laid with an average of seven being found in Ohio. It is estimated that individual females may lay from 18 to 51 eggs apiece.

The eggs overwinter and hatch the following spring. A critical period in the life of a spittlebug is from the time of hatching until the nymph finds and establishes itself on a suitable host. Apparently many nymphs do not survive this period. At Wooster, Ohio studies indicate that approximately equal time is spent in each of the five instars (about eight to ten days each). Although the nymphal period averages five to six weeks, the rate of development may be altered considerably by changes in temperature and moisture.

Nymphs usually rest head downward while feeding and as the spittle is formed it covers the insect. This material provides the moist habitat necessary for the survival of the nymph and appears not to be readily removed, even by heavy rains. Each mass of spittle contains one or more nymphs.

Spittle production ceases just prior to the final molt and the foam around it dries and forms a chamber, in which the molt occurs. The new adult then crawls or leaps out of the mass leaving a neat hole in the dried spittle ball. Adults may remain in fields where they developed until the foliage is removed, or fly to other crops which attract them. The direction of adult spittlebug migration appears to be greatly influenced by the wind direction.

Fully developed eggs begin to appear in ovaries of females in August. In September, females migrate into suitable fields for oviposition. Entomologists have found that intense oviposition usually occurs after the first week in September in Ohio. Females may continue to lay eggs until they die naturally or are killed by frost.

A combination of high humidity and an abundance of good legumes seems to be necessary for the spittlebug to develop as a serious pest. Humidity is an important condition determining survival of spittlebugs in all stages of their existence. The adults are attracted to and survive best on succulent foliage, and an abundance of this succulent foliage must be present to attract the adults for oviposition.

Control. Application of insecticides to infested fields early in September after the adults have ceased migrating extensively has resulted in excellent control of adult spittlebugs and has reduced nymphal infestations the following spring. For fall treatment, apply methoxychlor (1½ lb. active ingredient per acre) in early September at least seven days before harvesting or pasturing the treated crop.

For nymphal control in spring, apply either 2 oz. of endrin before plants are 2 inches tall or 1 lb. of methoxychlor per acre as a spray when the first small masses of spittle are produced in the crowns of the plants. Optimum time for applying insecticide in Ohio is when hatching is at its peak (when plants are 8 to 10 inches tall).

Thorough coverage of foliage with the insecticide is an important requirement for successful control. Airplane applications of insecticides and applications by low-volume, low-pressure sprayers have not given good results in dense foliage. Sprays have been reported more effective than dusts in some experiments. Various researchers have shown that low volume sprayers may be effective in applying these insecticides when the crop is 6 to 8 inches high.

Forage yields may be increased as much as 90 per cent by controlling meadow spittlebugs.

Selected References

Anon., *The Alfalfa Weevil: How to Control It*, USDA Leaflet 368, 1958.
Anon., *The Clover Leaf Weevil and Its Control*, USDA Farmers' Bull. 1484, 1956.
Anon., *The Spotted Alfalfa Aphid: How to Control It*, USDA Leaflet 422, 1957.
Anon., *The Velvetbean Caterpillar: How to Control It*, USDA Leaflet 348, 1959.
App, B. A., and R. T. Everly, *Insecticide Dusts to Control the Clover Root Borer and the Meadow Spittlebug*, U.S. Bur. Ent. and Plant Quar. E-811, 1950.
Dickason, E. A., and R. W. Every, *Legume Insects of Oregon*, Oregon Agr. Ext. Ser. Bull. 749, 1955.
Elliott, E. S., *Diseases, Insects, and Other Factors in Relation to Red Clover Failure in West Virginia*, West Virginia Agr. Exp. Sta. Bull. 351T, 1952.
Graumann, H. O., and C. H. Hanson, *Growing Alfalfa*, USDA Farmers' Bull. 1722, 1954.
Haws, B. A., and F. G. Holdaway, *Sweetclover Weevil and Its Control in Minnesota*, Minn. Ext. Folder 180, 1955.
Klostermeyer, E. C., *Alfalfa Seed Insects*, Washington Agr. Exp. Sta. Bull. 587, 1958.
Menke, H. F., *Insect Pollination in Relation to Alfalfa Seed Production in Washington*, Washington Agr. Exp. Sta. Bull. 555, 1954.
Miller, M. D., L. G. Jones, V. P. Osterli, and A. D. Reed, *Seed Production of Ladino Clover*, California Agr. Ext. Ser. Circular 182, 1951.
Palm, C. E., C. Lincoln, and A. B. Buchholz, *The Alfalfa Snout Beetle: Its Control and Suppression*, Cornell Agr. Exp. Sta. Bull. 757, 1941.
Pedersen, M. W., *et al.*, *Growing Alfalfa for Seed*, Utah Agr. Exp. Sta. in coop. with USDA, Circular 135, 1955.
———, *et al.*, *Cultural Practices for Alfalfa Seed Production*, Utah Agr. Exp. Sta. in coop. with USDA, Bull. 408, 1959.
Poos, F. W., *The Potato Leafhopper, a Pest of Alfalfa in the Eastern States*, USDA Leaflet 229, 1942.
Rockwood, L. P., *The Clover Root Borer*, USDA Bull. 1426, 1926.
Stern, V. M., R. F. Smith, R. van den Bosch, and K. S. Hagen, "The Integrated Control Concept," *Hilgardia* 29(2):81–101 (1959).
Tuttle, D. M., *et al.*, *The Spotted Alfalfa Aphid in Arizona*, Arizona Agr. Exp. Sta. Bull. 294, 1958.
Vansell, G. H., *Use of Honey Bees in Alfalfa Seed Production*, USDA Circular 876, 1951.
Watkins, T. C., *Clover Leafhopper* (Aceratagallia sanguinolenta Prov.), Cornell Agr. Exp. Sta. Bull. 758, 1941.
Weaver, C. R., and D. R. King, *Meadow Spittlebug*, Ohio Agr. Exp. Sta. Bull. 741, 1954.
Wehrle, L. P., *The Clover-Flower Midge* (Dasyneura leguminicola Lintner), Cornell Agr. Exp. Sta. Bull. 481, 1929.
Wildermuth, V. L., *Chalcid Control in Alfalfa-Seed Production*, USDA Farmers' Bull. 1642, 1931.
———, and F. H. Gates, *Clover Stem-Borer as an Alfalfa Pest*, USDA Bull. 889, 1920.
Wilson, M. C., *Prevent Leafhopper Yellows on Alfalfa*, Indiana Agr. Ext. Service Bull. 398, 1953.

Chapter 11 | INSECT PESTS OF
COTTON | *Robert E. Pfadt*

The pests

Cotton, with its green, succulent leaves, its large open flowers, nectaries on every leaf and flower, and its abundance of fruit attracts a great variety of insects and mites. In the United States over 125 injurious species attack cotton. The most destructive of these is the **boll weevil** (Fig. 11:10), a native insect of Mexico or Central America which crossed the border into Texas in 1892. It spread rapidly and now occupies more than 85 per cent of the Cotton Belt.

Other major pests of cotton include the bollworm, pink bollworm, cotton fleahopper, lygus bugs, cotton aphid, several species of spider mites and thrips, and the cotton leafworm.

The **bollworm**, *Heliothis zea* (Boddie), also called the corn earworm, feeds on many kinds of cultivated and wild plants (Fig. 9:12). It prefers young corn, but after corn matures the moths oviposit on cotton and other acceptable plants. Usually larvae of the second generation injure corn while larvae of the third and succeeding generations injure cotton.

The **pink bollworm** (Fig. 11:13) known as the most serious world-wide pest of cotton, is entrenched in and around Texas. Only stringent control measures have prevented its spread to the entire Cotton Belt. Hibernating larvae of this frail moth entered the United States in 1916 in cotton seed imported from Mexico.

The **cotton fleahopper** (Fig. 11:15), a widely distributed mirid bug in the United States, inflicts its greatest damage to cotton in Texas and Oklahoma. It feeds on a large variety of weeds in addition to cotton. **Lygus bugs,** also mirids, are most injurious to the cotton crop in New Mexico, Arizona, and California.

The **cotton aphid,** also called the melon aphid, is the most important of several species of plant lice infesting cotton (Fig. 11:1). Enjoying almost world-wide distribution, the aphid is found everywhere in the United States. Today it is mainly a pest of seedling cotton, but formerly, when growers applied calcium arsenate exclusively to control the boll weevil, it often increased to large, damaging populations on older plants. Several

Fig. 11:1. The cotton aphid attacking a cotton plant. Note the curled infested leaves at the top and the honeydew-covered lower leaf. *Courtesy USDA.*

other species—the cowpea aphid, green peach aphid, and potato aphid— may infest the foliage of seedling cotton, while several species attack the roots including the corn root aphid and the aphids *Trifidaphis phaseoli* (Pass.) and *Rhopalosiphum subterraneum* Mason.

A dozen or more species of **spider mites** are known to infest cotton in the United States. An important factor that has increased the seriousness of the mite problem on cotton has been the application of chlorinated hydrocarbon insecticides which have not only killed various cotton pests, but also beneficial, predaceous species. To correct this condition growers make suitable miticide applications whenever needed. Some of the important mite species are the two-spotted spider mite, four-spotted spider mite, strawberry spider mite, desert spider mite, Pacific spider mite, Schoene spider mite, tumid spider mite, and brown wheat mite.

Several species of **thrips,** at least nine, have been reported attacking cotton in the United States. Although thrips may injure mature plants, they are chiefly pests of seedling cotton.

In North America, one of the historical pests of cotton is the **cotton leafworm,** a tropical insect that, almost every year in the moth stage, invades the Cotton Belt by flight from Central or South America. As long ago as the eighteenth century, records show that during some years it destroyed 25 to 90 per cent of the crop (Figs. 11:2 and 11:3).

Cotton pests of somewhat less importance yet requiring control are listed below to show just how numerous and diverse the enemies of this crop are.

Collembola. Three or more species.

Orthoptera. The differential, migratory, red-legged, two-striped, American, and lubber grasshopper; the field cricket; snowy tree cricket.

Hemiptera. Rapid plant bug, superb plant bug, ragweed plant bug, and several other mirids; several stink bugs including the conchuela, Say stink bug, southern green stink bug, brown cotton bug, brown stink bug, and red-shouldered plant bug; and the cotton stainer.

Homoptera. The greenhouse whitefly, sweetpotato whitefly, and the whiteflies, *Bemisia tabaci, Trialeurodes abutilonea, T. vaporariorum,* and *T. pergandei;* several leafhoppers including the potato leafhopper and southern garden leafhopper.

Coleoptera. The sand wireworm and Pacific Coast wireworm; several species of false wireworms; striped blister beetle; white-fringed beetles; several species of *Colaspis;* the pale-striped flea beetle, elongate flea beetle, and sweetpotato flea beetle; the cowpea curculio; the corn silk beetle; and white grubs and May beetles, *Phyllophaga* spp.

Lepidoptera. A large number of noctuids including the black cutworm, pale-sided cutworm, variegated cutworm, granulate cutworm, army cutworm, beet armyworm, fall armyworm, yellow-striped armyworm, western yellow-striped armyworm, cabbage looper, tobacco budworm, brown cotton leafworm, leafworms (*Anomis* spp.), and the stalk borer; representatives of other families include the cotton leaf perforator and *Bucculatrix gossypiella;* the garden webworm, European corn borer, and greenhouse leaf tier; the cotton square borer; the salt-marsh caterpillar and the yellow woollybear; the white-lined sphinx; and several species of leaf rollers including *Platynota stultana* and *P. rostrana.*

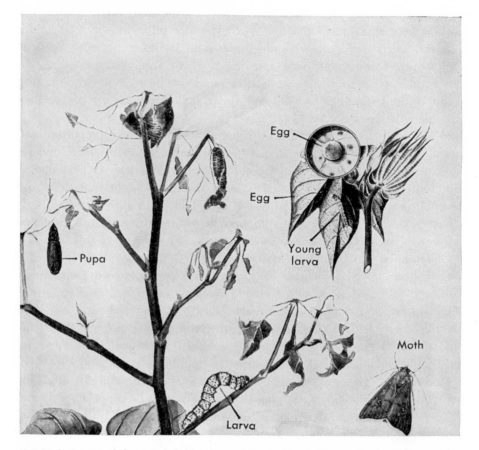

Fig. 11:2. Stages of the cotton leafworm and its feeding injury to the host plant. *Courtesy USDA.*

Diptera. The seed-corn maggot and the serpentine leaf miner.

The injury

Insect pests not only reduce yields of cotton lint and seed, but also lower their quality. Agricultural scientists have estimated that insects cause an annual loss of well over 200 million dollars to cotton growers. Pests attack cotton in the field from the time the seed is planted until the crop is harvested. Those that feed on cotton in its early stages of development probably have little effect on quality, but they definitely affect yields. Insects like wireworms, false wireworms, and seed-corn maggots may reduce or even prevent the establishment of stands by consuming the seeds and destroying the seedlings.

After the young plants emerge, they are attacked by both chewing and sucking insects. Thrips and the cotton aphid suck juices of seedling cotton and introduce salivary secretions which retard both growth of the plant and production of fruit. Chewing insects such as cutworms, beet armyworm, darkling beetles, May beetles, flea beetles, cowpea curculio, and field crickets feed on the leaves or the tender stems often killing the young plants.

Sometimes fields of seedling cotton show symptoms of injury—yellow, weak plants—without evidence of insects being present. One should then look for root feeding pests such as root aphids.

When the crop once begins to fruit, insects not only reduce yields of cotton, but also adversely affect its quality. They need not inflict this injury directly on the bolls but may do it indirectly through defoliation, feeding on the roots, or boring in the stem. Notorious defoliators include the cotton leafworm, spider mites, cotton aphid, yellow-striped armyworm, fall armyworm, cabbage looper, and cotton leaf perforator. Insects that bore in the stem are the European corn borer and the stalk borer.

Fig. 11:3. A close-up of the cotton leafworm showing its looping method of progression. *Photo by Bob Taylor.*

Some of the most serious pests of cotton attack the fruit directly, feeding on squares, blooms, or bolls. Mandibulate insects such as the boll weevil, bollworm, and pink bollworm feed inside the squares and bolls, ruining or devouring lint and seed. Sucking insects like the cotton fleahopper, lygus bugs, and stink bugs, suck juices from the squares and cause them to turn brown or black and fall from the plant. Lygus bugs and stink bugs also feed heavily on the bolls, causing young bolls to shed or staining the lint of older bolls.

On open bolls lint may become stained in other ways. The excrement of cotton leafworms may stain the lint. Honeydew from aphids causes gummy lint on which molds frequently grow that stain and weaken the fibers.

Insects are predisposing factors and vectors of several diseases of cotton. In piercing the bolls stink bugs and cotton stainers introduce yeastlike fungi which stain the lint and contribute to the injury known as stigmatomycosis. Insects that chew holes through the walls of the bolls, open avenues of entry for bacteria and fungi that cause boll rots. Some insects may transport the pathogen as they enter the boll. Thrip injury weakens seedling plants, making them more susceptible to sore shin disease caused by a fungus, *Rhizoctonia solani.* Insects also transmit several virus diseases of cotton. Two whiteflies, *Trialeurodes abutilonea* and *Bemisia tabaci,* transmit the virus of leaf crumple which affects cotton in the Southwest. In Russia aphids transmit the virus of cotton leaf curl and in Africa a whitefly transmits the virus of leaf curl.

Cultural control

Because many cotton pests are difficult to control solely with insecticides, growers must also employ cultural methods to achieve a profitable harvest. The chief objectives of cultural control are: (1) to have an early maturing crop so that it escapes peak populations of pests; (2) to harvest the crop early so that removal of the pests' host plant stops their multiplication; and (3) to reduce the numbers of pests that are able to overwinter.

Growers reach these objectives by: (1) locating cotton fields as far as possible from other crops which may serve as host plants of cotton insects and as far as possible from favored hibernation quarters of cotton insects, particularly the boll weevil; (2) planting reasonably early; (3) planting healthy seed of a recommended variety; (4) stimulating rapid growth and maturity through the adoption of recommended agronomic practices; (5) harvesting early; (6) destroying stalks with cutter-shredders immediately after harvest (Fig. 11:4); (7) plowing under crop residues; and (8) destroying weed patches which serve as hibernating quarters for several cotton pests.

Since gin trash may serve as hibernating quarters for boll weevil and pink bollworm, gin-plant sanitation is essential for reducing the overwintering populations. In regulated areas of the pink bollworm, state and federal laws require that gin trash be either burned, sterilized, run through a hammer mill or a special type fan, or composted.

Fig. 11:4. Cutting and shredding cotton plants after harvest aid in the control of insect pests of this crop. *Courtesy Texas A & M.*

Chemical control

For its protection from injurious insects and mites, cotton receives a wider variety and greater quantity of insecticides than any other single crop. Each year cotton growers normally purchase some 50 million dollars' worth of insecticides and spend another 20 million dollars in applying them.

Reasons for applying a variety of insecticides to cotton are that no one material controls all pest species, some materials used alone create problems with bollworms, aphids, and spider mites, still others have decreased effectiveness because of the development of resistance by several cotton insects.

The insecticides used on cotton include various chlorinated hydrocarbons, organic phosphates, several miscellaneous organic compounds, and a few inorganic chemicals. The principal insecticides for controlling important cotton pests are shown in Table 11:1. In addition to these, a number of more recently developed compounds, mainly organic phosphates, look promising, and some, no doubt, will become widely utilized. They include Delnav, Diazinon, Di-Syston, Trithion, ethion, and Tedion.

Since no one chemical controls all cotton pests, growers often make a practice of combining two or more insecticides in a single treatment. A popular mixture has been one including BHC and DDT, or BHC, DDT, and sulfur.

Because most insecticides kill beneficial predators and parasites as well

Table 11:1 | Recommended Dosages for the Principal Insecticides Used for the Control of Certain Cotton Pests

(Pounds Per Acre of Technical Material in a Dust or Emulsion Spray)

Pesticide	Boll Weevil	Boll-worm	Cotton Aphid	Cotton Flea-hopper	Cotton Leaf-worm	Cut-worms	Fall Army-worm	Grass-hoppers	Lygus and Other Mirids	Pink Boll-worm	Spider Mites [1]	Stink Bugs	Thrips
Aldrin	0.25–0.75			0.25				0.10–0.25	0.25–0.75				0.08–0.15
BHC (gamma)	0.30–0.45			0.1				0.3–0.45	0.3–0.45			0.45	0.1–0.2
Calcium arsenate [2]	7–15				7–10								
DDT		0.5–2.0		0.5		1–2.5 [3]	1.0–1.5		1.0–1.5	2–3			0.25–1.5
Demeton [4]			0.125–0.4								0.25–0.4		
Dieldrin	0.15–0.50			0.15		0.3–0.5 [3]		0.07–0.125	0.15–0.50			0.5	0.08–0.15
Dipterex			0.25–1.0		0.25–1.0				1.0–1.5			1.5	
Endrin	0.2–0.5	0.2–0.5		0.1	0.2–0.5	0.2–0.5	0.2–0.3	0.2–0.5	0.2–0.5				0.08–0.15
Guthion	0.25–0.50			0.25	0.25–0.5				0.2–0.5		0.25–0.5		0.25–0.5
Heptachlor	0.25–0.75			0.25				0.25–0.50	0.25–0.75			1.0	0.08–0.15
Malathion	0.5–2		1–2	0.25–1.0	0.25–0.5				0.5–1.0				0.5–1.0
Methyl parathion	0.25–0.75		0.25–0.5		0.25–0.5						0.25–0.5		0.25–0.50
Parathion			0.1–0.25		0.125–0.25						0.1–0.4	0.5	
Sevin	1–2	1–2		0.5–1.0	0.5–1.0					2.0–2.5			0.5–1.0
Strobane	2–4	2–4		1.0	2–3				2–3			4.0	0.75–1.0
Toxaphene	2–4	2–4		1.0	2–3	2–5	2–3	1.0–2.5	2–3			4.0	0.75–1.0

Source: 1960 Conference Report on Cotton Insect Research and Control, ARS, USDA, in Cooperation with 12 Cotton-Growing States.

[1] Not all species of spider mites are controlled with these materials. See state recommendations.
[2] Dust only.
[3] Does not control all species.
[4] Spray only.

as pest insects and thereby contribute to outbreaks of still other pests, informed growers use them only when needed. They apply insecticides early in the season to control infestations of cutworms, beet armyworms, grasshoppers, and aphids. Differences of opinion exist among entomologists on whether early-season control of the boll weevil is a good practice. In some states growers are advised to make early-season treatments for weevil and likewise for thrips, fleahoppers, and plant bugs. In mid-season and in late-season growers make treatments to control such serious pests as boll weevil, bollworm, leafworm, fleahopper, plant bugs, aphids, and spider mites. In outbreak years of the boll weevil they may treat cotton every four or five days, making as many as twenty or more applications during the season.

A grave problem in dealing with cotton pests is the development of resistance to insecticides. Resistance in cotton insects first appeared in 1953 in the cotton leafworm. But not until 1955 was the problem fully appreciated when in some areas it was found that the boll weevil had developed resistance to the chlorinated hydrocarbon insecticides. Entomologists have now found resistance in other species such as onion thrips, salt-marsh caterpillar, cabbage looper, four species of spider mites, cotton fleahopper, brown stink bug, cotton aphid, beet armyworm, southern garden leafhopper, cotton leaf perforator, and two species of lygus bugs. Methods of combating the resistance problem include the use of insecticides having different physiological actions than the ones to which the pests have become resistant, protection of beneficial predators wherever possible, and greater reliance on cultural methods.

As much valuable research is conducted every year on both cotton pests and cotton culture, agricultural scientists interested in this crop meet in an annual conference to exchange and discuss new findings and new field experiences. The Thirteenth Annual Conference on Cotton Insect Research and Control was held in 1960 at Memphis, Tennessee. Summaries of the deliberations are published each year by the National Cotton Council, Memphis 12, Tennessee.

To keep growers abreast of new developments, the extension service of each cotton state publishes annually detailed guides for control of cotton pests. These may be obtained from County Agricultural Agents and State Colleges of Agriculture.

Control equipment

From the year 1916 when calcium arsenate was found effective against several serious cotton pests, growers have applied insecticides to cotton plants mainly as dusts. With the discovery of the chlorinated hydrocarbons and organic phosphates, which are conveniently formulated as emulsifiable concentrates, a trend toward use of sprays has developed. Sprays are more efficient in covering seedling plants with insecticides and while both methods are equally effective later in the season, sprays drift less than dusts and can be applied under a wider range of weather conditions.

The types of dusters that growers use depend a great deal on the acreage of cotton they must treat. Hand dusters are practical for treating about five acres daily, horse-drawn traction dusters for treating 20 to 30 acres daily, and tractor or airplane dusters for treating larger acreages (Fig. 11:5).

Growers usually apply 10 to 15 lbs. of dust per acre except in the West where they may apply heavier dosages. On ground rigs they adjust nozzles so that there is one nozzle over each row about 10 inches above the plants.

Fig. 11:5. Dusting cotton with an airplane for control of mites and lygus bugs. *Courtesy Transland Aircraft, Torrance, Calif.*

A significant development in cotton dusting and spraying equipment is the introduction of self-propelled high-clearance ground machines (Fig. 11:6). These machines provide efficient coverage in rank cotton without injuring the plants mechanically. The machines are able to treat 75 acres daily, but they have the disadvantage of all ground rigs in their inability to operate in wet fields.

Instead of dusters some growers employ low-gallonage, low-pressure, boom-type sprayers. Normally from 1 to 8 gal. of emulsion spray are applied per acre although in the Far West up to 15 gal. may be applied. One nozzle above each row is used to spray seedling cotton. On larger plants three nozzles per row may be used, one above and one on each side, and in rank growth as many as five or six.

Fig. 11:6. A self-propelled, high-clearance, 8-row sprayer treating cotton with insecticide. *Courtesy John Blue Co., Huntsville, Ala.*

A third method of applying insecticides to cotton is to treat the seed. Applied in this way chlorinated hydrocarbons such as heptachlor and dieldrin, provide protection from wireworms, false wireworms, and seedcorn maggots.

Granules and fertilizer-insecticide mixtures show considerable promise for control of some cotton insects.

REPRESENTATIVE COTTON INSECTS

For our study of individual cotton pests, we have chosen the boll weevil, the pink bollworm, the cotton fleahopper, and the black cutworm.

Boll weevil

Anthonomus grandis Boheman [Coleoptera:Curculionidae]

The boll weevil causes more damage to cotton in the United States than any other insect. Native to Mexico or Central America, it was first reported in the United States in the fall of 1894 at Brownsville, Texas. Investigation showed that the boll weevil was established in several southern Texas counties and had probably crossed the Mexican border in 1892.

From the point of invasion, the boll weevil spread rapidly. It advanced at the rate of 40 to 160 miles a year, mainly by dispersal flights. By 1922 it attained its general distribution in the United States infesting more than 85 per cent of the Cotton Belt (Fig. 11:7).

Panic followed the boll weevil. As Southern agriculture and industry depended almost entirely on one crop—cotton, weevil destruction of one-third to one-half normal production in newly invaded areas bankrupted farmers, merchants, and bankers. Many farmers deserted their places and fled from the ravages of the weevil to other regions.

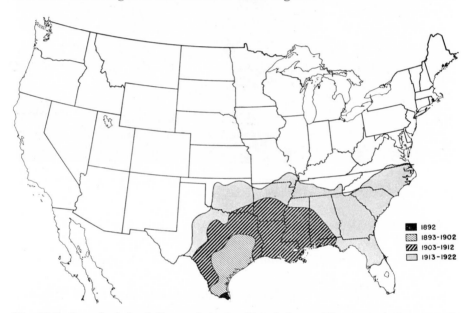

1892
1893-1902
1903-1912
1913-1922

Fig. 11:7. Spread of the boll weevil in the United States. The insect had apparently reached area of general distribution by 1922. *Courtesy USDA.*

By name and reputation, the boll weevil became known to every southerner. Songs were written about it. In the 1890's Texas Negroes began singing the "Ballad of the Boll Weevil," an early blues song.

The amount of damage varies from year to year due to fluctuation in numbers of weevil. From 1909 to 1949 agricultural scientists have estimated an average loss of cotton and cottonseed of more than 203 million dollars annually. The loss exceeded 500 million dollars in each of five years. In only 16 of the 41 years was the annual loss less than 100 million dollars.

In spring before cotton begins to fruit, boll weevils feed on growing terminals and destroy a few leaves by puncturing the leaf petioles. As soon as flower buds, the so-called "squares," start to form, the weevils feed on them, gouging out small cavities with their long snouts. Feeding on the squares often induces the bracts to open up or "flare," the color to fade to a yellowish-green, and the plant to shed the injured buds.

Further injury results when the female weevils lay eggs in the squares, usually one egg to a square. Upon hatching the larva feeds inside the square and quickly causes it to flare, fade in color, and in about three days to drop from the plant (Fig. 11:8). If the square does not drop, it ceases growth and becomes hard and dry.

Because heavy numbers can destroy all of the squares, a bad infestation of boll weevils may prevent cotton from blooming. In lighter infestations uninjured squares open up into flowers which eventually form fruit or bolls.

Fig. 11:8. Damage of the boll weevil. A, square with egg puncture; B, larva in square; C, pupa in square; D, adult emerging from square; E, infested squares fallen on ground; F, larva and pupa in boll. *Courtesy USDA.*

Weevils destroy young bolls as they do squares. Older bolls in which females oviposit usually stay attached to the plant and may continue to grow. A larva developing in a lock will cut, stain, and ruin the lint. If several larvae develop within a boll, as often happens when food is scarce, they destroy the entire boll.

Usually the spring infestation is light so that cotton plants produce a good "bottom crop" of bolls. As the season progresses and weevils increase in number, they may severely injure or completely destroy the "top crop."

In 1919 the citizens of Coffee County, Alabama, erected a monument to the boll weevil on the town square of Enterprise, Alabama (Fig. 11:9). They inscribed these words: "In profound appreciation of the boll weevil and what it has done as the herald of prosperity." Their reason for this action was the fact that the boll weevil forced diversification of crops and production of livestock in the South bringing about a more stable economy.

Another benefit attributable to the boll weevil is the establishment of the Federal and State extension services. In 1904 part of an appropriation to fight the boll weevil was made available to the Bureau of Plant Industry to demonstrate to cotton farmers how to control this pest. The demonstrations were so successful that the Farmers' Cooperative Demonstration Work grew into what is now the Agricultural Extension Service.

Cotton is the principal host plant of the boll weevil. It feeds occasionally on a few other Malvaceae and is able to develop on althea, *Hibiscus syriacus,*

Fig. 11.9. Monument to the boll weevil on town square of Enterprise, Alabama. *Courtesy, Enterprise Ledger.*

on Arizona wild cotton, *Gossypium thurberi,* and on portia tree, *Thespesia populnea.*

Description. Eggs of the boll weevil are pearly-white, elliptical, and approximately 0.8 mm. long. The eggs hatch into legless, white grubs with light brown heads. After feeding from seven to twelve days the larvae become full grown and pupate within the squares or bolls (Fig. 11:10B). The pupa is all white at first, but becomes suffused with brown as it develops. After a pupal period of three to six days, the adult boll weevil emerges. Adult weevils range from ⅛ to ⅓ inch in length and are reddish-brown or grayish in color (Fig. 11:10A). The conspicuous snout is about half as long as the body. A distinctive character is the spur on the inner surface of each front femur.

Life history. The boll weevil passes the winter in the adult stage sheltered underneath ground litter in cotton fields, along fence rows, in the edge of woods, in weed patches, and in other protected places. Many even seek shelter in clumps of Spanish moss hanging from trees.

Adult weevils start coming out of hibernation quarters as soon as the weather warms up in spring. Although the period of emergence may extend from March to the middle of July, the majority of weevils emerge in June. They often fly considerable distances in search of cotton fields. After finding a field of fruiting cotton they settle down to feed and reproduce.

Weevils that emerge before cotton plants have begun to square, feed on the leafbuds and growing terminals and live for only one to two weeks. Those emerging later feed on squares, their principal food, and live as long as four weeks.

To obtain food, weevils usually puncture the tips of squares where they feed internally on the developing pollen and other structures. After a few days of feeding, the females begin to produce eggs.

They prefer to lay in squares, but they also utilize bolls. They deposit eggs singly into cavities made with their mouth parts. After placing an egg deep in the cavity, they seal the hole with a gluelike substance. Though females rarely lay more than one egg in a square, they may lay several in a boll. Overwintering females usually produce fewer than 100 eggs, but females of later generations produce up to 300 or more eggs.

Eggs hatch in three or four days and the larvae, which develop inside the square or boll, feed upon the anthers and pollen or the lint. Influenced by temperature and by the nutritional value of their food, larvae complete development in seven to twelve days.

The larvae then pupate within the squares or bolls which afford protection for the delicate pupae. This stage lasts from three to six days after which the adult weevils cut their way out. Depending on latitude there are from two to seven generations annually in the United States.

Late in the season adult weevils again take to flying and dispersing. The exact time of the flights depend on densities of weevils, abundance of fruit, and percentage of infested fruit.

Outbreaks of the boll weevil are linked with favorable weather and adequate food and shelter. Cotton that is allowed to grow and to develop squares in late summer provides the weevils with an abundant supply of breeding sites and nourishing food. Because well-fed weevils enter hibernation with higher levels of accumulated fat, they survive in larger numbers.

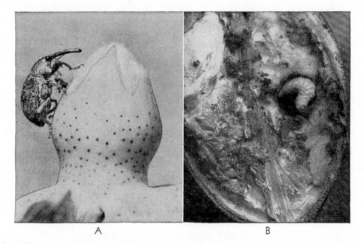

A   B

Fig. 11:10. The cotton boll weevil. A, adult resting on square; B, larva feeding in boll. A, *courtesy Shell Chemical Company; B, courtesy Hercules Powder Company.*

Dormancy of adults is not incited solely by colder temperatures in their habitat, instead they enter a state of diapause characterized by increased fat and decreased water content, lower respiratory rate, and atrophy of the sex organs. At least a few "hibernating" adults may be found in any month of the year.

Mild winters and satisfactory shelter favor survival of the hibernating weevils. Field studies have shown that winter mortality is usually quite high. Nevertheless, significant variations in survival occur as it may range from less than 1 per cent up to 20 per cent.

After weevils emerge in spring, frequent rains, moderate temperatures, and plenty of squares for food and for breeding sites promote high populations. On the other hand, prolonged hot, dry weather is lethal to developing larvae and effectively checks a potential outbreak. Excessive heat and low humidity kill the larvae inside squares, particularly those in fallen squares exposed to the sun.

Although as many as 23 species of parasites attack the boll weevil, they are only of slight value in limiting the population. Parasites normally kill about 6 per cent of boll weevil larvae; in a few localities parasitism may run as high as 20 per cent throughout the season. The commonest parasite is a small wasp, *Bracon mellitor* Say, which in its larval stage feeds on and destroys the weevil larva inside the square or boll.

Control. Satisfactory control of the boll weevil depends on the use of both cultural practices and insecticidal treatments. Beneficial cultural practices include: (1) planting of recommended varieties; (2) early planting; (3) stimulating rapid growth by thorough preparation of seed bed, by fertilizing, and by frequent shallow cultivation; (4) delaying thinning and leaving more plants per acre; (5) early destruction of cotton stalks; and (6) destroying favorable hibernation quarters.

Cultural methods have two main objectives. The first and foremost is to hasten development of cotton plants so that they set a crop before the weevil population has increased to ruinous numbers. The second objective is to reduce the overwintering weevil population and thereby minimize the problem for the next year.

As plant breeders improve cotton, a number of superior varieties are replacing the multitude formerly grown. Currently recommended varieties mature quickly, have determinate growth, yield well, and produce quality lint. So far no variety includes a useful level of resistance to boll weevil.

As soon as danger from frost has passed, early planting of all cotton within an area enables the crop to set bolls before the weevils become numerous.

Stimulating rapid growth and maturity by preparing a good seed bed, fertilizing, and cultivating likewise helps the crop to escape the large summer population of weevils.

Delaying thinning until the plants are several inches tall and leaving the plants thick in the row suppresses vegetative growth and stimulates early fruiting. Much of the cotton in Texas is now planted to a stand; that is, it is planted and not thinned.

Soon after the harvesting of the cotton crop, early community cutting of stalks prevents further multiplication of the weevil population and starves and weakens the adults that go into hibernation. Unfortunately this method is not practicable in the more northern areas where growers are unable to harvest the crop until October and later.

Destroying or reducing the number of favorable hibernating places such as weed patches in or near cotton fields, along fence rows, and in waste land decreases the number of weevils that successfully overwinter.

Chemical control. Because larvae develop inside squares and bolls and because adults feed mainly on internal tissues and migrate extensively, the boll weevil is a difficult insect to control with insecticides. On a single cotton crop during years of heavy infestation farmers may apply as many as twenty insecticidal treatments at three- to five-day intervals. During light years boll weevils may require no treatment in northern parts of the Cotton Belt and perhaps only two or three in southern parts.

From 1919 until 1947 growers made calcium arsenate dust the No. 1 boll weevil insecticide, applying it full strength at rates of 5 to 10 lbs. per acre. In 1947 they began turning to the newly discovered chlorinated hydrocarbons. In some areas development of resistance by the boll weevil to chlorinated hydrocarbons has compelled growers to revert to calcium arsenate or to use modern phosphate insecticides.

Table 11:1 shows the dosage of insecticides that have controlled the boll weevil in one or more areas of the Cotton Belt. Since applying these insecticides singly may create other insect or mite problems, they are often combined with insecticides that will counteract any side effects. Interestingly enough, entomologists have found a synergistic action between toxaphene and DDT, for a mixture of the two has given greater mortality of resistant boll weevils than that expected from the sum of the mortalities of the two toxicants used separately.

The timing of treatments is important for successful control of boll weevil, but varies with the region, weather, and severity of infestation. Some states recommend controlling boll weevils only during midseason (blooming period) and late-season (maturing period); whereas other states recommend treatment during early-season (pre-bloom period) as well.

A new approach in the use of insecticides against the boll weevil is being investigated by making treatments during the harvest period. Insecticidal treatments of methyl parathion combined with cultural methods prevent the insect from entering diapause and reduce the overwintering population to lower levels than cultural methods alone.

In spite of the great variety of modern insecticides, new application equipment, and the many years of investigating the pest, we still have not satisfactorily solved the problem of the boll weevil. This fact is indicated by the many entomologists devoting full or part time to its study and by the completion in 1961 of a $1,100,000 USDA Boll Weevil Research Laboratory on the campus of Mississippi State University. Preliminary plans call for around 25 scientists to be employed at the laboratory.

Pink bollworm

Pectinophora gossypiella (Saunders) [Lepidoptera:Gelechiidae]

The pink bollworm, a native of Asia, perhaps India, has become a major world-wide pest of cotton. Man, in shipping infested cotton seed, has spread this injurious species to all the important cotton growing countries of the world. Once the insect gains entry into a country, it may disperse widely by flight.

Egyptian seed, imported in 1911 into Mexico, carried the pink bollworm to North America. Not long afterwards, in 1917, entomologists found the insect in fields near Hearne, Texas. It apparently had entered the country in the fall of 1916 in a shipment of cotton seed sent to an oil mill at Hearne from the Laguna district of Mexico.

In spite of stringent quarantines and control measures, the pink bollworm has fanned out in Texas and crossed state lines into New Mexico, Arizona, Oklahoma, Arkansas, and Louisiana. Unrelated to this infestation a separate population attacks wild cotton in southern Florida and presents a threat to the Southeast's cotton crop.

Even though control measures have not yet stopped the gradual invasion of the Cotton Belt, they have kept injury down to an insignificant amount. The year 1952 was an exception as losses reached almost 35 million dollars in counties of the Coastal Bend Area of Texas.

Damage in foreign countries has often ranged from 15 per cent to as much as 70 per cent of the crop. In Puerto Rico the pink bollworm forced growers completely out of cotton production.

Pink bollworms damage cotton by feeding inside the squares and bolls. Since moths prefer to lay eggs on the bolls, and the larvae prefer to enter them, squares are only infested for a short period early in the season.

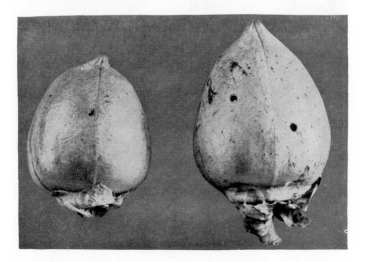

Fig. 11:11. Green cotton bolls a few days before opening, showing exit holes of the pink bollworm. *Courtesy USDA.*

Larvae burrow into the squares where they feed upon the pollen and other embryonic flower parts. Invaded squares do not open normally, as the pink bollworm spins a web of silk around the petals holding them together. This gives the flower a characteristic rosette appearance. Actual loss from square infestation is negligible, but the spring generation developing in squares is important as the progenitor of populations that may severely attack bolls.

Larvae prefer to feed on bolls usually attacking those one-half to three-fourths grown (Fig. 11:11). Boring into them at any point, larvae may go several routes and feed on several tissues. They may feed in the soft carpel tissues producing brownish discolored tunnels. The tunnels, commonly called "railroads," are characteristic of pink bollworm damage. Or the larvae may completely perforate the carpel wall entering and feeding on the immature lint. Some larvae go from one lock to another by cutting round or oval holes through the partitions. Eventually all reach the developing seeds on which they finish their feeding (Fig. 11:12).

In completing growth each pink bollworm eats out the contents of several seeds. From one to several larvae may infest a single boll and in heavily infested cotton there may be an average of six or seven larvae per boll.

Because of their tunneling and feeding within bolls, pink bollworms reduce yields and lower quality of the lint. Frequently cotton loses a full

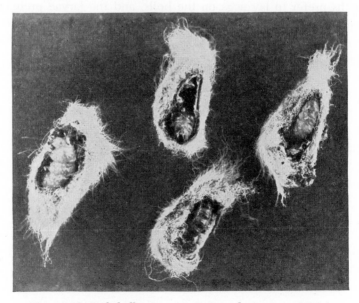

Fig. 11:12. Pink bollworm in cotton seed. *Courtesy USDA.*

grade because of pink bollworm damage. In addition they reduce the yield of seeds and the quantity and quality of the oil.

The pink bollworm is known to propagate on 39 plant species under natural conditions in this country. Okra is probably preferred after cotton and is considered in the same category as cotton in the overwintering of the species and quarantine regulations.

Description. The moths are grayish brown with irregular markings on the forewings. They have a wingspread of about ⅗ in. The eggs, usually laid in masses on the cotton plant, are elongate oval and 0.5 mm. long. They are pearly white with a greenish tint when first deposited but become reddish before hatching. The larvae are creamy white with dark brown heads and thoracic shields. Usually not until the fourth instar do they acquire the pink color that gives them the name "pink bollworm." The full-grown larvae measure about ½ in. long. The pupae are brown, pubescent, and about ⅜ in. long (Fig. 11:13).

Life history. The pink bollworm passes the winter in the larval stage. Beginning in spring and extending into summer, overwintering larvae pupate and about ten days later emerge as moths. Peak numbers usually occur before the first bolls appear.

The moths are seclusive during the day, hiding under trash, stones, and clods in the cotton field. At dusk they become active. Through the night they fly from plant to plant feeding on nectar, resting, mating, and laying eggs.

Though females prefer to deposit eggs on bolls, usually in clusters under the calyx, they may place them on all parts of the cotton plant, even in soil. During their lifetime of about 15 days, female moths produce from 100 to 200 eggs.

The eggs hatch in about five days and the young larvae bore through the carpel wall of bolls. Cutting into the tissues and throwing the fragments outside, they become completely hidden in 20 to 40 minutes. Much mortality occurs at this time, as only about 10 per cent of the larvae succeed in entering bolls.

Once larvae penetrate the bolls, they are protected from enemies and adverse weather and unless crowded by other larvae inside the boll, their chances of survival are good. Pink bollworms are antagonistic and often kill one another on contact. Having gained entrance into the boll they feed on the tender tissues, the inner carpel wall, the immature lint, the outer seed coat of immature seeds, and particularly the inside of older seeds. They molt three times and become full grown in 10 to 14 days. Then they either cut a round hole through the boll wall and drop to the ground or they remain in the boll, usually inside a hollowed-out seed.

In spring and summer the majority of larvae are the so-called short-cycle or summer larvae which spin light cocoons, pupate mainly in the soil, and give rise to succeeding generations. As the pink bollworm completes a generation in 25 to 30 days during summer, there may be as many as six generations a year.

Fig. 11:13. Life stages of the pink bollworm, larva, pupa, the adult moth, and cluster of eggs, *Larva, pupa, and adult, courtesy Hercules Powder Company; eggs, courtesy USDA.*

A few larvae in summer and almost all in fall enter dormancy. They are the long-cycle or resting larvae. Spinning a tough cocoon, they remain in the boll usually inside a hollowed-out seed, or inside two hollowed-out seeds that they tie together. Because the united seeds, called "double seeds," show up after ginning they serve as good indicators of pink bollworm infestation.

In warm, humid areas winter survival of resting larvae is greatest in bolls that remain attached to standing plants or that lie on the soil surface. Few survive the winter buried in the soil. In comparatively cold arid areas, minimum winter temperatures of 15° F. or lower, kill the larvae in bolls on standing cotton.

Several parasites and predators attack pink bollworms. Two common parasites are the wasps, *Bracon mellitor* Say and *Bracon gelechiae* Ashm. Neither species appears to contribute much toward economic control of the pest. Currently various disease organisms are being studied and investigated with the objective of exploiting biological control. Entomologists are attempting to use a nematode parasite which transmits a lethal bacterial disease to pink bollworms.

Control. Although insecticides are necessary at times to control heavy infestations of the pink bollworm in order to prevent crop losses, growers make cultural practices their first line of defense. The chief objectives of cultural control are to have an early maturing crop so that it escapes the high populations of pink bollworm which come late in the season, to harvest early to stop pink bollworm reproduction, and to reduce the numbers of overwintering pink bollworm. Mandatory cultural control zones have been established in the regulated areas of Arizona, Arkansas, Louisiana, much of Texas, and Mexico adjacent to Texas.

Recommended cultural practices include the following. (1) Plant at the optimum time and shorten the planting period. Select a recommended early-maturing variety. Use seeds which have been culled, treated with a fungicide, and tested for germination. (2) Leave as thick a stand of cotton plants as recommended for an area and type of soil. (3) Produce the cotton crop in the shortest practicable time. Early-season insect control has proved advantageous in some states. Protection of early fruit from insects will assure an early harvest. (4) Withhold late irrigation and use defoliants or desiccants to hasten opening of bolls. (5) Shred and plow under cotton stalks as soon as possible after harvest. Okra stalks should be shredded and plowed under at the same time. (6) In cold arid areas where winter irrigation is not feasible, leave stalks standing until lowest temperatures have occurred in order to obtain a maximum kill of pink bollworms infesting bolls on the stalks. But if a large amount of crop debris such as seed cotton or locks is on the soil surface, high survival of the pest may ensue, so the stalks should be shredded and plowed under as early and as deeply as possible. The flail type stalk shredder is more efficient than the horizontal rotary type for pink bollworm control.

When chemical control is required weekly applications of DDT, or DDT plus Guthion, or Sevin are effective.

Eradication of the pink bollworm is possible in areas which are not subject to constant reinfestation. Programs of this sort depend on the enforcement of cultural and chemical control measures.

Ever since the pink bollworm was first found in the United States Federal and State quarantines and sponsored survey and control programs have slowed down the spread of the pest. The Federal quarantine prohibits the entry of cottonseed and cottonseed hulls from most of Mexico and from all other countries. Cotton, cottonseed cake and meal enter only under restricted conditions.

Quarantines also govern the movement of cotton and cotton products produced in infested areas of the United States. In general the regulations require that cotton, cotton products, and all articles connected with the production of cotton be treated to render them free of pink bollworms before they are moved to nonquarantined areas.

Other regulations include deadlines for planting cotton and for harvesting and destroying stalks, and processing plant sanitation.

Entomologists and plant breeders are intensifying their efforts to transfer the natural resistance of several Old World species of cotton to pink bollworm into new varieties.

Cotton fleahopper

Psallus seriatus (Reuter) [Hemiptera:Miridae]

Several species of mirid bugs, the lygus bugs, *Lygus hesperus* and *L. elisus,* the tarnished plant bug, ragweed plant bug, superb plant bug, the black cotton fleahoppers *(Rhinacloa forticornis* and *Spanogonicus albofasciatus),* and the cotton fleahopper are serious pests of cotton. Although causing similar injury to cotton, the species vary in importance in different areas of the Cotton Belt.

Widespread in North America, the cotton fleahopper causes greatest damage in Texas, Louisiana, and Oklahoma. It is a native insect whose host plants include many weeds such as goatweed (*Croton*), horsemint (*Monarda*), primrose (*Oenothera*), horsenettle (*Solanum*), and orach (*Atriplex*). Cotton, the only cultivated plant seriously attacked, appears to be an acquired food plant of this bug.

Described in 1876 by Reuter from specimens collected in Texas, the cotton fleahopper attracted little attention as an economic pest until 1920, when investigators showed that the appearance of a new type of damage to cotton, excessive shedding of minute squares, was associated with the feeding of this insect.

In feeding, cotton fleahoppers prefer to suck juices from the tender growing terminals and squares, which causes the tiny squares to turn brown and fall from the plant. The bugs also feed on other parts inducing swelling and splitting of stems and deformities in leaves (Fig. 11:14). Although injury is of a local nature and is due to toxic salivary juices injected into the plant by the insect, mass attack brings about abnormal development of the whole plant. Fruiting is retarded, internodes are decreased in length but increased in number, plants either become bushy or become tall and whip-like and usually produce only a few bolls near the tops.

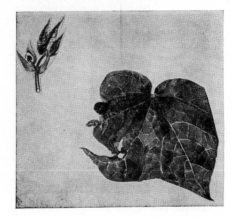

Fig. 11:14. Damage of the cotton fleahopper, blasted bud and deformed leaf. *Courtesy USDA.*

Description. The cotton fleahopper inserts small, glistening white eggs, about 0.8 mm. by 0.2 mm., into the stems of host plants. Previous to hatching the eggs become suffused with yellow. First instar nymphs are pale green, 1 mm. long, and have prominent scarlet eyes. Older instars become greener and densely mottled with black spots. The adults are light green, densely spotted black, and approximately ⅛ inch long (Fig. 11:15).

Life history. The cotton fleahopper passes the winter in the egg stage mainly inside the stems of wild host plants such as goatweed. Overwintering eggs hatch early in spring and populations build up rapidly as the bugs are able to complete 7 or 8 generations during a growing season in the South.

Development of large populations of cotton fleahoppers depend upon a favorable sequence of host plants as well as favorable weather. In early spring the bugs feed on early weeds such as evening primrose and crowfoot. In late spring and early summer they move to goatweed, horsemint, and horsenettle. When weed hosts become tough in summer, the bugs migrate to cotton which at this time is more succulent. In late summer and fall they return to wild hosts, principally goatweed.

Depending on temperature and moisture, eggs vary in rate of development. Under optimum conditions eggs may hatch in five days but on an average they hatch in seven or eight days. The nymphs develop rapidly passing through five instars, in as little as ten days, to reach the adult stage.

Fig. 11:15. The cotton fleahopper. Left, nymph; right, adult. *Courtesy Hercules Powder Company.*

Adult females feed for three or four days before they begin to deposit eggs inside the stems and other parts of the host plant. They lay the eggs singly by means of a strong swordlike ovipositor. Observations on bugs confined in cages indicate that females live from 14 to 29 days and produce around 21 eggs each. Males have a somewhat shorter lifespan.

Control. Though growers place main reliance on insecticides to control damaging infestations of cotton fleahopper, clean culture can be helpful in preventing outbreaks. Destruction of weeds near cotton fields eliminates important host plants and plowing under old cotton stalks destroys overwintering eggs.

Entomologists usually advise application of insecticide when cotton fleahoppers reach an abundance of 15 to 35 nymphs and adults per 100 terminals or 16 to 20 per 100 sweepings. Dusting or spraying with aldrin, BHC, DDT, dieldrin, endrin, Guthion, heptachlor, malathion, Sevin, Strobane, or toxaphene has provided adequate control. Applications are made at seven to ten day intervals, their exact number depending on intensity and duration of the infestation.

Black cutworm

Agrotis ipsilon (Hufnagel) [Lepidoptera:Noctuidae]

The Noctuidae, containing some 2,700 species in the United States and Canada, has many members that are serious crop pests in their larval stages. The larvae, named after their habits, are known commonly as cutworms, armyworms, loopers, semiloopers, leafworms, borers, and fruitworms.

Entomologists divide the cutworms into four main groups based on their ways of feeding: subterranean, surface feeders, climbers, and tunnel makers. Subterranean cutworms normally feed underground on the stems of plants and may pull young plants beneath the surface. The pale western cutworm, a serious pest of wheat and other grains in the West, is a notable example of this group. Surface feeders are species that feed at or near the surface of the soil and often cut plants down. Climbers are those which climb high on the plant to feed on leaves, flowers, and other aerial parts. Tunnel makers form tunnels in the soil and drag parts of plants into them to feed on. Some entomologists consider armyworms as climbing cutworms that have developed the habit of migrating in large bands.

As one might expect, cotton has more than its share of serious noctuid enemies. Grouping them into general categories, we may list the following cutworms and relatives:

Subterranean cutworms
 no cotton pests
Surface feeding cutworms
 army cutworm, *Chorizagrotis auxiliaris* (Grote)
 granulate cutworm, *Feltia subterranea* (Fabricius)
Climbing cutworms
 bollworm, *Heliothis zea* (Boddie)
 tobacco budworm, *Heliothis virescens* (Fabricius)
 variegated cutworm, *Peridroma saucia* (Hübner)
Tunnel making cutworms
 black cutworm, *Agrotis ipsilon* (Hufnagel)
 pale-sided cutworm, *Agrotis malefida* Guenée
Armyworms
 beet armyworm, *Spodoptera exigua* (Hübner)
 fall armyworm, *Laphygma frugiperda* (J. E. Smith)
 yellow-striped armyworm, *Prodenia ornithogalli* Guenée
 western yellow-striped armyworm, *Prodenia praefica* Grote

Leafworms
  cotton leafworm, *Alabama argillacea* (Hbn.)
  brown cotton leafworm, *Acontia dacia* Druce
  Anomis erosa Hbn.
  Anomis flava fimbriago Steph.
  Anomis texana Riley
Loopers
  cabbage looper, *Trichoplusia ni* (Hübner)
Borers
  stalk borer, *Papaipema nebris* (Guenée)

Cutworms in cotton are enemies chiefly of the seedling plants. The pests frequently develop in weeds, in legumes, and in other crops and will attack and often destroy stands of cotton planted in or adjacent to infested land.

The various species of cutworms are usually polyphagous in their feeding habits. The black cutworm, no exception to this rule, not only seriously attacks seedling cotton but also young corn plants, tobacco, and many vegetables. It likewise finds forage legumes highly palatable.

The black cutworm is a highly destructive species, much out of proportion to the amount of vegetation it consumes. Relatively small populations are able to destroy entire stands of cotton because of the cutworm's habit of eating into the stem of a plant, cutting it down near ground level, and then moving on to repeat the havoc on other plants.

The species is widely distributed throughout the world occurring in the United States, southern Canada, Mexico, South America, Europe, Asia, Africa, Australia, and elsewhere. Preferring moist or wet soil, the species exhibits a high tolerance to moisture. Outbreaks often arise in river bottoms after floods and in wet muck lands.

Description. The eggs are deposited in groups of one to 30 on leaves and stems near the ground. Each egg is sinuously ribbed, subconical in profile, and measures approximately .45 mm. high and .65 mm. in diameter. The egg is white when laid but becomes suffused with brown the second day. The larvae are almost unicolorous dorsally and vary from light gray to nearly black. Full grown, they measure from 1¼ to 2 in. long. The pupa is naked, brown, and ⅝ to ⅞ in. long. The adult moth has a wing expanse of 1½ to 2 in. The forewings are long, narrow, usually dark, and each is characteristically marked with three black dashes. One dash arises from the outer side of the reniform spot and the other two point toward the first one from near the outer margin of the wing (Fig. 11:16).

Life history. The black cutworm normally passes the winter in the pupal stage. In spring the adults emerge and mate. Females lay their eggs usually at night and dissection indicates that they have reproductive capacities ranging from around 500 to 2,250 eggs each. Preferring low or over-flowed wet soil, moths select plants growing in such sites for oviposition. They deposit eggs singly or in small clutches on the leaves and stems of plants. They also deposit eggs on soil in the laboratory and no doubt in the field.

Fig. 11:16. The black cutworm. A, adult; B, larva or cutworm; C, pupa in its soil cell; D, pupa removed from cell. A, C, D, *courtesy Can. Dept. Agr.*, B, *courtesy University of Nebraska.*

In three to six days the larvae hatch from the eggs, move to the soil, and begin to feed and grow. Young black cutworms feed first on the leaf surface, then later eat holes in leaves. Only the older larvae develop the cutting habit. Most feeding is done in the evening. Older larvae may drag their food into tunnels which they make in the soil. The black cutworm is noted for its aggressive, pugnacious, and cannibalistic nature. They are exceedingly antisocial, for $1 + 1 = 1$.

Although some larvae require seven instars and a few eight, the majority become full grown in six instars. Varying with temperature the larval period lasts from 25 to 35 days. The full grown larva forms a cell in the soil in which it pupates. During the summer the pupal period lasts around 12 to

15 days. The entire cycle from egg to adult takes around 45 to 55 days and a multiple number of generations are produced each year ranging from two to three in northern states and in Canada to four or more in southern states.

As with most cutworms, a number of parasites, predators, and diseases take their toll, but their importance in limiting outbreaks of the black cutworm is doubtful.

Control. Though growers place main reliance on insecticides to control damaging infestations of cutworms, cultural methods are helpful. They include clean cultivation at least three weeks prior to planting, elimination of weed host plants, and thorough seed-bed preparation.

For many years poisoned baits have been used to control cutworms, but the present trend is toward using sprays, dusts, or granules. The following insecticides with amounts of toxicant per acre have been recommended as sprays or dusts to control cutworms in cotton: toxaphene 2 to 5 lbs., DDT 1 to 2.5 lbs., endrin 0.2 to 0.5 lb., dieldrin 0.3 to 0.5 lb. These may be applied as a broadcast treatment of ground and plants or as a band treatment in crop rows. Since these insecticides vary in their effectiveness depending on species of cutworm and on environmental conditions, growers should get specific recommendations from local entomologists or county agents. Two of the most important considerations in preventing destruction of seedling stands is the early discovery of cutworms and then prompt insecticidal treatment.

Selected References

Adkisson, P. O., L. H. Wilkes, and S. P. Johnson, *Chemical, Cultural, and Mechanical Control of the Pink Bollworm,* Tex. Agr. Exp. Sta. Bul. 920, 1958.

Anon., *The Boll Weevil: How to Control It,* USDA Leaflet No. 2147, 1960.

Anon., *The Bollworm: How to Control It,* USDA Leaflet No. 462, 1960.

Anon., *The Cotton Aphid: How to Control It,* USDA Leaflet No. 467, 1960.

Anon., *The Cotton Fleahopper: How to Control It,* USDA Leaflet No. 475, 1960.

Anon., *The Cotton Leafworm: How to Control It,* USDA Leaflet No. 468, 1960.

Anon., *Official 1960 Cotton Pest Control Guides* (Memphis: National Cotton Council), 1960.

Anon., *The Pink Bollworm: How We Fight It,* USDA Leaflet No. 339, 1953.

Anon., *Thirteenth Annual Conference Report on Cotton Insect Research and Control,* USDA Entomology Research Division, 1960.

Brazzel, J. R., and D. F. Martin, *Resistance of Cotton to Pink Bollworm Damage,* Tex. Agr. Exp. Sta. Bul. 843, 1956.

——, L. D. Newson, J. S. Roussel, C. Lincoln, F. J. Williams, and G. Barnes, *Bollworm and Tobacco Budworm as Cotton Pests in Louisiana and Arkansas,* La. Tech. Bul. 482, 1953.

Chapman, A. J., L. W. Noble, O. T. Robertson, and L. C. Fife, *Survival of the Pink Bollworm under Various Cultural and Climatic Conditions,* USDA Production Res. Rpt. No. 34, 1960.

Crumb, S. E., *Tobacco Cutworms,* USDA Tech. Bul. 88, 1929.

Faulkner, L. R., *Hemipterous Insect Pests: Their Occurrence and Distribution in Principal Cotton Producing Areas of New Mexico,* New Mex. Agr. Exp. Sta. Bul. 372, 1952.

Fenton, F. A., and E. W. Dunnam, *Biology of the Cotton Boll Weevil at Florence, S.C.,* USDA Tech. Bul. 112, 1929.

Folsom, J. W., *Insect Enemies of the Cotton Plant,* USDA Farmers' Bul. 1688, 1932.

Gaines, R. C., *Ecological Investigations of the Boll Weevil,* USDA Tech. Bul. 1208, 1959.

Isely, D., *The Cotton Aphid,* Ark. Agr. Exp. Sta. Bul. 462, 1946.

Loftin, U. C., *Living with the Boll Weevil for Fifty Years,* Ann. Rpt. Smithsonian Institution, pp. 273–291, 1945.

Newsom, L. D., J. S. Roussel, and C. E. Smith, *The Tobacco Thrips: Its Seasonal History and Status as a Cotton Pest,* La. Agr. Exp. Sta. Bul. 474, 1953.

Ohlendorf, W., *Studies of the Pink Bollworm in Mexico,* USDA Tech. Bul. 1374, 1926.

Reinhard, H. J., *The Cotton Flea Hopper,* Tex. Agr. Exp. Sta. Bul. 339, 1926.

Telford, A. D., and L. Hopkins, *Arizona Cotton Insects,* Ariz. Agr. Exp. Sta. Bul. 286, 1957.

Watts, J. G., *A study of the biology of the flower thrips* Frankliniella tritici *(Fitch) with Special Reference to Cotton,* S.C. Agr. Exp. Sta. Bul. 306, 1936.

Chapter 12 | VEGETABLE CROP
INSECTS | W. Don Fronk

The pests

All vegetables grown in the United States are attacked by one or more insects and any grower, whether a backyard gardener or a commercial producer, is vitally interested in protecting his crop. Entomologists have estimated that insects caused an annual loss of at least $139,527,000 to vegetable producers during the years 1942 to 1952.

Many of the vegetables grown in the United States are of foreign origin. In their native land these plants are attacked by a number of insects. When such pests become accidentally introduced into the United States, certain controlling factors such as parasites, predators and diseases are often left behind. Enjoying the lack of enemies, the pests become much more serious than they were in their original home. For example, the European corn borer, whose name indicates its origin, is of little significance to corn production in Europe while in the United States it is considered one of the most serious pests of both sweet and field corn. Problems may also arise by native insects showing preference for introduced vegetables over original host plants. Table 12:1 shows the origin of several vegetables grown in the United States and the origin of their insect pests.

We can divide vegetable insect pests into two groups according to their selection of food plants: (1) those restricted more or less to one species of vegetable or to closely related species; and (2) those feeding on a wide variety of vegetables and often referred to as "general feeders." In the first group we may mention such pests as asparagus beetles, squash vine borer, onion maggot, tomato hornworm, and many species of aphids. In the second group we may especially note such pests as cutworms, grasshoppers, white grubs, wireworms, spider mites, blister beetles, vegetable weevil, and lygus bugs.

346

Table 12:1 | Geographical Origin of Some Vegetables and Their Insect Pests

Vegetable	Origin	Pest	Origin
Cabbage	Western Europe and north shore of Mediterranean	Cabbageworm	Northwest Europe
		Cabbage maggot	Northwest Europe
		Harlequin bug	Central America
Bean	North America	Bean weevil	Mediterranean area
Potato	North and South America	Potato tuber moth	Central America
		Colorado potato beetle	North America
Watermelon	Africa	Melon aphid	Central America
Cucumber	East Indies	Striped cucumber beetle	North America
Muskmelon	India	Squash bug	North America
Squash	North America	Squash vine borer	North America

The importance of vegetable insects will often vary in different sections of North America. Some species inhabit limited regions and for this reason may be only of local importance; others may be widely distributed yet reach injurious numbers only in certain areas favorable for their increase; still others, representing about half the total number of vegetable pests, attack and severely injure their hosts wherever they are grown.

Fig. 12:1. Adult of the Colorado potato beetle, a serious pest of solanaceous crops. *Courtesy Shell Chemical Company.*

Because vegetables belong to several different plant families, their insect enemies are many and diverse and we shall take time to mention only some of the most important ones.

Insects injurious to solanaceous crops—potato, tomato, eggplant, and pepper—include the Colorado potato beetle (Fig. 12:1), tomato hornworm, potato leafhopper, potato tuberworm, tomato fruitworm (Fig. 9:12), eggplant lacebug, potato psyllid, pepper weevil, blister beetles, cutworms, flea beetles, wireworms, and aphids.

Cruciferous crops—cabbage, broccoli, brussels sprouts, radish, turnip, and mustard—are attacked by the cabbage looper, imported cabbageworm (Fig. 12:12), diamondback moth caterpillar, cabbage webworm, cabbage maggot, seed-corn maggot (Fig. 12:15), harlequin bug (Fig. 4:9B), cabbage aphid, vegetable weevil, flea beetles, and cutworms.

The pests of cucurbits—cucumbers, squash, pumpkin, and various melons—include the striped cucumber beetle (Fig. 12:8), spotted cucumber beetle (Fig. 9:17B), pickleworm, squash vine borer (Fig. 12:2), squash bug (Fig. 4:9A), melon aphid, and cutworms.

Insects that damage beets, spinach, and chard—all members of the family Chenopodiaceae—include the beet webworm, beet armyworm, beet leafhopper (Fig. 12:17), sugar-beet root aphid, sugar-beet root maggot, sugar-beet wireworm, spinach flea beetle, and spinach leaf miner.

Beans are fed upon by the Mexican bean beetle (Fig. 12:10), bean leaf beetle, bean aphid, bean weevil, lima-bean pod borer, potato leafhopper, seed-corn maggot, and corn earworm. The two-spotted spider mite is a serious bean pest, particularly in hot, dry weather. Peas are attacked by the pea aphid, pea weevil, and pea moth.

Fig. 12:2. Squash vine borer in stem of squash plant. *Courtesy Iowa State University.*

Fig. 12:3. A white grub feeding on corn root. *Courtesy Shell Chemical Company.*

Onions are injured by the onion maggot, onion thrips, and wireworms.

Lettuce is set upon by the cabbage looper, six-spotted leafhopper, cutworms, wireworms, and aphids.

Vegetables belonging to the Umbelliferae—carrots, celery, and parsnips—are relished by the carrot rust fly (Fig. 4:28), carrot weevil, celery leaf tier, celery looper, parsnip webworm, six-spotted leafhopper, tarnished plant bug (Fig. 4:9C), wireworms, and aphids.

Asparagus is attacked by the asparagus beetle, spotted asparagus beetle, and asparagus miner (Fig. 4:29).

Sweetpotato suffers from the feeding of the sweetpotato weevil, sweetpotato leaf beetle, sweetpotato flea beetle, sweetpotato or tortoise beetles, and wireworms.

Sweet corn is damaged by the corn earworm, fall armyworm, European corn borer (Fig. 9:15), seed-corn maggot, corn sap beetle, cutworms, grasshoppers, white grubs (Fig. 12:3), and wireworms.

The injury

Insect injury to vegetables has many forms, the most obvious being the actual consumption of plant parts above ground. Chewing insects like cabbageworms often destroy heads completely; Colorado potato beetles sometimes strip all of the leaves from potato and eggplant; in satisfying their voracious appetites grasshoppers may eat everything but the stalks of sweet corn.

Many vegetable pests confine their feeding to particular parts of the plant. The larvae of the cowpea curculio, pea weevil, and bean weevil feed within the green seeds; corn earworms feed chiefly on the juicy kernels at the end of the cob, though they may also feed in the whorl of young

Fig. 12:4. A squash plant dying from attack of the squash vine borer. *Courtesy Iowa State University.*

corn plants; tomato fruitworms eat holes in the tomato fruit; larvae of the pepper weevil feed within the buds and pods of pepper plants. Some insects, such as the squash vine borer, burrow inside of the stems of vegetables (Fig. 12:4).

Just as serious and frequently just as noticeable as the damage of chewing insects is the damage caused by sucking insects, such as aphids, leafhoppers, stink bugs, and lygus bugs. Besides withdrawing juices from the plant, which depresses growth, they may inject toxic salivary secretions which cause disease. By their feeding potato leafhoppers produce a disease known as hopperburn. Conspicuous symptoms in potatoes are the upward curling of the leaves at the tips and sides, triangular necrotic areas at the edges of the leaves, and shortened internodes. Similar symptoms appear in beans though the edges of the leaves curl down rather than up.

Lygus bugs feeding on lima beans inject a toxin that causes the blossoms and small pods to shed and young seeds to shrivel. One aphid species causes white spots on celery leaves, another yellowing and chlorosis, and a third curling of the leaflets. Squash bugs feeding on cucurbits inject a toxin that produces anasa wilt, the symptoms of which resemble those of bacterial wilt.

A devastating systemic disease of potatoes and tomatoes called psyllid yellows results from the feeding of nymphs of the potato psyllid. In potatoes the symptoms are a marginal yellowing and upward curling of the leaflets; reddening or purpling of the terminal leaves of pigmented varieties, and stunting of the plant. In young plants infected with the disease tuberization is suppressed, while in older plants the tubers increase in number but remain small and worthless.

Another important way in which insects cause serious injury to vegetables is through their transmission of pathogenic fungi, bacteria, and viruses. A few examples will illustrate this kind of damage. The green stink bug transmits the fungus that causes yeast spot on lima beans. The striped and spotted cucumber beetles transmit bacterial wilt of cucurbits, while the toothed flea beetle and corn flea beetle transmit bacterial wilt of sweet corn. The seed-corn maggot and the onion maggot transmit bacterial soft rot of vegetables.

Insects are the most important vectors of virus diseases of plants; and of these vectors aphids transmit the greatest number of different virus diseases. They transmit common bean mosaic, squash mosaic, cucumber mosaic, potato leafroll, onion yellow dwarf, and many more.

But there are other insects important in transmitting plant viruses, such as the six-spotted leafhopper which transmits the virus of aster yellows to carrots, lettuce, and potatoes as well as asters; the beet leafhopper which transmits curly top virus to beets, tomatoes, and beans; and thrips which transmit the virus of tomato spotted wilt.

Vegetables are also bothered by injurious soil insects that eat the seed, cut off roots, shred underground stems, burrow in roots and tubers (Fig. 12:5), and even cut down entire plants. Numbered among the serious soil pests of vegetables are wireworms, whitegrubs, seed-corn maggot, cabbage maggot, corn rootworms, flea beetle larvae, and cutworms.

Insects need not necessarily feed on vegetables to be destructive. One of the chief concerns of the asparagus grower is the presence of asparagus beetle eggs on the spears. These eggs are difficult to remove and if too

Fig. 12:5. Sweet potato damaged by the feeding of a wireworm. *Courtesy Iowa State University.*

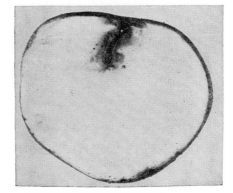

many are present the particular shipment of asparagus may be refused for canning purposes.

Cultural control

Growers cannot consistently produce good yields of high quality vegetables unless they control the insects that threaten their crops. There are several cultural control methods that vegetable growers should regularly employ to reduce insect injury. These have an advantage over chemical methods in usually being cheaper and in leaving no poisonous residues.

1. Rotation of crops tends to reduce some insect populations. The species most susceptible to control by rotation are those which are limited to a narrow range of food plants and are unable to move far in search of food and those confined to a limited area because of the nature of their life cycle.
2. Burying of crop remnants by plowing or disking helps to control several vegetable pests such as cabbageworms, European corn borer, and Mexican bean beetle by destroying their hibernating quarters.
3. Controlling weeds in and surrounding vegetable plantings reduces the threat of many pest species which breed in weeds. Included in this group are grasshoppers, flea beetles, stalk borer, garden webworm, and potato tuberworm.
4. Shallow plowing and cultivation may be used to expose insects living in the soil to freezing temperatures and to predaceous animals. Insects which pupate in the soil may likewise be killed by such treatment. Deep plowing may bury insects so deeply that they are fatally trapped.
5. Where the insect infestation is spotty, destruction of affected plants may prevent spreading and a general outbreak. Since vegetable crops are usually planted so that individual plants may be examined, this method of control is often practical. One should handle infested plants carefully to prevent pests from scattering to other plants.
6. Growers may use trap crops to control certain insects by planting a few rows of the vegetable in advance of the main planting. The insects tend to collect on the early plants where one can destroy them with strong sprays or dusts. Growers may also establish effective trap crops by seeding plants more attractive to pests than the main crop. Trap crops have been used particularly to advantage in protecting cole vegetables.

7. Mechanical barriers, commonly used by the home gardener, may also be used to advantage by commercial growers where labor costs are not prohibitive. Wrapping stems of transplants with paper will protect them from cutworms. Covering small plants with cheesecloth or screen will ward off insects until the plants reach a size sufficient to withstand attack. In this way some growers protect seedling cucurbits from cucumber beetle attack.

8. In small gardens hand picking is sometimes a feasible method of control. Hand picking is especially effective for use on large insects such as tomato hornworm.

9. Vegetable varieties resistant to insects have been developed by plant breeders. There are potato varieties which have varying degrees of resistance to leafhopper, Colorado potato beetle, flea beetles, aphids, and potato psyllid. Some beans are resistant to leafhoppers, peas to aphids, and squash to squash vine borer.

10. Variation in time of planting may help in insect control. In the north, early planted sweet corn may escape corn earworm damage; but in the south, corn earworn larvae are more common in the early planted sweet corn. Early planted squash tends to have a higher population of squash vine borers.

11. As a last resort, vegetable growers may curtail the production of certain crops for several years until pest populations have fallen to noninjurious numbers.

Chemical control

The modern vegetable grower is faced with the problem of producing quality vegetables uncontaminated by insects yet bearing no harmful residues. To a large degree modern insecticides have enabled him to meet this challenge.

One way in which the grower achieves this goal is by employing materials nontoxic to higher animals, such as the botanical insecticides pyrethrum and rotenone and to a less extent ryania and sabadilla. As used in agriculture today, these insecticides constitute no hazard to man or to his livestock. They are effective against a wide range of insect pests, but they possess little residual action and are relatively expensive. A second way in which the grower controls injurious pests and yet avoids toxic residues is by applying short-lived synthetic insecticides like TEPP, Dibrom, or phosdrin.

As a rule vegetable growers treat with the more residual and less expensive insecticides such as DDT, TDE, methoxychlor, perthane, aldrin, dieldrin, endrin, heptachlor, malathion, and parathion and then wait a minimum period of time for residues to disappear or to decrease to tolerable amounts before harvesting.

Because vegetable growers require a large number of insecticides to handle their many pest problems, entomologists have searched for a mixture of insecticides to simplify the task. One such mixture contains methoxychlor, malathion, and a fungicide. The so-called general-purpose dusts or sprays have found greater acceptance among home gardeners than among commercial growers.

To be sure, the control of insects on commercial plantings and the control of insects in the home vegetable garden present two different problems. The commercial grower, trained to use a wide range of chemicals, has an advantage in having available not only special application equipment to apply insecticides efficiently and effectively, but also special produce washing equipment to take care of residues of toxicant. Yet in some ways he has greater limitations than the home gardener, for he must consider closely labor costs and the prices of various insecticides.

In recent years vegetable growers have begun to recognize the injurious nature of soil insects and have taken measures to stop their losses. They have found that applying materials like heptachlor, aldrin, or dieldrin to the soil is quite effective and profitable. Another method used by growers to control soil pests is to treat the seed with insecticides and fungicides. Frequently the seedhouses make the treatment and so label the seed, but some growers coat their own seed before planting.

To protect crops of high-acre value from nematodes, wireworms, and other soil pests, vegetable growers may apply, two or three weeks before planting, fumigants such as D-D, ethylene dibromide, or chloropicrin. Some fumigants not only control nematodes and insects, but also reduce the population of disease-producing organisms and weed seeds.

In addition to the usual precautions one must take in using insecticides, the vegetable producer must guard against phytotoxicity and the development of off-flavors in his crop. Phytotoxicity may be hidden or clearly evident. An insecticide may cause a slight reduction in growth and yield or it may kill plants outright. Cucurbits are extremely susceptible to insecticide injury. Toxaphene will kill most cucurbits while technical DDT may cause severe injury.

Off-flavors usually arise through the misuse of soil insecticides applied to root crops. BHC is particularly dangerous to use as either a soil or foliar insecticide, but other insecticides such as lindane may also cause trouble.

Control equipment

While home gardeners find it convenient to use hand dusters or hand sprayers to treat their backyard vegetables, commercial producers with large acreages of vegetables employ power dusters or power sprayers. These are usually equipped with booms and drop nozzles to provide thorough coverage of plants. They are usually pulled through the field by tractors.

High pressure sprayers (Fig. 7:6) delivering up to 200 gal. of spray per acre cover the plants most thoroughly and provide the greatest control of both insects and plant diseases; however low pressure, low gallonage sprayers provide nearly as good insect control, but may be less effective in controlling plant diseases.

To further speed up pest control operations some vegetable growers employ large capacity, air-blast sprayers for low-gallonage spraying of row crops (Fig. 12:6). When fields are wet and untraversable by ground-rigs, growers may often hire airplane applicators to treat their crops. In some sections growers use lightweight, back-pack, power dusters to treat vegetables (Fig. 7:13).

Fig. 12:6. An air-blast sprayer dispensing insecticide on a commercial field of vegetables. *Courtesy Oliver Corporation.*

Some vegetable producers use special rigs for treating their crops. Growers of sweet corn control the European corn borer and corn earworm with high-clearance sprayers; growers of sweet potatoes or tomatoes may control soil insects with the transplanting machine by mixing insecticide in the transplant water.

REPRESENTATIVE VEGETABLE INSECTS

The vegetable insects which we have chosen to treat in detail are the: striped cucumber beetle, Mexican bean beetle, imported cabbageworm, seed-corn maggot, and beet leafhopper.

Striped cucumber beetle

Acalymma vittata (Fabricius) [Coleoptera:Chrysomelidae]

The American Indian cultivated cucurbits long before the coming of the white man and they likely had trouble with the striped cucumber beetle which is native to North America. The first published record of this beetle in America was by Fabricius in 1775.

The striped cucumber beetle is found throughout the United States except for the western-most states where it is replaced by the western striped cucumber beetle, *Acalymma trivittata* (Mann.). In Canada, the striped cucumber beetle is a common pest of cucurbits in Ontario, Quebec, New Brunswick, and Nova Scotia and an occasional pest in Manitoba and Saskatchewan. It is known to occur in Mexico and Panama and probably could be found in most of the tropical and temperate regions of South America.

Early in the season, even before all the plants are above ground, these beetles fly from their hibernating quarters into cucurbit fields where they feed on the young plants, frequently killing them. Later the beetles attack the flowers and may prevent a good set of fruit despite the fact that they may assist in cucurbit pollination. They also feed upon the fruits and gnaw deep pits in the rind making the produce unfit for market (Fig. 12:7). Of minor importance is the damage caused by the larvae feeding on the roots of the host plant and on the fruits where they come in contact with the soil.

During early spring and late fall the beetles feed upon other plants, chiefly members of the Rosaceae, but economic damage seldom results.

The striped cucumber beetle and the spotted cucumber beetle (Fig. 9:17B), are vectors of the serious cucurbit disease, bacterial wilt which is caused by *Erwinia tracheiphila* (E. F. Smith). Plants infected with the disease, wilt in warm weather. As the disease progresses, they become permanently wilted, the leaves dry out, and the plant eventually dies.

The causative bacteria overwinter in the bodies of the hibernating beetles which introduce the organisms into plants by contaminating feeding wounds

Fig. 12:7. Rind of squash fed upon by the adult striped cucumber beetle. *Courtesy Iowa State University.*

with feces. So far as is known, this is the only natural method of infection. These two beetles as well as aphids are vectors of squash mosaic virus.

Description. The adult striped cucumber beetle is oblong, yellowish green in color, ³⁄₁₆ to ¼ in. long, and is marked by three slate black stripes (Fig. 12:8). The head, scutellum, front tibia, tips of middle and hind tibia and the tarsi are dark. The elytra is covered with very small punctures. The egg is light yellow or orange in color, round to oval in shape, and about 0.6 mm. long. The worm-like larva is almost ⅜ in. long when full grown. The body is white with a dark head and tail plate. It has three pairs of true legs on the thorax and one pair of prolegs on the caudal segment. The whitish-yellow pupa is about ¼ in. long.

Life history. Adult beetles leave their hibernating quarters and begin to move about in spring when the weather has warmed to 65°F. or more. If there are no cultivated cucurbits available, the adults feed on the flowers of various plants such as serviceberry, haw, and wild cucumber. As soon as cultivated cucurbits begin to break through the surface of the soil, large numbers of beetles appear suddenly in the field and begin feeding on the seedling plants. Some even crawl into cracks in the soil to reach the sprouting seed.

The beetles soon start to mate and continue to do so throughout the summer. The eggs are laid from eight to 25 days after the first mating. To deposit its eggs, the female crawls into cracks or depressions about the base of a cucurbit plant, thrusts her abdomen into the soil and lays her eggs singly or in small clusters. The total number of eggs produced usually varies from 225 to 800 but some females may lay as many as 1,514 eggs. In general the beetles which have hibernated through the winter lay fewer eggs than do the females of other generations.

The incubation period varies with external conditions but averages from

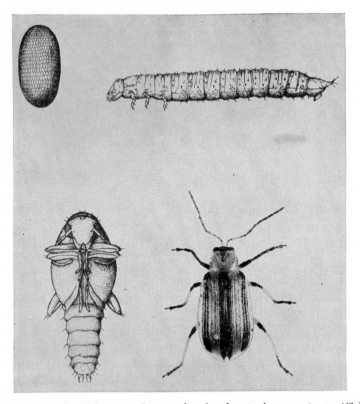

Fig. 12:8. Life stages of the striped cucumber beetle, *Acalymma vittata* (Fab.). *Egg, larva, and pupa, courtesy University of Arkansas; adult, courtesy Iowa State University.*

five to eight days. The larvae, which pass through three instars, spend 15 days feeding on roots and also on stems and fruit which come in contact with the soil. From two to ten days are spent as a prepupa in a small cell formed by the full-grown larva. The pupal period lasts six to seven days. The period from egg to adult for the first generation requires approximately a month while the succeeding generations require slightly longer for development.

Dates of emergence of adult beetles from hibernation and the number of generations depend a great deal on temperature. In Canada the adults leave hibernation in May or June while in Arkansas the beetles may become active in March. In the north the beetle has but one generation a year while in southern Texas it produces four generations.

With the beginning of cool fall weather and the maturing of the cucurbit plants, striped cucumber beetles start moving to their winter quarters. These are usually wooded or brushy areas where the beetles are able to find protection under litter. Hibernating quarters may be as far as a mile from the cucurbit field which produced the beetles.

Control. Recommendations such as covering the plants with cloth, dusting with Bordeaux, calcium arsenate, or lime, and the use of trap crops were common before the discovery of the new organic insecticides. Although there are a number of insecticides which control the beetle, only a few chemicals can be used on cucurbit crops due to their great sensitivity to chemical injury. Application of rotenone, cryolite, or methoxychlor is usually recommended as soon as the plants begin to break through the ground and thereafter at intervals of one to two weeks.

Aldrin and dieldrin are also effective. Even though technical grade of DDT causes severe burning and stunting and should not be applied to cucurbits, the purified form of DDT is effective and causes no phytotoxicity. In humid areas of the South and East, malathion and parathion have caused foliar burn on most cucurbits.

Mexican bean beetle

Epilachna varivestis Mulsant [Coleoptera:Coccinellidae]

Mulsant first described the Mexican bean beetle in 1850 from specimens sent to him from Mexico. It was first definitely known from the United States in 1883, when it was reported from Colorado. Some entomologists have pointed out that this beetle was known in New Mexico close to the time of the Mexican War of 1846–48 and they conjecture that its introduction into the United States might have resulted from the movement of food for the cavalry. It was not of great importance, however, until it appeared in the eastern part of the United States. In 1918 the beetle spread to northern Alabama where it may have entered in a shipment of hay from the West.

A native of Mexico, the beetle is now found generally east of the Mississippi River and in Arizona, New Mexico, Colorado, Utah, Wyoming, Nebraska and Idaho. An isolated infestation occurred in Ventura County, California in 1946 but an energetic control program eliminated it from this state.

Although the Mexican bean beetle is a mandibulate insect, it does not swallow solid food material. Both larva and adult chew off portions of the bean leaf, masticate it and suck the plant juices. The larvae move backward on the under or upper surface of the leaf with their heads swaying and their mandibles working. In this way they rake the plant tissues into ridges from which they suck the juice. The adults feed somewhat in the same manner. Both larvae and adults, usually feeding from the under surface of the leaves, rake up tissue from only one side, the membrane on the opposite side remaining unbroken. As drying sets in the unbroken membrane tears apart (Fig. 12:9).

Fig. 12:9. Bean leaf injured by the feeding of Mexican bean beetle larvae. *Courtesy Union Carbide Chemicals Co.*

The feeding is confined almost entirely to bush and pole beans (*Phaseolus vulgaris*) and to the lima bean (*P. limensis*). However, the beetle can live on other plants and has been found feeding on beggarweed, hyacinth bean, cowpea, soybean, and alfalfa. It may also feed to a limited extent on adsuki bean, kudzu, some clovers, okra, eggplant, and squash.

Description. The strongly convex adult beetles are about ¼ in. long. The elytra are usually copper red in color and are conspicuously marked with 16 black spots arranged in three rows over the back. The eggs are yellow, about 1.3 mm. long, and are laid in clusters on the under surface of bean leaves. Larvae are yellow and covered with dark, branched spines. Full grown larvae are about ⅓ in. long. Pupae are yellowish to copper-colored and about ¼ in. long. The back of the pupa is smooth but the spine-covered last larval skin remains attached to the caudal end of the pupa (Fig. 12:10).

Life history. Hibernating beetles arrive in bean fields about the time the earliest beans are showing their first true leaves. In the South they appear in late March or early April while in Maine they appear in early June.

After a preovipositional period of seven to ten days, females begin to lay batches of 40 to 60 eggs on the underside of bean leaves. Each female may lay an egg mass every two or three days and produce on an average 460 eggs. Some individual females may produce as many as 1,669 eggs. In spring eggs hatch in 10 to 14 days while in summer they hatch in five or six days.

The larvae, which pass through four instars, require about 35 days to reach the pupal stage in spring and 18 to 20 days in summer. When ready to pupate, each larva securely fastens its caudal end to the underside of a bean leaf or some other convenient object. The pupal period lasts from seven to 20 days. New females begin laying eggs within eight to 13 days after emergence. The Mexican bean beetle produces three or four generations in the South and one or one and a partial second in the North. In the Southwest one generation is the general rule.

With the coming of fall, the adults begin to seek shelter for hibernating. They usually select the litter in rolling woodlands and show a preference

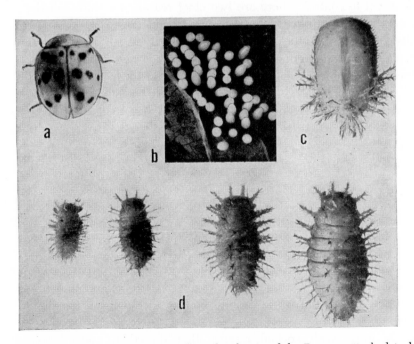

Fig. 12:10. Life stages of the Mexican bean beetle. A, adult; B, eggs attached to bean leaf; D, first to fourth instar larvae; C, pupa. *Courtesy Rutgers University.*

for woods of pine-oak mixture. They hibernate less frequently in the debris along fence rows, stone piles, under rubbish in gardens, and under wood-piles. Ordinarily they do not seek winter quarters more than a mile from the home bean field and the majority go no farther than a quarter of a mile. In the West, however, the beetles may fly many miles where they often enter alfalfa fields for hibernation. In the Southwest beetles do not truly hibernate since on warm days they do much moving about.

Weather plays an important part in controlling populations of Mexican bean beetle. Lack of proper cover during the hibernation period greatly increases winter mortality. During the summer unusually high temperatures accompanied by drought reduces populations.

A number of predaceous insects feed on the Mexican bean beetle but none of them hold populations in check. At times the adult Mexican bean beetle feeds on its own eggs. A tachinid fly, *Paradexodes epilachnae* Aldrich, is an important factor in reducing beetle numbers in Mexico but its intro-duction into the United States has not been successful.

Control. For many years the Mexican bean beetle was considered one of the most difficult insects to curb. Even now it is regarded as being a trouble-some insect to control. There are two chief reasons for this: (1) the pest is not greatly susceptible to the ordinary insecticides; and (2) larvae and adults live and feed on the undersides of the bean leaves where it is difficult to apply insecticides.

A commonly recommended insecticide for Mexican bean beetle is rote-none used either as a 0.015 per cent spray or 0.75 to 1 per cent dust. Also effective are methoxychlor at 1 to 2 lbs. per acre, malathion at 1 lb. per acre, parathion at ½ lb. per acre, Dilan at ½ lb. per acre, or Sevin at ½ lb. per acre.

If not applied thoroughly to bean plants, recommended insecticides will fail to control the beetle. For spraying bush varieties, it is necessary to use from 100 to 125 gal. of spray per acre. Adjust the sprayer boom so that drop lines fall on either side of the bean row. Point the nozzles upward at an angle of 45° so the spray strikes the underside of the leaves. Direct the third nozzle downward over the center of the row. The ends of the drop lines should be made of rubber hose to prevent their breakage in passing over uneven ground. On young plants lower the boom so that nozzles are about two inches above the ground and as the plants grow higher raise the boom.

Apply dusts with special nozzles that direct the dust upward and arrange nozzles to treat both sides of the row. Where there is danger of drift, as on a windy day, control can be improved by using a 10- to 15-foot cloth apron behind the duster so as to hold the dust down around the plants.

There are several farm practices which aid in Mexican bean beetle control. It is wise to burn or otherwise destroy all crop residue soon after the beans have been picked. Plowing refuse at least 6 inches deep in the soil destroys all stages of the beetle. Beans planted 3 to 4 inches apart produce less foliage in the row than beans planted closer, are easier to treat, and as a general rule, are not as heavily infested.

Imported cabbageworm

Pieris rapae (Linnaeus) [Lepidoptera:Pieridae]

The imported cabbageworm, nearly a worldwide pest of crucifers, was first introduced into North America at Quebec about 1860. Later it entered New York City in 1868 and Charleston, South Carolina and Apalachicola, Florida about 1873. From these points it spread rapidly through the United States and Canada, reaching California by 1883.

When cabbage plants are small, cabbageworms feed primarily on the underside of the developing leaves. Young larvae chew off the lower layers of the leaf leaving the upper layers untouched, but older larvae devour all cell layers and eat big holes into the leaves (Fig. 12:11). When the heads

Fig. 12:11. Cabbage damaged by imported cabbageworms. Note abundant excrement. *Courtesy University of Florida.*

develop, cabbageworms feed on the outer leaves and bore into the centers, making the cabbage unmarketable. Larvae also cause damage by contaminating the heads with their greenish-brown excrement.

The imported cabbageworm feeds on all forms of cruciferous plants but prefers cabbage and cauliflower. It frequently damages turnip, kale, collards, radish, mustard and horseradish and occasionally lettuce. Ornamentals often attacked are nasturtium, mignonette, sweet alyssum, and cleome.

Description. The imported cabbageworm adult, a familiar insect to all who grow cruciferous crops, is a white butterfly with a wing expanse of about two inches in the female and slightly less in the male (Fig. 12:12). The wings bear several black markings. Near the center of the forewing the male bears one black dot whereas the female bears two.

The eggs, laid singly on leaves, are light yellow, spindle-shaped, and about 1 mm. long. They have longitudinal ribs reticulated transversely.

When full grown the larva is about an inch in length, velvety green with a faint yellow dorsal stripe and a row of yellow spots along each side in line with the spiracles. The larva crawls slowly over the plant and does not show any looping movement which is common to the cabbage looper, another common cabbageworm.

The pupa is about ⅘ in. long, sharply angled, and greenish spotted with black. It is attached usually to the underside of a host leaf by an anal pad and a loop of silk.

Life history. The imported cabbageworm overwinters in the pupal stage on host plants. As the first warm days of spring bring the adults out, they frequently are the first insects to be noticed flying about in fields. Adults mate soon after emerging from the chrysalis and begin to lay eggs on their host plants. The eggs, deposited singly and on wild plants if no cultivated crucifers are available, hatch in four to eight days. The larvae, which pass through five instars, require ten to fourteen days to reach full growth.

When ready to pupate, the caterpillar spins a carpet of silk over the site chosen, fastens its anal end to the carpet and then spins a silken girdle around its body at the first abdominal segment. After the chrysalis forms, it is held in place by these bonds. The cabbageworm remains in the pupal stage for seven to twelve days.

The generations of cabbageworms greatly overlap due to the short larval and pupal periods and the long ovipositional period of the females. The time from egg to adult takes 22 to 42 days and from two to six generations develop annually. In certain parts of Canada the insect is unable to overwinter and infestations result from a northern migration of butterflies.

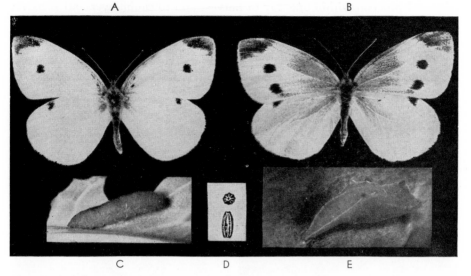

Fig. 12:12. Life stages of the imported cabbageworm. A, male butterfly; B, female; C, larva; D, eggs; E, chrysalis or pupa. *Courtesy University of Florida.*

Although a great many insect parasites and predators attack the imported cabbageworm, they are usually not present in sufficient numbers to hold the pest in check. Among the more important predators and parasites are the hymenopterous parasites *Apanteles glomeratus* (L.), *Pteromalus puparum* (L.); the wasp predator *Polistes metricus* Say, and ambush bugs *Phymata* spp. The imported cabbageworm also suffers from a bacterial disease caused by *Micrococcus pieridis* Burril. In addition a granulosis virus disease has been reported from California.

Control. The imported cabbageworm is not difficult to control if action is taken soon enough. Insecticidal treatment should start when there is an average of one cabbageworm per plant and continue at about ten-day intervals for as long as necessary. After the plants begin to head, cabbageworms are able to bore inside and so escape any insecticide which is applied. Either dusts or sprays are effective, but sprays require the addition of a spreader-sticker because the waxy leaves of crucifers readily shed water. Growers usually apply about 25 to 30 lbs. of dust or 100 to 150 gal. of spray per acre. Some growers use low pressure sprayers and apply from 15 to 20 gal. of spray per acre.

Insecticides effective against imported cabbageworm, and against cabbage looper and diamondback moth larvae as well, are endrin and phosdrin. Because of toxic residues, application of endrin is limited to the period before the formation of edible parts, but phosdrin may be applied to cabbage and broccoli within one day of harvest and to cauliflower and Brussels sprouts within three days.

Additional insecticides used to control cabbageworms include parathion, malathion, Dibrom, Perthane, rotenone, and pyrethrum. Combinations of Perthane and parathion or Perthane and malathion are superior to any of these materials used alone.

Seed-corn maggot

Hylemya cilicrura (Rondani) [Diptera:Anthomyiidae]

The seed-corn maggot, a widely distributed insect in the temperate regions of the world, was first recorded in North America in 1855 by Asa Fitch. In New York State he found large numbers of adults feeding upon the flowering heads of wheat during June.

Fig. 12:13. Seed-corn maggot that has devoured everything except the seed coat. *Courtesy Shell Chemical Company.*

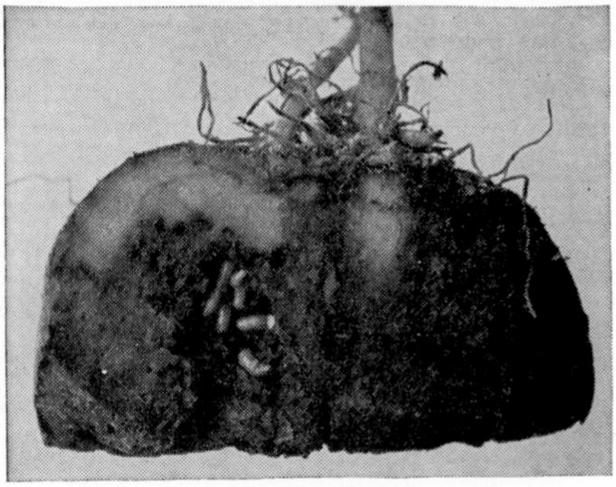

Fig. 12:14. Seed piece of potato being devoured by seed-corn maggots. *Courtesy USDA.*

Injury to plants results mainly from the feeding of the maggots on sprouting seed (Fig. 12:13) or on seedlings. They attack a variety of vegetable crops including beans, peas, corn, cabbage, cauliflower, cucurbits, spinach, potato seed-pieces, turnip, radish, and onion. The maggots burrow into the seed, feed on the endosperm, and often leave only a hollow shell. By breaking through the tough seed coat, they allow disease organisms to enter which cause the seeds to rot. Attacked seeds which manage to germinate often fail to develop true leaves. In some of the larger seeded plants, the maggots may be found feeding in the cotyledons above ground.

Seed pieces of potato are injured by the larvae entering the cut surface and honey-combing the seed piece with their feeding tunnels (Fig. 12:14).

The seed-corn maggot is an important agent in the dissemination and inoculation of potato blackleg which is caused by the bacteria, *Erwinia carotovora* (Jones). This disease causes an average annual loss of approximately two per cent of the potato crop.

Description. The adult fly is approximately ⅕ in. long (Fig. 12:15). The gray body has scattered bristles and the legs are black. The eggs are pearly white, somewhat banana-shaped, and about 1 mm. long. The larva is pearly white and when full grown about ¼ in. long. The pupa forms inside the last larval skin which hardens to form a protective puparium nearly ⅕ in. long. It is light reddish brown when first formed, turning darker as the pupa matures.

Life history. Adults and larvae of the seed-corn maggot are most abundant in cool periods of the year—spring and fall. In midsummer populations decrease to their lowest point and adults, chiefly females, survive to carry the species through. The insect remains active through the winter in North Carolina, but farther north it overwinters in the pupal stage.

The adult fly emerges from the puparium at night or early in the morning and with the aid of its ptilinum, a bladder-like structure on the head of the fly, works its way through the soil from depths as great as 7 inches. The flies feed on the nectar of flowers and plant juices. During June in the eastern United States, adults are common on the flowering heads of grasses. After a variable preoviposition period of from five to 55 days, depending on temperature, females lay eggs singly or in small clusters just beneath the

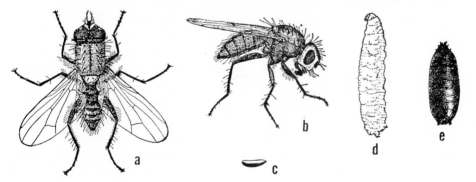

Fig. 12:15. Life stages of seed-corn maggot. A, male fly; B, female; C, egg; D, larva; E, puparium. *Courtesy USDA.*

surface of the soil near larval food. Favorite sites are near sprouting or decaying large seeds like beans, corn, or peas, near decaying crop remnants, and near organic fertilizers. Living for approximately one month, the females produce an average of 100 eggs with some individuals laying as many as 150.

Eggs hatch in from one to nine days. The larvae, which apparently have three larval instars, develop rapidly in an abundance of food and at temperatures of 70° to 85°F. Usually in one to three weeks the maggots become full grown and pupate.

The larval skin thickens and becomes darker to form the puparium. Within the puparium the seed-corn maggot passes approximately two days in the prepupal stage and seven to 26 days in the pupal stage. In the north central states, three to five generations develop each year.

There is a symbiotic relationship between the seed-corn maggot and several species of bacteria, one of which causes blackleg of potato. Larvae deprived of their bacterial flora and reared on sterile media are small and unthrifty while those possessing the usual gut bacteria develop into normal individuals.

The seed-corn maggot does not have many natural enemies. A parasite that has been reared from this insect is the hymenopteran *Aphaereta auripes* (Provancher). Several predators have been noted among which are a wasp *Ectemnius stirpicola* (Pack.), and a fly *Scatophaga furcata* Say. Spiders also kill a few seed-corn maggot adults. Fungi belonging to the genus *Empusa* attack the adult flies.

Control. Not until the advent of the chlorinated hydrocarbons was there a satisfactory chemical method for fighting the seed-corn maggot. Now growers can protect vegetable plantings by coating seeds with insecticide. A common slurry consists of ⅓ oz. of 75 per cent wettable powder insecticide, 1½ oz. of fungicide, and 8 fluid oz. of water per 50 lbs. of seed. Recommended insecticides include aldrin, dieldrin, lindane, and heptachlor. A fungicide quite often used is thiram. Some manufacturers offer a mixture already prepared for application to seeds and some seed houses make available treated seed. Growers may treat their own seed by placing the seed in any smooth container that can be sealed shut and tumbled. For small amounts of seed, a fruit jar suffices. The container should be only half filled with seed during each mixing operation. Use one teaspoonful of slurry for each pound of seed.

There are certain cultural practices which tend to lessen populations of the seed-corn maggot. Infestations tend to be lighter on warm, well-drained soils. If organic fertilizer is used, it should be well rotted and plowed into the soil during the fall. After a green cover crop is plowed under, it is best to wait about three weeks before planting.

Rapid germination of seed is desirable since less time is given for the maggot to attack. Growers can hasten germination of seed by working the seed bed thoroughly and planting as shallow as possible. If the spring is wet and cold, one should delay seeding until warmer weather.

Since maggots attack sound potato pieces only where the skin is broken or the surface injured, growers can prevent damage by allowing cut seed pieces to heal before planting. If the maggots have infested a stand of vegetables the best thing to do is disk it under and replant immediately. There is little danger from reinfestation.

Beet leafhopper

Circulifer tenellus (Baker) [Homoptera:Cicadellidae]

The history of the beet leafhopper is closely tied to the history of the sugar beet industry of the western states. The first successful sugar beet factory was erected at Alvarado, California in 1870 and by 1890 the industry was well founded and in full production. In 1898 a plant disease, called **curly top,** struck the sugar beets and from then on it occurred sporadically in most of the western beet growing areas. E. D. Ball, in 1905, suspected the beet leafhopper as being connected with the disease but could offer no experimental proof. In 1910 H. B. Shaw, working on the suggestion of Ball proved that the beet leafhopper was, in fact, the vector of curly top, a virus disease.

The beet leafhopper, a native insect of western North America, is distributed principally west of the Continental Divide. Entomologists have also found infestations of this insect or cases of the disease which it transmits in Florida, Illinois, Iowa, Minnesota, Nebraska, Indiana, and Kansas.

The beet leafhopper causes damage primarily by its acting as a vector of curly top, a serious disease of sugar beets, spinach, tomatoes, beans, squash, cantaloupe, and several other plants (Fig. 12:16). So far as known, the disease is carried only by this insect, although another species of leafhopper is the vector of a disease of sugar beets in Argentina which may be identical with curly top.

Symptoms of the disease vary more or less with the kind of host attacked. In beets the earliest signs are a clearing of the veins and inward rolling of the margins of young leaves. As the disease progresses, curling of the leaves increases, veins swell, and papillae develop on the underside of the leaves. Leaves become dull, dark green, distorted, thick, and brittle. Lateral rootlets die, which induces the beet to develop a mass of hairy and woolly lateral rootlets. Concentric circles of dark tissue alternate with light tissue in cross sections of the root. Plants infected with the disease suffer a general stunting and frequently die.

Fig. 12:16. Sugar beet plant infected with curly top, a virus disease transmitted by beet leafhopper. *Courtesy USDA.*

Curly top has forced sugar beet factories in many places in the West to close and to move to other locations not so seriously affected. Growers generally abandon badly infected fields. In 1944 this insect caused an estimated loss of $3,676,000 to vegetable crops in the intermountain region.

Description. The adult beet leafhopper, nearly ¼ in. long, is slender and tapers posteriorly with the widest point of the body just behind the metathorax (Fig. 12:17). Color of adults varies from gray to greenish yellow. Darker individuals have blackish or brownish markings on the front wings, head, and thorax.

The egg, 0.06 mm. long, is barely visible to the naked eye. It is long, slender, slightly curved and greenish white, later changing to a lemon yellow. As the egg develops, eye spots appear at the anterior end.

The nymphs resemble the parents but are smaller and have no wings. When first hatched, they are white in color but soon darken. Older nymphs are usually spotted with red and brown.

Life history. In northern regions of its distribution as in Washington and Idaho the beet leafhopper develops three generations annually; in southern regions as in California and Arizona it develops five or more. The species overwinters in the adult stage chiefly on overgrazed rangeland which has been invaded by wild mustards, the principal winter host plants of the insect. Whenever temperatures are favorably high during winter, the adults become active and feed. In the Southwest reproduction continues during every month except December and January.

Females usually begin to deposit eggs in quantity when mustards start growing in spring. They insert eggs inside leaves and stems of host plants in rows of two to five and produce an average of 300 to 400 eggs each. Eggs laid during cool, spring weather take as long as forty days to hatch, but eggs laid in summer may hatch in five days. The young nymphs immediately begin feeding on host plants by inserting their beaks and sucking juices. Molting five times, they develop to the adult stage in three to seven weeks. In spring a complete life cycle takes from six to ten weeks; in summer it may take only four weeks. The generations overlap each other so that all stages are present at any time during the growing season.

The first or spring generation develops on weed hosts, chiefly mustards. About the time the insects reach the adult stage the weeds mature and become dry inducing the leafhoppers to migrate. Flying with the wind, they infest summer hosts plants in their path, the infestation of crop plants

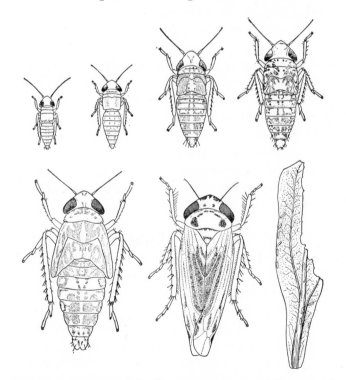

Fig. 12:17. Life stages of the beet leafhopper. The five nymphal instars, the adult, and the eggs embedded in tissue of sugar beet leaf. *Courtesy USDA.*

such as sugar beets, beans, and tomatoes being incidental to their general movement, as they do not actively seek these out but alight on any favorable host.

Russian thistle is the most important summer weed host in the western states. Mixed stands of Russian thistle and mustards are especially favorable for supporting large populations, since the leafhoppers can overwinter and reproduce their spring and summer generations in the same area. Of the cultivated plants, beets are the only important breeding host.

With the maturing and drying of summer host plants in fall, leafhoppers migrate back to their winter hosts. Until the annuals germinate they may have to feed on plants unfavorable to their survival, perennials like salt-bush, sagebrush, or mesquite, with a resulting heavy mortality. On the other hand, high leafhopper populations enter winter if the winter hosts germinate before the summer hosts dry or are killed by frost.

In studying the biology of the beet leafhopper, entomologists have found six main breeding areas in which the insects have an abundance of food plants and favorable weather conditions (Fig. 12:18). Leafhoppers from any one breeding ground infest the same cultivated areas year after year.

A number of parasites and predators attack the beet leafhopper. Three minute wasps, *Polynema eutettixi* Girault, *Abbella subflava* Girault and *Anagrus giraulti* Crawford parasitize the eggs. Members of the wasp genus *Gonatopus* act as both predators and parasites of nymphs and adults. The big-eyed fly, *Tömösváryella subnitens* (Cress.), is probably the most important parasite of the nymph and adult. *Geocoris pallens* Stål, a predaceous hemipteran, destroys the active stages of the leafhopper. Spiders, lizards and birds often prey on leafhoppers.

Control. Since the beet leafhopper is migratory and is able to transmit curly top virus in a few minutes of feeding, the usual practice of applying insecticides to crops needing protection from insects has not proven successful.

One approach to control is the development of plants resistant to curly top. Several varieties of sugar beets have been developed that are resistant and are well-adapted to the beet leafhopper area. Resistant varieties of Great Northern and of Pinto beans have been produced by the Idaho Experiment Station. Work is in progress on breeding resistant tomatoes but no completely resistant variety has yet been developed. Certain varieties of bean, squash, and pumpkin are naturally resistant to curly top.

In general early planted sugar beets are less injured by curly top but often other factors make early planting an unsatisfactory practice. In the coastal area of California beets planted after the spring movement of leaf-

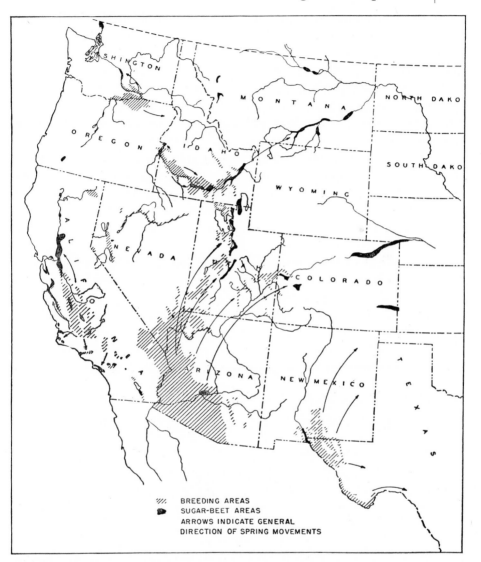

Fig. 12:18. The major breeding grounds of the beet leafhopper and the sugar beet areas affected by them. *Courtesy USDA.*

hoppers make a successful crop. It is wise to plant tomatoes as late as possible so as to miss the spring migration of leafhoppers. In Utah double-hill planting of tomatoes has given some protection from curly top; in New Mexico spacing tomatoes one foot apart in the row rather than 3 feet has resulted in less curly top and greater production.

Since direct control in commercial plantings has proven difficult, entomologists have attempted to control weed host plants before the leafhoppers migrate. Removing weed hosts deprives the leafhoppers of breeding sites; or spraying the weeds with insecticides kills the leafhoppers before they have a chance to migrate to cultivated plants.

The hosts carrying the leafhoppers through the winter and during the spring are mostly annuals which develop as weeds on overgrazed areas. One method of control is to limit grazing so that nonhost grasses come back to replace the weeds.

Russian thistle, the chief weed host that supports the summer and fall population of leafhoppers, grows principally on abandoned land and on overgrazed areas. Because leafhoppers tend to congregate on this weed for breeding, elimination of Russian thistle by hoeing, cultivating, or dragging a railroad rail over the plant has been suggested for controlling the insect.

Direct control of leafhoppers before they migrate in spring is helpful in preventing transmission of curly top. After survey crews determine and map the areas supporting large populations of leafhoppers, control personnel come in with trucks and planes and cover the area with insecticide, such as DDT.

Selected References

Anon., *The Mexican Bean Beetle in the East and Its Control*, USDA Bul. 1624, 1960.

Anon., *The Onion Thrips: How to Control It*, USDA Bul. 372, 1960.

Anon., *The Sweetpotato Weevil: How to Control It*, USDA Bul. 431, 1960.

Beckham, C. M., *Biology and Control of the Vegetable Weevil in Georgia*, Ga. Agr. Exp. Sta. Tech. Bul. 2, 1953.

Brindley, T. A., J. C. Chamberlin, and Ralph Schopp, *The Pea Weevil and Methods for its Control*, USDA Farmers' Bul. 1971, 1958.

Cannon, F. M., *Control of the Colorado Potato Beetle in Canada*, Can. Dept. Agr. Publ. 1071, 1960.

———, *Control of the Potato Flea Beetle in Eastern Canada*, Can. Dept. Agr. Publ. 1072, 1960.

Cockerham, K. L., O. T. Deen, M. B. Christian, and L. D. Newsom, *The Biology of the Sweet Potato Weevil*, La. Agr. Exp. Sta. Tech. Bul. 483, 1954.

Cook, W. C., *The Beet Leafhopper*, USDA Farmers' Bul. 1886, 1941.

Crosby, C. R., and M. D. Leonard, *Manual of Vegetable-garden Insects* (New York: Macmillan, 1918).

Drake, C. J., and H. M. Harris, *Asparagus Insects in Iowa*, Ia. Agr. Exp. Circ. 134, 1932.

Dudley, J. E., and T. E. Bronson, *The Pea Aphid on Peas and Methods for Its Control*, USDA Farmers' Bul. 45, 1952.

Dudley, J. E., B. J. Landis, and W. A. Shands, *Control of Potato Insects*, USDA Farmers' Bul. 2040, 1952.

Elmore, J. C., and R. E. Campbell, *The Pepper Weevil*, USDA Leaflet 226, 1951.

Fenton, F. A., and A. Hartzell, *Bionomics and Control of the Potato Leafhopper,* Ia. Agr. Exp. Sta. Res. Bul. 78, 1923.

Folsom, D., G. W. Simpson, and R. Bonde, *Maine Potato Diseases, Insects, and Injuries,* Me. Agr. Exp. Sta. Bul. 469, 1949.

Hayslip, N. C., W. G. Genung, E. G. Kelsheimer, and J. W. Wilson, *Insects Attacking Cabbage and Other Crucifers in Florida,* Fla. Agr. Exp. Sta. Bul. 534, 1953.

Kelsheimer, E. G., N. C. Hayslip, and J. W. Wilson, *Control of Budworms, Earworms and Other Insects Attacking Sweet Corn and Green Corn in Florida,* Fla. Agr. Exp. Sta. Bul. 466, 1950.

Linn, M. B., and J. M. Wright, *Tomato Diseases and Insect Pests: Identification and Control,* Ill. Agr. Exten. Serv. 683, 1951.

Michelbacker, A. E., W. W. Middelkauff, and N. B. Akesson, *Caterpillars Destructive to Tomato,* Calif. Agr. Exp. Sta. Bul. 707.

——, ——, O. G. Bacon, and J. E. Swift, *Controlling Melon Insects and Spider Mites,* California Agr. Exp. Sta. Bul. 749, 1955.

Miller, L. A., and R. J. McClanahan, "Life-History of the Seed-Corn Maggot, *Hylemya cilicrura* (Rond) and of *H. liturata* (Mg.) (Diptera: Anthomyiidae) in Southwestern Ontario," *Can. Ent.,* 92:210–221 (1960).

Pepper, B. B., *The Carrot Weevil,* Listronotus latiusculus *(Bohe) in New Jersey and Its Control,* N.J. Agr. Exp. Sta. Bul. 693, 1942.

Pletsch, D. J., *The Potato Psyllid: Its Biology and Control,* Mont. Agr. Exp. Sta. Tech. Bul. 446, 1947.

Read, D. C., *Control of Root Maggots in Rutabagas, Cabbages, and Related Plants in the Maritime Provinces,* Canada Dept. Agri. Publ. 1075, 1960.

Reed, L. B., and S. P. Doolittle, *Insects and Diseases of Vegetables in the Home Garden,* USDA Home and Garden Bul. 46, 1958.

Reid, Jr., W. J., and F. P. Cuthbert, Jr., *Aphids on Leaf Vegetables: How to Control Them,* USDA Farmers' Bul. 2148, 1960.

Reid, Jr., W. J., and F. P. Cuthbert, Jr., *Control of Caterpillars on Commercial Cabbage and Other Cole Crops in the South,* USDA Farmers' Bul. 2099, 1960.

Shands, W. A., and B. J. Landis, "Potato Aphids," USDA Yearbook *Insects,* 1952:519–27.

Simpson, G. W., and W. A. Shands, *Progress on Some Important Insect and Disease Problems of Irish Potato Production in Maine,* Me. Agr. Exp. Sta. Bul. 470, 1949.

Thomas, C. A., *Mushroom Insects: Their Biology and Control,* Pa. Agr. Exp. Sta. Bul. 419, 1942.

Wallis, R. L., *Ecological Studies on the Potato Psyllid as a Pest of Potatoes,* USDA Tech. Bul. 1107, 1955.

Westcott, C., *The Gardener's Bug Book* (Garden City: Doubleday, 1946).

Wilcox, J., A. F. Howland, and R. E. Campbell, *Investigations of the Tomato Fruitworm, Its Seasonal History, and Methods of Control,* USDA Tech. B. 1147, 1956.

——, and F. H. Shirck, *The Onion Thrips: How to Control It,* USDA Leaflet 372, 1954.

Wilson, G. F., *The Detection and Control of Garden Pests* (London: Crosby Lockwood and Sons Ltd., 1949).

Wilson, J. W., and N. C. Hayslip, *Insects Attacking Celery in Florida,* Fla. Agr. Exp. Sta. Bul. 486, 1951.

NOTE: Many experiment stations and extension services have issued publications on vegetable insects. One may usually obtain these on request.

Chapter 13 | INSECT PESTS OF
TREE FRUITS | *Carl Johansen*

The pests

A variety of insects and mites live on fruit trees—apple, pear, peach, apricot, cherry, prune, and plum. One well-known entomologist has estimated that some 400 species of insects infest the apple, though only 25 of these are of economic importance. Other tree fruits are also fed upon by many different kinds of insects, but the number of major pests are only a fraction of the total. For example, peach in Ohio has four major pests and about 36 minor ones and pear in California has ten major pests and 20 minor ones.

Orchard insects vary in their specificity for feeding on the different varieties of fruit. Some, like the pear psylla, attack only a single kind of host, but the majority are more general feeders and attack more than one or even all, as does the San Jose scale.

Two orders, the Lepidoptera and the Homoptera, contain the major number of species of tree fruit insects. Among the Lepidoptera, the most familiar species is the **codling moth**—the well-known "worm" in the apple (Fig. 13:15). Related caterpillars which cause severe damage to tree fruits include the **oriental fruit moth** (Fig. 4:17C), **cherry fruitworm,** and **eyespotted bud moth.**

Leaf rollers such as the **fruit-tree leaf roller** and **red-banded leaf roller** are common pests in the orchards of North America (Fig. 13:1). Two major pests of peach, the **peach tree borer** (Figs. 13:10 and 4:17A) and the **lesser peach tree borer,** are the larvae of clear wing moths. The **peach twig borer,** a species belonging to another moth family, attacks terminal growth and fruit of peach (Fig. 4:17B).

In the order Homoptera, scale insects and aphids are notorious tree fruit pests. The most important scale insect is the **San Jose scale** (Fig. 13:23),

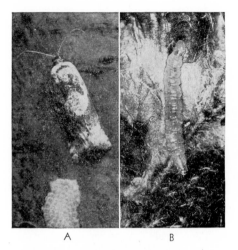

A B

Fig. 13:1. Red-banded leaf roller, *Argyrotaenia velutinana* (Wlk.). A, adult and egg mass; B, larva. *Courtesy Michigan State University.*

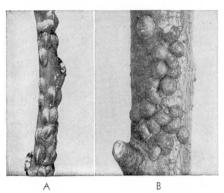

A B

Fig. 13:2. European fruit lecanium, *Lecanium corni* Bouché. A, immature scales; B, mature scales. A, *courtesy University of California; B, courtesy Ohio Agr. Exp. Sta.*

but other highly destructive species include the **European fruit lecanium** (Fig. 13:2), **oystershell scale,** and **scurfy scale.** Major species of **aphids** include the apple aphid, woolly apple aphid, rosy apple aphid, apple grain aphid, black cherry aphid, rusty plum aphid, mealy plum aphid, leaf curl plum aphid, thistle aphid, green peach aphid, and black peach aphid (Fig. 13:3). Other important Homoptera on fruit include several species of **leafhoppers,** which transmit virus diseases especially among stone fruits, and the **pear psylla** (Fig. 13:4), a pest only of pears, found in most orchard regions of America.

Various sucking bugs (Hemiptera), such as the **tarnished plant bug** (Fig. 4:9C), **apple red bug,** and a number of **stink bugs,** cause pitting or scabbing of apples and pears or "catfacing" of peaches and apricots.

Among the Diptera, several species of fruit flies feed internally on the fruit. The **apple maggot** is distributed in the eastern half of the nation, while the **cherry fruit fly** (Figs. 13:25 and 26) and the **black cherry fruit fly** are widely dispersed throughout North America.

A few species of beetles are major orchard pests. The **plum curculio,** found east of the Rocky Mountains, damages all types of fruit (Fig. 13:5). Various species of **roundheaded wood borers** and **shot-hole borers** injure the trunks and larger branches of orchard trees.

Since World War II, mites have become one of the greatest concerns of

Fig. 13:3. Black peach aphid, *Anuraphis persiscaeniger* (Smith) on peach shoot. *Courtesy USDA.*

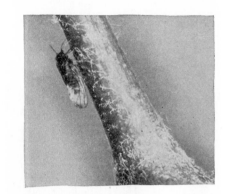

Fig. 13:4. Pear psylla, *Psylla pyricola* Förster, adult, a specific pest of pears. *Courtesy Michigan State University.*

fruit growers. **Spider mites** are particularly damaging, but **blister mites** and **rust mites** are also injurious.

The injury

Fruit damage. Although various insects and mites feed upon all parts of orchard trees, many of the most serious pests feed upon the fruit. Because of consumer attitudes, even small blemishes or feeding scars reduce the value of fruits. If one insect is discovered in samples from a truckload of fruits, the whole shipment is subject to rejection by the processor or fresh-fruit merchandiser. Therefore, special attention is given to those pests which feed directly upon or otherwise affect the fruit.

Certain insects damage fruits by tunneling directly into them. Codling moth caterpillars, cherry fruit fly maggots, oriental fruit moth caterpillars,

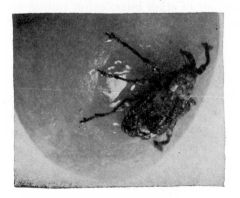

Fig. 13:5. The plum curculio, *Conotrachelus nenuphar* (Herbst), a general fruit pest. *Courtesy Pennsylvania State University.*

peach twig borer, and cherry fruitworm cause this type of injury. Sometimes maggots or caterpillars remain as a contaminant in processed fruits.

Scabs, blemishes, russeting and other disfigurations of the surface of the fruits are often caused by insects. Through their feeding on the fruit, bugs, such as the apple red bug, boxelder bug, and stink bugs, produce blemishes on apples and pears (Fig. 13:6A). The tarnished plant bug and other species of lygus bugs, as well as certain stink bugs, often cause misshapen or "catfaced" peaches and apricots (Fig. 13:6B). The pear leaf blister mite forms black spots on pear fruits as well as on the foliage. Pitting, stunting, and deforming of apples are caused by the attack of rosy apple aphids. Scabby areas are left by the feeding of climbing cutworms, green fruitworms, and leaf-roller larvae. Heavy injury by adult plum curculios produces warty and misshapen fruits. The Japanese beetle eats holes in developing peaches in eastern orchards.

Fruit drop of peaches is caused by feeding of the green peach aphid upon the blossoms. Feeding of pear midge larvae within developing fruits causes stunting, deforming, and dropping of pears. Fruits attacked by the plum curculio usually drop soon after the eggs hatch and the young begin to feed. Tunneling near the skin by the apple maggot causes the fruits to drop prematurely.

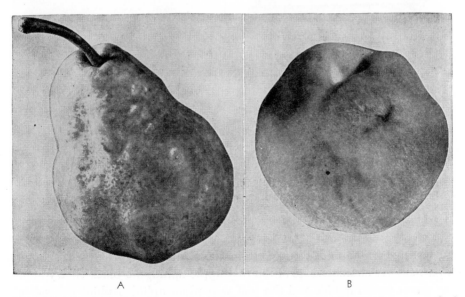

A   B

Fig. 13:6. Fruit injured by insects. A, stink bug damaged pear. Depressed areas resulted from bug's feeding on developing fruit; pear is corky under skin where bugs have fed. B, cat-faced peach caused by feeding of tarnished plant bug. A, *Courtesy University of California; B, Courtesy Ohio Agr. Exp. Sta.*

Honeydew produced by aphids, scale insects, and others feeding on various parts of the tree may get onto the fruit. Honeydew may cause blemishes and a black, sooty fungus, which often grows in the honeydew, causes further disfiguring.

Foliage damage. Insects and mites may damage the foliage by sucking up the cell contents of leaves, by injecting toxic substances, or by devouring leaf tissues. Leafhoppers, mites, and lace bugs remove the chlorophyll along with other cell contents and cause a white speckling of the foliage. If the injury is severe, the leaves usually turn brown and drop. Rust mites cause a general discoloration of the foliage. One species, the peach silver mite, often imparts a silvery appearance to the leaves. Pear and apple leaf blister mites form black blisters on the leaves (Fig. 13:7).

Fig. 13:7. Pear leaf blister mite, *Eriophyes pyri* (Pgst.), injury to leaf. Note the black blisters. *Courtesy Michigan State University.*

Fig. 13:8. Pear-slug *Caliroa cerasi* (L.), skeletonizes the leaves of pear and cherry trees. *Courtesy USDA.*

Most tree-fruit aphids cause a curling of the foliage. This type of symptom is particularly characteristic of the rosy apple aphid, the black cherry aphid, the green peach aphid, and the leaf curl plum aphid. Aphids concentrate on the tender growth of the terminals causing a killing back or stunting of these portions.

Foliage pests with chewing mouthparts, such as various leaf miners, pear-slug, cankerworms, and leaf rollers, consume leaf tissues and may seriously defoliate trees (Fig. 13:8).

By their damage of leaves and impairment of leaf function, foliage pests indirectly affect the fruit which may fail to develop properly and attain normal size.

Trunk, limb, and twig damage. Many pests of fruit trees feed on the surface of twigs, limbs, and trunk or bore into these structures. A variety of scale insects attach themselves on the surface, suck plant juices, kill branches, and weaken trees. Certain insects, such as the buffalo treehopper, the periodical cicada, and tree crickets lay their eggs in young branches and twigs and thereby injure or kill these parts.

Insects, such as the roundheaded apple tree borer, sinuate pear tree borer, and shot-hole borer, feed under the bark of the trunks and larger limbs (Fig. 13:9). The larvae of these beetles may weaken and even girdle the trees. Larvae of clear-winged moths burrow beneath the bark and are particularly destructive to young trees (Fig. 13:10).

Root damage. Only a few pests are found on the roots of fruit trees. The woolly apple aphid and the black peach aphid feed on roots as well as top growth and are especially damaging to nursery stock. White grubs sometimes cause minor root injury. In the Pacific Northwest, several species of rain beetles, *Pleocoma* spp., severely injure the roots of orchard trees in local areas.

Disease transmission. Several serious virus diseases of stone fruits are transmitted by insects. In the northeastern states, peach yellows and little peach are transmitted by the plum leafhopper. In the West, the geminate leafhopper and certain other species transmit the little cherry-western X disease complex to both cherries and peaches. Workers in California have recently demonstrated that an eriophyid mite transmits peach mosaic in the West.

Cultural control

Orchardists cannot rely solely on cultural methods to control insects. Modern consumer demands for top quality processed fruits have forced greater and greater use of insecticides in order to obtain nearly perfect control. Furthermore, since tree fruits have a high unit value, use of chemical controls is often economically sound where it might not be on other types of crops. But there are helpful cultural practices such as the following.

Use of nonlegume cover crops is suggested in some areas in order to reduce certain insect pest populations. This practice is particularly useful in peach and apricot orchards, since catfacing insects are attracted to legumes both for feeding and for overwintering. Leafhoppers which transmit stone-fruit virus diseases also prefer legume hosts.

Fig. 13:9. Peach limb showing gum exuding from injuries of shot-hole borer, *Scolytus rugulosus* (Ratzeburg). *Courtesy Ohio Agri. Exp. Sta.*

Several cultural methods are effective in lessening damage from shot-hole borers. Removal and burning of badly infested trees, together with all prunings, will reduce the possibility of further damage. Keeping trees in good condition, including watering and fertilizing when necessary, will protect them from both shot-hole borers and flatheaded borers. Removal of wild host plants near the orchards will help reduce shot-hole or round-headed borer populations in the area.

The plum and apple curculios winter in plant debris or rubbish on the ground or in other sheltered places. Keeping the orchards and surrounding lands free from such materials aids in the control of these pests.

Northern Spy apple rootstocks are used by nurserymen in some areas because of their resistance to the woolly apple aphid. This resistance to the attack of the aphid is due to the presence of antibiosis, an adverse effect of the plant upon the insect.

Chemical control

Consumer demands for top quality fruits, free from blemishes or contaminations of any kind, have forced orchardists to rely more and more heavily upon chemical control measures. As fruit trees are invariably attacked every year by a host of pests, growers regularly apply a series of treatments timed with seasonal development of the trees. These so-called **spray programs** or **spray schedules** for tree fruits have become very complex in recent years and vary from crop to crop and from region to region. Many states publish spray schedules annually as guides for growers to follow or to modify as actual insect and disease conditions in the orchard warrant.

Specific insect problems are complicated by the necessity of applying fungicides, chemical thinning sprays, hormone sprays, minor-element deficiency sprays, and fertilizers. When several materials are applied in combination, plant injury or other evidences of incompatibility may result. Insecticidal residues remaining on fruits at harvest time must be carefully controlled so as not to exceed the tolerances set by the Food and Drug Administration. Insecticide poisoning of honey bees has made it increasingly difficult to obtain pollination services in certain areas.

The standard dormant or delayed-dormant sprays of oil and lime-sulfur are applied in many areas against spider mites, rust mites, pear and apple leaf blister mites, scale insects, aphid eggs, fruit-tree leaf roller eggs, and pear psylla. Sometimes lead arsenate or nicotine is added to the dormant sprays for control of the peach twig borer or aphids, respectively. Dinitro compounds are also used in the dormant period against aphid eggs, scale insects, and eye-spotted budmoth. Summer dinitros are sometimes used to control mites.

Although it has been largely replaced by newer materials, lead arsenate is still used against apple maggot, various caterpillars and cutworms, plum curculio, cherry fruit flies, and codling moth in certain localities.

Several of the botanical insecticides are employed to control tree-fruit pests. Nicotine is used against aphids, leafhoppers, and sucking bugs; rotenone against cherry fruit flies and pear psylla. Rotenone or pyrethrum is sometimes injected into the burrows of roundheaded wood borers in eastern orchards. Ryania has aroused considerable interest throughout this country and Canada as a promising control for codling moth because it is relatively harmless to the natural enemies of both the codling moth and spider mites.

The chlorinated hydrocarbon insecticides are exploited against a wide variety of tree-fruit insects. Although it has often proven to be a major factor in the production of heavy mite populations, DDT is one of the most used insecticides in the orchard. It controls apple maggot, codling moth, Japanese beetle, leaf rollers, cutworms, caterpillars, oriental fruit moth, peach tree borer, shot-hole borer, pear-slug, pear midge, pear thrips, certain scale insects, sucking bugs, and leafhoppers. Methoxychlor is used against cherry fruit flies, cherry fruitworm, plum curculio, Japanese beetle, and apple maggot. TDE finds a specific use against two leaf rollers of the genus *Argyrotaenia* which are not controlled by DDT—the red-banded leaf roller in the East and the orange tortrix in the West. BHC and lindane can be used to control aphids, but they must not be applied near harvest time since they can cause off-flavors in the fruit. The plum curculio, cat-facing insects, and pear psylla are controlled with dieldrin. A carbamate insecticide, Sevin, has recently come into orchard use against pear psylla, codling moth, and aphids. It also shows promise as a chemical fruit thinner for Delicious apples.

Organic phosphorus compounds are widely utilized in orchard insect control. Parathion is effective against a greater variety of pests than any other material in use at the present time. It controls aphids, mites, scale insects, pear psylla, sucking bugs, leaf rollers, codling moths, cutworms and caterpillars, plum curculios, oriental fruit moths, cherry fruit flies, peach tree borers, shot-hole borers, and treehoppers. A prepink spray of

Fig. 13:10. Young peach tree infested with peach tree borer, *Sanninoidea exitiosa* (Say). *Courtesy Ohio Agr. Exp. Sta.*

parathion has largely replaced dormant sprays against mites, scale insects, and the pear psylla in certain areas of the Pacific Northwest.

Other useful phosphate insecticides in the orchard include malathion, EPN, Diazinon, Guthion, TEPP, schradan, and demeton. Promising newer phosphates include Phosdrin, Trithion, Phostex, and dimethoate.

The so-called "specific miticides," DMC, Genite, Mitox, Kelthane, Chlorobenzilate, Sulphenone, Fenson, Tedion, and ovex, are effective in controlling spider mites and rust mites. Each of these materials has limitations, being most useful when applied to certain kinds of fruit trees for control of certain species of mites.

Fumigants provide effective control of various tree borers. Paradichlorobenzene is placed in a trench in the soil around the base of the tree to kill the peach tree borer. It is mixed with carbon disulfide for injection into the burrows of roundheaded borers. Ethylene dichloride or propylene dichloride emulsions are also used in soil trenches for control of the peach tree borer.

Control equipment

Since 1948, there has been a rapid change from dilute to semiconcentrate and concentrate sprays for orchard pest control. The method consists of reducing the normal gallonage of spray material per tree and compensating by increasing the concentration of chemicals in the spray. Thus a "2X" means half normal gallonage applied per tree and double the amount of chemicals per 100 gal. of spray mixture. By 1954, 80 per cent of the tree fruits in New York were being sprayed at some degree of concentration by air-blast machines; 25 per cent of the tree fruit acreage in Michigan was being treated with spray concentrations averaging 2X to 4X; 90 per cent in northern California was by air blast; 75 per cent of the orchards in eastern Washington were being treated at 2X to 3X; and 90 per cent of the orchards in British Columbia were treated with concentrate sprays up to 10X. Air-blast sprayers, conventional sprayers with blower attachments, and mist blower concentrate sprayers are the main types of equipment utilized in commercial tree fruit operations (Fig. 13:11).

Hand-gun applications (Fig. 13:12) are still the mainstay in certain states, such as Utah; while almost all trees in the Willamette Valley of Oregon and in Montana are treated by means of power dusters.

Aerial application of orchard sprays or dusts is desirable under certain conditions. Orchardists with limited acreages often would rather hire aerial applicators than buy expensive equipment. Growers who own ground equipment may turn to aerial applications near harvest time when the tree branches are bending down with fruit and might be damaged by a spray

Fig. 13:11. Modern air-blast sprayer used to treat orchard with concentrate spray. *Courtesy Oliver Corp.*

machine. Aerial sprays are also useful in irrigated orchards in early spring or late fall when water may not be readily available.

The use of concentrate and semiconcentrate sprays has developed as a consequence of several factors. A major problem of the modern fruit grower is his labor costs. Even when high wages are paid, the orchardist is not sure of obtaining efficient and experienced help. One man with an air-blast sprayer can treat an orchard about twice as fast as three men with a conventional high-pressure machine and hand guns.

Potent insecticides like DDT and parathion have replaced lead arsenate and oil for many orchard-pest problems. Although an experienced man with a hand gun can put a more complete spray cover on the trees than can be accomplished with an air-blast sprayer, maximum coverage and deposit of sprays are no longer required.

It has also been shown that the use of semiconcentrate and concentrate methods of application results in a saving of up to 20 per cent in spray

Fig. 13:12. Grower spraying his small orchard with hand gun. *Courtesy Hudson Mfg. Co.*

materials. Sprays no longer must be applied till "runoff" from the foliage to be sure of adequate coverage. However, careful attention must be paid to the pruning of trees to obtain best results with concentrate applications.

REPRESENTATIVE TREE FRUIT PESTS

For detailed study we have chosen the following serious pests of tree fruits: codling moth, spider mites, San Jose scale, and cherry fruit flies.

Codling moth

Carpocapsa pomonella (Linnaeus) [Lepidoptera:Olethreutidae]

The familiar "apple worm" is an introduced pest from southeastern Europe. It was first observed in New England about 1750; in Iowa, 1860;

in Utah, 1870; and in Washington, about 1880. The increasing destructiveness of this pest closely paralleled the development of the commercial apple-growing industry in the United States. It is found wherever apples are grown in the world.

Codling moths feed upon apple, pear, English walnut, quince, crab apple, hawthorne, and wild apple and they infrequently attack various stone fruits. The larva often enters the fruit through the calyx end. Sometimes it will tunnel in where two fruits are touching or a leaf touches a fruit. The larva eats its way into the center of the apple and feeds upon the seeds and the core (Fig. 13:13). Later, it tunnels back out and leaves the fruit. **Stings** are shallow blemishes on the surface of the fruit, usually caused when a newly hatched larva has taken a few bites and then died from the effects of an insecticide.

Damage by the codling moth reached sizable proportions by 1880—ranging from nearly total loss in many areas down to 10 to 20 per cent crop destruction in the extreme northern apple and pear producing re-

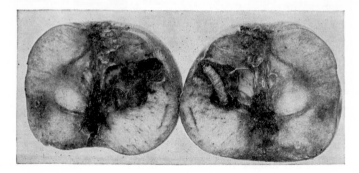

Fig. 13:13. Apple cut to show the damage of the larva of the codling moth. *Courtesy USDA.*

gions. About this time, arsenical insecticides were found effective, and for many years thorough and timely spray applications largely prevented codling moth injury. Gradually control became more difficult and the spray programs more intensive until, in the thirties and extending until about 1947, losses from this pest often reached 30 to 50 per cent or more of the crop, despite the heavy spraying. Since 1947, losses caused by the codling moth have been kept down to 1 to 5 per cent by the use of DDT. Yet the moth is present in all apple-growing regions and populations build up whenever a farmer is careless in his spray program.

Description. Female codling moths lay their eggs singly on the foliage or fruit. The egg is pearly white when first laid. It is oval in shape and flattened, resembling a minute drop of wax (Fig. 13:14). Newly hatched larvae are semitransparent white with a shiny black head and are about $\frac{1}{16}$ in. long. When the caterpillar is mature it is pinkish white with a brown head and about ¾ in. long. The full-grown larva spins a silken cocoon under bark or other suitable shelter.

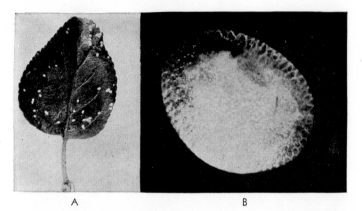

A   B

Fig. 13:14. Codling moth eggs. A, eggs laid on apple leaf; B, single egg greatly enlarged. *Courtesy USDA.*

The pupa is about ½ in. long and varies in color from yellow to brown, depending upon age. Adult moths are variable in size, the wing expanse being ¾ in. or less. The wings are brownish gray with dark bands. Near the tip of each forewing is a dark brown color spot in which are two irregular coppery lines (Fig. 13:15).

Life history. Codling moths overwinter as mature larvae in waterproof cocoons under the bark or in the ground at the base of the tree. In the spring, usually in April or May, the overwintering larva changes into a light brown pupa. The pupal stage may last four to six weeks in the cool weather of early spring. When about to emerge, the pupa works its way toward the surface. After part of its length is out of the cocoon, the shell splits and the adult moth emerges, leaving the brown pupal shell protruding from the exit hole.

Moths of the spring brood reach a peak of activity during May or June in most localities (April in southern areas). See Table 13:1. The females oviposit during late afternoon or evening when the temperature is 60°F. or higher. Temperatures during spring influence the extent of egg laying and the development of first-generation caterpillars, and are important in determining codling moth activity during the season. However, larval injury depends mostly upon the initial infestation. The greater the population of overwintering larvae, other things being equal, the greater the damage.

A   B

Fig. 13:15. Codling moth. A, larva and pupa in cocoons under bark; B, adult resting on apple leaf. *Courtesy USDA.*

Eggs of the first generation usually take 12 to 14 days to hatch because of cool weather. First-generation larvae enter the fruit over a period of five to six weeks. The caterpillars feed in the fruit about three weeks, then leave and search for a place to spin their cocoons. About one fourth of the caterpillars remain in the cocoons until the following spring. Most change to pupae within four to six days and the pupal period lasts from ten days to two weeks. First-generation moths appear by mid summer and may be present until cool weather in northern areas. The length of the first generation varies from 35 to 50 days in southern areas and 50 to 60 days in northern.

Eggs of the second generation hatch after six to seven days. Second-generation caterpillars appear in mid to late summer, depending on locality, and attack the fruit for about 6 weeks. In northern states, the second-generation caterpillars leave the fruit and go into winter quarters during August and September or later. A small portion may pupate, emerge, and lay a few eggs. In southern states, the second-generation caterpillars leave the fruit in July and August and give rise to a complete third generation. A fourth and a partial fifth generation may occur in some areas.

Table 13:1 | Typical Timing of Peaks of Codling Moth Activities in Selected Localities

Activity	Oregon	Massachusetts	New Mexico
Emergence of spring brood moths	Late May	Mid-June	Late April
Hatching of first generation eggs	Mid-June	Early July	Mid-May
Emergence of first generation moths	Late July	Early August	Late June
Hatching of second generation eggs	Early August	Mid-August	Early July
Emergence of second generation moths	Late August	——	Early August
Hatching of third generation eggs	Mid-September	——	Mid-August
Emergence of third generation moths	——	——	Early September
Hatching of fourth generation eggs	——	——	Mid-September
Number of generations per season	Two and a partial third	Two	Four

Control. During the forty years previous to 1947, lead arsenate was the standard control measure for codling moths. By 1925 the pest was becoming difficult to kill with this insecticide. Strains of codling moth from Washington and Virginia were shown to be resistant to lead arsenate in 1928. Growers in certain regions began applying as many as ten cover sprays in a single season in an attempt to reduce the fruit injury. The apple industry was in serious jeopardy in some areas just before DDT became available for agricultural work in this country. Since 1947, two to four summer applications of DDT have given effective control of the codling moth in most orchard regions. Resistance to DDT has been reported from New York, Colorado, and Ohio, but has been gradually increasing in all orchard areas. Methoxychlor, EPN, parathion, and Diazinon are also used for codling moth control. In localities where growers have had increasing difficulty in obtaining adequate control, there has been a shift to newer materials such as Sevin and Guthion.

As in all insect control work, timing is of utmost importance. Codling moth sprays are applied most effectively just before newly hatched larvae attempt to enter the apples.

Ascogaster quadridentata Wesm. is a braconid parasite which helps keep codling moth populations under control in eastern United States and Canada. It was introduced into the Pacific Northwest during the twenties, but apparently is not effective in this region.

Spider mites

European red mite *Panonychus ulmi* (Koch)

Two-spotted spider mite *Tetranychus telarius* (Linnaeus)

Schoene spider mite *Tetranychus schoenei* McGregor

McDaniel spider mite *Tetranychus mcdanieli* McGregor

Four-spotted spider mite *Tetranychus canadensis* (McGregor)

Yellow spider mite *Eotetranychus carpini borealis* (Ewing)

Brown spider mite *Bryobia rubrioculus* (Scheuten)

[Acarina:Tetranychidae]

Since the development and use of DDT and other synthetic organic insecticides in the orchard, spider mites have become major pests. The fact that DDT kills natural predators of spider mites is the most obvious reason for this sudden change in extent of damage caused by them. However, investigators have recognized that the problem of increase of mite pests on crops has a multiple origin. It is known that indirect effects of DDT and other chemicals upon the mite or its host plant are at least partly responsible. Another causal factor involves certain changes made in the spray program. In the past, an oil was usually added to the lead arsenate sprays and it helped to keep mites in check. Oils cannot be combined with DDT because such mixtures cause plant injury.

Spider mites were noted damaging tree fruits in California as early as 1854. The European red mite (Fig. 13:16) was first recorded in Oregon in 1911 and was causing injury in eastern United States and Canada by 1918. Two-spotted spider mite injury to orchard trees was noted in New England during the early 1800's. The brown mite was also observed in the east during the 1800's.

Twelve species of spider mites are known to infest deciduous fruit trees in the United States and Canada. Only seven of these are widely distributed or of serious consequence at the present time. Several species are usually present in any given orchard and different species usually predominate at

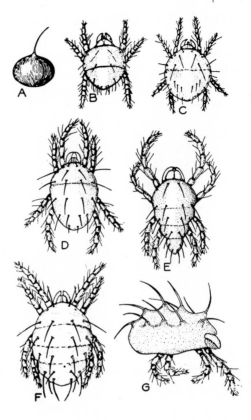

Fig. 13:16. Life stages of the European red mite. A, egg; B, larva; C, protonymph; D, deutonymph; E, adult male; F, G, adult female top and side views. *Courtesy USDA.*

different times throughout the growing season. Orchards in the same area will not necessarily contain the same kinds of spider mites.

The two-spotted spider mite is the most common species, being found throughout the country on a wide variety of crops (Fig. 13:17). It is nearly cosmopolitan in its distribution. It feeds upon tree fruits, small fruits, vegetable crops, forage crops, and florist and ornamental crops. It is a destructive pest of roses, beans, cotton, hops, strawberries, cucurbits, almonds, and apples.

European red mite is found throughout most of the United States and southern Canada, as well as in Europe, Russia, Australia, and Tasmania. It attacks all of the tree fruits as well as other trees, shrubs and berries.

Brown spider mite, which was formerly thought to be a tree-feeding race of the clover mite, is found in all parts of the United States and Canada and in South America, Europe, and Australia (Fig. 13:18). This mite feeds upon all tree fruits, various woody ornamentals, and also walnut and almond.

The Schoene spider mite and the four-spotted spider mite are mainly found in eastern orchards. They are also pests of various crops in southwestern United States. Schoene spider mite feeds on cotton, beans, various brambles, black locust and other shade trees as well as on apple. Four-spotted spider mite is found on apple, plum, cotton, and a number of shade trees.

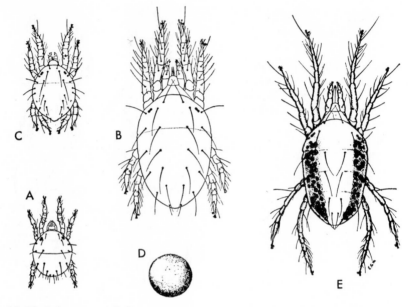

Fig. 13:17. Life stages of the two-spotted spider mite. A, larva; C, protonymph; B, deutonymph; E, adult female; D, egg. *Courtesy USDA.*

McDaniel spider mite is a serious pest of tree fruits in the Pacific Northwest and has also been collected in Utah, California, Montana, North Dakota, Michigan and New York. This is the same mite which was formerly called Pacific mite [1] on tree fruits in Washington. Yellow spider mite is damaging to apples, pears, cherries, several berries, and certain ornamentals from British Columbia to central California. This species was previously known as Willamette mite [1] in certain orchard areas.

Spider mites cause a general weakening of the trees. Studies have shown that 35 per cent or more of the chlorophyll in apple foliage may be removed by mite feeding. Initial damage to foliage appears as fine white speckling which extends and turns brownish as the mites continue to feed (Fig. 13:19). Photosynthesis and transpiration of the trees are depressed. In severe

---

[1] Pacific mite and Willamette mite are now known to be damaging to tree fruits only in localized areas.

infestations, the leaves may become entirely brown and drop from the tree. Injury caused by the brown spider mite on stone fruits is exceptional in that browning and dropping of foliage does not occur. Damage caused in early summer may cause a light set of fruit the following season. Mite stimulation of late summer or fall regrowth of the trees may result in winter kill of the terminals. Mites may cause a reduction in the size of fruits and also a reduction in the number of fruits produced per tree. They may also cause off-color in fruits and fruit drop.

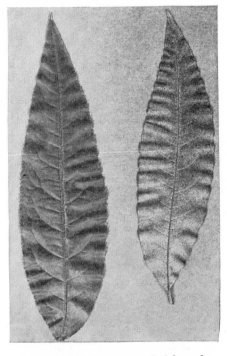

Fig. 13:18. The brown spider mite, *Bryobia rubrioculus* (Scheuten). Note the long front legs. *Courtesy University of California.*

Fig. 13:19. Injury to peach foliage by European red mite. Left, uninfested leaf healthy and green; right, heavily infested leaf injured and gray. *Courtesy Ohio Agr. Exp. Sta.*

Description. Spider mites are quite small—the adults being barely visible to the naked eye. The species being discussed vary from about 0.25 to 0.5 mm. in length. All of the spider mites go through five stages in their life cycle—egg, six-legged larva, eight-legged protonymph, deutonymph, and adult.

European red mite adults are brick red with prominent white spots at the bases of the dorsal spines. Nymphal stages are dull green to brown. A light green to straw color is typical of two-spotted spider mite adults and nymphs. Actively feeding adults have a large dark spot on each side of the body near the middle. Schoene spider mites and four-spotted spider mites are similar in color, being green with two black spots near the front of the body and two near the rear. Active female McDaniel spider mites are translucent green to greenish yellow in color with a double spot on each side near the middle and another pair of spots near the rear (Fig. 13:20). Yellow spider mites are light pink to pale yellow or greenish in color with two or three pairs of small dusky spots on the body in later life. Adult brown spider mites usually are dark brown on the front portion of the body and light brown to greenish or reddish on the rear portion.

Eggs of the European red mite are red and slightly flattened on top with a dorsal stipe. This species spins little or no webbing. The eggs of the brown spider mite are spherical, smooth and red. Adult females have long front legs and they spin no webbing. Yellow spider mites lay eggs that are

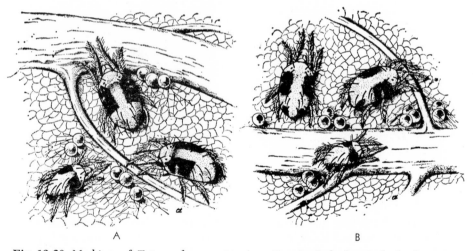

A   B

Fig. 13:20. Markings of *Tetranychus* species. A, pattern typical of actively feeding two-spotted spider mite, females above right, male below left; B, pattern typical of actively feeding four-spotted spider mite, McDaniel spider mite, and Schoene spider mite, females above, male below. *Courtesy University of California.*

spherical and clear with a fine dorsal stipe. They spin very little webbing. Two-spotted, four-spotted, McDaniel, and Schoene spider mites lay spherical, clear to pearly white, smooth eggs. The first two spin a moderate amount of webbing, while the others spin a copious amount of webbing.

Life history. Although most spider mites overwinter as bright orange adult females in plant debris on the ground, there are exceptions to this rule. European red mites and brown spider mites winter as bright red eggs on twigs and limbs. Yellow spider mites hibernate as bright yellow females under the bark. A high proportion of McDaniel spider mites survive the winter in cracks in the bark below the soil level.

Orchard mites usually develop six to eight generations per season, depending on the area. Schoene, European red, and two-spotted spider mites have nine to ten generations in Virginia. Brown spider mites have three to five generations per season. European red mites have only two full generations in Nova Scotia. Studies show that McDaniel spider mites normally produce ten to eleven generations per season in Washington and seven to nine in northern Utah.

Hibernating females become active in early spring and migrate to the opening buds. Two-spotted spider mites may winter under the bark, move to the cover crop to feed in early spring, and invade the trees again in early summer. McDaniel spider mites usually have a similar sequence of hosts. Eggs of the European red mite and the brown spider mite hatch with the first warm weather of spring and the larvae swarm to the young leaves.

Larvae feed for two or three days and then remain quiescent for about the same length of time. The protonymphs emerge from the split skin of the resting stage. They feed for two to four days and then pass a quiescent stage of about equal length. Deutonymphs emerge, feed for two to six days, and remain quiescent for an equal number of days. Adults emerge and mate or else the females reproduce parthenogenetically. When the latter occurs, only males are produced from the eggs. The complete life cycle is from one to three weeks in length, depending upon locality, seasonal variations, and species involved.

The average number of eggs laid per female varies from 25 for the European red mite to 150 for the McDaniel spider mite. Length of life of adult females is two to three weeks for the brown spider mite and up to nine weeks for the two-spotted spider mite. Apparently the brown spider mite is entirely parthenogenetic, since no males have ever been collected.

Brown spider mites lay their winter eggs early in hot, dry seasons and the population of active stages may be greatly reduced by mid summer. European red mite or McDaniel spider mite populations may replace the brown mites, building up peaks of infestation by mid to late summer. Yellow spider mites and two-spotted spider mites tend to develop heaviest populations in late summer or fall.

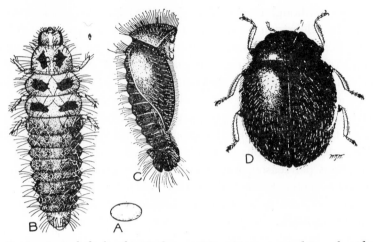

Fig. 13:21. A minute lady beetle, *Stethorus picipes* Casey, a predator of spider mites. A, egg; B, larva; C, pupa; D, adult. *Courtesy USDA.*

Several types of predators are effective in reducing spider mite populations. Small, black lady beetles of the genus *Stethorus* have been cited as the most important natural enemies in several regions. S. *punctum* is the common species in eastern orchards, while S. *picipes* is the western species (Fig. 13:21). Predaceous mites of the genus *Typhlodromus* and the minute pirate bug, *Orius insidiosus,* also feed upon spider mites. Other predators include certain plant bugs and thrips.

Control. Delayed dormant sprays of lime-sulfur and oil are used to help prevent the development of brown spider mite and European red mite populations.

Organic phosphorus insecticides such as parathion, malathion, EPN, TEPP, schradan, and demeton are effective against mites. However, strains of McDaniel, European red, and two-spotted spider mites have developed resistance to phosphate insecticides in some areas. Parathion and EPN often cause injury to McIntosh or related varieties of apples.

The specific acaricides, Sulphenone, Chlorobenzilate, Genite, Mitox, ovex, Aramite, Fenson, Tedion, Kelthane, and DMC will control the phosphate-resistant mites. However, resistance to most of these acaricides has also developed in certain orchards. Aramite is not effective against the brown spider mite, whereas Sulphenone is especially good for control of this species. Genite, Fenson, Mitox, DMC, and ovex may cause a russeting injury of apples, especially Golden Delicious, under slow-drying weather conditions. Chlorobenzilate is utilized for control of mites on pears, but may cause injury to apples or peaches. Aramite and Sulphenone may affect the size and color of the fruit under certain conditions. Aramite is no longer recommended on bearing trees, because it has a zero tolerance on fruit. Tedion in combination with parathion may cause russeting of apples.

Two sprays, seven to ten days apart, are often applied in mite control problems. If a prebloom spray of Genite, DMC, Mitox, ovex, or Fenson is applied, often at least one summer spray of Sulphenone, Kelthane, Tedion, or Chlorobenzilate, will also be required. Use of combinations of an organic phosphorus insecticide plus an acaricide are useful when resistant mites are present.

San Jose scale

Aspidiotus perniciosus Comstock [Homoptera: Diaspididae]

San Jose scale, potentially the most destructive orchard pest, is an introduced species, having been brought into California about 1870. By 1873 it had become a serious pest in the San Jose Valley. A "classic" early investigation was the trip by C. L. Marlatt to the Orient in 1901–02 to find the native home of the scale. He found that it had originated in the area north and west of Peiping on flowering Chinese peach. Meanwhile the insect had been inadvertently transported to New Jersey in 1886 or 1887 with a shipment of Kelsey plums. The two nurseries that received this material shipped nursery stock to various parts of the country and by 1895 San Jose scale had spread to most of the eastern states. It reached Oregon and Washington by 1882 and Nova Scotia by 1912.

Tremendous damage occurred before control measures were perfected and established. Besides rendering the fruit unmarketable, the scales killed the twigs and limbs, and eventually killed the trees. More than 1,000 acres of mature apple trees were killed in southern Illinois in 1922. The insects suck the plant juices from the twigs and larger branches and from the fruit and foliage. Infested trees show a general decrease in vigor and terminal twigs usually die (Fig. 13:22). The leaves characteristically remain on infested trees through the winter. This is especially typical of sweet cherry trees.

San Jose scale attacks all orchard fruits, most small fruits, and many kinds of shade trees and ornamental shrubs. It is most destructive to apple, pear, and sweet cherry; rarely is it found on sour cherry, pecan, or walnut. Records indicate that it is distributed throughout the commercial fruit-growing sections of the United States and Canada. It is also reported from the Orient, Australia, New Zealand, Russia, Germany, Austria, Africa, the Mediterranean Region, and South America.

Fig. 13:22. Peach tree injured by San Jose scale. Several branches have been killed. *Courtesy USDA.*

Description. Female San Jose scales are nearly round and about 2 mm. in diameter. The waxy shell is gray with a raised central nipple. The yellowish, saclike body of the female with its long thread-like sucking mouth parts remains protected under this cover of fibers and wax. Male scales are oval, about 1 mm. long and have a raised dot near the larger end of the shell. When mature the male emerges from the scale as a delicate, yellow, two-winged insect. **Crawlers** or young are borne alive under the female scale. These are very small, yellow nymphs with six well-developed legs and a pair of antennae. Individual scales usually become surrounded by a small reddish spot on the fruit or on the bark of young twigs. On heavily infested trees, the entire surface of the bark is covered with a gray layer of overlapping scales. The twigs appear as if they had been sprinkled with wood ashes when wet (Fig. 13:23).

Life history. Winter is passed as partly grown scales upon the tree. Up to 80 per cent of the winter forms may be first nymphal instars. Temperatures of minus 25° to minus 30°F. kill 90 per cent or more of the half-grown scales, while minus 15° to minus 20°F. kill about two-thirds. In spring, the scales continue their growth and become mature about the time the fruit trees bloom or a little later.

The active males issue from their scales and mate with the females which remain under scales throughout their lives. After being fertilized, the females begin producing living young ovoviviparously at the rate of nine to ten per day. They reproduce for six weeks or more, each scale bearing from 150 to 500 crawlers.

Young scales may crawl considerable distances during the first few hours of their lives. Often they are carried to other trees by the wind, on the feet

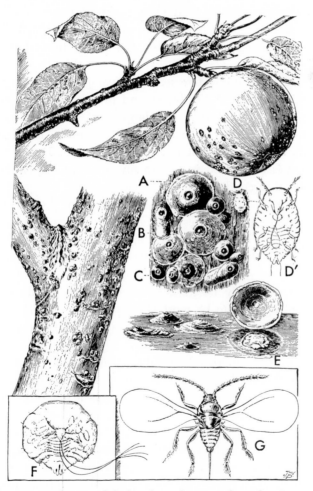

Fig. 13:23. San Jose scale. A, adult female scale; B, male scale; C, young scales; D, nymph just hatched; D', same, much enlarged; E, scale raised, showing body of female beneath; F, body of female much enlarged; G, adult male much enlarged. *Courtesy USDA.*

of birds, on the clothing of men working in the orchard, or on farm implements. The first waxy secretion is produced on the dorsal surface of the crawlers. Ordinarily they settle down within a few hours on the bark or on the leaves or fruit, insert their long, thread-like beaks into the plant tissue, and begin feeding.

About three weeks afterwards, they molt or shed their skins and with the old skin lose their legs and antennae. The scales become mere flattened yellow sacks with waxy caps, attached to the bark by their sucking mouth parts. As the insect grows, woolly secretions are given off from the body. These fibers are mixed with a waxy material to continue the formation of the shell. Portions of the shed skins are incorporated into the scales following molts. The female develops through two nymphal instars to the adult; the male, through four, the last two being termed the "propupa" and "pupa."

Two or more generations per season develop in various parts of the country—two in the Pacific Northwest and in the Northeast—three in the Sacramento Valley of California. Overlapping of broods is caused by the long reproduction period of each female which results in all stages being present on the trees throughout the growing season. During the summer each generation is completed in five to seven weeks, depending upon the locality and weather conditions.

Prospaltella perniciosi is a minute wasp parasite of the San Jose scale in the eastern states and as far west as Kansas. Parasitism up to 90 per cent has been reported. This species, together with the cosmopolitan *Aphytis proclia,* has apparently reduced the scale from a major to a minor pest in New England.

The twice-stabbed lady beetle is a common scale predator throughout the country, but appears to be most effective on the Pacific Coast. *Microweisea misella* is another small lady beetle which preys upon scale insects in both eastern and western orchards.

Control. In North America lime-sulfur was developed primarily as a San Jose scale treatment, and was first used in California in 1880. This material is still used as a scalecide, especially as a delayed dormant spray in the Pacific Northwest.

Spray oils are used against the scale throughout the country. A combination spray containing lime-sulfur plus oil is utilized in certain areas of the West. So-called "Superior oil" is applied in the East. Other special grades of oil have been developed for use in various orchard regions.

Malathion and parathion are also effective controls for the San Jose scale. A prepink phosphate spray has replaced the use of delayed dormant lime-sulfur and oil in some regions.

DDT will kill San Jose scale crawlers if applications are carefully timed to get the first generation when it appears in early summer.

Cherry fruit fly, *Rhagoletis cingulata* (Loew)

Black cherry fruit fly, *Rhagoletis fausta* (Osten Sacken)

[Diptera:Tephritidae]

The cherry fruit fly and the black cherry fruit fly are native North American insects. Until recently it was thought that the cherry fruit fly was an eastern species which had been introduced into the West. However, investigators in California have shown that the subspecies, *R. cingulata indifferens* Curran, is indigenous to the West in wild bitter cherry, *Prunus emarginata;* while the eastern subspecies, *R. cingulata cingulata* (Loew) is native to that area in wild black cherry, *P. serotina.*

Cherry fruit fly was reported from cultivated cherries in eastern United States and Canada prior to 1900 before its wild host plants were discovered. Western cherry fruit fly was first noted in cultivated cherries in Oregon in 1913 and in Washington in 1916. Although it was present in wild cherries, it did not become an economic pest of cultivated cherries in certain commercial cherry-growing areas of the West until after 1940.

The black cherry fruit fly was first recorded in British Columbia and later in eastern and midwestern states. This species is found in all cherry producing areas, but usually much rarer than the cherry fruit fly when the two species are associated. However, it was the only fruit fly attacking

Fig. 13:24. Cherries injured by maggots of the cherry fruit fly. *Courtesy Pennsylvania State University.*

cherries in the Flathead Valley of Montana until recent years. Pin cherry, *Prunus pennsylvanica,* is its primary native host in the East. The insect has been found in bitter cherry, *P. emarginata,* in the West.

Cherry fruit flies are mainly found in cultivated and wild cherries. The black cherry fruit fly prefers sour cherries to sweet cherries. Fruit fly maggots burrow to the center of the cherries and feed around the pits. Cherries become somewhat misshapen and undersized (Fig. 13:24). Usually one side of the fruit will become partially decayed and shrunken and closely attached to the pit. Exit holes are sometimes cut in the cherries by the maggots before harvest. Maggots are a contaminant when present in processed fruit.

Description. The cherry fruit fly is about two-thirds the size of a house fly, blackish in color, with yellowish head and legs and light green compound eyes (Fig. 13:26). Conspicuous dark bands extend transversely across the wings. The abdomen of the black cherry fruit fly is entirely black; while that of the cherry fruit fly is marked with white bands, four in the female and three in the male.

The white egg is slightly less than 1 mm. in length. The maggot is a dirty white color and about ¼ in. long when full grown (Fig. 13:25). The puparium is about ⅐ in. long and resembles a grain of wheat. Cherry fruit fly puparia are reddish brown; whereas those of the black cherry fruit fly are straw colored.

Life history. Cherry fruit flies overwinter as pupae within puparia in the soil. Adult flies begin emerging from the soil in the spring about one month after sweet cherries are in full bloom. Emergence usually begins during the first half of June in the Northeast and Midwest and towards the end of May in the Pacific Northwest.

Depending upon weather conditions, females begin egg-laying a week to

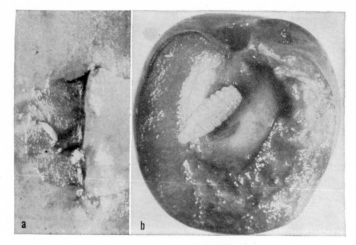

Fig. 13:25. Cherry fruit fly. A, egg exposed by removal of flap of skin of cherry; B, full-grown larva. *Courtesy Pennsylvania State University.*

10 days after emergence. Eggs are usually laid during any daylight hour when it is warm and sunny. The female makes feeding punctures near the bottom of the fruit with her ovipositor and feeds upon the juices which exude. Eggs are not usually deposited in heavily punctured cherries but in nearby fruits. They are inserted just under the skin.

Fig. 13:26. Cherry fruit fly. A, pupa; B, adult. *Courtesy Pennsylvania State University.*

Fruit fly eggs hatch in five to seven days and the small maggots begin feeding on the pulp of the cherry. Several maggots can develop in a single cherry. It is not uncommon to find five or six mature maggots in individual cherries from heavily infested orchards. The maggots feed for two to three weeks in the fruit. When they are full grown they leave the fruit, drop to the ground, and enter the soil to a depth of one to three inches.

There is one generation per season, except for about 1 per cent of the maggots which pupate and emerge the same season according to investigations in the Pacific Northwest. The few flies emerging in late summer or fall are lost because there is no suitable host present. Most of the pupae remain in the soil until the following spring.

Infestation of cherries varies considerably with weather conditions in spring and early summer. If cool weather retards the emergence of flies and fly activity after emergence, cherries may escape infestation to a large degree because either too few flies have emerged by harvest time or the female preoviposition period has been extended. Sometimes the season is late, so that cherry blooming, fly emergence, and cherry harvest are all delayed. Then, if high temperatures occur during the last two weeks before harvest, a high potential infestation of the fruit will result.

A number of parasites of the cherry fruit flies have been recorded from both eastern and western regions. Braconid parasites of the genus *Opius* are most common in maggots from wild cherries, while an ichneumonid has been reared from maggots in cultivated cherries. Parasitism only averaged about 2 per cent in an untreated cherry orchard in Washington.

Control. Lead arsenate spray or dust is still used in certain areas, but in other areas it is ineffective for practical control. It is recommended in two to four applications at 10 to 14-day intervals.

Methoxychlor is used in two to three applications at ten-day intervals. This material provides fair control of the cherry fruit fly. Parathion is the most effective insecticide currently recommended for control of the fly and it also kills the maggots within the fruit. Sometimes methoxychlor and parathion are applied in combination sprays. Diazinon and perthane will also control cherry fruit flies.

Malathion is recommended especially for use in orchards adjacent to town because of its low toxicity to animals. TEPP or rotenone are used during cherry harvest in some areas. Lead arsenate, methoxychlor, parathion, or demeton are sometimes applied as postharvest sprays to help reduce the fruit fly population for the following season.

Selected References

Cagle, L. R., *Life History of the Spider Mite* Tetranychus schoenei McG., Va. Agr. Exp. Sta. Tech. Bul. 87, 1943.

——, *Life History of the Two-spotted Spider Mite,* Va. Agr. Exp. Sta. Tech. Bul. 113, 1949.

Cox, J. A., *The Cherry Fruit Fly in Erie County,* Pa. Agr. Exp. Sta. Bul. 548, 1952.

Cutright, C. R., *Codling Moth Biology and Control Investigations,* Ohio Agr. Exp. Sta. Bul. 583, 1937.

Eyer, J. R., *Ten Years' Experiments with Codling Moth Bait Traps, Light Traps, and Trap Bands,* N.M. Agr. Exp. Sta. (Tech.) Bul. 253, 1937.

Frick, K. E., H. G. Simkover, and H. S. Telford, *Bionomics of the Cherry Fruit Flies in Eastern Washington,* Wash. Agr. Exp. Sta. Tech. Bul. 13, 1954.

Garman, P., and J. F. Townsend, *Control of Apple Insects,* Conn. Agr. Exp. Sta. Bul. 552, 1952.

——, *The European Red Mite and Its Control,* Conn. Agr. Exp. Sta. Bul. 418, 1938.

Gentile, A. G., and F. M. Summers, "The Biology of San Jose Scale on Peaches with Special Reference to the Behavior of Males and Juveniles," *Hilgardia* 27(10):269–85 (1958).

Lathrop, F. H., *Apple Insects in Maine,* Maine Agr. Exp. Sta. Bul. 540, 1955.

Marlatt, C. L., *The San Jose or Chinese Scale,* USDA Bur. Ent. Bul. 62, 1906.

Madsen, H. F., and M. M. Barnes, *Pests of Pear in California,* Cal. Agr. Exp. Sta. Circ. 478, 1959.

Morgan, N. H., and C. V. G. Anderson, "Life histories and Habits of the Clover Mite, *Bryobia praetiosa* Koch, and the Brown Mite, *B. arborea* M. & A., in British Columbia (Acarina: Tetranychidae)," *Can. Ent.* 90:23–42 (1958).

Newcomer, E. J., *Orchard Insects of the Pacific Northwest and Their Control,* USDA Circ. 270, 1950.

Newcomer, E. J., and M. A. Yothers, *Biology of the European Red Mite in the Pacific Northwest,* USDA Tech. Bul. 89, 1929.

Pritchard, A. E., and E. W. Baker, "A Guide to the Spider Mites of Deciduous Fruit Trees," *Hilgardia* 21:253–86, 1952.

Webster, R. L., *A Ten-Year Study of Codling Moth Activity,* Wash. Agr. Exp. Sta. Bul. 340, 1936.

Chapter 14 | INSECT PESTS OF
SMALL FRUITS | Carl Johansen

Small fruits are represented by a variety of crops—raspberries, loganberries, blackberries, and other cane berries, strawberries, gooseberries, currants, grapes, blueberries, and cranberries. These plants are grown under widely differing conditions and are attacked by a correspondingly diverse group of insects and mites.

The pests

Weevils are one of the commonest types of small fruit pests. Larvae of **strawberry root weevils**, *Brachyrhinus* spp., feed on the roots of strawberries, raspberries, and other small fruits in all parts of the United States and southern Canada. Root weevils are especially damaging in the Pacific Northwest. The **strawberry crown borer**, *Tyloderma fragariae* (Riley) (Fig. 14:1), is a weevil which attacks strawberries in the eastern states, especially

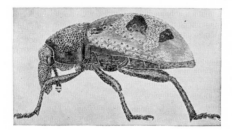

Fig. 14:1. Adult of the strawberry crown borer, *Tyloderma fragariae* (Riley). *Courtesy Ohio Agr. Exp. Sta.*

the Southeast. A closely related species damages strawberries in the Northwest. The **strawberry weevil**, *Anthonomus signatus* Say, is a small native species which occurs in the eastern United States and Canada and in Texas. **White-fringed beetles** damage strawberries in the Southeast.

Several other kinds of beetles are injurious pests of small fruits. Eastern and western **raspberry fruitworms** are small beetles whose larvae feed upon the receptacles and fruits of raspberries and loganberries. The **strawberry rootworm,** *Paria fragariae* Wilcox, is another type of small beetle which injures strawberry and raspberry plantings in the East. Both eastern and western species of **grape rootworm** feed on the roots of the vine.

Just as among tree fruit pests, we find that a good number of small fruit pests belong to the order Lepidoptera. Clearwing moth larvae feed upon all types of berries and grapes, for example larvae of the **strawberry crown moth** attack blackberries and raspberries as well as its preferred host; **raspberry crown borer** damages all cane berries; **currant borer** damages both currants and gooseberries; and **grape root borer** attacks both wild and cultivated grapes.

Caterpillars of several lepidopterous families roll the leaves of berries and grapes. The **strawberry leaf roller** is a pest in all parts of the country (Fig. 14:2); while the western strawberry leaf roller is only damaging on the Pacific Coast. **Red-banded leaf roller** (Fig. 13:1) feeds on grapes and berries in the East. The **oblique-banded leaf roller** and the **orange tortrix** attack cane berries and strawberries in the West.

A number of so-called **fireworms,** the larvae of certain small moths, are major pests of cranberries. In the Great Lakes region the **grape berry moth** is a serious pest as the larvae (Fig. 14:3) destroy the blossoms and fruit of grapes.

Sawfly larvae feed on the foliage of raspberry and blackberry. The **imported currantworm** is a sawfly which injures currants and gooseberries.

A number of Diptera are pests of small fruits. The **raspberry cane maggot** attacks both raspberries and blackberries. Fruit flies include the **blueberry maggot** and several species of **currant fruit flies.**

Various **sucking insects** are highly injurious including the bramble, grape, and rose leafhoppers; raspberry, strawberry, and grapevine aphids; tarnished plant bug and spittlebugs; strawberry whitefly and grape whitefly; grape mealybug and grape phylloxera (Fig. 14:4); and several species of scale insects.

A variety of **mites** commonly attack small fruits. Eriophyid mites include the redberry mite on blackberry, dryberry mite on raspberry and loganberry, the currant bud mite, and the grape erineum mite. Important spider mites infesting small fruits are the two-spotted spider mite on strawberry, raspberry, and blackberry; McDaniel spider mite and Schoene spider mite on raspberry; Pacific spider mite and Willamette spider mite on grape and raspberry; southern red mite on cranberry; strawberry spider mite on strawberry; and yellow spider mite on raspberry and blueberry. The cy-

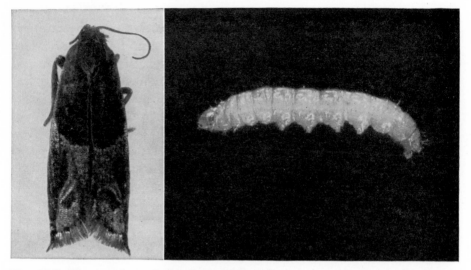

Fig. 14:2. The strawberry leaf roller, adult and larva, a major pest of strawberries. *Courtesy University of California.*

clamen mite feeds upon strawberries as well as various ornamentals. This minute pest is particularly injurious and difficult to control on both greenhouse and field grown crops.

Although many of the same pest species attack raspberry, loganberry, and blackberry, it is notable that certain ones are more damaging either to blackberry or to raspberry and loganberry.

The injury

Fruit damage. Many of the small fruit insects cause injury by direct feeding on and contamination of the fruits. Both the eastern and the western raspberry fruitworms feed upon the cores and into the drupelets of raspberries and loganberries. Larvae of the currant fruit fly and the blueberry fruit fly are maggots which feed within the fruits. The cranberry fruitworm is a caterpillar which literally devours the berries. It is also a pest of blueberries. Gooseberry fruitworms web together several berry clusters and feed upon the fruits. The grape berry moth is the only pest that causes extensive damage to grape berries (Fig. 14:5).

The redberry mite causes the red berry condition of blackberries as a toxic effect of its feeding. Dryberry mites cause similar symptoms, often referred to as "dryberry disease" of loganberries and "sun-scald disease" of raspberries.

Tarnished plant bugs and spittlebugs suck the juices of strawberry and raspberry fruit buds resulting in small, hard, seedy "nubbins." Strawberry weevils cut the pedicels of the buds thereby destroying them. Second brood black-headed and yellow-headed fireworms usually feed upon the flower buds and the fruits of cranberries.

Honeydew from grape mealybugs will "gum" up the bunches of berries. A black, sooty mold usually develops on the honeydew. Grape juice processors reject fruits which contain honeydew and sooty mold.

The orange tortrix is a rather unique pest of red raspberries. Its only damage is contamination of the berries by the caterpillars themselves. When the canes are disturbed during harvest, the larvae drop from the foliage and lodge in the depressions of the fruits where they cannot be washed out. Their direct injury to the foliage is insignificant. Oddly enough, orange tortrix caterpillars do feed directly into the cores and drupelets of loganberries, blackberries, boysenberries, and other berries.

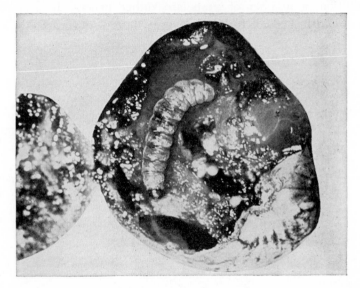

Fig. 14:3. Larva of the grape berry moth feeding inside a grape. *Courtesy Michigan State University.*

Foliage damage. Insects which injure the foliage include various leaf roller caterpillars (Fig. 14:6), raspberry sawfly larvae, the imported currant-worm, and several species of cranberry fireworms. Sucking pests also attack the foliage. Strawberry whitefly and grape whitefly, various aphids, spider mites, the cyclamen mite, bramble leafhoppers and grape leafhoppers are especially notable.

Cane damage. Canes are attacked by cane maggots and cane borers. Scale insects infest the stalks or canes of brambles, currants, grapes, and cranberries. The currant borer feeds in the center of the canes of currants and gooseberries (Fig. 14:7).

Crown and root damage. The crowns and roots of small fruits harbor a variety of pests. Strawberry crowns are attacked by two kinds of caterpillars—the strawberry crown moth and the strawberry crown miner. Certain weevils, such as the strawberry crown borer, also feed in the crowns of strawberry plants. Roots are eaten by the strawberry rootworm and strawberry root weevils. Raspberry, loganberry, and blackberry crowns are tunneled by the raspberry crown borer and the strawberry crown moth. Grape roots are destroyed by grape rootworms. A kind of sod webworm, the cranberry girdler, feeds upon the crowns, stems, and roots of cranberries. Only a few sucking insects attack the roots. The strawberry root aphid and the grape phylloxera are the most important species in this category.

In addition, a number of pests are rather general feeders upon the crowns or roots of small fruits. Cutworms and wireworms are damaging

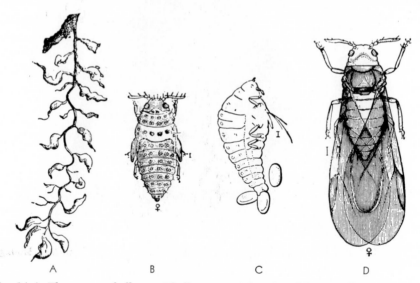

Fig. 14:4. The grape phylloxera *Phylloxera vitifoliae* (Fitch). A, galls on grape root inhabited by root generations of insect; B, female nymph; C, wingless female laying eggs on roots; D, winged female (migrant form). *After Riley.*

wherever such crops are raised. White grubs, particularly of the genus *Phyllophaga* in the East and the genus *Polyphylla* in the West, cause considerable injury (Fig. 14:8). The garden symphylan (Fig. 15:18) feeds upon the smaller roots and root hairs of many kinds of crops. Although symphylans are mainly soil inhabitants, ripe strawberries touching the soil surface sometimes become infested.

Disease transmission. Virus diseases represent the major limiting factor in the production of berries in some regions. The yellows disease of strawberries is transmitted by the strawberry aphid, while the raspberry aphid is the vector of raspberry mosaic. Certain leafhoppers, sometimes called sharpshooters, transmit Pierce's disease of grapes.

Cultural control

Since small fruits are shorter-term crops than tree fruits, cultural methods are more useful against the small fruit pests. Some of the commoner methods are: (1) removal and burning of infested canes or plants; (2) rotation, isolation, and planting in uninfested land; (3) plowing or cultivating to bury or destroy soil insects; (4) use of resistant varieties of plants; and (5) flooding of cranberry bogs.

Removal and destruction of infested canes is a standard practice used against the raspberry crown borer, raspberry cane borers, and the currant borer. Cutting raspberry canes close to the soil or destruction of pruning stubs in the spring removes the pupation site of the raspberry crown borer. Tips of canes infested with raspberry cane maggot are cut several inches below the girdled area. Plants injured by the strawberry crown moth are removed and burned. Raking and burning of fallen leaves in winter destroys pupae of the grape berry moth.

Crop rotation helps reduce populations of strawberry rootworm. New plantings should be established at least 300 yards from old fields to lessen the chance of strawberry crown borer infestation. Uninfested plants should be used and the old fields should be destroyed after harvest.

Vineyards are plowed before May 15 to bury the overwintering pupae of the grape berry moth. Often a low ridge of soil is thrown under the trellis about 30–45 days before harvest so that winter cocoons will be exposed. During the following spring, the ridge is pulled back into the row centers and disked to cover the cocoons. Plowing or cultivation is also utilized to destroy grape rootworm and currant fruit fly pupae.

Use of rootstocks resistant to the attack of the grape phylloxera is a common practice among nurserymen. Lloyd George raspberry is highly resistant to the raspberry aphid. This variety is used in breeding programs to obtain mosaic-escaping qualities in new hybrids, since the raspberry aphid transmits the mosaic virus.

Barriers placed around the perimeters of fields help protect them from the attacks of strawberry crown borers and strawberry root weevils. These

Fig. 14:5. Grape cluster damaged by larvae of the grape berry moth. Deflated berries injured by third generation larvae, dried berry (top) by second generation larva. *Courtesy Pennsylvania State University.*

pests are flightless and migrate by crawling. Fields should not be planted next to woodlots, nor should hedgerows or overgrown fences be allowed nearby, because these are overwintering places for strawberry weevil and strawberry rootworm adults.

Flooding is used as a method of control in cranberry bogs against several pests. Bogs are flooded for ten hours during the night or on a cool day about the end of May to kill small caterpillars of the black-headed fireworm. Winter flooding continued into May reduces the yellow-headed fireworm and certain cutworms. Fall flooding is effective against the cranberry girdler.

Chemical control

Although cultural measures are effective against some small fruit insects, insecticides must be relied upon for control of others. In general, the control programs are less complicated than those for tree fruit pests. Some of the reasons for this are: (1) smaller size of plantings, (2) lesser permanence of plantings, (3) fewer major introduced pests, and (4) smaller industry, with less disruption and problems caused by man.

In recent years, soil treatments with the chlordane-like materials have come into widespread use. This type of application has provided excellent control of many soil-inhabiting pests which previously were difficult to control.

As with tree fruits, one of the oldest practices is the use of lime-sulfur and/or oil in dormant or delayed dormant sprays. These are applied against grape mealybug, San Jose scale, redberry mite, and dryberry mite. Dormant dinitro sprays are used to destroy aphid eggs on certain small fruits in the East.

The inorganic insecticides are still used against certain chewing pests— lead arsenate for raspberry sawflies, strawberry rootworm, imported currant-worm, and strawberry leaf roller; calcium arsenate for blueberry maggot and strawberry weevil. Calcium arsenate and sodium fluosilicate are used in baits for control of strawberry root weevils. Cryolite is applied against orange tortrix, strawberry rootworm, and strawberry weevil.

Fig. 14:6. Injury of the strawberry leaf roller. *Courtesy Ohio Agri. Exp. Sta.*

Botanical materials are especially effective against pests which feed on the fruits. Raspberry fruitworms, spittlebugs, blueberry maggot, cranberry fruitworm, strawberry flea beetles and leaf beetles, imported currantworm, and gooseberry fruitworm are controlled with rotenone. Pyrethrum is used against the black-headed fireworm and the strawberry weevil. Sabadilla controls stink bugs and nicotine controls aphids.

At present, the chlorinated hydrocarbons rank first in number of small fruit pest control uses. DDT is utilized against a wide variety of insects—Japanese beetle adults, white-fringed beetles, grape berry moth, strawberry crown miner, cranberry tipworm, leafhoppers, leaf rollers, cane borers, rootworms, fruitworms, cutworms—at least 35 of the more important species. Chlordane, dieldrin, heptachlor, and aldrin are particularly useful for soil insects such as strawberry root weevils, white-fringed beetles, white grubs, wireworms, rootworms, and strawberry crown borers. Chlordane is also used against spittlebugs, mole crickets, and earwigs, dieldrin against blueberry blossom weevil. Thiodan is applied for control of aphids and cyclamen mite on strawberries and endrin is effective as a post-harvest spray against the cyclamen mite. Methoxychlor controls some of the same pests that DDT does. TDE is effective against the orange tortrix and the strawberry leaf roller. The leaf form of the grape phylloxera is controlled with lindane. Toxaphene is useful for strawberry crown borers and Kelthane is applied for spider mites on several crops.

Organic phosphate compounds are not as generally used on small fruits

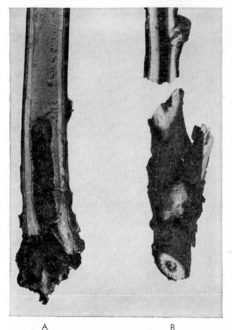

A   B

Fig. 14:7. Injury by larvae of clearwing moths. A, burrow of raspberry crown borer in blackberry cane; B, burrow of currant borer in currant cane. *Courtesy Wash. State Univ.*

Fig. 14:8. A portion of a strawberry row severely attacked by white grubs. *Courtesy Ohio Agr. Exp. Sta.*

as they are on tree fruits. TEPP, parathion, diazinon, and malathion are standard recommendations for spider mites and aphids. Parathion also controls grape berry moth, grape mealybug, raspberry crown borer, currant borer, and European fruit lecanium. EPN has some of the same uses as parathion. Grape mealybug, imported currantworm, rose scale, grape leafhoppers, and the currant fruit fly are treated with malathion. Trithion is effective against spider mites. Parathion is used as a soil treatment against the garden symphylan.

Fumigants are resorted to for control of certain pests. Ethylene dibromide is sometimes used as a soil treatment against wireworms and certain root weevils. Methyl bromide treatment of strawberry plants for cyclamen mite is conducted in fumigation chambers. In California, this pest is controlled in the field by covering the strawberry rows with plastic tarpaulins and releasing the methyl bromide underneath. Planting stock is fumigated with methyl bromide to kill the strawberry crown borer.

Control equipment

Several kinds of insecticide application equipment are suitable for use in small fruit production. Standard high-pressure power sprayers are efficient in various situations. They are equipped with horizontal booms for strawberries and vertical booms for cane berries and grapes. Sometimes a vertical boom is built in an inverted "U" shape so that it extends over the row of cane berries or grapes with nozzles directed inward from both sides (Fig. 14:9). This gives good spray coverage.

Power dusters are similarly used, with horizontal arrangement of fish-tail outlets for strawberries and vertical for cane berries and grapes. Rotary hand dusters and knapsack sprayers are adequate in plantings of a few acres.

Spraying or dusting of cranberry bogs poses a special problem. Some growers use stationary spray plants with long pipelines to carry the material to the ends of the bogs. Hoses and hand guns are attached to the pipeline during the spraying operation. Mobile equipment can be used by carrying long hoses into the bog and spraying with hand guns or multiple-nozzle broom guns. Long horizontal booms which extend out over the planting are sometimes utilized. Many growers apply insecticides through sprinkler systems. Power dusters and airplane equipment have also been used on cranberries.

Soil treatments should always be applied before planting. It is difficult to treat the soil efficiently in an established planting of small fruits. Sprays or dusts are evenly distributed on the soil surface by any suitable method

Fig. 14:9. Sprayer for treating grapes, covered U-boom. *Courtesy Pennsylvania State University.*

and then thoroughly mixed into the soil to the prescribed depth. Devices which inject the treatment behind a ditching tool or chisel, or in a plow furrow have also been used.

Soil treatment with parathion for control of garden symphylan is a critical procedure. Disk harrows are dragged immediately behind the spray machine so that the insecticide does not remain uncovered for more than a few minutes. Sometimes the initial disking process is followed by rotary tilling to mix the insecticide thoroughly with the soil.

REPRESENTATIVE PESTS OF SMALL FRUITS

For detailed discussion we have chosen the following insects that are serious pests of small fruits: strawberry root weevils, raspberry fruitworms, redberry mite, and grape leafhoppers.

Strawberry root weevil *Brachyrhinus ovatus* (Linnaeus)

Black vine weevil *Brachyrhinus sulcatus* (Fabricius)

Rough strawberry root weevil *Brachyrhinus rugosostriatus* (Goeze)

[Coleoptera:Curculionidae]

All three of the major species of strawberry root weevils were introduced from Europe. The strawberry root weevil was recorded in Massachusetts in 1852 and in the Pacific Northwest by 1904; the black vine weevil was collected in Massachusetts in 1831; and the rough strawberry root weevil was found in New York in 1891. They have become established throughout the United States and southern Canada.

Other root weevils are sometimes associated with the three listed above. In New York, the alfalfa snout beetle, *Brachyrhinus ligustici*, also attacks the strawberry; *B. singularis*, the clay-colored weevil, feeds on strawberries in British Columbia, *B. cribricollis* and *B. meridionalis* damage strawberries in California. In the Pacific Northwest, gray root weevils (genus *Dyslobus*) and the so-called raspberry bud weevils (genus *Nemocestes*) sometimes are locally important.

The strawberry root weevils attack a wide range of host plants. They attack all types of small fruits and berries. In addition, the strawberry root weevil and the black vine weevil attack ornamentals and nursery stock. Strawberry root weevil is very damaging to primroses. Black vine weevil is known as "cyclamen bulb borer" or "taxus weevil" in certain areas because

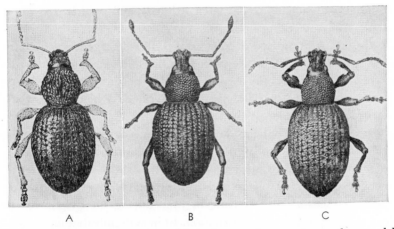

A B C

Fig. 14:10. Three species of root weevils. A, the strawberry root weevil, normal length 5 mm; B, the rough strawberry root weevil, normal length 8 mm; C, black vine weevil, normal length 10 mm. *Courtesy Eide, Wash. Agr. Exp. Sta.*

of its injury to these ornamentals. Root weevil grubs will also be found among the roots of legumes and grasses and have been known to cause serious damage to grasses grown for seed, peppermint and spearmint, and hops.

Adult *Brachyrhinus* weevils feed upon the foliage or fruits of plants. However, this injury is usually limited and minor in importance as compared to that of the larvae. The grubs feed on the roots of the plants. Heavy infestations are capable of killing entire plantings of strawberries. Damaged plants become stunted, the foliage turns red, and the fruit remains small and seedy.

Description. The strawberry root weevil is about ⅕ in. long. It is usually shiny black, sometimes brown, with rows of small, round punctures on the wing covers. The rough strawberry root weevil is similar except that it is about ⅓ in. long. Black vine weevil is the largest of the three, being about ⅖ in. long. It is black, but has several yellowish or gray spots on the wing covers (Fig. 14:10).

The larvae of strawberry root weevils are white to pinkish in color, have no legs, and have brown heads. They vary in length, being ¼ to ½ in. long when full grown (Fig. 14:11).

Life history. Strawberry root weevils winter as grubs or adults in the soil or plant debris. The larvae become active during the spring and form earthen cells in which they pupate. Adults usually emerge during May or June depending on the locality and the season. Black vine weevils emerge somewhat later than the strawberry root weevil. Rough strawberry root weevils emerge about two weeks later. Adult weevils which pass the winter will usually start emerging in April.

Eggs are laid starting two to four weeks after emergence and continuing for about two months. These are placed on the soil near the plants. All three species are parthenogenetic as only females occur. The strawberry root weevils usually lay 150 to 200 eggs per individual. A black vine weevil has been recorded to lay more than 2,000 eggs.

The eggs hatch in about ten days and the larvae burrow down as much as 6 or 8 inches into the soil. They feed upon the fibrous roots and tend to be most destructive in the spring.

Adult weevils feed on foliage and fruit at night. They make two distinct migrations per season—one starting in June during the oviposition period, the other in fall, possibly for hibernation. In heavily infested areas, the adult beetles may enter houses in sizable numbers and become household pests.

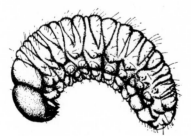

Fig. 14:11. Larva of the strawberry root weevil. *Courtesy Dept. Agr. British Columbia.*

Late emerging adults may pass the winter and lay more eggs the following season. Sometimes the adults are able to survive into a third season, which results in overlapping generations.

Control. Baits containing dried fruit or bran plus sodium fluosilicate or calcium arsenate have been used for root weevil control for many years. Apple waste or "pomice" is commonly utilized in commercial bait preparations. An apparatus consisting of a funnel and a metal tube is useful in applying baits to the crowns of strawberry plants.

In recent years, soil insecticides have been proven effective against strawberry root weevils. Aldrin, dieldrin, heptachlor, or chlordane is applied as a preplanting treatment. The insecticide is dusted onto the soil surface and then worked in with a disk harrow or rotary tiller to a depth of about 4 inches. Even on established plantings, dusting with these insecticides has given better control than baits.

In fields where soil insecticides have been used for several seasons, damage from *Nemocestes* or *Dyslobus* weevils may occur. This is particularly true on newly cleared land. In such cases, a return to poison baits has been required. Heavily infested fields may be cleaned up with ethylene dibromide injected into the soil behind a chisel which slices through the center of the strawberry crowns.

Eastern raspberry fruitworm *Byturus rubi* Barber

Western raspberry fruitworm *Byturus bakeri* Barber

[Coleoptera:Byturidae]

The two major raspberry fruitworms in North America are indigenous to this continent. Apparently these closely related species have evolved because the Continental Divide acted as a barrier to keep them separated. Other species of *Byturus* are recorded in this country but are not of economic importance. The eastern raspberry fruitworm is a pest in the eastern United States and Canada; while the western raspberry fruitworm is present in Oregon, Washington, Idaho, Montana, and British Columbia.

Raspberry fruitworms attack red raspberry and loganberry, and to a lesser extent, black and purple raspberries, blackberry, and strawberry. In the Pacific Northwest, the fruitworm has also been recorded from wild blackcap raspberry, wild dewberry, thimbleberry, and salmonberry.

The overwintered beetles feed on the unfolding leaves, especially those of the small, new canes. As the season progresses, they move up and feed upon foliage of the old canes, flower buds, and open flowers (Fig. 14:12).

When the leaves become distended, the injury appears as narrow slits between the secondary ribs. This injury is somewhat typical of the beetles and is often used as a reference point for insecticide applications.

Fig. 14:12. Damage to leaves and buds of raspberry by adult raspberry fruitworms. *Courtesy Conn. Agr. Exp. Sta.*

Larvae of the fruitworms usually feed upon the receptacles, scoring or tunneling them. Sometimes they feed upon the drupelets causing misshapen fruits (Fig. 14:13). Adult feeding in fruit buds will destroy them completely or cause the developing fruits to be distorted.

Fig. 14:13. Damage to raspberry fruit by raspberry fruitworms. Note larva feeding on drupelet. *Courtesy Conn. Agr. Exp. Sta.*

Description. The western raspberry fruitworm beetle is about ⅙ in. long and the eastern species is about ¼ in. long. They both are light brown in color, the eastern form being somewhat paler than the western. The full-grown larvae are ¼ to ⅓ in. long and white or yellowish in color with light brown areas on the upper part of each segment. Pupae are ⅙ to ⅕ in. long and are white (Fig. 14:14).

Life history. The overwintering adults emerge from the soil in the spring, starting in March and April in the Pacific Northwest and May in New England. Eggs are usually deposited singly on the buds or in the flowers about the time the first blooms appear. Sometimes they are placed on bud pedicels, leaf petioles, or even on a leaf.

The eggs hatch in about one to three weeks. Newly emerged larvae may feed in the blossoms or on the developing fruits for a few days. Some bore through the calyx into the receptacle or between developing drupelets the first day after hatching. The larvae feed in the fleshy receptacles or the drupelets for about four to six weeks.

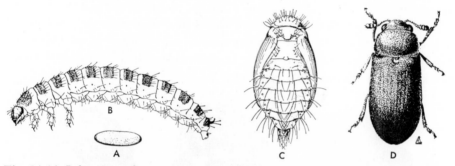

Fig. 14:14. Life stages of western raspberry fruitworm. A, egg; B, larva, C, pupa; D, adult. *Courtesy Wash. Agr. Exp. Sta.*

Mature larvae drop to the ground and enter the soil. They burrow in the soil for several days and pupate in late summer or fall. Fully-colored adult beetles are formed before winter, but they do not leave the pupal cells before the following spring.

Control. The standard control measure for raspberry fruitworms is rotenone applied to kill the beetles before they deposit their eggs. Usually several treatments are required—the first about a week after the first raspberry blooms open, the second about ten days after the first, and sometimes a third about ten days after the second.

In eastern Canada, lead arsenate plus Bordeaux mixture or lead arsenate plus hydrated lime are the materials usually applied. DDT is also recommended in some areas.

Redberry mite

Aceria essigi (Hassan) [Acarina:Eriophyidae]

The redberry mite was apparently introduced into California from Europe about 1921. When it was discovered in this country, the mite was confused with the dryberry mite, another European species. However, the mite was properly described by Hassan in 1928. It has become established in Oregon, Washington, and California.

At first it appeared that the mite would attack only Himalaya blackberries. Later observations showed that it would feed upon all varieties of blackberries tested, as well as red and black raspberries, wild dewberry, loganberry, and boysenberry. It is primarily a pest of Evergreen and Himalaya blackberries.

While in the berry, the mites feed near the bases of the drupelets around the core. The fruits grow to full size but do not ripen normally. All or part of the drupelets remain bright red and hard (Fig. 14:15). Berries become hardened and roughened and remain on the plants until the old canes die during the winter. **Redberry disease** varies in extent with the numbers of mites present. As many as 683 mites have been recorded in an individual red berry during September. Injury ranges from a single red drupelet in a black berry to a completely red berry.

Fig. 14:15. Injury of redberry mite to blackberries. Left berry, normal; middle berry with part of drupelets red and hard; right berry, all drupelets red and hard.

A closely related species, the dryberry mite, *Phyllocoptes gracilis* (Nalepa), causes so-called **dryberry disease** in loganberries and red raspberries.

Description. The redberry mite is very small, white, and worm-shaped. It varies in body length from 0.125 to 0.155 mm. Like all eriophyid mites, this species has only two pairs of legs which are attached near the cephalo-thoracic region. The slender, tapered abdomen is marked with eighty fine grooves which encircle the entire body (Fig. 14:16).

Although the mite is usually white, winter forms may be yellowish or amber. The male is slightly smaller than the female. Eggs are dull white, spherical, and 0.005 mm. in diameter.

Life history. The redberry mite overwinters in the adult stage under the bud scales. Some eggs may be laid during the winter in temperate localities. Reproduction is greatly increased in the spring when the foliage buds begin developing. Egg laying starts in late February or early March. The first brood is usually active by mid-March in the Pacific Northwest. The mites feed in the buds and sometimes move into the unfolding leaves. As the fruits begin to form there is a migration from the scales of the winter cane buds to the green berries. It appears that mites are carried from row to row of a planting by air currents. When migrating from the buds, they may be easily picked up by the wind and carried to adjacent rows.

In California, the migration is directly from the cane buds to the developing flowers. In Washington, not all mites leave the scales of the winter cane buds until the following fall. The mite population is built up by continual increase which starts in March, reaches a peak during September, and decreases during the fall and winter.

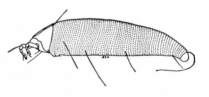

Fig. 14:16. Adult of redberry mite, *Aceria essigi* (Hassan). *Courtesy Ore. Agr. Exp. Sta.*

Each season there are a number of overlapping generations, which are indefinite due to the overlapping of egg and immature stages. The length of the life cycle from egg to adult may be as short as ten days under favorable conditions. During the summer, a heavily infested field may contain an average of several hundred mites per berry. Early in the fall the majority of the mites on the new canes are found in the axis of the cane buds and the compound leaf rather than inside the cane bud. As winter advances, more are found beneath the bud scales.

The mortality from midsummer to the following spring is very high. Two hundred mites per berry in the summer may be reduced to ten per berry by the next spring. Eggs have been observed as late as December. Some injured fruits retain a faded red or purplish color and hang on into the winter. Mites have been recorded in such berries as late as January.

Control. Lime-sulfur or sulfur sprays have been used against redberry mite in California since 1923. Lime-sulfur still is the best control measure for the mite. It is usually applied in a delayed dormant spray during February or March. Sometimes a second application is required in May.

Lime-sulfur is a standard treatment for eriophyid mites, including the pear leaf blister mite, apple rust mite, dryberry mite, and citrus rust mite.

Important natural enemies of the redberry mite are also mites. They belong to the predaceous genus, *Typhlodromus*. The life history of these predators is closely related to that of their host. They winter as adults under the bud scales but remain active, feeding upon the redberry mite throughout the winter.

Grape leafhopper *Erythroneura comes* (Say)

Western grape leafhopper *Erythroneura elegantula* Osborn

Variegated leafhopper *Erythroneura variabilis* Beamer

Three-banded leafhopper *Erythroneura tricincta* Fitch

Virginia-creeper leafhopper *Erythroneura ziczac* (Walsh)

Other species *Erythroneura dolosa* Beamer & Griffith, *E. vitifex* Fitch, *E. vulnerata* Fitch, *E. vitis* Harris, and *E. octonotata* Walsh

[Homoptera:Cicadellidae]

Many of the native North American species of *Erythroneura* attack grapes. *E. comes, E. tricincta, E. vulnerata,* and *E. vitis* are found in the Northeast, central states, and Southeast. *E. ziczac* inhabits the northeastern states, central states, and northwestern states. *E. octonotata* is only recorded from the central states. *E. vitifex* is found in the Northeast, Southeast, central states, and the Southwest. *E. variabilis* inhabits only the southwestern states. *E. elegantula* is a major species in the Southwest, Northwest, and certain central states; while *E. dolosa* is restricted to the Pacific Northwest.

All species of *Erythroneura* overwinter as adults. Nearly all live on woody plants, especially oaks and grape. Other hosts of the various grape leafhoppers are Virginia creeper, currant, gooseberry, raspberry, blackberry, dewberry, apple, plum, cherry, wild cherry, hawthorn, hollyhock, dahlia, Boston ivy, and various grasses and weeds. Shelter from wind provided by such plants as holly, wild strawberry, wild blackberry, dewberry, curled dock, and dandelion may be a primary consideration rather than their use as host plants.

The grape leafhopper has been known as an injurious pest of grape foliage since 1825. Major outbreaks have been recorded beginning in the early

1900's. In New York, peaks occurred in 1902, 1911, 1922, and 1938–47. California records indicate that the western grape leafhopper was particularly abundant in 1907–08, 1913–14, and 1929–32.

The two major damaging effects caused by grape leafhoppers are lowering of the quality of fruit and reduction in yield. Removal of chlorophyll and other cell contents causes a white speckling of the foliage. As the feeding punctures become more numerous, the light areas become larger and the leaf appears mottled (Fig. 14:17).

In advanced cases the whole leaf may turn pale, die and turn brown, and then fall. If a large portion of the foliage drops, the bunches of grapes may be sunburned. Lesser damage may cause deformed leaves, low sugar content in the grape berries, poorly maturing canes in the fall, and weak growth of vines the following spring. The droplets of honeydew which are exuded by the leafhoppers may disfigure the grapes. Dust may accumulate in these sticky droplets and sooty molds may also develop on them.

Description. Grape leafhoppers are small, agile insects about ⅛ in. long. The grape leafhopper adult is pale yellow with red, brown, and black markings (Fig. 14:17). Western grape leafhoppers are pale yellow with reddish and dark brown markings. The variegated leafhopper usually is darker than the above species with larger areas of cloudy brown on the forewings. Three-banded leafhoppers have a pair of dark markings across

Fig. 14:17. Grape leafhoppers and injury. A, white speckling of leaf due to feeding of leafhoppers; B, three-banded leafhopper (left) and grape leafhopper (right); C, nymphal leafhopper. *Courtesy USDA.*

the thorax and two more pairs forming color bands across the forewings. Overwintering adults have darker red markings than those of the spring and summer broods.

Grape leafhopper eggs are less than 1 mm. long, slightly curved, and white to pale yellow in color. Newly hatched nymphs are very small and nearly white. As they develop, they become more yellowish or brownish. Faint indications of wing pads occur in the second instar and continue to enlarge with each molt until the adult form is reached.

Life history. All of the grape leafhoppers overwinter as dark-colored adults in plant debris. These adults become active and migrate to the grapevines during March and April in California. Farther north, they become active in May. In New York there are two generations per season; in Kentucky there are two and a partial third; and in California there are three. Mating takes place on the grapes. Females begin inserting their eggs singly under the surface tissue of the leaves. Each female may lay up to 100 eggs over a period of one to two months. Eggs of the first brood hatch in 15 to 20 days depending upon the locality and the species. The newly-hatched nymph emerges through a slit in the egg and the leaf. Eggs are mainly laid in the lower surfaces of the leaves and the leafhoppers prefer to feed upon the lower surfaces. Development through the five nymphal instars is completed in about 15 to 25 days. First generation adults appear in late May in California and about Mid-June in more northern areas.

Mating takes place about two weeks after the adults emerge and egg laying commences about a week later. Second generation eggs take only five to 15 days to hatch. The nymphal stages are completed in about two weeks. A third generation develops during August and September in California. The adults overwinter in old leaves, dead grass, and straw along fence rows, ditches, and in alfalfa fields. There is a greater mortality of adults during winters with long periods of cold, wet weather than during mild winters.

Control. In most cases, grape leafhoppers are quite readily controlled with sprays or dusts of DDT. If sprays are used, they should be applied before bloom to avoid spotting of the grape berries. One application may be enough up until the first generation adults begin laying eggs. Then another treatment is best applied after all first brood eggs have hatched but before the second generation adults begin laying eggs.

Malathion is used close to harvest time (it is permitted up to two weeks before harvest). It is used in crowded residential areas because it has very low toxicity to warm-blooded animals. Malathion is also utilized against DDT-resistant leafhoppers.

A number of natural enemies of the grape leafhoppers are recorded in the literature. One which is sometimes present in numbers large enough to provide some control is a wasp egg parasite, *Anagrus epos* Girault. Weather conditions have been shown to be largely responsible for variations in the prevalence of the grape leafhoppers from year to year. The entomogenous fungus, *Entomopthera sphaerosperma,* is often an important natural factor adversely affecting populations of the leafhoppers.

Selected References

Allen, W. W., *Strawberry Pests in California,* Calif. Agr. Exp. Sta. Circ. 484, 1959.

Andison, H., *Common Strawberry Insects and Their Control,* Canada Dept. Agr. Pub. 990, 1956.

Baker, W. W., S. E. Crumb, B. J. Landis, and J. Wilcox, *Biology and Control of the Western Raspberry Fruitworm in Western Washington,* Wash. Agr. Exp. Sta. Bull. 497, 1947.

Barber, H. S., *Raspberry Fruitworms and Related Species,* USDA Misc. Pub. 468, 1942.

Breakey, E. P., D. H. Brannon, and P. M. Eide, *Controlling Insect Pests of Small Fruits,* Wash. Ext. Bull. 450, 1957.

Chamberlain, G. C., and W. L. Putman, *Diseases and Insect Pests of the Raspberry in Canada,* Can. Dept. Agr. Pub. 880, 1952.

Essig, E. O., *The Blackberry Mite, the Cause of Redberry Disease of the Himalaya Blackberry, and its Control,* Calif. Agr. Exp. Sta. Bull. 399, 1925.

Franklin, H. J., *Cranberry Insects in Massachusetts,* Mass. Agr. Exp. Sta. Bull. 445, 1948; Parts II–VII, 1950; Suppl. 1952.

Hanson, A. J., *The Blackberry Mite and its Control,* Wash. Agr. Exp. Sta. Bull. 279, 1933.

Lamiman, J. F., *Control of the Grape Leafhopper in California,* Calif. Ext. Circ. 72, 1933.

Neiswander, R. B., *Insect Pests of Strawberries in Ohio,* Ohio Agr. Exp. Sta. Res. Bull. 763, 1955.

Smith, L. M., and E. M. Stafford, *Grape Pests in California,* Calif. Agr. Exp. Sta. Circ. 455, 1955.

Stearns, L. A., W. R. Haden, and L. L. Williams, *Grape Leafhopper and Grape-berry Moth Investigations,* Dela. Agr. Exp. Sta. Bull. 198, 1936.

Taschenberg, E. F., and F. Z. Hartzell, *Grape Leafhopper Control—1944 to 1947,* N. Y. (Cornell) Agr. Exp. Sta. Bull. 738, 1949.

Vaughan, E. K., and R. G. Rosenstiel, *Diseases and Insect Pests of Cane Fruits in Oregon,* Ore. Agr. Exp. Sta. Bull. 418, 1949.

Walden, B. H., *The Raspberry Fruit Worm,* Conn. Agr. Exp. Sta. Bul. 251, 1923.

Chapter 15 | INSECT AND OTHER PESTS OF FLORICULTURAL CROPS | *John A. Naegele*

The floricultural industry in the United States is a multibillion dollar enterprise which produces a diverse number of crops grown for flowers and for foliage to satisfy the esthetic appetite of modern Americans. Because these crops must be appealing, insect damage need not be destructive to be economically important. Any impairment of the beauty or form amounts to a reduction in quality. Hence, floricultural crops must be virtually pest free in order to command top prices.

The pests

The concentrated units in which floricultural crops are grown, such as in greenhouse, lath house, and cloth house are ideally suited for the buildup of injurious populations of insects, mites, and other pests. The mild, regulated environment provides ideal conditions for the survival and multiplication of a variety of species. Furthermore, the length of time some plants are maintained in one location not only allows for the perpetuation of populations but also sets the stage for knotty problems such as insect resistance to insecticides.

Many of the pests are indigenous and are normally of only moderate importance, but when introduced to the floricultural crop, growing under optimum conditions, the pests assume a major destructive role. The known enemies of floricultural crops exceed 370 species distributed among 93 families and 13 orders. For this reason the following survey of pests can treat only the most important species.

The Lepidoptera contain by far the greatest variety of floricultural pests, but because of new and effective control measures they no longer are the most destructive. At the present time the most serious pests in the Lepidoptera are found in the following groups: the leaf rollers and leaf tiers, plume moths, tussock moths, loopers, cutworms, sphinx moths, Pierids, and leaf miners. Particularly important species in this order are the **orange tortrix, omnivorous looper, rose leaf tier, carnation leaf roller, rose budworm, greenhouse leaf tier** (Fig. 15:1), **snapdragon plume moth, cabbage looper** (Fig. 15:2), **variegated cutworm, corn earworm,** and **azalea leaf miner.**

Mites are the most common and destructive pests in floriculture. There are a large number of species; the most important are those called red spiders or spider mites, family Tetranychidae. In this family, the **two-spotted spider mite** is the Number One pest (Fig. 15:22). Spider mites generally are small and unobtrusive, but when present in large numbers they may completely web over plants and thus call attention to themselves. Mites may also be detected by observing ball-like aggregations of them at the tips of leaves.

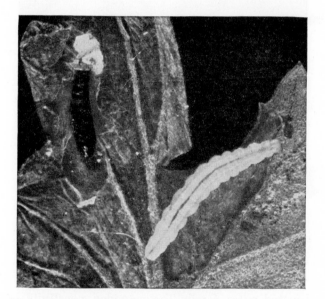

Fig. 15:1. Greenhouse leaf tier, larva and pupa on chrysanthemum.

Besides the two-spotted spider mite, there are a number of other spider mites commonly found on floricultural crops, such as the clover mite, asparagus spider mite, tumid spider mite, luden spider mite, oxalis spider mite, and hydrangea spider mite.

The false spider mites, family Tenuipalpidae, closely related to the true spider mites, cause similar foliage damage. They are distinguishable from the spider mites because they are exceedingly small, red or yellowish, and noticeably flat. The eggs are bright red and are usually more easily seen than the mites themselves. They do not produce silken webs. The most important species in this family is the **privet mite** (Fig. 15:3). This pest is bright red and very easy to spot on its favorite hosts, azalea and fuchsia. It has been widely distributed in America through commerce by the shipment of azalea plants. A false spider mite commonly found on orchids, particularly phalaenopsis orchids, is the **phalaenopsis mite.** This pest, which is yellowish or reddish in color, forms pits on the upper surface of phalaenopsis leaves.

Fig. 15:2. Cabbage looper feeding on snapdragon.

The thread-footed mites, family Tarsonemidae, constitute another group extremely important on floricultural crops. Their feeding characteristically produces deformity of the growing tips and young leaflets of the plants. The most widespread and destructive species of thread-footed mite found in greenhouses throughout the country is the **cyclamen mite.** It is found on many plants, for example African violets, gloxinia, gynura, English ivy, aralia, fuchsia, azalea, pepperpot, begonia, and snapdragon. This mite is particularly important in the production of African violets, gloxinias, and cyclamen.

A thread-footed mite similar to the cyclamen mite in appearance and in the injury it produces is the **broad mite.** Unlike the cyclamen mite, it occurs more generally over the plant rather than just in the developing buds and feeds on the undersurface of the leaves causing them to curl outward and take on a brittle appearance.

The **bulb scale mite** is found principally on the stems, leaves, and bulbs of narcissus. The principal damage is done to the bulbs and bulb scales.

The louse mites, family Pyemotidae, are generally found on grasses or grains and are occasionally pestiferous to humans. One species attacks floricultural plants, namely the **grass mite,** which burrows into the carnation bud to feed on the developing flower parts. They carry on their bodies the spores of the fungus responsible for carnation bud rot and a similar disease of grasses called silvertop. The mites are peculiar in that the abdomen of the female swells enormously to the shape of an egg or ball which contains as many as 200 eggs. These eggs hatch within the female and the young mites develop to maturity before they emerge from the parent.

Of increasing importance on bulbs, the fungus mites, family Acaridae, have been generally associated with the soil or moldy plant tissue. In the past they were considered to be secondary organisms associated with decay

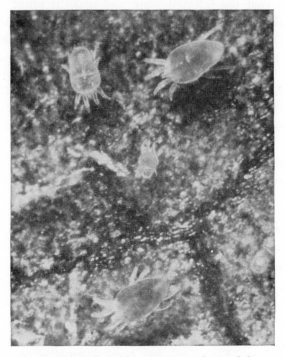

Fig. 15.3. The privet mite, *Brevipalpus obovatus* Donnadieu, adults, nymphs, and larvae. *Courtesy R. N. Jefferson.*

of organic material. However, it has been recently demonstrated that these mites can be the primary cause of injury in narcissus and related bulbous crops. The mites are usually found in enormous numbers on decayed or partially decayed bulbs which has brought about the confusion concerning their importance. The common species of bulb mite, *Rhizoglyphus echinopus* (F. & R.), may comprise a species complex since there are a number of closely related and difficult to distinguish species found in bulbs at the present time (Fig. 15:4).

Among the blister or rust mites, family Eriophyidae, the only species of importance in floriculture is the **carnation bud mite,** *Aceria paradianthi* Keifer, which causes a grassiness of the carnation often confused with boron deficiency.

Numerous pests of floricultural crops are to be found in the order Homoptera, such as scale insects, mealybugs, whiteflies, and aphids. Of the scale insects the soft scales constitute the most important group found in greenhouses. A common and destructive species is the **brown soft scale** (Fig. 15:5). The adult female is flattened, quite soft and yellowish or brownish in appearance. This insect produces large amounts of honeydew which tend to coat the infested plant and make it unsightly.

The **hemispherical scale** is commonly found in greenhouses throughout the country. The females are very convex, hard, brown, shiny, and smooth. The hemispherical scale infests a large number of plants and is particularly fond of ferns. The **black scale** is also common on a large number of hosts. It is readily recognized by the raised H shaped ridges on its back. The **cottony camellia scale** is found on camellias and several other plants under greenhouse conditions. There are other species of soft scales periodically important.

Numerous species of armored scales attack greenhouse plants. Perhaps the most common is the **oleander scale** (Fig. 15:6). It has a circular shield with a central nipple. The **Florida red scale** is found on a large variety of floricultural plants. The **Boisduval scale,** recognized by the cottony mass in which the males are clustered, is common on certain orchids (Fig. 15:7). Often the females become so numerous that the entire stem is encrusted. The **fern scale,** and the **rose scale** are common pests.

Mealybugs, close relatives of scale insects, are important pests of floricultural plants. Plants infested with mealybugs are often covered with waxy white cottony sacks in which they lay their eggs. The most common species is the **citrus mealybug** which is found on a wide variety of plants. The **Mexican mealybug** (Fig. 15:8) has been destructive on chrysanthemums and other host plants. The **grape mealybug** is an important pest of ferns.

Fig. 15:4. Fungus mites, *Rhizoglyphus* sp., on decayed plant tissue. Eggs, immature forms, and adults are shown. *Courtesy R. N. Jefferson.*

The **ground mealybug** is occasionally found on the roots of a large variety of plants, particularly cactus and palms. In addition other species are occasionally destructive, such as the **long-tailed mealybug** and the **citrophilus mealybug**.

The whiteflies, also related to scale insects, are notorious pests in greenhouses. The principal damage is caused by the larvae which suck sap from the plants and excrete large quantities of honeydew. The **greenhouse whitefly** (Fig. 15:9) is the most common species in greenhouses and infests many kinds of plants. Other destructive species include the **iris whitefly, fern whitefly**, and **azalea whitefly.**

Aphids are common pests of floricultural crops and include a number of important greenhouse species. Some of these attack a wide variety of plants, for example the **green peach aphid, foxglove aphid, potato aphid, melon aphid**, and **ornate aphid**. Others are more restrictive, such as the **crescentmarked lily aphid, rose aphid** (Fig. 15:10), and **tulip bulb aphid**. Of particular importance to chrysanthemums, the **chrysanthemum aphid** and the **greenfly** constitute an aphid complex on mums difficult to control.

Leafhoppers are not usually found in greenhouses, but on outdoor floral plantings they can be serious pests because of their ability to transmit virus diseases, such as aster yellows.

Thrips are of importance to florists. In greenhouses, various species of thrips occur as a result of their being blown by the wind through the vents. Of special importance to gladiolus, is the **gladiolus thrips,** found wherever these flowers are grown.

Several Hemiptera are common enemies of floricultural crops, in particular the **tarnished plant bug** and the **four-lined plant bug** (Fig. 15:11). The **azalea lace bug,** the **chrysanthemum lace bug,** and the **rhododendron lace bug** are periodically destructive.

Beetles are well-known pests of floricultural crops. In most cases the adult beetle is responsible for the injury and such groups as the **cucumber beetles,** the **tortoise beetles,** and **blister beetles** are destructive flower feeders. **Flea beetles** are particularly damaging to the foliage of several crops. Both adults and larvae of the **black vine weevil** may destroy the foliage and roots of several crops. Adult scarabs such as **Japanese beetle** (Fig. 15:12), **rose chafer, Asiatic garden beetle,** and **oriental beetle** are generally wholesale skeletonizers of the foliage and flowers in outdoor floricultural production. The larvae of some beetles feed directly on the foliage,

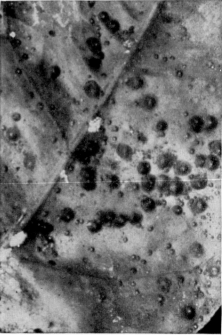

Fig. 15:5. The brown soft scale, *Coccus hesperidium* L. on ivy. Note the two groups of scales along two of the veins.

Fig. 15:6. The oleander scale, *Aspidiotus hederae* (Vallot), a common armored scale on greenhouse plants.

such as those of the **three-lined potato beetle,** which attack several kinds of plants. The larvae of this beetle have the peculiar habit of plastering their bodies with their own excrement.

Only a few species of Diptera are destructive to floricultural crops. In the Northwest, the **narcissus bulb fly** is particularly important in narcissus production. Common on outdoor columbine is the **columbine leaf miner.** The **seed-corn maggot** and several other root maggot species are occasionally serious pests on outdoor floral crops.

The Hymenoptera are of relatively little importance on floricultural crops. With the exception of several sawfly species on rose and violet the other Hymenopterous pests are no longer important. At one time however, the **orchidfly** was the major pest of orchids and often a limiting factor in orchid production. Gall wasps, ants, and stem nesting bees may cause some concern.

Occasionally grasshoppers and cockroaches are pests, but infestations of these insects are easily controlled in greenhouses. In certain areas of the South and West, grasshopper damage to plants grown outdoors can be severe.

Springtails, termites, earwigs, pillbugs (sowbugs), and millipeds, often found associated with the production of floral crops, are sometimes destructive. Of major importance, are **slugs** (Fig. 15:24) and the **garden symphylan** (Fig. 15:18).

The injury

The kinds of injury produced by pests of floricultural crops can be summarized conveniently into seven categories.

(1) Consumption of plant parts by the external feeding of pests. This type of injury is produced by enemies with chewing mouthparts and is usually the most obvious kind of injury. The pests that are responsible for the damage may not be as obvious, for many do their work at night or leave the scene of the crime when through feeding. In this kind of injury, generally associated with lepidopterous pests, the plant may be completely eaten or skeletonized by free feeding larvae, or the leaves and flowers may be first folded and then devoured, as by leaf rollers and leaf tiers. Slugs are direct feeders with huge appetites. Their feeding is not confined to one location, for they can easily climb the plant ignoring the green leaf tissue and sample flower parts like a practiced gourmet, and some species can burrow into the soil and destroy the underground stems and roots.

(2) The mines produced by miners in leaf tissue are conspicuous blemishes (Fig. 15:13). The azalea leaf miner, whose handiwork is easily

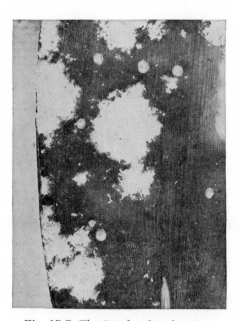

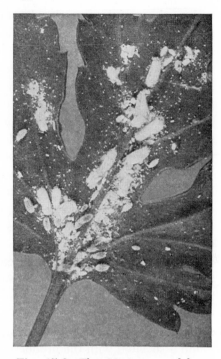

Fig. 15:7. The Boisduval scale, *Dias-pis boisduvalii* Sign., on cattelya or-chid. Note individual female scales and large cottony masses of male scales.

Fig. 15:8. The Mexican mealybug, *Phenacoccus gossypii* T. & C., on chrysanthemum leaf.

visible, is usually not responsible for wholesale destruction of leaves except in the Northwest. The mines of several species of leaf miners are unsightly, and if present in large numbers may reduce quality. Leaf miners generally do not constitute an economic threat, since they are controlled by many of the insecticides used against other pests.

(3) Borers working in the stem, crown, or base of the plant cause serious damage. Generally the first indication of their presence is the wilting or breaking of the infested stem. Usually the injury does not become apparent until considerable time and effort has gone into the growing of the crop and the flowers are ready to harvest. The destruction of shoots that may have born flowers is another way by which borers cut profit. While not considered true borers, narcissus bulb flies produce a somewhat related type of injury, for these species burrow into the mature bulb and destroy it. Likewise the iris borer completely destroys the rhizome.

(4) Probably the greatest amount of damage is that caused by pests which produce by virtue of their feeding; discoloration, curling, stunting of the leaves and flowers, and on occasion necrosis of the injured tissue. At the present time the most common and destructive of the sucking pests are the mites. They are responsible for general discoloration, loss of vigor, and decrease of flower production (Fig. 15:14). Rose bushes, severely infested with two-spotted spider mite, take on a brown dried appearance, termed "hardness" by growers. By its injection of toxic salivary secretions, the tarnished plant bug induces serious malformations in developing flower buds and developing foliage.

Fig. 15:9. The greenhouse whitefly, *Trialeurodes vaporariorum* (Westwood). Adults, white in color, congregated on leaf and shed skins of the "pupae."

Defects in the flowers and leaves due to feeding of thrips have caused serious financial problems to many growers (Fig. 15:15). The damage they produce is largely confined to the flowers although some species may injure the foliage as well. Flower damage is particularly annoying since the crop is generally ready for market.

(5) Apart from the general loss of vigor and loss of productiveness, some

sucking insects contribute to the general unsalability of floricultural crops by the excretion of messy honeydew. Several aphid and scale species are responsible for this type of injury.

(6) The presence of insect bodies or the scales of insects are unsightly and hence responsible for loss of quality in floricultural plants. Whiteflies contribute to quality reduction by the attachment of the nymphs to leaves and by the annoying presence of adult whiteflies flitting about the plant.

Fig. 15:10. An aggregation of rose aphids, *Macrosiphum rosae* (L.), on buds and stems of rose.

Aggregations of aphids on the host plant make an unsightly appearance and lower quality.

(7) The transmission of plant diseases by insects and mites also contribute to the problems of growers of floricultural crops.

Cultural and biological control

Methods other than chemical have not been extensively adopted in floricultural pest control. With the exception of Japanese beetle control by spread of milky disease, biological control has generally been incompatible with the almost universal use of chemicals. Cultural methods employed in the control of slugs and snails and the garden symphylan, will be discussed in detail later. On occasion pests such as the tarnished plant bug and other Hemiptera and bumble bees (which fertilize snapdragons and cause them to "shatter") have been excluded by keeping the side vents closed, or by erecting screening to cover the vents. This method has also been used to exclude Japanese beetle adults and when the screening is impregnated with chemicals to exclude thrips (Fig. 15:16).

Chemical control

Because of their rapidity of action, effectiveness, and general reliability, chemicals are the principal means of controlling floricultural pests today. The phenomenal decimation of extremely destructive pests by chemicals such as parathion and DDT has revolutionized control practices in floriculture. Prior to the introduction of modern insecticides, chemical and mechanical methods were largely inadequate. These older methods included the use of nicotine painted on the steam pipes, naphthalene fumigated from hot plates, lead arsenate and paris green sprayed on plants, and forceful streams of water to wash off the pests.

While the intrinsic properties of the new organic insecticides were largely responsible for their success, the development of the aerosol method of distribution firmly entrenched them as favored agents for the control of floricultural pests. Another advancement came with the discovery of the first effective systemic insecticide, sodium selenate, which provided an easy way to combat certain sucking pests.

Fig. 15:11. Four-lined plant bug, *Poecilocapsus lineatus* (F.), nymph and adult on chrysanthemum leaf. Note dark round necrotic spots resulting from feeding of bug.

At the present time virtually every insecticide in use in agriculture has been or is being used in floriculture. The initial introduction of DDT was followed by a variety of chlorinated hydrocarbons, phosphates, and other classes of insecticides. The list of pests successfully controlled by these compounds is impressive, for many of the pests were serious limiting factors in the production of floricultural crops.

Along with the good results achieved by these compounds came also some problems unique to greenhouse insect control. While parathion was effective for most pests, it was not very effective against brown soft scale. As a consequence populations of this species became prevalent in most rose houses. The introduction of other phosphates such as malathion and sulfotepp, however, has alleviated the problem. Likewise DDT was not especially effective against several leaf rollers, but subsequently other materials such as Sevin and TDE provided control of these pests.

Phosphate systemic insecticides are now used on several crops, particularly lilies and chrysanthemums. Although demeton is the most popular systemic utilized today, materials like phorate, Dimethoate, Di-Syston, and others still under code numbers are being tested for possible exploitation.

Fig. 15:12. Adults of the Japanese beetle, *Popillia japonica* New., feeding on blossoms.

Systemic insecticides are recommended and employed for the control of aphids and mites. Some initial trials using systemics for control of thrips have been undertaken and appear quite promising.

The chlorinated hydrocarbons such as chlordane and lindane have found a place in the control of soil inhabiting pests, particularly sowbugs. Lindane has been widely used to control symphylans and aphids. The phosphates have found favor as both general insecticides and as acaricides. Specific miticides such as Aramite, Kelthane, Chlorobenzilate, ovex, and others are especially effective against the two-spotted spider mite. Endrin and Kelthane provide good control of the cyclamen mite.

Baits are employed in the control of pillbugs, though surface applications of DDT or chlordane are also effective. Baits, sprays, and dusts of metaldehyde are successful in controlling slugs.

Because most floricultural crops are subject to serious damage from more than one pest, a single application or chemical or procedure may not be sufficient. The approach that is generally taken is to make several applications or to use several chemicals.

There are generally two types of control programs: preventive programs and watch and wait programs. **Preventive programs** are the preferred approach to insect control in floricultural crops. In this type program, insecticides are applied on a regular schedule regardless of whether pests are present or not. In this way insecticide applications become part of the

Fig. 15:13. Columbine leaf miner injury to columbine. The mines are conspicuous blemishes that detract from the beauty of the plant.

routine of growing the plants instead of a special event. The principal strength of the preventive program is that it does not allow insects to develop into large, destructive populations. Such programs also encourage the purchase and installation of adequate equipment for regular applications.

Watch and wait programs, in general use today, consist of applying insecticides when an infestation occurs. This type of program requires a minimum of labor and materials, but in order to be effective must have as a necessary part of the program daily checks on the plants to determine the presence of insects. It is at this point that the program generally breaks down, for observation of pests is generally not a part of the growing routine. Consequently, an infestation generally becomes large, injurious, firmly established, and difficult to control before it is noticed.

In establishing any control program several considerations must be made, such as determining what pests are consistently serious and what pests are only periodically serious. A preventive program can become wasteful if every pest of unpredictable importance is accounted for. What in fact happens in successful preventive programs is that the regular appearing pests are anticipated by a prearranged application schedule and the irregularly appearing pests are kept under surveillance. When the latter pests are observed in damaging numbers they are combatted by putting into effect prearranged treatments.

Preventive programs do not consist solely of chemical treatment. The wise use of other control methods such as cultural and mechanical play an important part. A well planned program correlates the life history of the pest, the culture of the host, and any peculiar characteristic of the control procedure.

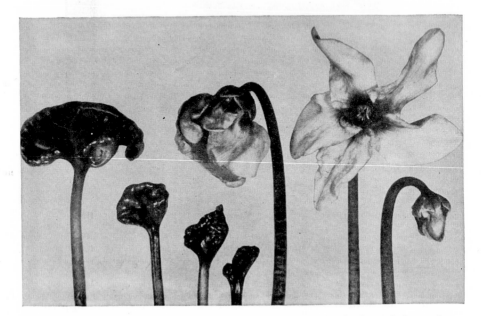

Fig. 15:14. Deformed leaves and buds of cyclamen caused by feeding of the cyclamen mite.

The following preventive program for the protection of chrysanthemums has been successfully employed commercially and is presented as an example. It has been designed to combat the insects and diseases listed below.

Chrysanthemums: Preventive Control Schedule
Midge—thrips—aphids—red spider mites—
leaf nematode—leaf miner—virus—leaf-
spot—Verticillium—Botrytis

Buy all cuttings or renew stock plants frequently from commercial houses using an indexing program.

In Greenhouse

1. Sterilize bench soil annually or after any diseased crop.
2. Ventilate and keep humidity down.
3. Apply DEMETON (SYSTOX) soil drench 7 to 10 days after benching at 1 pint 23 per cent DEMETON (SYSTOX) per 1,000 square feet.
4. Two months after DEMETON (SYSTOX) application (3)—(a) apply DEMETON (SYSTOX) again (at the same rate as 3), or (b) use PARATHION, MALATHION, OR ARAMITE AND LINDANE every two weeks until disbudding is finished, or (c) if crop will be in the bench longer than 4 months, apply DEMETON (SYSTOX) (at the rate used in 3). Two months later PARATHION, MALATHION, or ARAMITE-LINDANE can be used every two weeks until disbudding is finished.
5. Be prepared to put on weekly applications of MALATHION, LIN-DANE, or PARATHION for thrips if they become a problem; continue until influx from outdoors ceases.
6. Keep weeds around greenhouse, cloth house or field planting cut, chemically controlled or cultivated.

In Field

Spray lower and upper leaf surfaces with FERBAM, DDT and PARA-THION every 7 to 14 days until plants are about 14 to 16 in. tall. With standards (and with pompoms in bad Botrytis areas) mist-spray the buds and blooms with ZINEB, THYLATE or CAPTAN (½ lb. to 100 gallons) weekly or oftener, or use ZINEB or CAPTAN dusts.

Control equipment

There is considerable variation in the way control chemicals are applied to floricultural crops. The method used is dependent in part on the kind of structure in which the crop is being grown. The use of hydraulic sprays has been popular on crops grown out-of-doors or under lath or cloth. Hydraulic applications are also used in greenhouses, but for most crops, other than roses, there are more effective methods of distributing the chemical. One of the difficulties with hydraulic applications is obtaining adequate coverage, which is affected by several factors such as proper amount of emulsifier, appropriate nozzle, sufficient pressure at nozzle, pump capable of sufficient volume, and proper application technique such that the spray is placed on the under surface of the foliage as well as on the upper surface.

Dust applications have been effectively used to control floricultural pests on the west coast but they have been neither very popular nor widespread on the east coast. Part of the difficulty with dust applications is the redistribution of the dust when the plants are handled either to remove cut flowers or to tie or "pinch" them.

Fig. 15:15. Thrips damage to carnations. Note the injured petal edges.

There has been an increased interest in the use of small mist blowers or mist concentrate machines for applying insecticide in floricultural establishments. The advantage of this type of machine is the virtually invisible residue which results from the application, which of course means that the chemical residue on the foliage does not detract from the quality of the plant. Loss of quality due to residues is a problem in both hydraulic and dust applications. At the present time there are several mist blowers being employed in floriculture, but none of them have proven themselves to be perfectly adequate for all situations. They are under continual study.

The aerosol method is the most popular means of dispensing insecticides in the greenhouse. The method employs a liquefied gas in a container in which insecticide is dissolved with auxiliary solvents. The liquefied gas is discharged through a nozzle and immediately evaporates upon its discharge leaving small particles of insecticide suspended in the air. These particles fall rapidly, settle on the foliage, and to some extent volatilize producing a fumigant effect. The aerosol method of applying insecticides in green-houses has been popular because of its economy of time and labor. Proper use of aerosols, however, demands proper safety equipment. The insecti-cides employed are generally quite toxic to mammals so that precautions must be taken to avoid inhaling them. Furthermore, the propellent gas, often methyl chloride, can be toxic at high concentrations. Aerosoling is generally done with a full face gas mask and with an appropriate canister

A   B

Fig. 15:16. Screening the side vents of a greenhouse with dieldrin-impregnated cheese cloth to control thrips. A, erecting the screen; B, completed job.

attached to mask. Protective clothing to cover all exposed skin is also necessary. The aerosol method of application is applicable only in green-houses or closed areas because the particles are so small (generally 1 to 10 microns) that the slightest breeze or air current will influence their distribu-tion and produce uneven coverage.

A type of areosol generator called the **Hi Fog** machine has been exten-sively used on the west coast for the control of floriculture pests. This method of application utilizes an insecticide concentrate under extremely high pressure. The insecticide is released through a small nozzle under pressures of 350–1,000 psi which results in fine break-up into small droplets. The resultant particles are not quite as small as liquefied gas aerosol particles and consequently Hi Fog particles settle more rapidly producing a heavier deposit on plants. The Hi Fog can be used under lath, under cloth, and even in the open field on calm days (Fig. 15:17). It has been used exten-

A   B

Fig. 15:17. The Hi Fog aerosol sprayer. A, close up of sprayer; B, Grower treating greenhouse carnations with Hi Fog sprayer.

sively in custom pest control operations on the west coast providing efficiency and economy similar to aerosol application and effectiveness comparable to spray applications on most crops. The Hi Fog machine, however, has some limitations and hydraulic spraying is still used on roses.

Smoke generators are often used against floricultural pests in greenhouses. The smoke generator burns a low-temperature combustible material in which insecticide is dissolved. The smoke which is emitted is a mixture of combustion by-products and insecticide in intimate contact and is distributed throughout the greenhouse by convection currents. The particles, generally less than 1 micron in diameter, are smaller than aerosol particles. Consequently they are much more subject to breezes and convection currents than liquefied gas aerosol particles and have not been effective for treating plants under lath or cloth or in the field. The number of insecticides that can be successfully formulated as smokes are limited because insecticides of relatively high volatility and heat stability are required.

Traditional fumigation has been effectively employed in the past to control insects in greenhouses. The fumigant, calcium cyanide, while widely used at the turn of the century, was replaced because of some serious drawbacks. Not only was its mammalian toxicity high but in addition it would often cause serious damage to a number of plants. Naphthalene evaporated from a hot plate has been used as a fumigant in greenhouses where it effectively controls red spiders. It was rapidly displaced, however, by more effective compounds. At the present time fumigation by volatilizing insecticides painted on the steam pipes in greenhouses is often undertaken. Before the advent of the new organic insecticides, nicotine was volatilized from the steam pipes. This was an effective way of controlling aphids but was also very toxic to the operator and many growers were seriously injured. In recent years other materials have been volatilized from the steam pipes with varying degrees of success. This method of application consists of painting a slurry of a wettable powder or an emulsifiable concentrate on the steam pipes. Azobenzene has been used in this manner for spider mite control as have other materials, such as Chlorobenzilate and Aramite. Lindane has been volatilized from steam pipes for aphid control.

Recently systemic insecticides applied to the soil have been used to control several sucking pests, but the method has not been particularly effective against chewing insects. The insecticide is generally distributed in water used to water the crops.

REPRESENTATIVE FLORICULTURAL PESTS

Garden symphylan

Scutigerella immaculata (Newport) [Symphyla:Scutigerellidae]

The garden symphylan is one of the serious subterranean pests that attack floricultural crops. Symphylans are particularly injurious to seedlings of such plants as tomatoes, snapdragon, and sweet peas. They also have been reported injurious to the seeds and root hairs of lettuce, spinach, celery, cucumber, stock, roses, chrysanthemums, asters, gladiolus, smilax, lilies, ferns, and a number of other plants. In California they may seriously injure field asparagus and in the East field plantings of lettuce.

Much of the damage done by these pests is to the roots, for symphylans eat off root hairs or chew cavities into the larger roots and crowns. On plants such as sweet peas the stems may be hollowed out and the new roots destroyed as quickly as they are produced.

Symphylans can also be a serious problem to growers of African violets. This is particularly true when these plants are grown on a large scale and plunged into soil or moist sand. Symphylans will then infest the whole bench and every pot made up from the bench. Whole benches of chrysanthemums and other florist crops have also been infested. On occasion the infestation is confined to a relatively small area or several discontinuous areas.

Description. The garden symphylan is a tiny creature, never more than 8 mm. long and ½ mm. wide (Fig. 15:18). It is usually pure white and when adult has twelve pairs of legs and fourteen body segments. Occasionally the alimentary canal is visible through the body wall as a darker streak. Symphylans have long conspicuous antennae made up of about 50 to 60 segments in adults. The egg is about 0.5 mm. in diameter and pure white or pearl colored.

Life history. The symphylan adult lays her eggs in groups of five to 25 in cavities in the soil. Usually these eggs are deposited deep in the soil where the soil is undisturbed and normally moist. In ground beds this is generally in the subsoil. In the greenhouse the eggs hatch in ten to twelve days, whereas in the field they take from one to three weeks. Upon hatching the young symphylan is about 1.6 mm. long and looks very much like its parents except that it has only six pairs of legs and six antennal segments. Young symphylans molt six times before reaching adulthood.

As adults they continue to molt for a long period of time undergoing as many as fifty molts. Symphylans are long-lived. Several investigators have reported them as living for four years and longer. Symphylans have silk

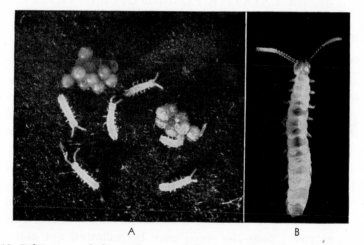

A   B

Fig. 15:18. Life stages of the garden symphylan. A, eggs and newly hatched young; B, adult. A, *Courtesy University of California; B, Courtesy Oregon State University.*

glands located in the two appendages that project from the rear of their body. They can produce fine sticky silken threads and it has been suggested that these threads help guide the symphylans through the soil.

Symphylans are very active creatures and are quite sensitive to changes in their environment. While they will often come up to the surface to feed on seeds or seedlings, they generally remain under cover of the soil. When disturbed they quickly run away from the light and escape into the soil. They are delicate animals and apparently are unable to make their own burrows. Instead they depend upon burrows of earthworms, normal air cavities, and holes left by decayed plant material.

Optimum activity of symphylans occurs between 50° to 70°F. They are, however, active and present at soil temperatures as high as 85°F., but do not do well at 90°F. and quickly die when the temperature reaches 100°F. They survive outdoor soil temperatures during the winter.

Control. Control of symphylans has largely centered about soil sterilization and incorporation of certain chemicals into the soil. Though symphylans have a number of natural enemies such as predatory mites, diseases, the larvae of several species of beetles, and several centipedes, these have never been effectively employed to provide biological control.

Cultural methods have been effective in control. As the garden symphylan occurs outdoors in manure piles, leaf mold, and other decayed material, soil obtained from such places should be sterilized before bringing it into the greenhouse. One should also avoid bringing in infested potted plants. Commercial experience has demonstrated that entire beds can be infested by bringing in one or two pots containing the garden symphylan.

Growing plants on raised beds has been suggested as a preventive measure. Symphylans which may infest the walks and area under the raised beds do not crawl up the dry posts from the ground soil to the bed. Raised beds, nevertheless, can be contaminated in other ways. The incorporation of cinders or other drainage material in the bottom of the bed provide for rapid movement of symphylans throughout the bed. Yet in spite of this, drainage material should not be omitted with the intention of thereby controlling symphylans.

A helpful adjunct to soil sterilization practices is the employment of solid bottom beds. Many floriculturalists who grow their crops in ground beds have not been able to obtain adequate control of the garden symphylan by sterilization methods because the pests will travel down into the soil below where the heat or chemical can reach them. Putting solid bottoms in ground beds permits sterilization throughout the soil mass.

In addition to these suggestions, the cultivation of empty beds between crops has been helpful in that it kills many symphylans and eggs by the mechanical action of turning the soil. Heating empty greenhouses during the summer has also been suggested, but the practice is not very effective in ground beds because the active stages can always reach cool, moist soil. It has also been suggested that compaction of the soil would delay or inhibit the rapid spread of symphylans.

Steam is probably the earliest and most effective soil sterilant for eliminating symphylans in raised beds. The use of carbon disulphide along with steam is even more effective but increases the cost.

Chemicals have also been used to control symphylans in the soil. Carbon disulphide was one of the earliest. This material is poured or injected into holes in the top of the bed and the holes are covered with soil. After application of the fumigant the soil surface is wetted or covered with a tarpaulin to retain the gas. For best results with carbon disulphide, soil temperatures must be above 60°F. and moisture condition adequate for planting. If the soil is too dry the gas quickly escapes and if the soil is too wet it does not penetrate sufficiently. Because the eggs of symphylans are not killed by carbon disulphide, repeated treatment is necessary. There are other sterilant chemicals, such as choropicrin and methyl bromide that work well against symphylans.

A regular program of soil sterilization with chemicals can be helpful in keeping symphylan damage to a minimum since it does take some time for the symphylans to again reach injurious numbers. Consequently a grower on a regular program of soil sterilization whether it be with chemicals or with steam can effectively prevent serious damage from symphylans most of the time.

Beds are often infested with symphylans when the crop is in place and soil sterilization methods, whether steam or chemical, cannot be used without damage to the plants. In these cases soil treatment with chemicals such as DDT or lindane has been effective. Lindane is probably the most effective chemical and provides long lasting action against symphylans. Protection up to three to five years has been reported from one application of the material in raised beds as well as ground beds. Lindane can be applied as a dust or as a spray over the surface of the soil and raked in or mixed into the soil so that the symphylans will come in contact with it. Potted plants can be treated with lindane by watering the plants with an emulsion of the insecticide. Lindane has proved so effective that it is now the mainstay of symphylan control in the greenhouse. Research on the activity of phosphate insecticides against symphylans is disclosing highly promising materials even more effective than lindane.

Flower thrips

Frankliniella tritici (Fitch) [Thysanoptera:Thripidae]

Because thrips are wind-blown into greenhouses, a complex of species are involved in the injury caused to floricultural crops. Though composition of the complex varies with location and season, important species include the flower thrips, tobacco thrips, onion thrips, pear thrips, composite thrips, and greenhouse thrips (Fig. 15:19).

Thrips cause damage in several ways. They may directly injure the flowers, for with their rasping-sucking mouthparts they puncture the surface of petals and suck the liberated juices. Their feeding produces streaks and browning of the tips of these parts. On some plants they induce a stippling and silvering of the leaves. The excrement they leave on foliage creates an unsightly residue. Thrips may also attack and injure bulbs and seeds.

A   B

C   D

Fig. 15:19. Adults of four species of thrips commonly found in greenhouses. A, greenhouse thrips; B, pear thrips; C, onion thrips; D, flower thrips. A, *courtesy USDA; B, courtesy Can. Dept. Agr.; C, courtesy Hasso von Eickstedt; D, courtesy Fla. Agr. Exp. Sta.*

We shall discuss the flower thrips to illustrate the life history and control of this group of insects.

Description. Adults of flower thrips are small insects, about 1 mm. long and ⅓ mm. wide. They vary in color from brown to yellow. Their wings are narrow with a noticeable fringe around the margins. The immature stages are lighter in color, smaller than the adults, and without wings. The eggs are bean-shaped, 0.2 mm. long, and are inserted into plant tissue (Fig. 15:20).

Life history. Dependent on several factors, this pest requires from seven to 22 days for the completion of one generation. In warmer areas of the country there may be from 12 to 15 generations per year. The females have a preoviposition period of from one to four days or longer depending upon the temperature. The eggs generally hatch in about three days and the first nymphal instar requires two days. The mean period of the second instar is three days, while the next instar, sometimes designated "propupa" requires about one day. The "pupal" instar requires 2.5 days. The total developmental period from egg to adult takes on the average from 11 to 12 days. Under favorable conditions, the short developmental period allows

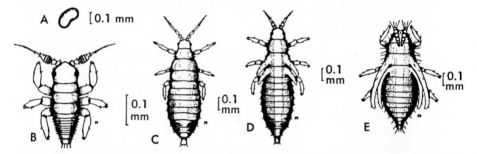

Fig. 15:20. Immature stages in the development of thrips. A, egg; B, newly emerged nymph; C, full-grown nymph; D, first resting stage or "propupa"; E, second resting stage or "pupa". *Courtesy University of California.*

a very rapid increase in numbers. Thrips live on the foliage or in the flowers of the host. The "pupa," however, generally resides in the soil. The adult insect is a weak flier but is strong enough to launch into air currents and be carried by winds. Heavy populations of thrips are often carried from southern areas to northern parts of the country.

Control. Control of thrips in greenhouses is complicated by the fact that wind-borne adults continually invade these structures and thereby place tremendous pressure on any chemical used to destroy them. Thrips are blown in through both upper and lower vents and intensity of infestation is influenced by location of the greenhouse, prevailing winds, density of thrips outdoors, and location of fields in which they live and multiply.

Application of insecticides, such as tartar emetic or paris green mixed with brown sugar, or lindane, dieldrin, or malathion, to plants has given varying degrees of success because of differences in numbers of thrips invading the greenhouse from time to time.

A more effective method of control consists of draping insecticide impregnated cheesecloth over vents. The impregnated cloth provides both a physical and chemical barrier to migrating thrips. When both top and side vents are screened, tests have demonstrated 100 per cent control. In some areas just screening the side vents has been sufficient for adequate control. Emulsifiable concentrates of dieldrin are used to impregnate the cheesecloth.

Another method of thrips control has been investigated which consists of circulating an insecticide in the wash water of pad and fan cooled houses. The method, though initially successful, was attended with certain difficulties, such as phytotoxicity associated with large amounts of solvent that occasionally got into the air.

Systemic insecticides, applied to the soil in granular form or sprayed on the plants, have also been used successfully for thrips control.

Two-spotted spider mite

Tetranychus telarius Linnaeus [Acarina:Tetranychidae]

The two-spotted spider mite, probably the most serious pest in floriculture today, attacks a wide variety of hosts. Carnations, cymbidium orchids, gardenias, hydrangeas, and roses are greenhouse crops constantly under attack. Roses are especially vulnerable because the cultural conditions of high temperature the year round provide a favorable habitat for the mite to survive and multiply (Fig. 15:21).

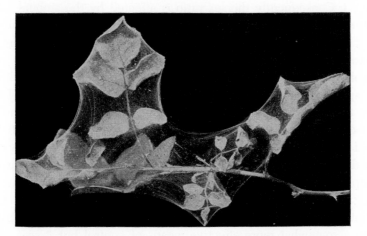

Fig. 15:21. Severely infested rose shoot completely webbed by the two-spotted spider mite.

The feeding of mites produces a speckled appearance in leaves and flowers. Heavy infestations cause leaves to drop and plants to lose vigor and bear fewer flowers.

Description. The two-spotted spider mite (Fig. 15:22) is less than 0.5 mm. long. Males are slightly smaller than the females. When looked at carefully all four stages of this mite can be seen to be covered with bristles. The body has a dark spot on each side and varies in color from a dark green to light oránge depending upon the feeding activity and several other obscure factors. The eggs are clear to pale green, spherical, and about 0.1 mm. in diameter.

Life history. The female two-spotted spider mite lays from three to fourteen eggs per day. The average female usually lays about seventy eggs in her lifetime, but some females will lay as many as 200. Incubation lasts from two to fifteen days depending on temperature. Upon hatching from the egg, the first or larval stage has only six legs. Depending on temperature, this stage lasts from 1½ to 4¼ days. Larvae go into a quiescent period, at the end of which they shed their skin and emerge as protonymphs. This stage has eight legs and lasts from 1½ to 3¼ days. A quiescent period again occurs at the end of which the skin is cast and the deutonymphal or second nymphal stage appears. The mite remains in this stage from one to sixteen days depending again on temperature, with the male having a shorter deutonymphal stage than the female.

The adult female which emerges after the quiescent period has a pre-oviposition period of about 1½ days. Females live on the average for three to four weeks and produce eggs throughout this time. Interestingly, the male offspring of any female are haploid while the female offspring are diploid. Consequently the sex ratio is affected by the amount of sperm transferred from the male parent to the female parent, since all of the unfertilized eggs will become males. The length of the cycle from egg to egg varies from as little as five days to as long as forty days.

Control. Prior to 1935 there was no uniform method of controlling two-spotted spider mites on roses. Soaps and flour pastes were used by many growers to stick the mites to the leaves. Pyrethrum and rotenone and certain oils were also used and gave varying degrees of control. High pressure and volume water sprays or "syringing" of rose plants was often employed to wash the mites off the leaves but this method also introduced the complication of blackspot, a serious disease which was spread by the splashing water.

The introduction of naphthalene volatilized from specially built heaters provided a somewhat more effective means of control but it was not until the introduction of Selocide, a complex selenium compound, used as a spray that any one material received widespread use by the growers. The second year of Selocide usage brought about sudden and unexplainable control failures. Several investigators now look upon these failures to be the initial demonstration of resistance in the two-spotted spider mite, but no specific evidence to support this thesis was obtained at the time.

Fig. 15:22. Two-spotted spider mite, *Tetranychus telarius* L., adults and eggs.

Selocide was followed by sodium selenate, which was the first systemic insecticide used on floricultural crops. This material was applied to the soil and was absorbed by the plant producing a "poisoned" sap to kill the two-spotted spider mite and many other sucking insects. Sodium selenate, effective on many crops, was not very successful on roses.

For a while azobenzene fumes were used to control mites on roses and apart from the fact that they occasionally bleached certain red varieties the material was effective. Azobenzene, however, was soon replaced by the organic phosphates in the late 1940's, and materials such as HETP, TEPP, and parathion were applied by many growers. Because of their widespread use they served as effective selecting agents and it was at this time that resistance was definitely recognized in the two-spotted spider mite. The initial success enjoyed by the use of parathion came to a sudden and disappointing halt.

Since its first appearance, resistance to virtually every other acaricide has developed in the two-spotted spider mite. Combinations of materials have been applied in an attempt to combine chemicals with different modes of action and thus improve control. Combinations such as Aramite and azobenzene, or Tedion and Aramite, or Chlorobenzilate and schradan, or Chlorobenzilate and demeton have been used with varying degrees of success. In addition certain acaricidal sequences have been used, for example, several applications of sulfotepp followed by an Aramite treatment, or Aramite followed by sulfotepp. Other growers have alternated materials not waiting for a compound to fail. Which of these approaches is best in providing control and avoiding resistance has not been clearly demonstrated. All are plagued by the presence of a high degree of cross resistance. That is to say, when a population develops resistance to one material, it may at the same time be developing resistance to other materials. For example parathion resistant mites are resistant to Aramite as well; and mites that have been selected with Aramite are also resistant to parathion. Consequently the use of parathion or Aramite in sequence or combinations may not have much advantage.

At the present time thousands of new compounds are being tested for their effect against resistant strains of the two-spotted spider mite. A constant search is going on for a non-selective acaricidal agent, one that will not select out a resistant strain under continued use. It is hoped that research will provide answers to the problem of controlling resistant spider mites.

Gray garden slug, *Deroceras reticulatum* (Müller)

Gray field slug, *Deroceras laeve* (Müller)

Spotted garden slug, *Limax maximus* (Linnaeus)

Greenhouse slug, *Milax gagates* (Linnaeus)

[Stylommatophora: Limacidae]

Slugs are common inhabitants of greenhouses and floricultural plantings. Because there are a large number of economic species throughout the United States, we shall discuss slugs as a group instead of concentrating on one species.

Slugs, favored by high humidity, are a common pest in greenhouses, but they may also damage crops grown outdoors. They prefer to feed on seedlings and the more succulent parts of plants, and devour leaves, stems, or roots. In feeding young slugs rasp away surface tissues, older slugs make irregular holes (Fig. 15:23).

Through commerce slugs are spread from greenhouse to greenhouse with plants and plant parts. They may also enter greenhouses in soil and flats from the outdoors.

Fig. 15:23. Slug injury on gerbera.

Description. The most vivid description of slugs is that they are snails without shells. They vary in size depending upon the species and age from ¼ in. to 7 in. long. They secrete a characteristic slime which they leave behind when they locomote. This slime trail is typical and a good diagnostic character for identifying slug damage. The color of slugs also varies with species ranging from a dark black brown to a light gray with darker spots. Some have a mantle of lighter color. Also characteristic of slugs are the soft slimy bodies and the extensible eye stalks which give the creature a Martian-like appearance (Fig. 15:24). The eggs are gelatinous and watery in appearance. They range in size from ⅛ to ¼ in. and vary in shape from round to oval. They are usually colorless, but often reflect the color of their surroundings (Fig. 15:25). Baby slugs resemble their parents but may not be as fully colored.

Life history. All slugs lay eggs. Each species requires a different length of time for the development of its eggs and the maturing of its young.

Slug eggs are laid in clusters in concealed, moist locations. The number of eggs laid at one sitting by one slug may approach 100 but averages 20 or 30. Young adult slugs apparently lay fewer eggs than older ones.

In many states slug eggs may be found out-of-doors during any month of the year. Most species overwinter in the egg stage. In spring, the eggs hatch and the slugs reach maturity and lay eggs by fall. During periods of particularly favorable climatic conditions, the rate at which the eggs and slugs develop may be increased to such an extent that eggs are laid in mid-summer instead of in the fall, thus making possible a second generation. Some species which overwinter as adults may lay eggs any time during the spring or summer. Usually, mating takes place from August until mid-October, and eggs are laid from 30 to 40 days after a successful mating. In greenhouses, where climatic conditions are always favorable, egg laying occurs the year around.

Eggs are generally laid on the soil surface but are usually deposited in places of concealment. Mulch, dead leaves, empty flowerpots, plant flats, rocks, and boards all serve as shelter. Particularly preferred are spots beneath clay flowerpots and similar materials where the nature of the cover keeps the surroundings relatively cool and moist. At least one species, the greenhouse slug, habitually buries its eggs in tunnels beneath the soil surface. Other species may also bury their eggs, particularly in the fall.

Little or no development takes place in the overwintering eggs until warm weather arrives in spring. The minimum temperature at which egg development will take place varies with the species of slug but is in the range of 32° to 40°F. At the minimum temperature, as long as 100 days may be required for the eggs to develop. However, at higher temperatures, such as those encountered in greenhouses, development is usually completed in ten days to three weeks.

As soon as slugs hatch, they are active and begin to crawl or feed if the temperature and humidity conditions are right. Otherwise they may remain motionless and concealed until nightfall provides suitable conditions for activity.

The rate of growth of immature slugs depends on the type and amount of food available. Dry conditions usually result in a loss of weight which is regained rapidly when moist conditions return.

Slugs reach full adult size in three months to a year depending upon environmental conditions. However, both large and small slugs can reproduce. Under the high temperature conditions of greenhouses, slugs may lay fertile eggs when only six weeks old.

Slugs are hermaphroditic, that is, they can be both males and females at the same time. Usually slugs first develop mature male sexual organs. Afterwards, female organs may develop in addition to the male organs, or the male organs may degenerate leaving a strictly female individual. In some species of slugs, the time of change from male to female is strongly influenced by the amount and nature of available food. Usually cross-fertilization occurs, that is, two slugs mate with each other and both individuals subsequently lay fertile eggs. However, self-fertilization can also occur, and a single slug raised in isolation may lay fertile eggs.

The rituals associated with the mating behavior of some species of slugs

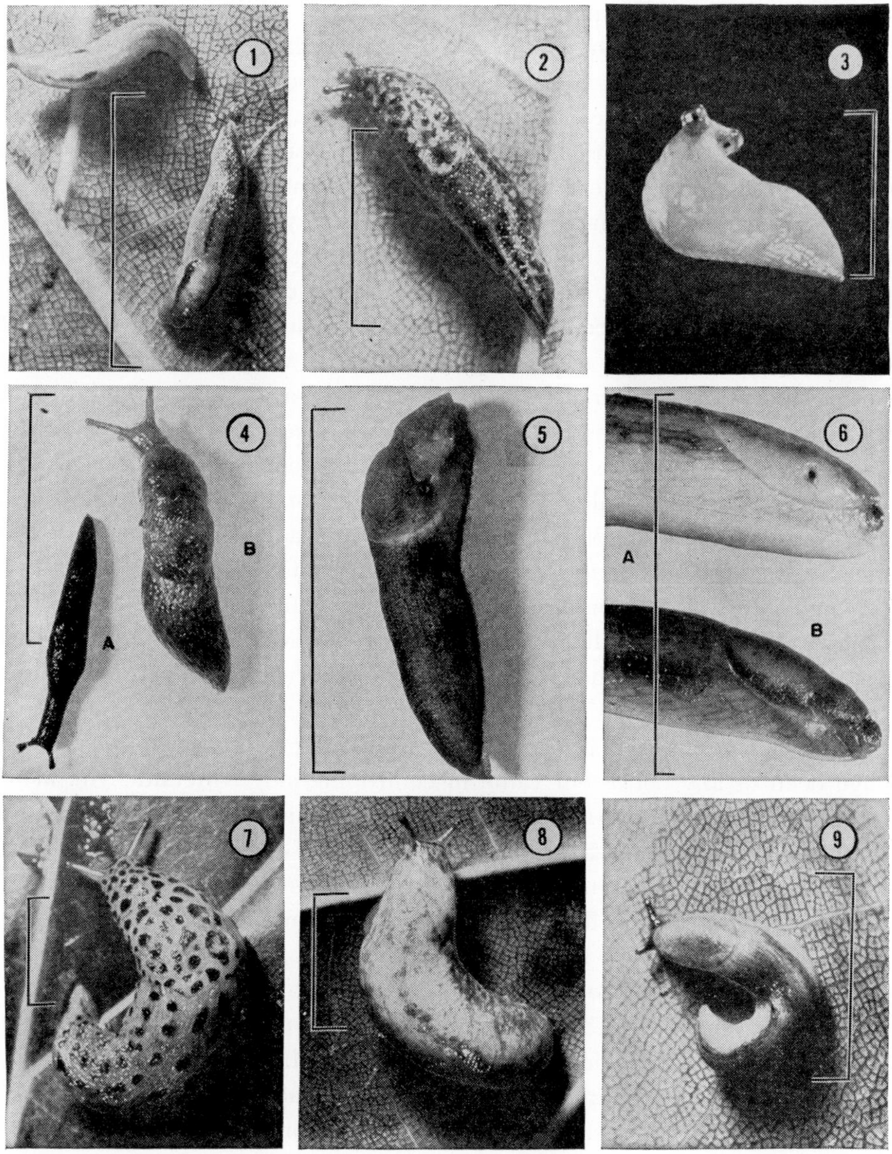

Fig. 15:24. Several species of slugs found in greenhouses. 1. *Limax marginatus;* 2. *Limax maximus,* striped form; 3. *Deroceras reticulatum,* young; 4. (A) *Deroceras laeve,* (B) *Deroceras reticulatum;* 5. *Milax gagates;* 6. (A) *Arion circumscriptus,* (B) *Arion subfuscus;* 7. *Limax maximus,* spotted form; 8. *Philomycus carolinianus,* common outdoors but uncommon in greenhouses; 9. *Arion circumscriptus.* Scale in each figure, except figure 3, is equal to 4 cm. (1½ in.). The scale in figure 3 equals 5 mm (⅕ in.). *Courtesy Cornell University.*

are quite complex. The spotted garden slug mates while suspended several feet above the ground on slime threads and the gray garden slug engages in a "nuptial dance" which lasts for an hour or more before mating.

Very little is known concerning the maximum length of life of slugs under greenhouse conditions. Out-of-doors in a temperate climate, slugs usually live less than a year. Overwintering eggs which hatch in the spring provide the nucleus of the new population every year. A few adults of all species, but particularly the spotted garden slug, survive the winters. In greenhouses, many adult slugs live for more than one year.

Control. Formal slug control suggestions were first made during the last decade of the nineteenth century. Home remedies were probably used even earlier. Protective barrier rings of coal tar, soot, ash, lime and other substances are old suggestions and occasionally are used today. Space limitations make such methods impractical in most greenhouses.

The discovery of metaldehyde as a slug killer in 1934 provided the most important chemical weapon against slugs known today. This discovery was the result of an accidental exposure of slugs to the English "Metafuel" (canned heat) which contains metaldehyde as a principal ingredient. This chance observation is all the more remarkable when one considers that several closely related chemicals are of no value whatsoever in controlling slugs.

None of the common insecticides or fungicides which have been tested have been of any consistent value in controlling slugs. Metaldehyde alone or combined with the arsenicals is the best chemical method available for the control of slugs on floricultural crops at the present time.

Although metaldehyde baits are frequently used, most growers who use baits are not satisfied with the results. The baits mold rapidly and must be replaced frequently. For this reason a 15 per cent metaldehyde dust or the 20 per cent metaldehyde liquid used according to label directions is preferred over baits. The 15 per cent metaldehyde dust is preferable to the 20 per cent metaldehyde liquid for slug control. Initial kill from liquid formulations are approximately the same as that achieved with dust. However, the dust gives satisfactory residual action for as long as three weeks, while the liquid formulation becomes ineffective in a much shorter period of time. Several applications are recommended.

Metaldehyde has also been used as a dust against snails in orchid houses and elsewhere. The degree of control achieved against snails is much poorer than that against slugs. More experimental work needs to be done on snail control before definite recommendations can be made.

Metaldehyde has been used without any phytotoxic effects on a great number of floricultural and vegetable crops.

Sanitation is a necessary part of slug control. This clean-up program will reduce slug problems within and around greenhouses. Appropriate cultural control measures are: (1) Do not scatter empty flowerpots indiscriminately throughout the greenhouse; avoid underbench pot storage; stack pots on a clean dry wooden surface on their sides, not on ends. If pots are stored under a bench, keep the pots dry. (2) Stack boards only in a dry area. Store wooden flats in a dry area and turn on end or with open sides down.

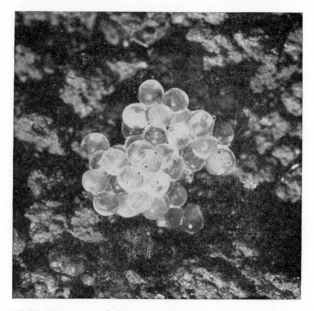

Fig. 15:25. Egg mass of the spotted garden slug. *Courtesy USDA.*

(3) Remove weeds from the aisles and underneath the benches. Keep areas beneath benches dry and clear. Gravel and cinders aid in underbench drainage and provide unsuitable habitats for slugs. (4) Use cinders, gravel or sandy soil in benches where potted plants are held. Soil should be present only when plants are grown directly in the benches. (5) Do not bring new plants of any sort into the greenhouse without examining them for insects, slugs and snails. The number of growers who attribute their troubles to a specific importation of plants but who do not examine the plants when they first arrive is surprisingly large. Without this cultural clean-up, money spent for attempted chemical control is largely wasted.

Hand-picking, crushing, or drowning slugs is a good idea. The time consumed is amply repaid. Even in the most severely infested ranges, an hour or two spent in a deliberate effort at hand-picking will noticeably reduce the slug population.

Individual plants of special value can be protected by placing the pots upon boards in a tray of water, by wrapping the stems in cotton batting, or by the use of electrical circuits surrounding the plants. None of these procedures are practical on a large scale.

Many insects, reptiles, amphibians and birds have been recorded as occasional predators upon slugs. None as yet offer an effective and practical means of control. This is an interesting field for future investigations, for it is possible that a tropical species could be introduced that would accept greenhouse conditions but which would not be able to spread if accidentally introduced out-of-doors in areas of low winter temperatures.

Selected References

Blauvelt, W. E., *The Internal Morphology of the Common Red Spider Mite* (Tetranychus telarius *Linn.*), Cornell Univ. Agr. Exp. Sta. Memoir 270, 1945.

Compton, C. C., *Greenhouse Pests,* Illinois State Natural History Survey Division, Ent. Series Arc. 12, 1930.

Filinger, G. A., *The Garden Symphylid* Scutigerella immaculata *Newport,* Ohio Agr. Exp. Sta. Bull. 486, Wooster, Ohio, 1931.

Gibson, A., and W. A. Ross, *Insects Affecting Greenhouse Plants,* Can. Dept. Agr. Publ. 695, 1940.

Howitt, A. J., "Control of the Garden Symphylid in the Pacific Northwest, *Down to Earth,* 15:6–10, 24 (1960).

Karlin, E. J., and J. A. Naegele, Biology of the Mollusca of Greenhouses in New York State, Cornell Univ. Memoir 372, 1960.

Karlin, E. J., and J. A. Naegele, "Screening Greenhouses with Insecticide-Impregnated Cloth for Thrips Control," *J. Econ. Ent.,* 50:55–58 (1956).

Karlin, E. J., and J. A., Naegele, *Slugs and Snails in New York State Greenhouses,* Cornell Univ. Bull. 1004, 1958.

Michelbacher, A. E., "The Biology of the Garden Centipede, *Scutigerella immaculata,*" *Hilgardia,* 11:55–148 (1938).

———, *Chemical Control of the Garden Centipede,* Calif. Agr. Exp. Sta. Bul. 548, 1932.

Miles, H., and Miles M., *Insect Pests of Glasshouse Crops* (London: Crosby Lockwood and Son, 1948).

McDaniel, E. I., *Insect and Allied Pests of Plants Grown Under Glass,* Mich. Agr. Exp. Sta. Bul. 214, 1931.

Pritchard, A. E., *Greenhouse Pests and Their Control,* Calif. Agr. Exp. Sta. Bul. 713, 1949.

———, and Baker, E., *Revision of the Spider Mite Family Tetranychidae,* Memoir Series, Vol. 2, Pacific Coast Ent. Soc., San Francisco, Cal., 1955.

Russell, H. M., *The Greenhouse Thrips,* USDA Bureau of Entomology Bul. 64, part 6, 1909.

————, *The Greenhouse Thrips*, USDA Bureau of Entomology Circular 151, 1912.

Severin, H. C., *Insect and Other Enemies Harmful to Greenhouse Plants*, in Fifteenth Annual Report of the State Entomologist of South Dakota, Brookings, S.D., 1924.

Smith, F. F., "Spider Mites and Resistance," in *Insects, The Yearbook of Agriculture*, USDA, 1952.

————, Hennebery, T. J., and E. A. Taylor, "How Thrips Get In," USDA, *Agr. Research* 7(7):14 (1959).

Thomas, C. A., *The Symphylid or Greenhouse Centipede* Scutigerella immaculata *Newport and Other Pennsylvania Greenhouse Soil Pests*, Pa. Agr. Exp. Sta. Bul. 508, 1949.

Watson, D. L., and J. A. Naegele, "The Influence of Selection Pressure on the Development of Resistance in Populations of *Tetranychus telarius* (L.)," *J. Econ. Ent.*, 53:80–4 (1959).

Watts, J. G., *A Study of the Biology of the Flower Thrips*, Frankliniella tritici *(Fitch), with Special Reference to Cotton*, S.C. Agr. Exp. Sta. Bul. 306, 1936.

Weigel, C. A., *The Gladiolus Thrips*, USDA Bul. E-300, 1934.

————, *Insects Injurious to Ornamental Greenhouse Plants*, USDA Bul. 1362, 1925.

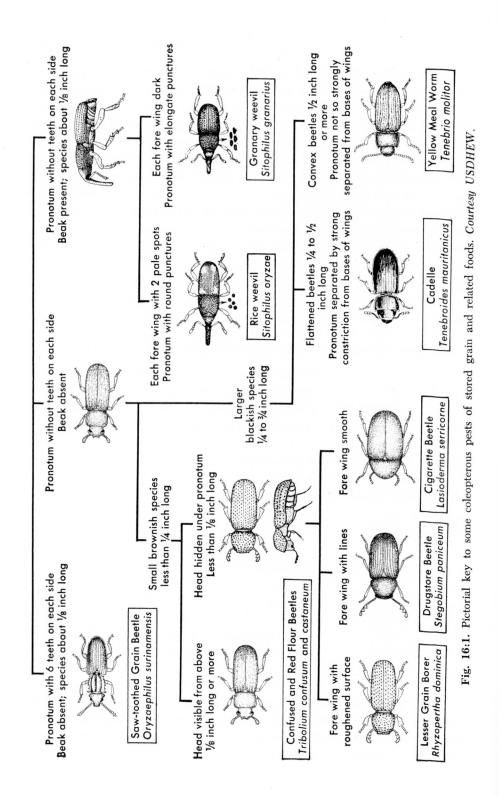

Pronotum with 6 teeth on each side
Beak absent; species about 1/8 inch long

Saw-toothed Grain Beetle
Oryzaephilus surinamensis

Pronotum without teeth on each side
Beak absent

Small brownish species
less than 1/4 inch long

Head hidden under pronotum
Less than 1/8 inch long

Head visible from above
1/8 inch long or more

Confused and Red Flour Beetles
Tribolium confusum and castaneum

Fore wing with
roughened surface

Lesser Grain Borer
Rhyzopertha dominica

Fore wing with lines

Drugstore Beetle
Stegobium paniceum

Fore wing smooth

Cigarette Beetle
Lasioderma serricorne

Larger
blackish species
1/4 to 3/4 inch long

Flattened beetles 1/4 to 1/2
inch long
Pronotum separated by strong
constriction from bases of wings

Cadelle
Tenebroides mauritanicus

Convex beetles 1/2 inch long
or more
Pronotum not so strongly
separated from bases of wings

Yellow Meal Worm
Tenebrio molitor

Each fore wing with 2 pale spots
Pronotum with round punctures

Rice weevil
Sitophilus oryzae

Each fore wing dark
Pronotum with elongate punctures

Granary weevil
Sitophilus granarius

Pronotum without teeth on each side
Beak present; species about 1/8 inch long

Fig. 16:1. Pictorial key to some coleopterous pests of stored grain and related foods. *Courtesy USDHEW.*

vironmental conditions such as high or low moistures or temperatures, poor sanitation, out-of-condition grain or with limited geographical areas.

Examples of minor pests are: **booklouse,** feeds on flour and other organic materials in mills and granaries; **foreign grain beetle,** feeds on molds in grain with high moisture; **black carpet beetle** (Fig. 17:2A), larvae feed on all types of animal products and grain and milled products; **cigarette beetle,** feeds on many dried vegetable materials especially tobacco, grain and cereal products; **long-headed flour beetle,** in mills and granaries; **hairy spider beetle,** in mills and granaries; **drugstore beetle,** feeds on dried vegetable materials of all kinds; **yellow mealworm,** feeds on out-of-condition grain and milled products; **larger cabinet beetle,** larvae feed on miscellaneous dried animal products and on grain and milled products; **tobacco moth,** larvae feed on many vegetable products including grain and milled products; **meal moth,** larvae feed on flour and out-of-condition grain.

3. **Incidental pests** consist of approximately 150 species of insects and mites. Certain of these occasionally attack grain, but others occur in grain frequently and in large numbers along with major and minor pests. They do not, however, damage the grain except by the contamination resulting from their presence. They may serve as a warning that the grain needs attention and thus be beneficial. The food of numerous of these species consists of fungi and other microorganisms. The families of Blattidae, Tenebrionidae, Ptinidae, Dermestidae, Bostrichidae, Ostomatidae, Cucujidae, Cryptophagidae, Nitidulidae, Phycitidae and Tineidae provide the more common species among the incidental pests.

4. **Parasites and predators** comprise an unknown number of insects and mites that prey on the other three groups. They have not been observed to be a factor in controlling infestations of stored grain insects with the exception of the tiny wasp *Bracon hebetor* Say. This parasite frequently reduces dense populations of Indian-meal moth.

Stored grain as food and environment for insects. *Food.* Stored grains provide all of the essential nutritive requirements for insects capable of chewing into the hard dry kernels. Yet only thirteen major pest species of an estimated 700,000 different insect species have been able to adapt to the food and environment provided by stored grain conditioned for safe storage. It has been commonly observed that the populations of adapted species frequently become very large. Only 25 insects in a quart of grain is equivalent to 800,000 in 1,000 bushels. The biotic potential of adapted species is enormous; by the end of six months in the absence of restrictive influences the progeny of a single pair of rice weevils would attain 675 million adults. However, in actual performance this potential is missed by wide margins in spite of an almost unlimited food supply, a relatively stable physical environment, and a remarkable scarcity of insect parasites and predators. The normal feeding and other activities of the insects alter the grain mass by causing heating and subsequent moisture translocation so that the grain becomes moldy and unsuitable for most forms of insect life. Only certain mold feeding insects and scavengers are adapted to moldy grain.

Moisture and temperature. The behavior and habits of stored grain insects are closely attuned to the moisture and temperature of their food media. For the most part the major stored grain pests are restricted to a narrow moisture band between 11.5 and 14.5 per cent. A moisture content about 12.5 per cent favors feeding and reproduction of most major pests. Moistures above 14.5 per cent permit the development of molds and germination. This results in heating, molding, and caking of the grain. The same molds that attack the grain also kill the insects. A few species can utilize grain below 11.5 per cent moisture though their ability to do this varies with the species, the temperature, and the physical condition of the food. If temperatures are increased to approximately 90°F., rice and granary weevils can reproduce in grain of 10 per cent moisture and can survive on a minimum of 9 per cent moisture. Confused flour beetles cannot maintain a culture on whole kernel wheat of 10 per cent moisture but on like grain of 12 and 14 per cent moisture they maintain vigorous cultures. They can survive on such dockage as broken kernels and on flour of 6 per cent moisture if the temperature is favorable. The Mediterranean flour moth can live on a 1 per cent moisture food medium. Kansas farm-stored grain below 12 per cent moisture will rarely have damage from weevils although infestations of saw-toothed grain beetles, cadelles, and lesser grain borers will occur. Under most circumstances dry wheat of 10 per cent or less moisture can be stored indefinitely without serious damage from insects.

Structural and physiological adaptation. Certain structural and physiological adaptations are essential to enable stored grain insects to inhabit such a rigorous low-moisture environment. Their exoskeleton is relatively impermeable to water preventing the loss of body fluids by evaporation. All moisture is withdrawn from the body wastes that assemble in the hind intestine and is returned through the intestinal walls to the blood leaving the excrement powder dry. In addition the **water of metabolism** resulting from the conversion of fats and starches to digestible foods is fully utilized.

The damage

Much of the damage from grain-infesting insects is done directly to the kernels (Fig. 16:2). The rice weevil, granary weevil, lesser grain borer, and Angoumois grain moth consume varying amounts of the endosperm. The germ is consumed by Indian-meal moth larvae and by flat and rusty grain beetle larvae. Cadelles, dermestids, and flour beetles first eat the germ and then turn to the endosperm which may be completely destroyed. The extent of the destruction of germ and endosperm, called **shrinkage**, is determined by such factors as insect species, temperature, moisture, and length of storage.

Grain-infesting insects are solely responsible for **dry grain heating** in all kinds of grain. This in turn frequently results in molding, caking and spoilage. The activity of assemblages of any of the grain-infesting insects within the grain mass may produce heat up to 106°F. even in winter. The

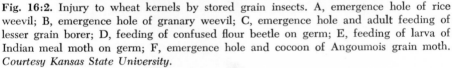

Fig. 16:2. Injury to wheat kernels by stored grain insects. A, emergence hole of rice weevil; B, emergence hole of granary weevil; C, emergence hole and adult feeding of lesser grain borer; D, feeding of confused flour beetle on germ; E, feeding of larva of Indian meal moth on germ; F, emergence hole and cocoon of Angoumois grain moth. *Courtesy Kansas State University.*

warmed air rises to the surface carrying moisture with it. At the surface the air is cooled and deposits moisture on the surface grain which encourages growth of molds and stimulates germination. Caking and spoilage result. Dry grain heating develops in grain of less than 15 per cent moisture.

Grain-infesting insects do not survive in grain with a moisture content above 15 per cent. This much moisture is adequate to activate molds and fungi and eventually the germ itself and thus produce wet grain heating. The microorganisms responsible for wet grain heating destroy any grain-damaging insects, though certain fungus-eating species may survive.

Lowered germination of seed grains results when either the germ or the endosperm are damaged. Germination is also impaired or destroyed by heating and by high moisture.

Insects living in grains, which are used as human foods, are responsible for the presence of such **filth** as excrement, molted exoskeletons, and disintegrated insect bodies in the milled grain products. Certain species as lesser grain borers and flour beetles impart noxious and persisting odors to the grain. Indian-meal moth larvae leave silken webbing wherever they have been in grain. Much of this filth and odor cannot be removed by cleaning procedures in grain processing plants.

Insect activity in grain inevitably results in dust, flour, excrement, and broken kernels that contribute to the amount of grain **dockage** determined by the Official Grain Graders. Lesser grain borers and cadelles reduce the grain to dust in such exorbitant quantities that successful fumigation is not attainable unless the dust is removed.

Cadelle larvae, lesser grain borers and dermestid larvae tunnel into the wooden parts of granaries, box cars and ship holds to such an extent that the structures are weakened (Fig. 16:3). Their holes provide hiding places

Fig. 16:3. Cadelle larval tunnels in wooden grain bin. Note accumulation of wood dust on surface of grain. *Courtesy Kansas State University.*

for other species of insects and lodging places for nutritious dusts and cracked kernels upon which these insects feed. The holes also prevent thorough cleaning of grain residues from the granaries.

Grain-infesting insects carry grain damaging molds to bins of grain and distribute the molds throughout the grain mass. If moisture conditions are favorable for the development of these molds, damage is certain to occur.

An indirect damage from grain-infesting insects frequently results from the presence of internal infesting insects that are not removed from the grain during the grain cleaning procedures prior to milling. After fumigation live or dead insects are processed into flour and other cereal products. Exoskeleton fragments in flour or in baked products can readily be detected by simple laboratory techniques. Cereal products containing insect fragments are considered filthy under the articles of the Food, Drug and Cosmetic Act. The products are liable to seizure and the manufacturers or processors may be prosecuted.

Field damage resembling damage by stored grain insects. There are several types of insect injury to wheat kernels done prior to harvest in the central Wheat Belt that superficially resemble injury by stored grain insects. Except in the southeastern states, stored grain insects rarely are found in the fields. Rather, the injury is done by certain pests of the growing crop at the time the kernels are ripening. Holes in the kernels superficially resembling weevil emergence holes frequently are made by young wheat head armyworms, young cutworms, and cowpea curculios. When these kernels are opened, entrance from the outside is evident since the walls of the hole are parallel and the cavity is free of excrement. Grasshoppers, cutworms, and armyworms frequently gnaw on the soft developing kernels leaving scars that resemble feeding of cadelles.

Several species of stink bugs extract the fluids from the developing kernels and inject saliva causing shriveled kernels resembling drouth damage. This damage does not occur in the southern and central Wheat Belt because the stink bugs are not abundant until after harvest. In the northern Wheat Belt these stink bugs, known as **gluten bugs,** are abundant when the wheat is maturing and their injury may be extensive. Gluten bug damage frequently is serious in Eastern Germany, Poland, Russia and the Near East.

Field infestations. Field infestations in corn by Angoumois grain moth, rice weevil, and certain other species are an annual problem in the southeastern United States. The area in which damage occurs coincides closely with the area in which the Angoumois grain moth survives normal winters. Combine harvesting has greatly reduced or eliminated field infestations in wheat.

Many elevator men throughout the Wheat Belt contend that grain brought to them directly from the combine frequently is "rolling with weevils." Repeated attempts by experienced investigators to capture stored grain insects in fields throughout this area just prior to harvest and to rear insects from newly harvested wheat obtained at the combine have had negative results.

Grain storage and sources of insect infestation

Storage on the farm. Enormous stocks of grain are stored on the farm either as feed or as market grain. On July 1, 1960, the farm storage contained almost two billion bushels according to USDA estimates. Feed grains are usually for livestock consumption on the farm and are normally retained for extended periods; market grains are for disposal through commercial channels and are moved within the year following harvest. There is a close correlation between insect damage and length of storage. Feed-grain infestations are more frequent not only because of the longer storage period but because less importance is attached to such infestations and little effort is made to provide adequate sanitation. The extent of shrinkage due to insect feeding is scarcely realized because feed grains are rarely weighed in or out of the granaries and the filth factors are ignored.

Farmers store market grains on the farm for two reasons; either they choose to do so as a part of a planned grain marketing program or they store because they must do so when the local elevators are full, when box cars and shipping are not available, or when truck drivers are scarce. Out of expedience they place the grain, often near infested grains, in temporary bins in animal shelters, chicken houses, and under haymows (Fig. 16:4). Grain sanitation procedures are unknown or ignored. When grain storage is a part of a planned marketing program, most farmers are acquainted with and are prepared for proper grain sanitation procedures and other adequate storage methods.

The important sources of insect infestation in farm-stored grain include: bins of old grains; stocks of animal feeds whether home prepared or commercial; granaries and cribs, particularly those with double walls and floor, cracks, and cadelle tunnels; feed and seeds from infested sources; accumulations of waste grain and feed in any of the buildings and in machinery and implements; migration of insects by flight from nearby infested sources; field infestations brought into the bins at harvest (in the South).

An intensive survey of grain storage conditions on Central Kansas farms which are typical of farm storage over a wide area revealed that accumulations of grain or feed could be found in most farm buildings including

Fig. 16:4. Bin of market wheat stored in a cow and hay barn. The heat from the animals and the manure and the insulation by the hay prevents normal cold winter temperatures from inhibiting activity of insects infesting the grain. *Courtesy Kansas State University.*

garages, machine sheds, all types of animal shelters and hay barns and under granaries. During the summer months, with a peak in September, many of these grain and feed accumulations were infested with some or all of the insect species found in the granaries. Farm grain sanitation, therefore, cannot be confined to the granaries but must extend into and around each of the farm buildings.

Commercial and government storage. Grain stocks in terminal elevators, Commodity Credit bins, and interior mills totaled over three and a quarter billion bushels on July 1, 1960. For handling and storage of such huge quantities of grain a system of elevators was developed. Country elevators constructed along railroads, received grain from farmers and funneled it directly to terminal elevators. Many old country elevators designed solely for this purpose are still in use. Of recent years a considerable number of country elevators have expanded their operations to include grain storage and feed manufacture, storage, and sale. These developments have greatly complicated and aggravated the problems of insect sanitation. It has resulted in elevator management turning to grain sanitation specialists, usually a part of the agricultural chemicals industry, to advise or to take care of stored grain insect problems.

In older elevators and in elevators under improper management, insect infestations stem from the elevator premises. Insects reside permanently in tunnels, in cavities in walls, in dead stocks in grain moving equipment, in holes and cracks in wooden or concrete bins, in any accumulations of grain. Frequently infested grain from farm storage is binned directly with uninfested grain without fumigation. A procedure practiced by some elevators is to place all newly received infested grain in isolated bins for fumigation before storage. When feed mills are a part of the elevator business and heavily infested grain is run through the mill machinery, the disturbed insects migrate in all directions and particularly to the grain in storage. Infested sweepings and cleanings frequently are sold back to farmers for scratch feed thus infesting the farm premises.

Grain in commercial channels can become infested from insects present in box cars during shipment. This is especially true from July to November when nearly all box cars are infested. The months of highest populations of stored grain insects coincide with the period of greatest grain shipping activity.

Control through management practices

Control of insects in stored grain calls for the application of all known measures for combating the pests. The granaries should be constructed so as to hold the grain securely and to exclude moisture, rodents and birds. The bins should be made tight enough to retain fumigant gases. In farm storage the removal of double-walled construction in bins and feed rooms where they are not required for structure reinforcement will eliminate important lodging places for grain and hiding places for insects. If the foundations of bins and granaries are sealed, grain cannot accumulate under the floor by spillage or through the activities of rodents. When the new grain is binned, ample head room should be left over the grain for inspection and treating.

Clean-up of the granary by removing accumulations of infested grain and feed from the premises or by fumigation is important. This clean-up is most effective if done in early spring when the insect populations are lowest. Leftover grain should be removed from the bins and the walls swept and vacuumed before new grain is binned. Grain and feed accumulations frequently overlooked include empty feed sacks, nutritious dusts created by the feed grinders (Fig. 16:5), seed litter from the haymows, grain left in truck and wagon beds, in combine and elevator hoppers, and in unused animal self-feeders.

Grains should be stored apart from feed rooms and feed bins since animal feeds support all grain infesting insects. Feed rooms are difficult to clean and cannot be adequately treated with residual sprays. Grains should not be stored in buildings that shelter animals and hay. The heat from the animals and from their manure may prevent the grain from cooling and may enable insects to remain active throughout the winter. Mangers, feed boxes, and feed troughs are continuously infested with insects that can move directly to grain stored nearby. Large bulks of hay alongside or over grain bins insulate the bins from the winter's cold.

Fig. 16:5. Accumulations of nutritious dusts produced by the feed grinder in the granary provide food and shelter for stored grain insects. *Courtesy Kansas State University.*

The drier the grain, the less it will deteriorate during storage as a result of insect activity. When storing grain of 12 per cent or more moisture, treatment with a grain protectant or one or more fumigations each year will be required in some parts of the country. The most serious insect problems would be avoided if harvest could be delayed until the grain is dry. When this is not possible, it may be necessary to resort to commercial driers as is done in the harvest of rice and of hybrid corn. Mistakes made by harvest crews that result in high moisture grain include harvesting too early or too late in the day when atmospheric moisture makes the grain tough and failure to cut around unripe patches in the field. When green weeds or insects, such as grasshoppers and cutworms, are harvested with the grain, the grain may require screening if a moisture problem is to be avoided.

Chemical control

Residual insecticides for granaries. After granaries and bins have been swept out and the old grain disposed of in preparation for the reception of new grain, there usually are many stored grain insects remaining in double walls, in cracks and crevices, and in cadelle tunnels. These insects cannot be reached by brooms or vacuums. If a suitable residual insecticidal spray is applied to the walls and floor about three weeks before the new

Fig. 16:6. Treating a bin with residual deposit of insecticide three weeks prior to binning new grain. Note that farmer is applying too much spray at one spot so that there is considerable runoff. *Courtesy Food Machinery and Chemical Corp.*

grain is binned, many of the insects will emerge from their hiding places, walk over the treated areas and receive a lethal amount of the chemical (Fig. 16:6). Several quarts of dead cadelles have been destroyed in this manner in certain treated wooden farm bins in Kansas. Residual sprays alone have prevented infestations from developing in many bins of new wheat where the chief source for reinfestation was from within the granary itself.

Residual insecticides approved for treatment of grain bins include sprays of pyrethrins 0.5 per cent synergized by piperonyl butoxide, methoxychlor 2.5 per cent, and malathion 2.0 per cent. They should be applied at the rate of 2 gal. per 1,000 square feet of surface, since ordinarily this is just enough to wet the surface without appreciable runoff.

Grain protectants. Grain protectants are formulations of chemicals having residual toxic or repellent action or both that are applied directly to grain to prevent damage by grain-infesting insects. Various pulverized rocks have been applied to grain for many years but at present their use is limited to seeds and to grain for animal feeds. Modern grain protectants have been in use since 1950. They are applied either as sprays or as powders to uninfested grain to avoid infestation. Application to farm stored grain is made by hand or by small sprayers at some convenient place between the

Fig. 16:7. Farmer applying wheat protectant to grain as it is transferred from combine hopper to truck. *Courtesy Kansas State University.*

combine and the bin (Fig. 16:7). Mechanical applicators are used in treating grain in commercial storage as it is being turned. Thorough good housekeeping measures should accompany the use of protectants.

Grain protectants have certain advantages over fumigants:

1. Grain can be treated while it is uninfested so that infestations are avoided.
2. Protectants are effective when the grain is stored in bins too loose to be fumigated. Much of the grain in emergency storage can be treated effectively only by protectants.
3. Protectants are less dangerous than most chemicals and may be applied by unskilled persons.
4. Generally one application at harvest time will be adequate for an entire year.
5. Protectants do not affect germination adversely.

Protectants now approved for use include:

1. Pyrethrins synergized by piperonyl butoxide. This combination is the safest insecticide formulation known. It is available as a powder, 1.1 per cent piperonyl butoxide and 0.08 per cent pyrethrins impregnated in pulverized wheat, and applied at the rate of 75 lbs. per 1,000 bu. of grain. In spray formulations the insecticide is available in a fumigant carrier and applied at 2 gal. per 1,000 bu. or it is available as emulsifiable concentrates to be diluted with water and applied at rates of 4 or 5 gal. per 1,000 bu.
2. Premium grade malathion. This insecticide may be applied directly to grains either as a 1 per cent dust at a rate of 60 lbs. per 1,000 bu. of grain or as a spray containing one pint of 57 per cent emulsifiable concentrate in 2 to 5 gal. of water per 1,000 bu.

Fumigation. Grain fumigants are chemicals used alone or in combination which in their vapor phase are toxic to grain damaging insects. The ideal fumigant is one that is highly toxic to insects, not harmful to warm-blooded animals, inexpensive, vaporizes rapidly, easily applied, nonflammable, nonexplosive, harmless to the grain, highly penetrating, and effective at all temperatures. Fumigants in use today fall short of these qualifications in one or more counts.

Chemicals have been used as grain fumigants since 1854 when carbon disulphide was first applied to kill granary weevils. The use of hydrocyanic acid began in 1886, chloropicrin in 1907, ethylene oxide and the 3:1 mixture of ethylene dichloride and carbon tetrachloride in 1927, and methyl bromide in 1932. For most insecticides the miracle poisons are of recent development; for fumigants, the first fumigant was the miracle poison. About thirty chemicals are now available for fumigation of grain but only one-third of them are in common use. Few new grain fumigants have been developed during the past 25 years but new formulations have been made by combining two or more chemicals.

Grain handlers and farmers depend almost entirely on fumigants to solve their stored grain insect problems not only because fumigants are more toxic and cheaper than grain protectants but also because they are reluctant to purchase grain insecticides until after insects are active in the grain.

The limitations of fumigants should be borne in mind. Once the toxic concentration of gas is dispelled, fumigants have no continuing effects. Fumigants are useful only when the structure that holds the grain is sufficiently tight that a concentration of gas can be maintained long enough to be lethal. Most fumigants are anesthetics. When the fumigant vapors are not sufficiently concentrated to be lethal, the insects may recover completely.

Types of fumigants. There are three physical types of fumigants used for treatment of stored grain.

1. **Gaseous fumigants** such as methyl bromide and hydrocyanic acid are chemicals that are liquid under pressure or low temperatures but which become gases upon the release of the pressure or at normal room temperatures. The gaseous types of fumigants are especially adapted for fumigation of grain using the closed recirculation type of forced distribution.

2. **Liquid fumigants** include those chemicals that are liquids under normal temperatures but vaporize rapidly when exposed to air at room temperatures or higher. Though there are many different formulations of liquid grain fumigants, the two basic mixtures are: the 3:1 mixture of **3 parts ethylene dichloride and 1 part carbon tetrachloride;** the 80–20 mixture of **4 parts carbon tetrachloride and 1 part carbon disulphide.** The following formulations are popular modifications of the basic mixtures. Additional additives have been included in some of the formulations to provide additional toxicants, and irritant and warning gases.

Carbon tetrachloride 78%; carbon disulphide 20%; sulphur dioxide 2%.

Carbon tetrachloride 95%; ethylene dibromide 5%.

Carbon tetrachloride 76%; carbon disulphide 19%; ethylene dibromide 5%.

Carbon tetrachloride 60%; ethylene dichloride 35%; ethylene dibromide 5%.

Carbon tetrachloride 75%; trichloroethylene 10%; benzene 12%; sulphur dioxide 3%.

3. **Solid fumigants** include certain granules and tablets that form a toxic gas on exposure to atmospheric moisture. Generally they are applied to the grain as it is being binned though the tablets can be inserted into binned grain through hollow tubes. Examples of solid fumigants include calcium cyanide that forms hydrogen cyanide (HCN) and aluminum phosphide that forms phosphine (PH_3).

Methods of application. The most important recent developments in fumigating grain have been in the methods of applying fumigants. These include the use of aeration systems designed to circulate air through the grain mass, to distribute or to recirculate fumigant vapors, and subsequently to remove them. These developments have resulted in greater efficiency, greater economy, and greater safety both to the grain and to the fumigator. The following methods are used in applying fumigants:

1. **Mixing the fumigant with the grain as the bin is being filled.** Liquid and solid fumigants can be applied to the grain stream by hand or by automatic applicator. Turning the grain from one bin to another is required if grain already in storage is to be treated.

2. **Gravity penetration of the vapors of liquid fumigants into the grain mass.** The surface grain is leveled and the fumigant is sprayed uniformly over the surface grain in a coarse, wet spray (Fig. 16:8). The heavier-than-air vapors penetrate the grain mass and replace the air in the spaces between the kernels. This method is used almost entirely in the fumigation of farm stored grains and is widely used with commercially stored grains.

Fig. 16.8. Farmer applying liquid grain fumigant to stored wheat. He is risking health by not wearing an approved gas mask. *Courtesy Dow Chemical Company.*

Uneven distribution may occur when hot spots or accumulations of dockage are in the grain mass since the vapors tend to flow around such obstructions. Longer exposures and higher dosages must be employed to overcome these difficulties. This occasionally results in damage to the grain by lowering germination and by increasing deposits of harmful residues and objectionable odors.

3. **Forced distribution of fumigant vapors throughout the grain by any mechanical or physical force other than gravity.** Usually this is accomplished by motor driven fans. Forced distribution has been employed in Europe for many years. Recent improvements in the techniques of gas sampling and of gas analysis have stimulated research in this country on the problems of forced distribution. Already various adaptations are in practice in large grain storage projects because they permit the use of reduced dosages, cause quick and uniform distribution of the vapors, and provide a means for their removal. Most of the installations for forced distribution of fumigants are adaptations of existing aeration systems, following tests to determine how much air is being moved and where it is going. The air flow pattern in a grain mass can be determined by measuring the static pressures exerted on the air as it is moved through the grain. Static pressure readings indicate the total amount of air being moved per minute of fan operations. From this, the time required for the fan to produce a single change of air within the bin can be determined. There are two general types of forced distribution:

a. **Single pass** uses an aeration system without modification. The fan operates long enough to produce one complete change of air within the grain mass. This is adequate to replace the air with the vapors which have resulted from the application of fumigant to the surface of the grain. If desired, the fan can be reversed and the heavy vapors lifted to the surface again, after which gravity penetration takes over.

b. **Closed recirculation** requires a return duct incorporated in the aeration system (Fig. 16:9). A fumigant in the vapor stage is introduced into the aeration system at any place and is recirculated through the grain for a period equal to one or more air changes.

Fumigant dosage rates. In spite of technical developments in materials and methods, grain fumigation remains more of an art than a science. Developments in the use of gas analyzers and of air moving equipment to grain fumigations may hasten the science of fumigation.

The art and science of fumigation lie in the proper appraisal of conditions at time of treatment. These conditions have so many variable factors associated with the storage buildings, the grain to be treated, the insects involved, and the chemicals available for use that standard recommendations are only approximations. The following list of storage conditions together with their demands on fumigant dosages suggest the considerations that should be given these variables.

Fig. 16:9. Closed recirculation system for fumigation of grain in steel tanks. Note lateral leading from beneath the load to the blower and the tube which conducts fumigant back to top of load. *Courtesy Dow Chemical Company.*

	Amount of fumigant required	
Storage conditions	Less	More
Bin structure	Steel or concrete	Wood
Bin condition	Tight	Loose
Dockage and chaff	Little	Much
Percentage moisture	Low	High
Condition of grain	Normal	Heating
Extent of grain surface to volume	Smaller	Greater
Depth of grain	Deep	Shallow
Compaction of grain	Loose	Tight

Precautions in use of fumigants. All chemicals used in grain fumigation are poisonous to human beings and animals. In handling them, the operator should take all necessary precautions and follow all directions given on the manufacturer's label. In addition, fumigators should recognize that nearly all grain fumigants are anesthetic in their effects on man and animals. After the first breath the sensory nerves may be paralyzed to varying degrees and the sense of smell reduced so that the fumigator may be unaware that he is breathing fumigants. Extreme care should be taken not to breathe the vapors or spill the liquids on the skin or clothing.

In handling and applying fumigants, the operator should wear an approved full-faced gas mask equipped with an approved black canister labeled "for organic vapors." The canister should be replaced with a fresh one after a 30-minute exposure to the fumes. Canisters are designed to protect fumigators from light concentrations of gas only. Canisters quickly become useless in heavy gas concentrations. It is sound practice to fumigate grain only when help is on hand for emergencies.

REPRESENTATIVE STORED GRAIN INSECTS

The following major pests of stored grain have been selected for detailed study: granary and rice weevils, confused and red flour beetles, cadelle, and Angoumois grain moth.

Granary weevil, *Sitophilus granarius* (Linnaeus)

Rice weevil, *Sitophilus oryzae* (Linnaeus)

[Coleoptera:Curculionidae]

These weevils were present in grain stored in the tombs of Ancient Egypt. Today they are the most destructive insect pests of grain in farm and in commercial storage in many parts of the world.

Rice and granary weevils are world-wide in distribution. Rice weevils are better adapted to southerly regions where they frequently fly to fields of grain and oviposit on the developing kernels. They also fly to shocked, stacked, or cribbed grain. In northern regions they infest grain in protected commercial and farm storage.

Granary weevils are better adapted to northern areas. In the Wheat Belt of the Central States granary weevils are more prevalent in farm stored grain while rice weevils are more prevalent in commercially stored grains. Both species can live throughout the bulk of stored grain no matter how deep the bins.

Description. Granary weevils are larger than rice weevils when they develop on the same host grain. However, rice weevils of the small strain reared on corn may be as large as granary weevils reared on wheat. Adult weevils are approximately ⅛ in. long and have the head capsule prolonged into a slender snout with chewing mouthparts located at its tip (Fig. 16:10). They may be distinguished by the following characteristics:

Granary weevil	Rice weevil
1. Larger (when reared on the same food)	1. Smaller (when reared on the same food)
2. Uniformly shiny black or reddish brown	2. Black or reddish brown with four light yellowish spots, two on each elytron.
3. Larger oval pits on pronotum	3. Smaller, closely compacted, rounded pits on pronotum
4. Without functional wings	4. With functional wings

There are two strains, or species, of rice weevils in the United States. The larger strain is more prevalent on corn in the Southern States while the smaller strain commonly infests commercially stored wheat throughout the country. Some authorities consider these forms to be species, the larger

Fig. 16:10. Adult of the rice weevil, *Sitophilus oryzae* (L.). *Courtesy Kansas State University.*

being *Sitophilus oryzae* (L.) and the smaller S. *sasakii* (Tak.). They appear to have behavioral and minor structural differences.

The sexes of granary weevils and rice weevils can be determined by observing certain characteristics of the snout. Snouts of males are shorter, thicker, and rougher while snouts of females are longer, more slender, and smoother.

Life history. The life history and habits of the two species are similar. Under the optimum conditions of 85°F. and 14 per cent moisture, rice weevils require about 23 days to develop from egg to emerged adult. Granary weevils require from five to seven days longer.

The females deposit up to 400 eggs each during their adult life. Rice weevils have a longevity of four to five months and granary weevils six to eight months. Females may deposit as many as five eggs per day. The female selects a site and eats a narrow cylindrical hole into the kernel. On wheat kernels the favorite oviposition sites are in two narrow bands, a band margining the germ and a band at the brush end of the kernel. When

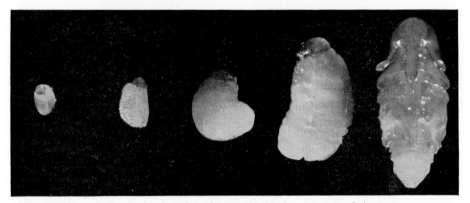

Fig. 16:11. Rice weevil, the four larval instars and the pupa (right). *Courtesy Kansas State University.*

the hole in the kernel is completed, a whitish egg is deposited in it by the ovipositor. As the ovipositor is withdrawn, the hole is filled to the surface of the kernel with a gelatinous material known as the **egg plug.** Parthenogenesis among the rice and granary weevils has been reported but it has not been substantiated by recent investigations.

The eggs hatch into white footless wrinkled larvae. There are four larval instars (Fig. 16:11). On the day before pupating, the last larval instar elongates into a prepupa. Adults may remain in the kernel for several days before eating their way out.

A granary weevil larva consumes approximately 55 per cent by weight of the interior of a wheat kernel. A rice weevil larva usually stays on one side of the crease of the wheat kernel where it consumes about 25 per cent of the kernel (Fig. 16:12). Two rice weevil larvae may inhabit a single wheat kernel if each remains on its own side of the crease. However, if one invades the area occupied by another, cannibalism results.

A granary weevil adult chews its way out of the kernel leaving a large irregular hole in the bran coat which contrasts with the roundness and neatness of a rice weevil emergence hole (Fig. 16:2A and B). Kernels with weevil emergence holes are known as **weevil-cut kernels** by the grain trade. Samples of wheat taken from mills in different parts of the United States have indicated that, for every kernel exhibiting an emergence hole, there are likely to be four internally infested kernels.

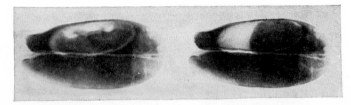

Fig. 16:12. Radiograph of rice weevil infesting wheat kernel (dark object top center in each kernel); left, pupa; right, larva. *Courtesy Kansas State University.*

Determination of internally infested kernels. It is of great importance to grain buyers for milling companies that they know the full extent of the internal infestation by rice and granary weevils. The following techniques are the most useful for this purpose:

1. X-ray grain inspection units have been designed to obtain radiographs of grain. All internal stages from egg to preemerged adults can be detected on these radiographs or on photographic prints made from the radiographs. X-ray units are widely used by the grain storing and processing industries as well as by inspection and research organizations.

2. Stains of acid fuchsin or gentian violet have an affinity for the gelatinous egg plugs so that when properly treated these plugs show a highly contrasting cherry red or violet spot against an unstained bran coat. The more commonly used acid fuchsin stain is prepared by adding 0.5 g. of acid fuchsin to a mixture of 50 cc. of glacial acetic acid and 950 cc. of distilled water. Grain, which has been wetted by soaking for about two minutes in warm water, is covered with the dye solution for about three minutes after which the dye is strained off and the grain washed under the tap to remove excess dye before examination.

3. A cracking-flotation method has been widely used by flour mill technicians. A sample of grain is cracked or coarsely ground so that the insects are released and can be floated to the surface when gasoline or mineral oil is added to the sample.

4. A specific gravity or flotation method provides a rough test that is particularly useful to country elevator operators. A solution of sodium silicate (water glass) is prepared with water so that the specific gravity is between 1.16 and 1.19 with the latter preferred. An ordinary filling-station hydrometer is adequate to determine the specific gravity. When a sample of wheat is added to this liquid and stirred, most of the infested kernels will float while the uninfested kernels will sink.

Confused flour beetle, *Tribolium confusum* duVal

Red flour beetle, *Tribolium castaneum* (Herbst)

[Coleoptera:Tenebrionidae]

The flour beetles, like the rice and granary weevils, are cosmopolitan insects that have been associated with grain stored by man at least since early Egyptian times. In nature they lived under bark where they were semipredators feeding on both living and dead materials. Today they are found in stored grains of many kinds and in the innumerable products manufactured from grain. They are known to millers as "bran bugs" since erroneously they were thought to feed only on flour and broken kernels rather than on whole kernels. In addition to grain they attack dried fruits, nuts, spices and numerous other stored food products.

About 85 per cent of all insects in flour mills in the midthirties were flour beetles. At that time they populated all available dead flour stock located throughout the milling machinery turning it a dirty gray. When disturbed the beetles secrete a vile smelling liquid into the flour. Modern sanitation procedures practiced by millers and bakers have largely corrected this situation. The two species are believed to be equally abundant in flour mills in the central states. North of this region the confused flour beetle is considered to be the dominant species while in the South it is the red flour beetle. Flour beetles together with saw-toothed grain beetles and Indian-meal moths are the most serious food pests in grocery stores and in home kitchens.

Description. The two species closely resemble one another in appearance, behavior and life cycle. They are flat, reddish brown beetles approximately $\frac{1}{7}$ in. long (Fig. 16:13). They may be distinguished by the following characteristics:

Confused flour beetle	Red flour beetle
1. Larger	1. Smaller
2. Antennae gradually enlarged toward the tip	2. Antennae with the last three segments abruptly enlarged
3. Eyes smaller	3. Eyes larger
4. On underside of head, the width of each eye is about ⅓ the distance separating them	4. On underside of head, the width of each eye is equal to the distance separating them
5. Wings not functional	5. Wings functional

The sexes of the confused flour beetle can be distinguished by the patterns created by the keels and grooves of the apical halves of the elytra. The sixth strial groove of females curves with the curvature of the apex of the wing and unites with the third strial groove. This never occurs on males.

The eggs are small and white. When laid each egg is covered with a fluid to which food particles stick making the egg difficult to find. Eggs hatch into yellowish white larvae that bear small darker forked processes on the tip of the abdomen (Fig. 16:14).

Life history. Each female may deposit from 400 to 500 white eggs among the food particles; frequently eggs are pushed through the mesh of sacks containing cereal products. A 5XX mesh bolting cloth will remove all flour beetle eggs from flour. When the food medium becomes overpopulated, the adults become cannibalistic and consume the eggs.

The number of larval instars varies between five and 12. On a suitable food more than half of both species will have seven or eight instars. The time required to develop from egg to adult depends upon the moisture and temperature. Like most grain-damaging insects, within the limits required

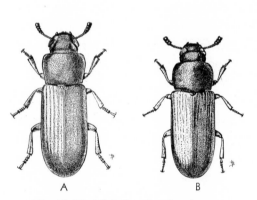

Fig. 16:13. Adult flour beetles. A, confused flour beetle; B, red flour beetle. *Courtesy USDA.*

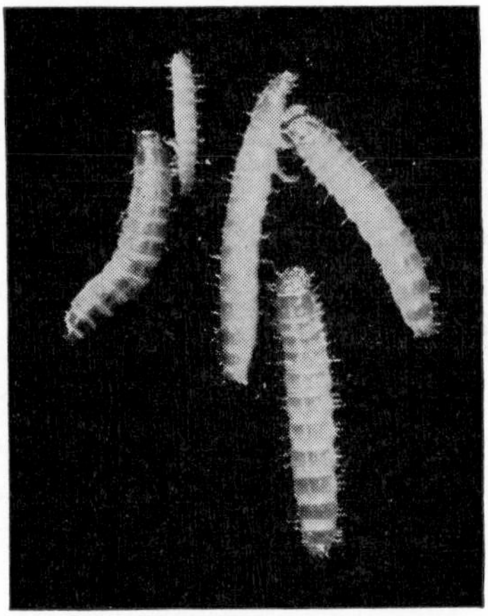

Fig. 16:14. Larvae of the confused flour beetle. *Courtesy USDA.*

by the species, the higher the humidity and the temperature, the shorter the developmental period. Under optimum conditions of environment and food the developmental period is approximately thirty days. As they mature the larvae come to the surface of their food medium to transform into naked pupae.

Cadelle

Tenebroides mauritanicus (Linnaeus) [Coleoptera:Ostomatidae]

The cadelle frequently is the first of the stored grain insects to infest newly harvested wheat in the Central Wheat Belt; also it is one of the most destructive. Cadelle larvae are generally known to farmers as "flour worms" because of the large amount of grain dust left in the bins after cadelle infestations. This is particularly noticeable when the grain is moved from the storage bins to be marketed. Formerly cadelles were known to millers as "bolting cloth beetles" because of their habits of eating holes in the bolting cloth. Today these insects rarely occur in flour mills. Cadelles are found in all parts of the world where grain products are stored. In nature they are believed to have lived out-of-doors under bark as predators.

Description. The adults are shiny black beetles of about ½ in. long with the body divided into two units. The head and prothorax are distinct from the rest of the body. Full grown larvae are about twice as long as the adults. They are the largest insects likely to be encountered in grain in suitable storage condition. The males can be distinguished by numerous punctures

Fig. 16:15. The cadelle, larva and adult. *Courtesy Kansas State University.*

on the under side of the abdomen some of which are very fine. There are fewer punctures in the same region of females and they are always coarse. Larvae are highly contrasting black and white; the black areas are the head, parts of the dorsal surface of each thoracic segment and a plate with two projections on the tip of the abdomen (Fig. 16:15).

Life history. The females insert white, slender, elongate eggs in cracks and crevices. Under favorable conditions they are prodigious egg producers; more than 3,500 have been reported from a single female. Oviposition continues throughout the summer and larvae of all sizes may occur in the grain until the larvae migrate to their hibernation sites. The larvae tunnel into the wooden parts of bins, boxcars, and shipholds to hibernate and to pupate. Pupation takes place in early spring; beetles emerge in late spring and in early summer. Beetles are exceptionally long lived, some surviving for more than three years. Only full-grown larvae and the adults normally survive the winters.

The tunnels constructed by cadelle larvae frequently cause storage structures to collapse. Also they provide lodging places for grain and grain dust and hiding places for other grain-damaging insects.

Angoumois grain moth

Sitotroga cerealella (Olivier) [Lepidoptera:Gelechiidae]

Since it was first reported in this country in 1728, the Angoumois grain moth has been the most destructive Lepidoptera of stored grains in the United States. Its larvae feed inside the kernels, weevil fashion, and consume the endosperm. Greatest damage is done in the southeastern states but the range extends into southeastern Kansas and across southern Illinois.

A pioneer in monographs dealing with injurious insects is the "History of an Insect which Devours the Grain of Angoumois" written by H. L. Duhamel du Monceau and M. Tillet in 1762. The authors, who were investigators representing the Royal Academy of Sciences, discussed the life history, habits and control of the Angoumois grain moth during a particularly disastrous outbreak in Angoumois province of France.

Description. The adults are buff to grayish or yellowish-brown moths with an average wingspread of ½ in. (Fig. 16:16). The moths range in weight from 0.7 mg. to 11.2 mg. depending on the larval food. Each front wing has two or three tiny dark spots and the apical tip of each hind wing is narrowed and pointed like "accusing" fingers. The hind wings are grayish white and are heavily margined with long hairs. The eggs are 0.6 mm. long. The larvae are white with a yellowish-brown head and reach a length of about ⅕ in. when full grown (Fig. 16:17).

Life history. Eggs are deposited outside of the kernels. On ears of corn they are likely to be pushed deep between the kernels; on wheat in the field, shock, or stack, eggs are placed anywhere on the head; on shelled corn and wheat in the bin, they are laid on kernels at the surface or within a few inches of the surface.

A newly hatched caterpillar first constructs an entrance cocoon on the outside of the kernel before eating an entrance hole into the kernel. Usually there is only one caterpillar per wheat kernel, but there may be more than one per corn kernel. When infestations occur in sorghum grain with kernels too small for larval entrance, a larva ties several kernels into a ball with

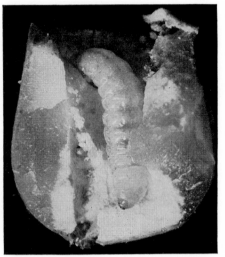

Fig. 16:16. Angoumois grain moth reared on corn. Left, female; right, male. *Courtesy Kansas State University.*

Fig. 16:17. Larva of the Angoumois grain moth feeding in a kernel of corn. *Courtesy Kansas State University.*

silk and lives inside the cluster but outside the kernels. There are four larval instars. Before pupating the mature larva extends the cavity to the inner surface of the seed coat and then spins a tough cocoon lining the cavity.

Presently an escape lid is prepared through the seed coat. Viewed from the outside this escape lid in a kernel of corn looks like a glass window. Upon completion of the pupal stage the moth easily pushes its way out of the kernel through the escape lid, frequently dragging the cocoon along with it (Fig. 16:2F). Development from hatching to adult emergence under optimum laboratory conditions requires a minimum of 23 days. Under field conditions this developmental period takes from five to seven weeks.

The winter is spent largely as mature larvae that pupate in the spring and emerge in late May or early June. There are from two to four generations in a year depending on environmental conditions. The moths are sufficiently strong fliers that they can infest wheat and corn in the field, shock, or stack. The harvesting of wheat by combine has largely eliminated the Angoumois grain moth as a wheat pest but it is still the most important pest of stored corn in those regions in which it can survive the winters.

Selected References

Anon., *Stored Grain Insects and the Clean Grain Program,* Kan. State College Ext. Service L-30, 1957.

Cotton, R. T., *Pests of stored grain and grain products* (Minneapolis: Burgess, 1956).

——, and N. E. Good, *Annotated List of the Insects and Mites Associated with Stored Grain and Cereal Products, and of their Arthropod Parasites and Predators,* USDA Misc. Publ. 258, 1937.

——, H. H. Walkden, G. D. White, and D. A. Wilbur, *Causes of Outbreaks of Stored-Grain Insects,* Kan. Agr. Exp. Sta. Bul. 416 (Revision of North Central Regional Publ. 35), 1960.

Daniels, N. E., "Damage and reproduction by the flour beetles, *Tribolium confusum* and *T. castaneum,* in wheat at three moisture contents," *J. Econ. Ent.,* 49(2):244–7 (1956).

Fraenkel, G., and M. Blewett, "The Natural Foods and the Food Requirements of Several Species of Stored Products Insects," *Trans. Roy. Ent. Soc.* (London) 93:457–90 (1943).

Frankenfeld, J. C., *Staining Methods for Detecting Weevil Infestation in Grain,* USDA, Bur. Entom. and Pl. Quar. Circ. ET-256, 1948.

Good, N. E., *The Flour Beetles of the Genus Tribolium,* USDA, Tech. Bul. 498, 1936.

Gray, H. E., "The Biology of Flour Beetles," Milling Prod. 13(12):7, 18–22 (1948).

Howe, R. W., "The Biology of the Rice Weevil, *Calandra oryzae* (L.)," *Ann. Appl. Biol.,* 39(2):168–80 (1952).

Linsley, E. G., "Natural Sources, Habitats, and Reservoirs of Insects Associated with Stored Foods Products," *Hilgardia* 16(4):187–224 (1944).

Milner, Max, "New Methods to Detect and Eliminate Insect-infested Grain," *Advances in Food Research,* Vol. 8: 111–31 (1958).

——, M. R. Lee, and R. Katz, "Application of X-Ray Technique to the Detection of Internal Infestation in Grain, *J. Econ. Ent.,* 43:933–5 (1950).

Parkin, E. A., "Stored Product Entomology," *Ann. Rev. of Ent.,* 1:223–40 (1956).

Richards, O. W., "Observations on Grain-Weevils Calandra (Col.-Curculionidae) I. General Biology and Oviposition," *Proc. Zool. Soc.* (London), 117:1–43 (1947).

Robinson, W., *Low Temperature and Moisture as Factors in the Ecology of the Rice Weevil,* Sitophilus oryza L. *and the Granary Weevil,* Sitophilus granarius L., Minn. Agr. Exp. Sta. Tech. Bul. 41, 1926.

Simmons, Perez, and G. W. Ellington, *Life History of the Angoumois Grain Moth in Maryland,* USDA Tech. Bul. 351, 1933.

Stored Products Insects Section, AMS, *Stored Grain Pests,* USDA, Farmer's Bul. 1260, 1958.

Walker, D. W., *Population Fluctuations and Control of Stored Grain Insects,* Wash. Agr. Exp. Sta. Tech. Bul. 31, 1960.

Wilbur, D. A., and George Halazon, *Pests of Farm-Stored Wheat and their Control,* Kan. Agr. Exp. Sta. Bul. 373, 1955.

——, and Lloyd O. Warren, "Grain Sanitation on Kansas Farms, *Proc. Tenth Int. Cong. of Ent.,* 4:29–31 [1956 (1958)].

Chapter 17 | HOUSEHOLD

INSECTS | *John V. Osmun*

From the day that man first started providing shelter for his family, he was accompanied by insect pests in the household. Early biblical references frequently mention ants, flies, and moths as part of man's abode. The destructiveness and undesirability of these insects were noted when James wrote, "Your riches are corrupted, and your garments moth eaten," and when Matthew suggested that proper preparation should be for heaven where moths do not consume. As people have improved their homes, they have gradually increased the opportunities for insects to adapt themselves to these desirable environments. In addition, food in an attractive form has been kept in increasing quantities. Ideal conditions for many insects exist today in many households.

The pests

At first consideration, the insects which one might think of as household pests are flies and mosquitoes. These pests, however, are incidental to the house, having been attracted by food odors or the presence of man. Generally the two groups do not breed or complete life cycles in structures, unless abnormal situations exist. For this reason, mosquitoes and house flies are considered elsewhere in this book as insects affecting man. We are concerned here with so-called structural insects which commonly utilize our homes and buildings for their chosen environments.

The most common insects in this category are the cockroaches. Although some nine species of roaches are found in buildings, four of them predominate: **German cockroach** (Fig. 17:8), **oriental cockroach** or "waterbug" (Fig. 17:9), **American cockroach** (Fig. 17:10), and **brown-banded cockroach** (Fig. 17:11). The first three names suggest origins from countries of the world; more likely the nomenclature arose at various times in history as

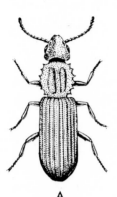
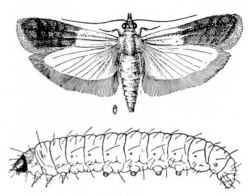
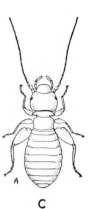

A   B   C

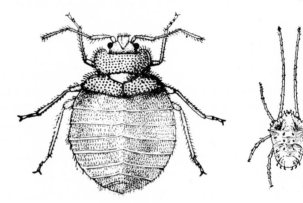

D   E   F

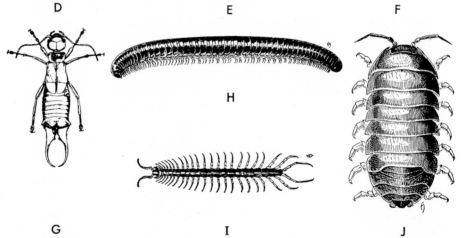

G   H   I   J

Fig. 17:1. Minor household pests (not to scale). Pantry pests: A, saw-toothed grain beetle; B, Indian-meal moth and larva; C, booklouse. Pests of various locations: D, silver fish; E, bed bug; F, clover mite; G, earwig; H, millipede; I, centipede; J, pillbug. *A and G, courtesy Washington State University; F, Courtesy USDA; rest, Courtesy University of California.*

a slander to a neighboring country. Whatever the origin, the connotation of "cockroach" or "waterbug" is not a pleasant one. These pests are widely distributed in the temperate areas of the world.

Clothes moths are commonly associated with the destruction of woolen clothing and rugs, although of equal importance in this category of household pests are the several species of carpet beetles (Fig. 17:2) and sometimes silverfish. Two species of clothes moths are common, the **webbing clothes moth** (Fig. 17:14) and the **casemaking clothes moth.** The web forming type is the more abundant and destructive.

Many species of ants invade the household and several species are able to nest and complete their life cycles completely within the structure without contact with the ground (Fig. 17:15). As a group, the ants are numerous and highly successful. Those completely adapted to household existence are the **black carpenter ant, Pharaoh ant,** and the **odorous house ant.** Other forms which normally nest in the foundation soil and range through dwellings include the **pavement ant,** field ants, **thief ant,** and in the southern and western parts of the United States, **Argentine ant.** The much publicized imported fire ant in the South is primarily a pest of agricultural land.

Throughout our country, one of the most feared insects is the termite (Fig. 17:18). As common as these insects are, most people know very little about them, and perhaps it is the element of the unknown that causes such great anxiety. Historically the relatively ancient and socially organized termite has been considered a useful organism. It serves its place in the balance of nature by reducing fallen timbers and dead roots in the ground. Only because man has placed wood of his dwellings in situations accessible to termites, have these insects become destructive. **Subterranean termites,** which normally colonize in the ground and move upward into buildings, predominate and are reported from 49 states. **Drywood termites,** which can colonize in homes without soil or moisture connection, are generally limited to the Gulf states, Texas, Arizona, California and Hawaii. The less important dampwood termite has a similar distribution.

There are many insects of lesser importance associated with the household (Fig. 17:1), such as bed bugs, silverfish, pantry pests, and powder post beetles, but the most important and most frequently encountered ones are those mentioned first, the cockroaches, fabric pests, ants, and termites.

The damage

In considering the economic importance of household insects, one must take into consideration more than just injury or damage. Monetary sig-

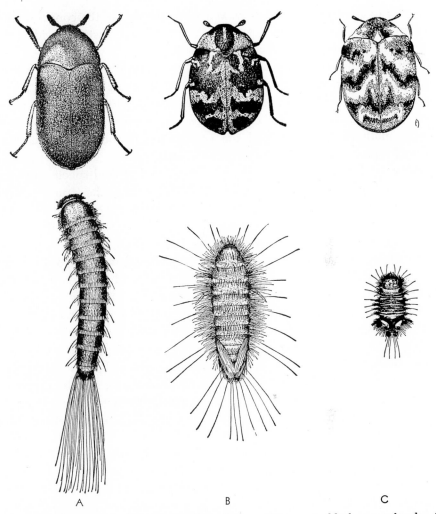

Fig. 17:2. Three species of carpet beetles, adults and larvae. A, black carpet beetle, *Attagenus piceus* (Oliv.); B, carpet beetle, *Anthrenus scrophulariae* (L.); C, varied carpet beetle, *Anthrenus verbasci* (L.). *A and B, courtesy Connecticut Agricultural Experiment Station; C, courtesy University of California.*

nificance is also attached to insects as contaminators of food and as factors in the esthetic well-being of people. No one likes insects in his food or crawling about in his home. Such things are as real to the homeowner as is a cornborer to a farmer.

Cockroaches are important in all of these categories. Through their ability to chew, they will attack book bindings, other sized paper and cloth, and will devour the nutrient material of a gummed surface (Fig.

17:3). They are odorous, obnoxious pests and habitually leave trails of fecal droppings. The German cockroach is often rightfully associated with unsanitary conditions and poor disposal of dirt and waste. In addition, this species at least is apparently a vector of gastroenteritis. The oriental cockroach can be found the year around in homes, but in the northern climates, it increases in numbers as individuals move in from the outside during the fall for protection from the cold. American cockroaches prefer

Fig. 17:3. Damage of American cockroach to paper products. Note staining as well as chewing damage. *Courtesy Purdue University.*

a warm, moist environment which results in infestations in steam rooms, moist basements, and in regions where the temperature is high, in sewers and areas under homes. Due to the large amount of intersectional moving of people during World War II, the brown-banded roach, once an inhabitant of the South is now scattered throughout the country. This insect is not as gregarious as the German cockroach it resembles, and it is found widely dispersed in household cupboards and drawers, behind pictures, in electric clocks, and in furniture.

Nearly everyone has at one time or another experienced the misfortune of having woolens attacked by clothes moths, and this situation is nicely summarized in the verse:

> Friends may criticize my clothes
> And all the furnishings I buy
> But moths and carpet beetles like them
> Equally as well as I.

These keratin-loving insects possess a keratinase enzyme which permits protein disintegration and nutrient consumption of wool fibers. Soiled wool is especially attractive to developing larvae, the only stage which feeds. The adult moths are active at night, moving readily from closet and drawers to furniture, rugs, feather pillows, and even pianos, in order to lay their eggs. Damage occurs not only to pure wool fabrics but also to mixtures of wool with synthetic fibers (Fig. 17:4).

From pants to pantry, ants can be important in a home; when their activities conflict with those of man, they are a problem. Food is a normal attractant to these insects and the resulting contamination can be considerable. Soiled spots on clothing are also attacked, resulting in damage. In addition, ants are annoying because of their presence and because of their ability to bite and insert irritating formic acid into the wound. Some ants, such as the fire ants, have retained the ability to sting. One group of

Fig. 17:4. Characteristic damage of the webbing clothes moth on wool and fur. *Courtesy Purdue University.*

ants, commonly called carpenter ants, are economically quite important because of their destruction of wood. These ants do not derive nourishment from wood but frequently hollow out supporting timbers in homes and other structures to provide protected nesting sites for colony development (Fig. 17:5).

Termites are injurious due to their ability to penetrate wood and wood

products and devour cellulose. The principal economic damage done by these insects is the weakening of structural timbers in homes and buildings (Fig. 17:6). The activity of a strong colony can be considerable, causing severe damage to foundation plates, joists, wall supports, and flooring. Man seemingly builds his homes for termites in that he places wood members of his dwelling in situations accessible to them. Subterranean termites, those which colonize in the ground and extend their activities from such focal points, can attack wood in buildings by finding protected passage from the soil to the source of food or by building connecting earthen tubes. Since warm temperature accelerates development, extensive damage occurs where extended periods of warmth occur. For many years, the predominately high incidence of infestation occurred in our southern states. Today, however, homes are better constructed. Basements are well heated; many are wood paneled; foundations are hollow, permitting undetected soil to wood passage of termites; slab homes are usually equipped with floor heating which makes the soil beneath an ideal environment for termite development. Combine this "better living" with the cryptobiotic nature of the termite, and it is little wonder that undetected damage can occur to harass the homeowner.

Control through sanitation and building management

Although household insects are in general difficult to eliminate by means other than chemicals, they can be kept to a minimum by good housekeeping practices. Cockroaches and ants enter a building either by their own volition or they are carried in with commodities. Their chance for survival, however, may depend on the degree of sanitation or household management that exists there. Included in these categories would be rapid and proper disposal of wastes, general cleanliness in the kitchen areas, protected storage of food, clean, well-ventilated basements, a minimum of concealed areas suitable for hiding, and storage free of superfluous accumulations. In the case of fabric pests, such as the clothes moth, seasonal airing of woolens, washing or dry-cleaning before storage, and thorough vacuuming of rugs, baseboards, and closet space are good preventive practices. Even when infestations of household pests do occur, such procedures will greatly enhance the possibility of success when chemicals are applied.

In the case of termites, certain measures can be taken that will decrease the chance of termite attack, but certainly will not guarantee it. During construction, efforts should be made to prevent the accumulation of scrap lumber in the soil around the house or in crawl spaces beneath it. Struc-

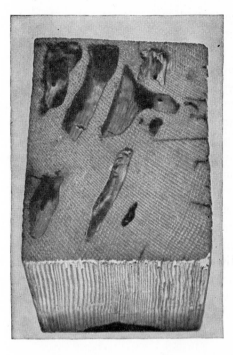

Fig. 17:5. End view of block of wood excavated by carpenter ants to provide nesting place. *Courtesy Purdue University.*

tural wood should not touch the soil or be in protected proximity to it. Proper drainage of the soil around buildings will decrease the possibility of moist environments attractive to termites.

Chemical control

The use of chemicals to control household insects is widely accepted. Even more important than in agriculture, however, is the necessity of employing safety in their use. The inhabitants of the household, whether pets, children, or adults are living organisms just as are insects. Insecticides can be hazardous if not properly used. The safest material, yet the one most rapid in toxic action to insects, is pyrethrum. It has no appreciable residual life, but is useful in initial knockdown or kill and may be used alone or in combination with other insecticides. Two of the cyclodienes, chlordane and dieldrin, are highly effective against all of the household insects discussed, but preference of choice as discussed later is dependent on the surfaces to be treated and the residual life desired. Malathion, an organic phosphate insecticide, is increasing in popularity, and is especially desirable where resistant German cockroaches are encountered. Household insecticides are formulated commonly in solutions of refined, nonstaining petroleum oil. Some emulsifiable concentrates are available for dilution with

Fig. 17:6. Wooden beam damaged by subterranean termites. Damage was not visible until torn apart. *Courtesy Purdue University.*

water, and there are on the market several very reliable dust formulations. Wettable powder suspensions are not recommended for use in household insect control.

Control with chemicals is only as good as the quality of application. Any of these insecticides must be applied thoroughly and, based on the habits of each particular pest, placed where most needed. One should keep in mind the operating procedure of diagnosis, prescription, and proper application. In many cases, especially with termite control, the householder will not be competent to utilize insecticides effectively against household insects. Fortunately there are several thousand reliable pest control operators in the country who are specially trained and competent to serve the public.

Control equipment

The best single piece of equipment for household insect control is a one-gallon compressed air sprayer equipped with a precision nozzle that produces a fan-shaped spray pattern (Fig. 17:7). It is convenient for the application of small quantities of insecticide in selected areas, and at the same time it can be used for fairly liberal spraying where needed. Most packaging devices, including aerosol dispensers and "handy" plunger sprayers, are quite limited in their effectiveness and can be relied upon only where light application is desirable. Although dusts are less used than sprays in the household, good equipment is needed to dispense them. Small, squeeze-type dusters are available as are rubber bulb applicators. Equipment for termite control includes highly specialized power equipment, modified nozzle assemblies, and drilling devices. Although a householder could purchase such specialities, they are most readily available as part of the service of a pest control operator.

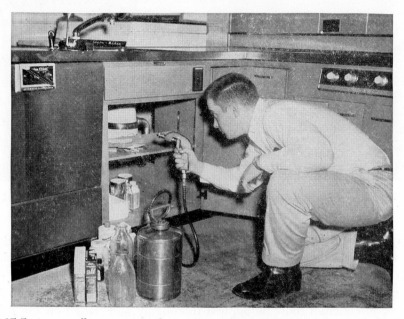

Fig. 17:7. A one-gallon compressed air sprayer for applying insecticides in the home. Items apt to be contaminated are removed before spraying. *Courtesy Purdue University.*

Precautions

The introduction of an insect toxicant into a household automatically implies the possession or use of a hazardous household chemical. Children are often present and human error can lead to difficulties. Consider each container of a household spray or dust as a potential hazard and store it in a safe place. Replace caps securely and keep dusts away from food supplies where they could be mistaken for flour or seasoning. Storage away from cold is also desirable because cold temperatures cause precipitation of the active ingredient.

When applying household insecticides avoid contamination of foods and food preparation surfaces. In addition do not apply materials where infants will be apt to crawl across treated surfaces. Prolonged and repeated exposure to aerosol mists should be considered hazardous. Actually, most of our insecticides bearing federal registration for household use can be considered safe providing they are used according to direction. Read the instruction label.

REPRESENTATIVE HOUSEHOLD INSECTS

German cockroach

Blattella germanica (Linnaeus) [Orthoptera:Blattidae]

The German cockroach is one of our most gregarious household pests and is distributed widely in the temperate regions of the world. This insect is seldom found outdoors, but breeds and lives generation after generation in buildings without influence of seasons. In apartment buildings, German cockroaches move readily from floor to floor following pipe lines or moving through wall voids. Since they generally carry their egg capsules until nearly hatching time, the spread of these pests is facilitated. This species is commonly introduced into buildings by means of infested food cartons, laundry, and various containers. Importance is attached to this insect's undesirable presence, not generally to any damage that it could cause. Food and dishes become contaminated by the excreta and by various secretions. The German cockroach tends to congregate under tables, in and between cupboards, in wall cracks and behind wall hangings, inside beer and soft drink cartons, and in similar secluded places. In recent years, an apparent change in its habits has been noted in areas where considerable insecticides have been used and where resistance of this species to chlorinated hydrocarbons occurs. The effect has been one of scattering, and individuals may be found almost anywhere in homes or other buildings. As a result of this change in behavior, control is more complicated.

Description. The German cockroach is pale brown in color with two, parallel, dark stripes on the pronotum (Fig. 17:8). When full grown, these insects are ½ to ⅝ in. long, boat-shaped in appearance, and possess fully developed wings covering the abdomen; their antennae are longer than the body. The wings are functional but used usually only for downward flight. The nymphs, which are without wings, resemble small editions of the adults; the visual impression is one of an insect with a light area in the center of the thorax. The egg capsules or oothecae are slender and light brown.

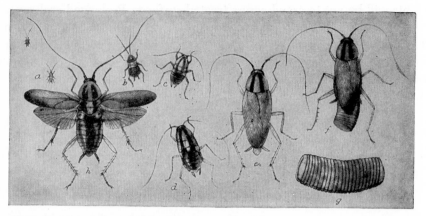

Fig. 17:8. German cockroach life stages, winged adults, nymphs, and egg cases. Note female carrying egg case. *Courtesy USDA.*

Life history. Each egg capsule contains up to 48 eggs. The female carries the capsule throughout most of the three-week incubation period, and produces about five capsules during her life. Growth is by gradual metamorphosis and takes an average of three months. Provided maximum hatching and optimum developmental conditions prevail, it is theoretically possible for one female to be the progenitor of more than 30,000 offspring in one year. The species is, from the standpoint of population development, the most efficient of the cockroaches. The productivity is an important consideration in understanding the development of chemical resistance in this insect.

Oriental cockroach

Blatta orientalis Linnaeus [Orthoptera:Blattidae]

The oriental cockroach is more commonly called a "waterbug," a term freely used to avoid the apparent stigma attached to having cockroaches in a household. This insect is found in homes and other buildings where dark, protected areas, food, and water are available. Basements most frequently provide such environment, but these insects will also migrate to higher levels. In most regions of the country, oriental cockroaches are common outdoors in warm weather and may become unusually abundant around trash and garbage. Although they are more sluggish and less wary than other cockroaches, they migrate readily and, especially in the fall of the year, find their way into buildings through drains, wall openings, and open doors. These insects are annoying and may do considerable damage to book bindings and starched materials.

Description. The oriental cockroach is shiny black, although occasionally the wings of the male are a mahogany color. The female is oval and has only wing stubs; its length is 1¼ in. Males have developed wings nearly covering the abdomen, are more slender, and about 1 in. long. Egg capsules are very dark and bulky in appearance. Nymphs of both sexes resemble miniature adult females (Fig. 17:9).

Life history. The oriental cockroach has retained the seasonal influence on its development cycle. The egg capsules, containing a maximum of 16 eggs, are dropped as soon as formed and often are glued to objects. Incubation may take two months. Since nymphs mature in the spring, the period of development may be just short of a year to over two years.

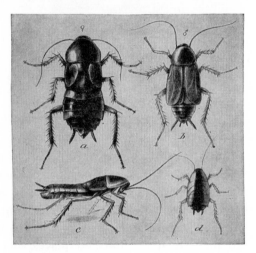

Fig. 17:9. Oriental cockroach. A, adult female; B, adult male; C and D, nymphs. *Courtesy Purdue University.*

American cockroach

Periplaneta americana (Linnaeus) [Orthoptera:Blattidae]

Humidity and high temperatures favor the development of the American cockroach. It is less of a household pest than the other three considered in this chapter, but it frequents the steam tunnels of apartment buildings and works upward from such focal environments. In the southern states this species and others of the same genus are more common as household pests, frequently migrating in from the outside where climatic conditions permit their existence. These insects are capable of moderate flight. They are economically important for the same reasons as are oriental cockroaches.

Description. The American cockroach is reddish-brown except for a light brown margin around the side and back edges of the pronotum (Fig. 17:10). These are large roaches with both males and females being winged, about

1½ in. in length, and bearing long, active antennae. The nymphs are wingless, but otherwise resemble the adults except for size. The dark brown or blackish capsule resembles that of the oriental species.

Fig. 17:10. American cockroach adult, actual size. *Courtesy Purdue University.*

Life history. As many as 16 nymphs can hatch from an ootheca, incubation taking less than two months to complete. Like the other cockroaches discussed, development of the nymphs is influenced by temperature, and may take as little as 285 days or as long as a year and a half. Adults are long lived, and females may produce as many as 50 capsules in a lifetime, dropping them in protected places soon after formation.

Brown-banded cockroach

Supella supellectilium (Serville) [Orthoptera:Blattidae]

The influence of war played a very great part in the present distribution of the brown-banded cockroach. Confined principally to the tropical regions and the southern states before World War II, this species hitchhiked in household goods of military personnel to establish itself successfully in heated homes in the North. This cockroach is not strictly gregarious. Adults, nymphs, and well-attached egg capsules are found in such secluded places as stationery drawers, inside furniture, beneath loose wall paper and pictures, behind moldings and kitchen utensils, in closets, and not infrequently in electric clocks. Their food is varied, and they have the annoying habit of removing glue from stamps and envelopes.

Description. This dimorphic cockroach is about the size of the small German, but bears a light tan band across the base of the wings and a broken band across the center of the wings. The male has functional wings covering the tip of its slender abdomen; the female is broad with stubby wings. The name, brown-banded, is especially appropriate for the nymphs on which

Fig. 17:11. Nymphs of the brown-banded cockroach, natural size. *Courtesy Purdue University.*

the banding on the abdomen is prominent in the absence of wings (Fig. 17:11). Egg capsules are small, nearly equilateral, and tan in color (Fig. 17:12).

Life history. Capsules of this species can have as many as 18 eggs each, and hatching occurs in a little over two months. (Note below this relationship to control practices.) The development period for the nymphs allows just two generations a year.

Cockroach control

Knowledge of the species and the specific habits and habitats of each are essential for good cockroach control. This information has always been important because of the distinct differences among our common species (Fig. 17:13), but is even more so now because of the insecticide resistance problem present with the German cockroach.

Except for the German cockroach, the several species may be readily killed with chlordane or dieldrin providing these materials are applied properly. Chlordane is used at 2 per cent in either an oil solution or emulsion; it is available also as a 5 per cent dust. Dieldrin is recommended at 0.5 per cent in liquid formulations and as a 1 per cent dust.

Liquid applications should be made with a reasonably coarse-droplet spray applied in such a way that a uniform residual will remain. If re-infestations are a problem, no longer than two weeks protection should be expected without reapplication. Dusts can be used only where moisture is not a factor and where they will not be unsightly. Whatever the material, effort must be made to apply it where the particular cockroaches concerned will be most apt to contact it for a rather prolonged period of time.

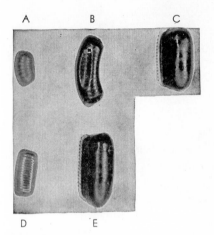

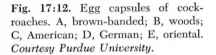

Fig. 17:12. Egg capsules of cock-roaches. A, brown-banded; B, woods; C, American; D, German; E, oriental. *Courtesy Purdue University.*

In the case of the chlorinated hydrocarbon-resistant German cockroach, the most favorable present success is with 1 per cent deodorized malathion and 1 per cent diazinon emulsions. Still effective is sodium fluoride dust used alone or in combination with pyrethrum. Provided application is thorough, success can be achieved using the new silica gel desiccant dusts which impart a dehydrating action on the cockroaches.

Certain special uses of insecticides should be noted. Two per cent phosphorus paste is attractive to American cockroaches and in some localities to the oriental species. The paste must be applied out of reach of children and pets and away from foods. Lindane, dispensed in a vaporized form continues to be the best control of well-scattered, brown-banded cockroaches, but reapplication is often necessary in two months to kill nymphs hatched from capsules. Pyrethrum, applied as an aerosol, is very useful in locating hiding places of all roaches since it stimulates almost immediate activity which will guide one to the localities where more persistent insecticides should be used.

In areas where certain of these cockroaches may migrate in from outdoors, a thorough application of the emulsion form of chlordane (1.0 per cent) or dieldrin (0.25 per cent) on the soil and base of the foundation around a structure is a good preventive practice.

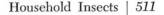

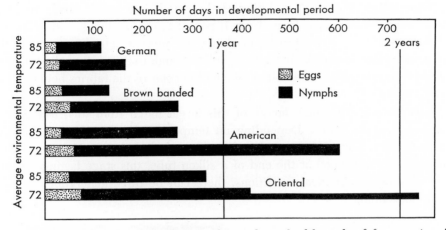

Fig. 17:13. The duration of developmental periods in the life cycle of four species of cockroaches. Note effect of temperature and the great variation between species. *Based on Gould and Deay.*

Webbing clothes moth

Tineola bisselliella (Hummel) [Lepidoptera:Tineidae]

The larvae of the webbing clothes moth are the only forms of this insect capable of doing damage. They readily attack keratin-containing materials such as wool, fur, hair, feathers, and occasionally skins. Although the highly specific enzyme keratinase permits this type of digestion, other nutrients such as B vitamins are necessary. These requirements mean that freshly hatched larvae will seek fabrics which are slightly soiled with food, residue of drinks, saliva, and urine, and only after they are well established will they attack entirely clean material. The presence of infesting larvae is detected by the characteristic silken tubes which are spun on or in the infested fabric; here the larvae spend most of their developing period.

Damage varies according to the intensity of infestation. The work of a single larva will leave a small hole or a groovelike etching on the nap of woolens. Heavier infestations result in numerous irregular holes, and often little is left of the fabric. When mixtures of wool and synthetic fabric are attacked, the larva shows little discrimination although the synthetic fibers are not digested, but simply passed through the insect's digestive system. The lint which accumulates in closets and along baseboards is often attractive to these pests, and such material serves as a residual source of infestation in a home or woolen goods store. The larvae avoid light and also very dry environments; infestations are therefore in protected places away from both light and air currents.

Description. The adult webbing clothes moth is a small, rather fragile, buff colored moth about ¼ in. long. It possesses narrow wings with a fringe of long hairs. No characteristic markings are present. The larvae range in size, according to age, from 1/16 to ½ in. Although they are normally creamy appearing caterpillars, they often take on the color of the fabrics being eaten (Fig. 17:14).

Life history. The small larvae of this insect hatch from tiny, oval ivory eggs laid in the fabric. Depending on temperature and nutritional factors present, larval development takes from five weeks to several months. The pupal stage is formed at the end of a silken tube, this stage lasting two to four weeks. Under ideal conditions, there can be three generations a year in a household.

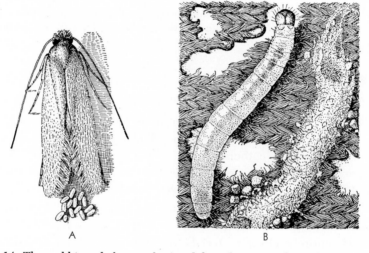

A   B

Fig. 17:14. The webbing clothes moth. A, adult and eggs; B, larva feeding on woolen cloth and silken tube of larva. *Courtesy Conn. Agr. Exp. Sta.*

The moth stage, which is more commonly seen than the larval stage, does not feed. These moths shun light, flitting weakly from place to place in darkened rooms.

Control. Preventive measures must be the key to fabric protection, because once the "hole" is made, the damage is done! There are three steps involved in clothes moth control: (1) preventive sanitation and chemical measures, (2) control of existing infestations, and (3) fabric protection.

Much can be done to prevent trouble by means of household cleanliness, thorough and frequent cleaning with a vacuum cleaner, by brushing, airing, and dry cleaning susceptible clothing, and by avoiding having locations predisposed to infestation like wall-to-wall carpeting and prolonged storage of discarded garments, bedding, and old rugs. Remember that a clean environment is not conducive to clothes moth activity. Several approaches can be made to the use of insecticides as preventive treatment. The most common one is the use of paradichlorobenzene (PDB) as a repellent and continuous fumigant in storage. Woolens to be stored should be interspaced with crystals of this material placed on clean paper as the fabrics are packed into very tight trunks or boxes. Application is at the rate of 1 lb. per 30 cubic feet of space. Naphthalene (moth balls), although less desirable to use, is effective at the same rate. Cedar closets and most cedar chests are seldom effective. Fur storage in cold vaults is a worthwhile preventive measure. When wool carpets are to be placed in a room preventive measures are recommended as follows: a thorough spraying of baseboards with 5 per cent DDT or 1 per cent dieldrin, or a dust application of either insecticide. An additional application to the underside of the carpets with 10 per cent DDT dust or 2 per cent dieldrin dust will afford protection for years.

Control of clothes moths, once an infestation is established in a household, is another problem. Insecticides cannot be used promiscuously without regard for the nature of the article to be treated. When clothes moths do occur, the first step is washing or cleaning the infested materials if practical. Chemicals can be sprayed on some woolens if care is taken. For this purpose, light oil solutions of 2 per cent DDT or 0.5 per cent dieldrin have been effective. For control of pests in drawers, closets, wall voids, and air vents, the addition of 0.25 per cent lindane to either 5 per cent DDT or 0.5 per cent dieldrin is especially useful. Professional assistance is usually desirable if extensive control measures are necessary, this being especially so if either a house or articles in it require fumigation for complete eradication.

So-called "moth-proofing" or fabric protection is more readily done during the manufacture of fabrics than after the latter become household goods. Certain organic chemicals related to dyes can be introduced as an integral and essentially permanent part of the basic threads of the fabrics. There are, however, available materials for home fabric protection. These include the inorganic fluorides such as sodium aluminum fluosilicate and others. These are water-base materials which must be applied with care to avoid shrinkage; they are not wash-proof. Dieldrin and DDT are both available in spray formulations and in emulsifiable concentrates which may be added to laundry water; these are not dry cleaning-proof.

Black carpenter ant

Camponotus pennsylvanicus (De Geer) [Hymenoptera:Formicidae]

Three genera of ants will be considered in detail as reasonably representative of the multitude of these insects encountered in a household. Probably because of its large size, usually black color, and roving habits, the black carpenter ant is one of the best known of the ants invading households. This particular species is a wood nesting form, its colonies occurring in logs, stumps, trees, posts, and the wooden structures of buildings. The latter nesting sites include beams, sills, rafters, and hollow wooden doors. When wooden members of a house are hollowed out for nesting purposes, serious damage is likely to result. Evidence of nesting is the presence of small or large piles of coarse sawdust thrown out during excavation. Whether the carpenter ant nests inside or outside, it readily enters homes in search of food, and thus is a source of annoyance and sometimes damage to fabrics and paper products which are heavily sized or soiled with food. The occurrence of these ants in buildings can be involuntary also, since they are commonly introduced in fire wood stored in basements or by the hearth. The workers of the carpenter ant are carnivorous and predaceous; they also attend honeydew excreting insects such as aphids and scales which provide a source of converted carbohydrates. They are known to feed on moist portions of meat, bread, fruits, and other foods found in a household. Like other ants, this species will bite vigorously when molested. Members of the genus *Camponotus* are well distributed throughout the United States.

Description. The stout workers of the black carpenter ant vary in size from ¼ to ½ in. in length, this polymorphic condition being related to the age and development of the colony, not to the individual. The winged females may reach nearly an inch in length. Like other ants, they are readily distinguished from termites by the presence of a distinct head, thorax, slender waist, large abdomen and clear wings of unequal length. The prominent gaster has a silky pubescence, and the 12-segmented antennae bear no enlarged terminal segments (Fig. 17:15).

Life history. Colonies of the carpenter ant vary in size from a queen and a few workers to organizations containing several friendly queens and as many as 5,000 workers. There are, like other ants, normally three distinct castes: males, females and workers (female, but seldom sexually functional). After mating, the winged male dies, leaving the female to develop a colony. She is long lived and propagates the colony through many years of growth. Ants have four developmental stages: egg, larva, pupa, and adult (Fig.

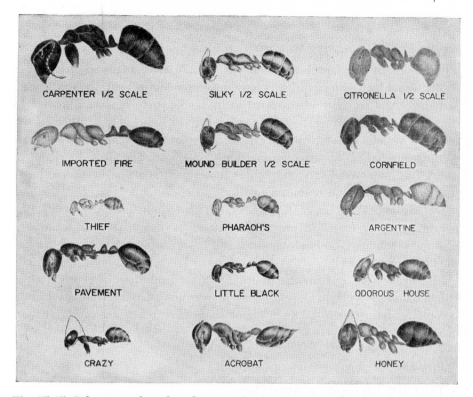

Fig. 17:15. Side views of a selected group of common ants (enlarged). Antennal clubs and number and shape of nodes located on abdominal petiole are characters used in identification. *Courtesy Wallerstein, Purdue University.*

17:16). The egg is nearly microscopic in size and hatches in about three weeks. The larvae, which are nourished by the workers, develop in about the same time in warm weather but this stage is greatly prolonged in winter. The pupae, which most people mistake for "ant eggs," require three weeks. The winged, sexual forms, are produced only by mature colonies and emerge commonly in July. Two generations of workers are possible in a year.

Pharaoh ant *Monomorium pharaonis* (Linnaeus)
Little black ant *Monomorium minimum* (Buckley)
[Hymenoptera:Formicidae]

The principal species here is the Pharaoh ant which, although small, is the most persistent of our household ants. Even in regions having cold winters, this ant commonly nests in inaccessible places in buildings and continues colony development and activity the year around. Nests are found in almost any protected place such as between walls, under floors, inside foundation voids, in boxes, articles of clothing, and piles of papers. In addition to their adaptability, colonies usually have many reproductives, a situation which allows quick colony development and subdivision to new localities. Add to these characteristics its tendency to explore almost anything and its omnivorous choice of foods which include not only other insects, but also sweets, breads, meats, grease and vegetable oils, and we have a well-distributed, most troublesome household pest. The little black ant is much less numerous and adaptable; it nests principally in the soil and rotting wood, but enters homes readily.

Description. Workers of this genus, *Monomorium*, are very small (approximately $\frac{3}{32}$ in.) and are characterized by antennal clubs composed of three segments. The Pharaoh ant is rather inconspicuous, being yellowish in color (Fig. 17:15).

Life history. Except for the unusually large proportion of reproductives, colonial life is typical. Development in warmly heated dwellings can be completed from egg to adult in about six weeks, increasing in length with cooler environments.

Fire ant *Solenopsis geminata* (Fabricius)

Thief ant *Solenopsis molesta* (Say)

Imported fire ant *Solenopsis saevissima richteri* Forel

Southern fire ant *Solenopsis xyloni* McCook

[Hymenoptera:Formicidae]

Most members of the genus *Solenopsis* are southern in distribution and are found from coast to coast. They are characterized by a fiery sting and great activity. Their nests occur usually in rather exposed areas under stones and boards and at the base of plants. Some species are mound builders which choose locations in the open. These ants readily enter homes and have a wide range of feeding activity. They are aggressive, often attacking poultry, small animals, babies, as well as both soiled and clean fabrics. They not only attend honeydew excreting insects, but commonly chew insulation from telephone wires, steal seeds, and attack plants and fruit. The exception to the rule in this genus is the smallest of our common ants, the thief ant, which does not sting but enters kitchens where it is attracted in large numbers to grease and sweets alike.

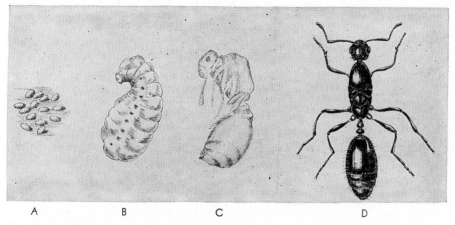

A   B   C   D

Fig. 17:16. Life stages of an ant. A, eggs; B, larva; C, pupa; and D, adult. *Courtesy Purdue University.*

Description. Ants of this group are yellowish to reddish-brown, range in size from $\frac{1}{16}$ in. (thief ant) to $\frac{3}{16}$ in., and bear only two segments in their antennal clubs (Fig. 17:15).

Life history. Most members of *Solenopsis* are prolific, with queens laying up to a thousand eggs a day in warm weather. Development to adults takes 1.5 to 2 months.

Ant control

Adequate control of ants is obtained only when the species and its habits are taken fully into consideration. In general, preventive methods are limited to good household sanitation and, where wood infesting forms are concerned, to keeping fire wood outdoors. Where the species of ant is a ground nesting form and is not apt to maintain colonies in houses or other structures, the use of insecticide banding is advocated. This method is accomplished by treating the soil surface to a width of 2 ft. around a house with a suitable insecticide. This may be done by liberally spraying either 0.5 per cent chlordane emulsion or 0.1 per cent dieldrin emulsion on the soil surface and base of the foundation, or by sprinkling wettable powder of either of these two insecticides on the soil surface and thoroughly watering.

For indoor corrective treatment, solutions or emulsions of 2 per cent chlordane or 0.5 per cent dieldrin are highly effective when applied properly. Satisfactory results depend on finding all of the sources of infestation, noting carefully the trails of activity, and applying adequate insecticide to assure a prolonged exposure of the individual workers to it. When nesting occurs in the house, destruction of the colony is desirable, otherwise workers will continue to appear in various new locations. When the nests occur outdoors, the materials recommended above for preventive application are effective as are also 5 per cent chlordane dust and 1 per cent dieldrin dust.

Many proprietary baits are available for ant control. Some are liquid, others are solid; some contain sweets, some contain greasy substances. Most of these materials bear labels explaining against which species of ants they are most effective. The toxic ingredient is usually thallium sulfate or sodium arsenite. These are acute poisons and must be placed in localities inaccessible to pets and children. Baits are seldom the single answer to control, but often they are useful adjuncts to the other methods recommended.

Eastern subterranean termite *Reticulitermes flavipes* (Kollar)

Western subterranean termite *Reticulitermes hesperus* Banks

Arid land subterranean termite *Reticulitermes tibialis* Banks

[Isoptera:Rhinotermitidae]

Inhabiting every state except Alaska, the subterranean termites of the genus *Reticulitermes* are the most destructive termites in this country (Fig. 17:17). Because they are cryptobiotic in nature and confine their destructive efforts to the inside of wood, they are seldom seen in the worker form. Swarms of termites are a familiar sight, however, and serve as indicators of the fact that an active colony exists nearby. The act of "swarming" occurs commonly in the early months of the year. It is characterized by the presence of black insects, ⅕ in. long, with four opaque, white wings twice that length. These swarmers, which are primary reproductive forms, represent one of the perpetuating forces of a termite colony. In this stage, the insects are positively phototactic and are seen around windows or outside at the base of walls. Swarming in itself does not mean that a building is necessarily infested, it simply indicates that a termite colony is somewhere in the vicinity. The active colony of feeding termites is quite unlike the swarmers in appearance, as it is composed of small, white, wingless, but very active crawling insects (Fig. 17:18). Only the latter form is destructive.

Damage occurs to almost anything containing cellulose, including rolls and piles of paper, the bindings of rugs, cotton cloth, books, adobe wall material containing straw binding, dead roots in the ground, and of course, timbers found in buildings. Termites will attack most woods, oak being as susceptible as pine; least apt to be attacked are teak, foundation grade redwood, and juniper. In addition considerable incidental damage is caused to noncellulose products through which termites may chew in search of food and shelter. One of the best examples is the penetration of underground, rubber-insulated cables, an intrusion which results in serious damage. Termites are capable of handling cellulose as part of their diet due to

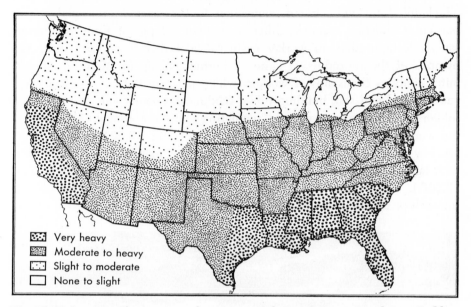

Fig. 17:17. Intensity of termite attack in continental United States. Based on a Building Research Advisory Report.

the presence in their gut of protozoa and other microorganisms which reduce cellulose to digestible carbohydrates. In addition, a balance of other nutrients is necessary and these in part are supplied by the microflora present in the wood and soil.

In the case of the subterranean form of termite, moisture is an essential part of the environment. These insects also avoid light, a behavior associated with avoidance of dehydrating air rather than light itself. Humidity conditions are maintained by occupying moist soil and traveling to food sources through protected passage such as the earthen tubes which termites so skillfully construct (Fig. 17:19). If one were to break the connection with a moisture supply, then the first step toward destroying the colony would be effected.

In northern climates, a great deal of colony movement occurs as the temperature changes. Winters are spent below the frost line unless the termites have access to a heated building. In warm weather the insects move nearer the ground surface and in some instances can be located entirely within the wood of a building.

Description. Termites are characterized by colonial existence and the caste system. In the subterranean termites of the genus *Reticulitermes* there are three forms: workers, soldiers, and reproductives. Drywood termites, which inhabit wood without connection to the ground or availability of particular moisture supplies, differ in caste development from the subterranean form in that no worker caste exists. Labor is performed by the nymphs of the reproductive caste. A normal colony of subterranean termites contains thousands of workers which perform the functions of excavating wood and soil, building tubes, feeding the young and more helpless soldiers and reproductives, and regulating the environment. Members of the worker caste are small and creamy white (Fig. 17:20A). The soldiers are few in number, about ¼ in. long, and are morphologically modified with large, dark, muscle-encased heads bearing sabre-like mandibles (Fig. 17:20B). Their function is to protect the colony from attack by placing themselves at airholes and other points of entry into the interior of the

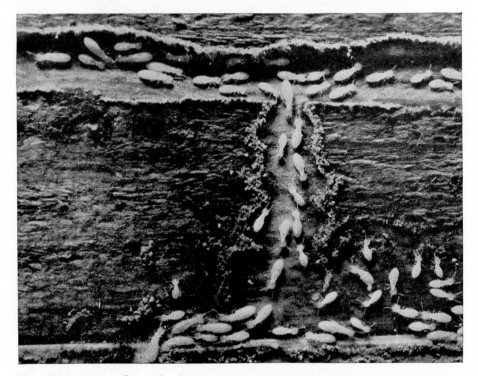

Fig. 17:18. Active colony of subterranean termites. A few slightly larger reproductive forms can be seen among the workers. *Courtesy Purdue University.*

galleries. The reproductives usually consist of more than one form. The primary (macropterous) form has been described above as the form which swarms (Fig. 17:21). The sole function of the primary reproductive is to establish new colonies, a feat seldom accomplished due to the hazards of life and general vulnerability of this form. At the end of swarming, the wings are shed and the dealated insects seek mates and a suitable wood niche for initiation of the colony. Natural enemies and unsuitable environment usually preclude success. The secondary (brachypterous) forms are the backbone of the reproductive strength of a colony. Often several hundred males and females are present, the females producing a few eggs per day, and sometimes moving individually to other areas together with a few workers to develop secondary colonies beneath the ground or in wood. Tertiary (apterous) forms are sometimes present; their importance as reproductives seems to be minor. Colony size of the subterranean form may be as few as a dozen or as many as one hundred thousand.

Life history. Close relatives of the termites are the cockroaches, and like the latter, development from egg to adult is by gradual metamorphosis. The eggs are tiny, white, and kidney-shaped. The nymphs, resembling miniature adults, look alike during the first two instars. Following this early development, they can be separated into the large headed, early stages of the sterile forms (leading to workers and soldiers), and the small headed reproductives. Workers and soldiers take one year for development; primary reproductives require two years. All stages of development can usually be found in a colony whether it is located in wood or in the ground. Once established, colonies exhibit strength due to individual longevity, cryptobiotic habits, continuous reproductive capacity, ceaseless industry, highly sensitive responses, and unusual adaptability.

Control. Because of the unusual ability of subterranean termites to enter homes and other structures and because control has to be complete to be effective, termite control has evolved into an applied science with definite standards. Basically, it involves separating or insulating the colony in the ground from its sources of food in a structure. There are four basic steps to control. These are modified only insofar as particular infestations and circumstance may require. The steps are: removal of wood debris and mechanical alteration; soil treating; foundation treating; wood treating.

Before one undertakes control, several questions should be considered. Must the building be treated? It should be treated if active infestations are present or if an owner wants the premise protected against future attack. Must it be treated immediately? Seldom is immediate treatment necessary; there is always time to investigate the situation thoroughly as to need and the particular pest control operator desired. Must the whole foundation area be treated? It is generally desirable to have a complete treatment if a chance exists for termite reentry in various new places. If partial treatments are to be satisfactory, they usually should include all four steps of control. Can termite control be undertaken by the average homeowner? Treatment of buildings by individuals is seldom successful due to the complexity of most situations. Professional help is usually advisable.

The first step in control corresponds to cultural control in agricultural entomology. Since there is a close relationship between the incidence of termite infestation and an optimum moisture content of the soil, drainage and proper water disposal are important. Closely related to this is the improvement of ventilation beneath structures. Improvement of such conditions through installation of foundation ventilators will decrease humidity and dry both the wood and soil. Vapor barriers on the soil surface beneath buildings are also helpful. All miscellaneous wood should be removed from areas near the building. Mechanical alterations include measures which may be as extensive as raising the house on its foundation or simply breaking soil contact of wooden posts erected through a concrete basement floor.

Fig. 17:19. Earthen tubes of subterranean termites in semi-excavated area beneath house. *Courtesy R. R. Heaton.*

Fig. 17:20. Eastern subterranean termite. A, worker; B, soldier. *Courtesy Purdue University.*

Fig. 17:21. Eastern subterranean termite. Adult winged primary reproductive termite, characteristic of the form which swarms. Black body, no abdominal constriction, and wings of equal length are characters of identification. *Courtesy Purdue University.*

Suitable chemicals for termite control include emulsions of chlordane at 1 per cent, dieldrin at 0.5 per cent, aldrin at 0.5 per cent, and heptachlor at 0.5 per cent. Sodium arsenite, formerly extensively used at 10 per cent, is good but limited in soil application to areas where no vegetation occurs. Pentachlorophenol at 5 per cent is excellent for wood treatment since it deters decay; it is seldom used in the soil because of the preference for the cyclodienes.

Soil treatments for eradication or as a protective barrier must be thoroughly applied. Around foundations, the normal procedure is to trench the soil and flood or rod-inject the formulation into the soil. The rate for shallow foundations is 2 gal. per lineal 5 feet; for deep foundations, 4 gal. per lineal 5 feet. Beneath slab porches, and slab floors which should be excavated or drilled, the rate is a minimum of 1 gal. per 10 square feet. Special equipment is needed for subslab treatments and for drilling and treating block wall voids.

The general practice is to drill infested wood and treat with a protective chemical. Pentachlorophenol is especially useful for this purpose. It is often good practice to drill and pressure treat unexposed ends of joints and wood supports.

There are no short-cuts to subterranean termite control. Each step is a part of the complete procedure, and must be done thoroughly.

Pretreatment of buildings. The best time to assure protection of a building from termite attack is at the time of construction. Several methods are feasible. One is the use of metal shields or barriers installed on the top of the foundations. These shields are only as good as the quality of installation; unfortunately this is seldom satisfactory, providing only a false sense of security. Another deterrent is the use of pressure treated wood (impregnated with a preserving chemical such as pentachlorophenol or copper naphthenate) in critical areas such as the plates and joists. This procedure is helpful and should be encouraged, but it cannot be expected to be a protection against attack elsewhere in the building. Soil treatment with a pro-

Fig. 17:22. Method of treating soil and fill with insecticide during new home construction for prevention of subterranean termite damage. *Courtesy Purdue University.*

tective insecticide expected to last for at least five years is the method of choice. The method consists of treating the soil just before pouring concrete slabs, and of thoroughly treating the soil completely around the outside of foundations (Fig. 17:22). The insecticides and the rates of application are those given under the corrective procedures discussed above.

Selected References

Anon., *Clothes Moths and Carpet Beetles. How to Combat Them,* USDA Home and Garden Bull. 24, 1953.

Anon., *Insect Control for Motels, Resorts, and Cottages,* Mich. State Univ. Cir. R-203, 1958.

Gould, G. E., and H. O. Deay, *The Biology of Six Species of Cockroaches which Inhabit Buildings,* Purdue University, AES Bul. 451, 1940.

Mallis, Arnold, *Handbook of Pest Control* (MacNair-Dorland, 3rd ed., 1960).

Osmun, J. V., "Recognition of Insect Damage," reprinted from *Pest Control,* 23:1, 4, 7, 10 (1955).

Snyder, T. E., *Our Enemy the Termite* (Comstock, 1948).

St. George, R. A., H. R. Johnston, and R. J. Kowal, *Subterranean Termites, their Prevention and Control in Buildings,* USDA Home Bull. 64, 1960.

Wheeler, W. M., *Ants, their Structure, Development, and Behavior* (New York: Columbia Univ. Press, 1926).

Chapter 18 | LIVESTOCK INSECTS AND RELATED PESTS | *Robert E. Pfadt*

Livestock—cattle, swine, sheep, and horses—are harassed, weakened, and sometimes killed by the assault of many different kinds of arthropod parasites. The attack is maintained the year round, some pests such as lice and mites are worse during the winter while other pests such as various flies and mosquitoes are injurious during the summer.

The pests

Just as among the crop insects we have studied, livestock pests include monophagous members, those which attack only a single class of host, and polyphagous members, or general pests, those which attack not only all kinds of domestic stock but wild animals as well. The flies, members of the order Diptera, contribute the greatest number of species to the group of general pests. Included are the cosmopolitan **house fly** and **stable fly** (Fig. 18:1) and the introduced **horn fly** (Fig. 18:15). Native species that attack livestock are many kinds of **mosquitoes, black flies** (Fig. 20:2), **horse flies** (Fig. 18:2), several **blow flies,** and the **screw-worm** (Fig. 18:16). A recently introduced cattle pest, the **face fly,** *Musca autumnalis* (DeG.), is rapidly extending its range in North America. It was first taken in 1952 at Middleton, Nova Scotia.

Throughout the world a variety of ticks parasitize livestock. In North America at least seven species are important pests: the **cattle tick, lone star tick, Gulf Coast tick, black-legged tick, winter tick** (Fig 18:20), **Rocky Mountain wood tick,** and **ear tick** (Fig. 18:3). None of these has a general distribution over the whole of North America, but all inhabit large sections of the continent. The cattle tick, which once infested 15 southern states, has been eradicated from this area by an organized program of cattle dipping and quarantine. It is, however, still present in Mexico.

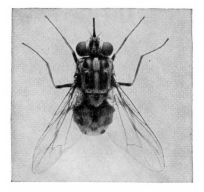

Fig 18:1. Adult female of the stable fly, *Stomoxys calcitrans* (L.), a cosmopolitan species of bloodsucking fly. *Courtesy USDA.*

Fig. 18:2. The black horse fly, *Tabanus atratus* F., a native injurious livestock pest. *Courtesy USDA.*

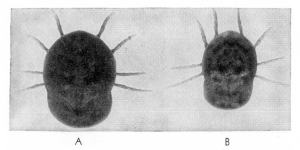

A   B

Fig. 18:3. The ear tick, *Otobius megnini* (Dugés). A, female; B, male. Indigenous to the Southwest but now more widely distributed. *Courtesy USDA.*

Among the more serious and widespread pests are those that attack specific classes of livestock. These parasites, of foreign origin, came to America along with their hosts and because of their importance, we have listed them at length in Table 19:1.

The injury

Livestock are sensitive to the attacks of insect pests and react by general unthriftiness, stunted growth, and sometimes death. The constant annoyance and irritation of biting flies make livestock restless and induce them to bunch up during the day when ordinarily they would be grazing. Pests such as the horn fly, lice, and ticks withdraw large amounts of blood, producing anemia in their hosts (Fig. 18:5). In attempting to lay eggs female heel flies (adults of cattle grubs) and horse bot flies cause stock to flee in terror and whole herds to stampede. Cattle grubs migrate in body tissues, make holes in the skin of the back, and spoil meat underlying the cysts in which they live.

Table 18:1 | Insect and Mite Parasites of Livestock in America

Cattle

Lice	cattle biting louse, *Bovicola bovis* (Linnaeus) (Fig. 18:10D)
	little blue cattle louse, *Solenopotes capillatus* Enderlein (Fig. 18:10C)
	long-nosed cattle louse, *Linognathus vituli* (Linnaeus) (Fig. 18:10B)
	short-nosed cattle louse, *Haematopinus eurysternus* (Nitzsch) (Fig. 18:10A)
	cattle tail louse, *Haematopinus quadripertusus* Fahrenholz
Grubs	common cattle grub, *Hypoderma lineatum* (de Villers) (Fig. 18:14)
	northern cattle grub, *Hypoderma bovis* (Linnaeus)
Mites	chorioptic mange mite, *Chorioptes bovis* (Hering)
	scab mite, *Psoroptes ovis* (Hering) (Fig. 4:6B)
	itch mite, *Sarcoptes scabiei* (De Geer)
	cattle follicle mite, *Demodex bovis* Stiles

Swine

Lice	hog louse, *Haematopinus suis* (Linnaeus) (Fig. 18:21)
Mites	itch mite, *Sarcoptes scabiei* (De Geer) (Fig. 18:23)
	hog follicle mite, *Demodex phylloides* Csokor

Sheep

Lice	sheep biting louse, *Bovicola ovis* (Linnaeus)
	African sheep louse, *Linognathus africanus* Kellog & Paine
	sheep foot louse, *Linognathus pedalis* (Osborn)
	goat sucking louse, *Linognathus stenopsis* (Burmeister)
Ked	sheep ked, *Melophagus ovinus* (Linnaeus) (Fig. 18:17)
Bot	sheep bot fly, *Oestrus ovis* (Linnaeus) (Fig. 4:27D)
Mites	scab mite, *Psoroptes ovis* (Hering) (Fig. 4:6B)
	chorioptic mange mite, *Chorioptes bovis* (Hering)
	itch mite, *Sarcoptes scabiei* (De Geer)
	sheep itch mite, *Psorergates ovis* Womersley
	sheep follicle mite, *Demodex ovis* Railliet

Horse

Lice	horse biting louse, *Bovicola equi* (Linnaeus)
	horse sucking louse, *Haematopinus asini* (Linnaeus)
Bots	horse bot fly, *Gasterophilus intestinalis* (De Geer) (Fig. 18:4)
	nose bot fly, *Gasterophilus haemorrhoidalis* (Linnaeus)
	throat bot fly, *Gasterophilus nasalis* (Linnaeus)
Mites	scab mite, *Psoroptes ovis* (Hering)
	chorioptic mange mite, *Chorioptes bovis* (Hering)
	itch mite, *Sarcoptes scabiei* (De Geer)
	horse follicle mite, *Demodex equi* Railliet

Screw-worms infest wounds and feed on living tissues, often causing the death of untreated animals (Fig. 18:6). Parasitic mites cause contagious skin diseases known as mange or scab in which the hair coat is lost and the skin becomes thickened, wrinkled, and covered with gray or yellow scabs.

Transmission of livestock diseases by insects results in untold losses to livestock growers. Certain flies such as horse flies, stable flies, blow flies, and house flies transmit the bacilli of anthrax, infectious keratitis, mastitis, and "swollen joints." Hog lice may carry swine pox and possibly other infectious diseases of swine. Tick paralysis is caused by the feeding and injection of toxins into the blood stream of the host by the Rocky Mountain wood tick and several other ticks. Ticks transmit the protozoans which live in the red blood cells of stock causing anaplasmosis or piroplasmosis.

Cattle tick fever or bovine piroplasmosis is a serious and often fatal disease in which the red blood cells are destroyed by a protozoan known as *Babesia bigemina* (Smith & Kilbourne). In the southern states the organisms were found to be transmitted solely by the cattle tick, *Boophilus annulatus* (Say). This discovery by Theobald Smith and Fred L. Kilbourne in 1889 marked an epoch in medicine, as it led not only to eradication of cattle tick fever from the United States by eliminating the tick through systematic dipping, but also firmly established the idea that certain other livestock diseases as well as certain human diseases like malaria, yellow fever, and typhus are transmitted by insects.

Another important way in which insects cause injury to livestock is by serving as intermediate hosts for parasitic worms. The gullet worm, *Gongylonema pulchrum* Molin, of cattle, sheep, swine, and wild ruminants requires certain dung beetles and cockroaches for the intermediate stage. Livestock become infested by swallowing the beetles. Dung beetles also serve as intermediate hosts of three species of stomach worms of swine; white grubs serve as the intermediate host of the thorn-headed worm of swine. The broad tapeworms, *Moniezia expansa* (Rudolphi) and *M. benedeni* (Moniez), which infest sheep, cattle, and several other ruminants, require oribatid mites for intermediate hosts.

Control through management

The initial defense against insects is always the elimination of breeding sources wherever possible and avoidance of conditions that predispose animals to attack. Many of the flies that torment livestock develop in accumulations of manure, wet straw, spilled feeds, carrion, and in drainage water. Hence, a program of farm sanitation can stop much needless fly propagation. Proper disposal or treatment of manure is essential to prevent

Fig. 18:4. The horse bot fly, *Gasterophilus intestinalis* (De G.), primarily a parasite of horses, mules, and donkeys. *Courtesy USDA.*

house flies from becoming so abundant that insecticidal applications are rendered impotent. Stockmen should take care in disposing of wet straw, since it is a major source of stable fly development. In stacking straw it is advisable to select a high, dry location.

Spilled feeds that become soaked with water serve as ideal breeding sites for both house flies and stable flies. By carefully handling feeds, not only is the propagation of noxious flies prevented but also wastage. If feeds are accidentally spilled, sweep them up and return them to bins. Dispose of spilled feeds that have become wet or scatter them thinly on the ground to dry out. Because dead animals are not only potential sources of disease but also breeding sites for blow flies, haul away carcasses to reducing plants or bury them deeply or burn them completely. Drain or fill low places where water collects and mosquitoes and horse flies breed.

Providing deep dark sheds so stock can retreat from the attack of flies during the height of fly activity is of much value. Groves of trees in pastures can likewise serve as retreats.

To protect livestock from injury by screw-worms and blow flies, a program of scheduling births before the fly season starts and of wound prevention and treatment during the fly season is advisable. Stockmen can prevent many accidental cuts and wounds by eliminating excessive amounts of barbed wire and by removing projecting nails and jagged boards from fences, corrals, and buildings.

Raising smooth, open-faced breeds of sheep aids in controlling insects, particularly wool maggots and screw-worms. Because wrinkled sheep are difficult to shear, they receive more skin cuts attractive to blow flies. Blow flies are also attracted by the feces and urine caught in the wrinkles of the breech. In Australia where the problem of wool maggots is grave, the Mules operation, named after its discoverer Mr. J. W. H. Mules, is usually performed on ewe lambs. The operation consists of removing loose skin from each buttock with hand shears. Upon healing of the wound the skin stretches from the vulva drawing the wool away from the midline and from the path of urine and dung.

Fig. 18:5. A heavily louse-infested cow. Note the languor and the dark, dirty hair coat on normally white areas of the Hereford. This animal died one night of anemia due to gross infestation by the short-nosed cattle louse. *Courtesy USDA.*

Keeping stock in good condition through adequate nutrition makes them less susceptible to some pests and appears to hold populations of mites, lice, and sheep keds at low levels. Of great importance in preventing the spread of parasites and disease is the temporary isolation and treatment of all new animals before introducing them into the herd.

Chemical control

In spite of good management practices and preventive measures, parasites often establish themselves on livestock and cause injury. We then should consider treatment with insecticides. The use of chemicals on livestock is complicated by restrictions imposed on growers because of the residues that accumulate in fat and milk when animals are treated. Yet many insecticides are available to stockmen for protecting their animals if precautions are taken. Greatest limitations occur on dairy animals since zero tolerances of insecticidal residues have been established for milk.

The insecticides recommended for livestock belong to several chemical groups. Chlorinated hydrocarbons such as DDT, lindane, methoxychlor, and toxaphene are widely used to control lice, various flies, keds, mites, and ticks. Recently some of the less toxic phosphate insecticides, such as ronnel and Co-Ral, have proved effective in controlling cattle grubs and screw-worms, livestock pests that were formerly difficult to control. Malathion and Delnav are also recommended for the control of several pests of stock.

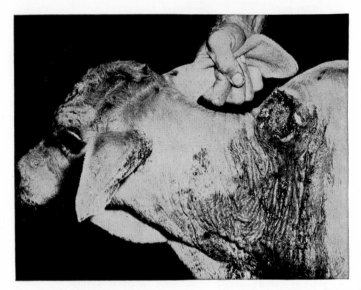

Fig. 18:6. A wound infested with screw-worms. The larvae feed on living flesh and may eventually kill the host. *Courtesy USDA.*

Among the botanical insecticides rotenone and pyrethrum are still used in considerable amounts, particularly on dairy animals. Several other chemicals are also applied directly to livestock including allethrin, organic thiocyanates as lethane and thanite, synergists as piperonyl butoxide and MGK 264, and repellents as butoxy polypropylene glycol.

Control equipment

Stockmen apply insecticides to their animals in the form of dips, sprays, washes, dusts, ointments, and boluses. The most common methods are dipping and spraying. To dip cattle or sheep, growers employ permanent concrete vats which vary in length from 30 to 100 feet. The stock enter at one end of the vat, swim through an insecticidal bath, and leave at the opposite end. Dipping requires a fairly large crew of men to force the animals into the dip and to attend them as they swim through. Men with dipping forks along each side of the vat dunk the heads of animals and prevent accidents (Fig. 18:7). Also available for dipping are portable steel or wooden vats 10 to 20 feet long. Dipping is a thorough and rapid method of treating animals with insecticides.

Because of their mobility and adaptability sprayers are widely employed to treat animals with insecticides. Confining animals in crowd-pens or chutes, growers apply sprays with spray guns at pressures varying from lows of 50 to 75 lb. p.s.i. to highs of 300 to 400 lb. (Fig. 18:8). A special spraying device for livestock is the so-called spray-dip or box-spray machine into which cattle are driven one at a time and held until completely soaked. The spray-dip machine is an effective though somewhat expensive and sometimes troublesome piece of equipment.

Fig. 18:7. Dipping cattle in an acaricidal bath to control mange. *Courtesy the Denver Post.*

Stockmen apply dusts by hand, by hand dusters, or by power dusters. The power dusting of sheep to control keds has gained favor among owners of large range flocks. If done after shearing it is effective, rapid, and less hazardous than dipping or spraying because there is no wetting of the animals and no rough handling.

Washes and ointments are convenient for treating animals infected with screw-worms or other blow fly maggots.

A self applicating device, the back-rubber, has become quite popular among cattle growers for fly control. Several designs are available but all are based on the principle that cattle like to rub themselves against posts and other objects. Burlap or canvas is wrapped around barbed wire or chains strung between deeply set posts and saturated with insecticide. When cattle rub against the treated materials, small amounts of the insecticide adhere to the hair and skin (Fig. 18:9).

Other self-applicating devices used to control flies on cattle, particularly dairy cattle, are the treadle sprayer, the lever sprayer, and the automatic photoelectric sprayer. These devices, placed at barn exists or at gates, dispense small amounts of concentrated spray when they are actuated by the passage of an animal.

Fig. 18:8. Spraying cattle with a systemic insecticide for the control of cattle grubs and lice. *Courtesy University of Wyoming.*

Stockmen may control certain pests of livestock such as the house fly and stable fly by applying residual sprays to buildings, fences, and other resting sites.

Precautions

Because spraying or dipping excites livestock causing them to mill about, one should make corrals and chutes safe by eliminating protruding nails and boards and by picking up hazardous objects lying on the ground. One can also prevent serious injuries by handling animals as gently as possible, never driving them with clubs or metal bars. Dairy cows are less frightened if they are treated while stanchioned. Since horses are sensitive to the hissing of sprayers and are particularly skittish about treatment, the most successful method is to use a low pressure, almost noiseless compressed air sprayer adjusted to dispense a coarse spray.

Even though animals are reasonably tolerant to wetting during cold weather, it is advisable to select a day that is warm and sunshiny for spraying or dipping. When nights are cold, stop control operations early enough to allow animals to dry off before sunset. Keep swine out of sunlight until

Fig. 18:9. A self-applicating device, the back-rubber, for controlling flies on cattle. *Courtesy South Dakota State College.*

they are completely dry to prevent skin blistering. Though there is usually no hazard to the health of livestock in applying recommended dosages of insecticide, very young animals (up to three months old) may be susceptible to some chemicals. Read the precaution statement on label before treating.

Avoid contamination of milking utensils, water tanks, feed troughs, feeds, and vegetation when applying insecticides to livestock or around the barn.

In disposing of excess spray or dip do not allow the formation of pools from which animals may drink toxic doses or allow runoff into streams.

REPRESENTATIVE LIVESTOCK PESTS

For our detailed study of livestock pests we have chosen cattle lice, cattle grubs, the horn fly, the screw-worm, the sheep ked, the winter tick, and the hog itch mite.

Cattle lice

Short-nosed cattle louse *Haematopinus eurysternus* (Nitzsch) [Anoplura:-Haematopinidae]

Long-nosed cattle louse *Linognathus vituli* (Linnaeus) [Anoplura:Haematopinidae]

Little blue cattle louse *Solenopotes capillatus* Enderlein [Anoplura:Haematopinidae]

Cattle tail louse *Haematopinus quadripertusus* Fahrenholz [Anoplura:-Haematopinidae]

Cattle biting louse *Bovicola bovis* (Linnaeus) [Mallophaga:Trichodectidae]

Lice are important pests of cattle in all parts of the world. In North America four species of sucking lice and one biting louse do considerable damage chiefly during winter and spring. As cattle lice have preferences for particular breeds and ages of cattle, rarely do all four kinds coexist on one animal. The long-nosed cattle louse more often parasitizes dairy breeds, especially young animals. The short-nosed cattle louse more commonly infests mature animals of the beef breeds. The cattle biting louse occurs on animals of all ages, but is more frequent on dairy than on beef cattle. The little blue cattle louse appears to have no special preferences as it infests young and old alike of all breeds.

Intense irritation set up by lice causes cattle to rub and scratch. Among grossly infested animals large areas of skin become raw, bruised, and denuded of hair due to constant rubbing against posts and fences. Because of the irritation, accompanying nervousness, and loss of blood, cattle neither thrive nor gain weight normally. Although the exact effects on milk production are still unknown, observation indicates that heavy lice infestations cause substantial decreases in yields.

When sucking lice become numerous, anemia may develop. Heavy infestations of the short-nosed cattle louse have been found to reduce the red blood cells to one-fourth the normal number and to bring about the death of infested animals. Cattle biting lice cause a skin reaction which results in loosening and falling out of hair. They also produce lesions resembling those of scab or mange. Underneath the scabs colonies of lice live on the raw skin. As yet cattle lice have not been incriminated as vectors of disease.

Description. Cattle lice are small wingless insects which as adults (Fig. 18:10) range in size from about 2 mm. long, the size of the little blue cattle louse and the cattle biting louse, to 3.5 mm. long, the size of the short-nosed cattle louse. The cattle tail louse may reach a length of 4.5 mm. Except for smaller size the nymphs look much like the adults. The species can be distinguished from each other by the shape of their heads and by color. The biting louse is reddish brown; the abdomen of the short-nosed louse and tail louse is gray-brown and that of the little blue louse and the

A   B   C   D

Fig. 18:10. Four common species of cattle lice. A, short-nosed cattle louse; B, long-nosed cattle louse; C, little blue cattle louse; D, cattle biting louse. *Courtesy Cornell University.*

long-nosed louse dark blue. Eggs of the short-nosed louse are opaque white to brown and 1 mm. long; eggs of the long-nosed louse are dark blue and 0.95 mm. long; eggs of the little blue louse are dark blue and 0.76 mm. long; and eggs of the cattle biting louse are translucent, colorless to light brown, and 0.64 mm. long. The eggs are also distinguishable by their shape and by the way they are attached to the hairs (Fig. 18:11). Eggs of the cattle tail louse are 0.76 mm. long and are found mainly on the hairs of the tail brush.

Life history. The life histories of cattle lice are in general similar, those of the short-nosed louse and the cattle biting louse being best known. All cattle lice are obligate parasites, that is they must remain on their hosts to survive. If eggs or lice fall off with shedding hair, they survive only a few days. Cattle lice are never found on other animals, and lice from other animals do not live on cattle.

Female lice glue their eggs close to the skin on hairs. Sometimes a single hair will bear two, three, or more eggs. The short-nosed cattle louse, cattle tail louse, and the cattle biting louse have preferred oviposition areas where females congregate and lay clusters of eggs. Summaries of the life cycle of three species are set forth below:

Period	Long-Nosed Cattle Louse Average Days	Short-Nosed Cattle Louse Average Days	Cattle Biting Louse Average Days
Incubation	8	12	8
1st nymphal instar	7	4	7
2nd nymphal instar	4	4	5.5
3rd nymphal instar	4	4	6
Preoviposition	2	4	3
Egg to adult	25	24	29.5

Adult males of the short-nosed cattle louse live up to ten days while adult females live up to 16 days. During their lifetime females lay 30 to 35 eggs each, depositing two to three a day. To obtain food sucking lice pierce the skin and suck blood, whereas biting lice scrape material off the surface of the skin and from the base of hairs. Striking features of cattle biting louse biology are the scarcity of males and parthenogenesis as the normal method of reproduction. The cattle tail louse, as the name implies, prefers to inhabit the long hair region of the tail, yet they also may infest the regions around the eyes, the neck, and other areas of the body.

Lice populations fluctuate with the seasons. They are lowest in summer, begin building up in fall, and reach their peak in winter and early spring. These variations have been found to be related mainly with temperature. In summer it becomes too hot in the hair coat for lice to stay in favored regions of the host and to maintain normal reproduction. During the hot months many animals probably become entirely free of lice, while a few highly louse-susceptible animals called **carriers** perpetuate the infestation. The cattle tail louse is an exception, for it reaches greatest abundance in late summer and early fall and is scarce in winter.

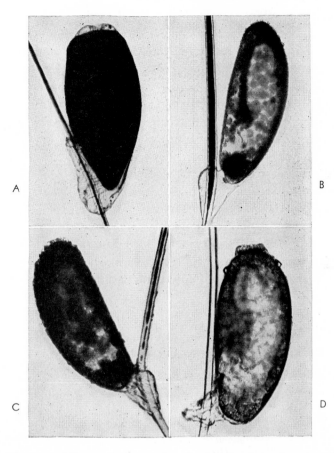

Fig. 18:11. The eggs of four common species of cattle lice (greatly enlarged). A, short-nosed cattle louse egg; B, long-nosed cattle louse egg; C, little blue cattle louse egg. Note the characteristic bend of the hair at the point of attachment; D, cattle biting louse egg. *Courtesy Cornell University.*

Control. Since nearly all herds develop infestations of lice, it is best to treat routinely in fall of the year before the onset of cold weather. Treatment at this time prevents heavy winter infestations. Stock growers usually either dip or spray cattle, but if numbers are small one may conveniently apply washes or dusts.

For control of lice on dairy cattle, only the application of rotenone or pyrethrins plus synergists (piperonyl butoxide or MGK 264) is permissible. Rotenone is used as a spray (1 to 2 lb. of 5 per cent rotenone powder in 100 gal. of water) or as a 0.5 to 1 per cent dust. Pyrethrins plus synergists are used as sprays at concentrations of 0.025 per cent and 0.25 per cent, respectively.

Several of the synthetic insecticides as well as the above materials may be applied to beef cattle. Recommended sprays include 0.03 per cent lindane, and 0.5 per cent ronnel, methoxychlor, toxaphene, malathion, or Co-Ral; recommended dips 0.5 per cent toxaphene or 1 to 2 lb. of 5 per cent rotenone powder per 100 gal. of water; a recommended dust is 10 per cent methoxychlor. Treatment with Co-Ral has the additional advantage in that it controls cattle grubs systemically. Recently Delnav at 0.15 per cent has been recommended for lice control as either a spray or dip and Co-Ral at 0.125 to 0.25 per cent as a dip.

Two treatments at a two- to three-week interval are generally needed to control infestations satisfactorily in the North; in the South one treatment with a residual insecticide usually suffices.

The cattle tail louse, prevalent in the southern states, is more difficult to control than other species of cattle lice. To do a satisfactory job, increase the insecticide concentration of sprays suggested above two or three times and apply this concentration only to the infested tail. Treat other areas with normal strengths.

Cattle grubs

Common cattle grub *Hypoderma lineatum* (de Villers)

Northern cattle grub *Hypoderma bovis* (Linnaeus)

[Diptera:Hypodermatidae]

Cattle grubs and their adult stage, heel flies, are among the most destructive insects attacking cattle. They are distributed principally in the northern hemisphere where they occur in North America, Europe, northern Africa, and Asia. In North America the common cattle grub is found in Canada, the United States, and in parts of Mexico. The northern cattle grub is somewhat less widely distributed, being found in Canada and in all the United States but the ten most southern states.

Unlike most flies attacking cattle, grubs cause injury not only in the fly or adult stage, but also in the grub or larval stage. For several months the larvae migrate through the body damaging tissues, until they eventually reach the back where they perforate the skin (Fig. 18:12). In this location they are enclosed in cysts which are often invaded by bacteria that produce pockets of pus. Heavily infested range animals are weakened. According to some studies, infested feed lot cattle do not realize their full potential of weight gain. A test with dairy cattle indicated that the presence of numerous grubs reduces milk flow.

When infested cattle are slaughtered, packers incur direct losses since grubs spoil the best part of both carcasses and hides. Because yellowish gelatinous areas develop in the meat near grub cysts, carcasses must be trimmed lowering not only weight but value. Hides with five or more grub holes are discounted one cent a pound.

Fig. 18:12. Hereford showing the position (bumps) of nearly full-grown cattle grubs in the back. *Courtesy University of Wyoming.*

Probably the greatest loss to the livestock grower and to the milk producer results from the attack of the adult flies. The females, in laying their eggs on cattle induce an uncontrollable fear which causes the animals to run wildly with tails high in the air seeking shelter in water holes or in the shade of sheds or trees (Fig. 18:13). During the months that heel flies are active, cattle graze less and consequently fail to put on flesh normally and to produce as much milk. The annual loss due to cattle grubs in the United States has been estimated at about 100 million dollars and some estimates place the loss as high as 300 million. The discrepancy in estimates points out the fact that much is yet to be learned about cattle grub injury and losses.

Description. The eggs of both species are elongate, pale yellow, and have a smooth and shining surface. They are 0.7 to 0.8 mm. long. The eggs of the common heel fly are laid in rows on the hair of cattle, while the eggs of the northern fly are laid singly. There are three larval instars. Young larvae are dull white and 0.5 to 0.7 mm. long. The last larval instar changes color with age, first becoming yellow, then brown, and finally black. It reaches a length of around ¾ to 1 in. In this instar the larvae of the two species are easily separated by the shape of the posterior stigmal plates. Those of the common grub are somewhat flat, while those of the northern grub are funnel shaped. The puparium is black and around ¾ in. long. The shape of the stigmal plates remain the same allowing identifica-

Fig. 18:13. Cattle running from heel flies. Note characteristic way of holding tails high. *Courtesy University of Wyoming.*

tion of the pupae. The adult flies are hairy, beelike insects measuring about ½ in. long. They are distinctively marked by transverse bands of black and yellow. The species can be distinguished by the band of hairs covering the end of the abdomen. In the common heel fly, the hairs are orange yellow and the band 3 mm. or less wide, in the northern heel fly they are lemon yellow and the band 5 mm. wide. In all stages the northern species is larger than the common (Fig. 18:14).

Life history. Although the life histories of the two species of grubs are similar, there are important differences. One significant difference is that all stages of the northern cattle grub appear from two to ten weeks later in the season than do those of the common cattle grub.

Adult flies of the common species emerge in spring. After mating the female deposits up to 500 or 600 eggs on the hairs of the legs and other lower parts of cattle. Several eggs are laid at a time one immediately above another in a straight row. When a cow lies down the common heel fly sometimes approaches so stealthily that many eggs are laid on the hairs of the udder, escutcheon, or sides without causing any disturbance.

The northern heel fly is bolder and more vicious in its attack. It deposits one egg at a time and often chases an animal about the pasture, striking it repeatedly on the thighs and rump. As heel flies neither sting nor bite, much conjecture but little study has been made on why cattle are frightened by them.

The eggs of both species hatch in four or five days and the tiny white larvae immediately crawl down the hair and bore through the skin to the connective tissue. From this point, common grubs migrate through connective tissue, chiefly to the esophagus where they remain for several months. They then resume migration until they reach their subdermal positions in the back where they produce tumerous swellings. Migrating by a different route, northern grubs accumulate in the spinal canal before reaching the back. The period from hatching to arrival in the back lasts from seven to eight months for both species.

When larvae reach the back they make holes in the skin through which they obtain air. Cysts form about the grubs but the holes are kept open. Growth of grubs occurs mainly in the cysts, as the entire migration is made by the small first instar larvae. Full development of common grubs in the back requires an average of about 55 days, while that of northern grubs an

A   B   C   D

Fig. 18:14. Life stages of the common cattle grub. A, adult or heel fly; B, eggs attached to hair; C, nearly full-grown larva; D, pupa. *A, B, D, courtesy USDA; C, courtesy Dow Chemical Company.*

average of about 70 days. Individual grubs, arriving in the backs early, spend approximately three weeks longer in the cysts than do those arriving toward the end of the season. The variations are apparently correlated with the different amounts of heat absorbed from the sun by grubs in their sub-dermal positions.

Upon attaining full growth grubs crawl from the cysts and drop to the ground where they pupate in litter. Depending on temperature the pupal period lasts from 15 to 75 days. The majority of flies emerge in spring on bright sunny mornings. As their mouthparts are nonfunctional, life is sustained and eggs nurtured from stored food acquired during the larval stage. Within an hour after emergence females may mate and start to lay eggs. The life span of individual adults is believed to be short. The complete life cycle requires about a year.

Densities of grubs in the same herd often vary widely from year to year. These variations have been found to be related to weather conditions during the pupal and adult stages.

Control. One of the most exciting developments in veterinary entomology has been the discovery that certain phosphate insecticides act systemically and are effective in controlling internal parasites. Two compounds are already recommended for control of cattle grubs and several more now being investigated look promising. One treatment with an approved systemic insecticide kills the grubs before they reach the back, thereby preventing damage to carcass and hide. This damage was not prevented by the old standard treatment with rotenone, since it could not be used effectively until after the grubs had arrived in the back and cut holes in the hide. Moreover, to achieve adequate control with rotenone, stockmen had to make from two to four spray treatments at regular intervals during winter.

The first systemic insecticide to be approved for control of cattle grubs was ronnel or Trolene. It is administered orally in bolus form (large pills) with a balling gun at a rate of one bolus (37.5 gram bolus of 40 per cent active ingredient) per 300 lb. body weight. Treatment is best made as soon as heel fly activity stops. In the United States, proper timing of treatment may range from July in the South to early November in the North. Treated cattle sometimes have reacted adversely, but symptoms usually have been mild and have ended within 24 hours. Stockmen should read and follow label directions faithfully to prevent injury to animals. Do not treat lactating dairy cattle or any cattle within 60 days of slaughter.

The second systemic insecticide to be approved was Bayer 21/199 which now bears the trade name Co-Ral. It acts systemically when applied as a spray or dip. For successful treatment each animal must be thoroughly wet to the skin over the entire body. About 1 gal. of 0.5 per cent spray is sufficient. Merely wetting the hair coat is not enough. Make treatments as soon as possible after the heel fly season is over. The recommended dip concentration is 0.25 per cent. Do not treat lactating dairy cattle, calves less than three months of age, cattle within 45 days of slaughter, or sick animals.

As cattle grub control with systemic insecticides is an active field of research, agricultural scientists will no doubt discover newer and better chemicals and simpler and easier methods of application. Entomologists are currently studying the advantages of putting ronnel in feed and in salt, of injecting dimethoate and Ruelene into the animal, and of applying Ruelene and Neguvon as "pour on's." The latter method consists simply of pouring 100 ml. (less than ½ cup) of emulsion or solution of the material from a beaker onto the back of each animal.

Because many entomologists believe that the ideal grub systemic has not yet been discovered, there is little doubt that the agricultural chemical industry will continue to investigate new materials. Not only for this reason but for reasons such as determining the effect of systemics on the health of animals and on weight gains and profit, the best methods of application, the advantages of area control, and the biology of heel flies, much research still remains to be done in the years ahead on cattle grubs.

Horn fly *Haematobia irritans* (Linnaeus) [Diptera:Muscidae]

Throughout North America one of the most abundant and persistent of cattle pests during the summer months is the horn fly. It is not uncommon for a herd of cattle to average 4,000 to 5,000 flies per animal; indeed as many as 10,000 to 20,000 may infest individual bulls. Horn flies pierce the skin and feed on the blood twice daily, each fly consuming an average of 2.5 milligrams of blood. Horn flies irritate and annoy cattle provoking them to fight back by tail switching, head throwing, licking, and kicking.

Several tests conducted in different parts of the United States and in Canada have demonstrated increased gains of 15 to 55 pounds by beef cattle accruing from horn fly control during a single season. Calves in treated herds gained as much as 75 pounds more. Tests have also indicated that milk production increases when horn flies are controlled. In the South, indirect losses occur due to screw-worms infesting wounds made by horn flies. One study in Texas showed that horn flies were responsible for 32 per cent of screw-worm infestations in cattle.

Description. The adult horn fly is a small insect approximately 4 mm. long, dark gray in color with bayonet-like piercing mouth parts. The eggs are reddish brown and about 1.2 mm. long. The white maggots develop rapidly in cattle droppings and are 10 mm. long when full grown. The puparium is barrel-shaped and dark brown (Fig. 18:15).

Life history. Horn flies appear with the first warm days in spring and are present on cattle until cold weather in fall. They cluster in large numbers on animals, particularly resting on the backs; or if the day is hot or rainy they congregate on the belly. They remain constantly with the host, female flies leaving only long enough to lay one to several eggs on freshly voided cow pats. The eggs hatch in 16 to 20 hours and the small maggots crawl down into the pat where they feed and develop. The larval stage lasts four to five days. On becoming full grown, larvae pupate either in the dung or in the soil beneath whichever offers the more favorable moisture condition. Soils containing less than 0.25 per cent of moisture or more than 14.5 per cent inhibit development of pupae. For highest survival soil holding 7 per cent moisture is optimum. After five days in the pupal stage, horn flies transform to adults and in two or three hours begin feeding

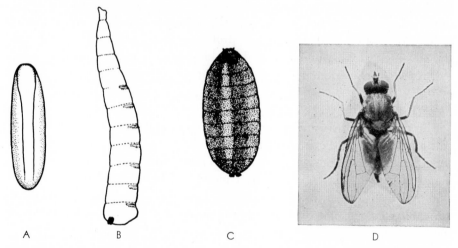

Fig. 18:15. Life stages of the horn fly. A, egg; B, larva; C, pupa; D, adult. *Courtesy USDA.*

on the blood of cattle. Mating takes place as early as the second day after emergence, while oviposition may begin on the third day. Females produce up to 24 eggs during their life time of approximately three weeks. When cold weather arrives, horn flies hibernate in the soil as pupae, but in the deep South they may continue to breed and develop the year round.

In the North, populations reach a peak in summer. In the South they reach a peak in spring, decline during summer due to hot dry weather, then reach a second peak in fall. Horn flies prefer dark colored animals over light colored and half grown or mature animals over calves.

Control. Horn flies are readily controlled by application of insecticides to the backs of animals. On beef animals 1 to 2 quarts of 0.5 per cent sprays of methoxychlor, toxaphene, or malathion give protection for three to four weeks. Treatment is then repeated as often as needed. Another way of using methoxychlor or toxaphene is to apply a tablespoon of 50 per cent wettable powder or dust by hand to the backs of animals.

A self-treatment method of applying insecticides for control of horn flies has become popular among raisers of beef cattle because of its saving of labor in handling cattle. This is the backrubber in which a burlap covered cable is saturated with a 5 per cent oil solution of methoxychlor, DDT, or toxaphene at a rate of 1 gal. per 20 feet of cable. Cattle treat themselves by rubbing against the cable and removing small amounts of insecticide.

Because of the necessity of meeting zero tolerances in milk, insecticides for control of horn flies on dairy cattle are restricted to methoxychlor or malathion dust or to sprays of pyrethrins, lethane, or thanite. Entomologists have found labor saving devices such as dust-charged backrubbers, treadle sprayers, lever sprayers, and automatic photoelectric sprayers useful in treating dairy animals. Since control of biting flies—chiefly horn flies, stable flies, and horse flies—is a field of active research, dairymen will profit by writing to their agricultural college for latest recommendations. Stable flies and horse flies are difficult to control solely with insecticides, and for this reason many recommended spray formulations contain repellent chemicals.

Screw-worm

Callitroga hominivorax (Coquerel) [Diptera:Calliphoridae]

One of the most dangerous pests of livestock in subtropical and tropical America is the screw-worm, the larval stage of a blow fly that confines its egg laying to wounds on warm-blooded animals. Of the domestic animals, cattle, sheep, goats, and hogs suffer most. When the adult flies are active, any minor cuts, as well as serious breaks in the skin of an animal, invite egg laying. Upon hatching the larvae tear into healthy tissues and create a characteristically foul smelling, bleeding wound. The odor attracts other flies which lay eggs and increase the severity of the infestation. Because of repeated egg deposition screw-worms of different sizes and ages infest untreated wounds (Fig. 18:6).

Infested animals appear nervous and make frantic attempts to scratch and lick the wound. They often leave the herd to hide away in secluded places. The majority of untreated infestations terminate in the death of animals. Death may be caused by the direct action of the maggots themselves or indirectly by the female flies introducing pathogenic organisms. The causative bacterium of the disease "swollen joints," *Streptococcus pyogenes,* is carried mechanically to the navel of calves by egg laying screw-worm flies, while the feeding activities of the larvae appear to facilitate the infection.

In favorable years screw-worms widely populate the southern half of the United States, which they invade from their overwintering ranges in southern parts of Florida, Texas, New Mexico, Arizona, California, and in Mexico. From late spring to early fall the adult flies spread northward by flight to states as far away as Colorado, Kansas, Missouri, Kentucky, and Virginia, migrating as much as 35 miles each week. Nearly all outbreaks north of these states originate from maggot-infested animals shipped from the South and not from migration of flies.

Description. Eggs of the screw-worm are deposited in oval, shingle-like clusters at the edges or on dry surfaces of wounds. Eggs are 1 mm. long, elongate, and white or cream colored. Maggots are creamy white and vary in length from 1.2 mm. at hatching to 16 mm. (⅔ in.) at full growth. The puparium is dark brown and 10 mm. long. The fly is somewhat larger than the house fly being 8 to 10 mm. long. It has a blue to bluish green body and a reddish orange to brown head (Fig. 18:16).

Life history. Under favorable temperatures the species develops and reproduces the year round. During cool weather it survives in the pupal stage which may last two months. If cool weather—average daily temperatures lower than 54°F.—prevails longer than two months the pupae die in the soil. For this reason screw-worms usually are able to overwinter only in the most southern parts of the United States and in countries further south.

In nature screw-worms develop solely in wounds of live animals; they cannot exist in carrion. Adult flies feed on the juices of manure and the exudations of wounds. Gravid female flies are attracted to wounds where, on the edges or dry surfaces, they deposit 200 to 400 eggs cemented together in shingle-like clusters. Each female produces several clusters at four-day intervals and may lay as many as 3,000 eggs. The eggs hatch in about 12 hours into tiny white maggots which invade the wound, feed close together, and form a pocket in the living flesh. They pass through three instars in four to eight days to become full-grown larvae. These drop to the ground and burrow into the soil to pupate. Under Texas conditions the pupal stage lasts from seven days in summer to 54 days in winter. Within two to five days after emerging, flies are ready to mate. During her lifetime a female fly copulates only once with a male. In summer the average life cycle of about 20 to 25 days allows several generations to develop annually.

Fig. 18:16. Life stages of the screw-worm. A, cluster of eggs; B, larva; C, pupa; D, adult. *Courtesy USDA.*

Control. Stockmen control screw-worms in three ways: first, by preventing wounds; second, by preventing infestation through wound treatment; and third, by treating infested wounds. Gentle handling of livestock prevents many needless wounds. Do not drive sheep, cattle, and other livestock with whips or sticks or biting dogs. Holding corrals should not have protruding nails and broken boards on which animals can snag themselves.

If possible limit operations such as dehorning, branding, castration, shearing and lamb docking to months when screw-worm flies are inactive. If operations are necessary at other times, treat the wounds with EQ 335, Korlan smear, 0.5 per cent Co-Ral dust, or another effective remedy.

It is also advisable to have lambs, calves and other young dropped during months of reduced fly activity. In the extreme southern areas of the United States this time will be in February and March. Young animals are highly susceptible to navel infestation. All young born during the screw-worm season should receive special attention. In treating the navel of a new born calf, tie off the umbilical cord and cut the surplus away. Then apply iodine and follow with an application of EQ 335. It is also advisable to treat the vulva of the dam with screw-worm remedy before and after she gives birth.

Some wounds are difficult to prevent. The bites of insects such as horse flies and stable flies and the bites of ticks produce breaks in the skin attractive to screw-worm flies. Equally attractive wounds can result from animals brushing against thorny shrubs or barbed wire. The feeding of sheep and goats on prickly pear cactus causes mouth injuries that allure flies. Moreover, warts, pink eye, and cancer eye may attract egg laying females.

In the deep South treat all wounds with EQ 335 at all seasons. In the northern areas one may restrict treatment of wounds to the screw-worm season. Screw-worm remedy EQ 335, a fluid, can be conveniently applied with a 1-inch brush. Give uninfested wounds a light coating of the material, but work the material well into infested wounds and paint the surrounding area. Give deep pockets of maggots special attention. A light application to drainage areas below wounds on sheep and goats is helpful in preventing future attacks of the fly. Infestations in beef cattle may also be treated successfully by spraying animals with 0.5 per cent ronnel or 0.25 per cent Co-Ral. Dairy cattle may be treated with EQ 335 or an older screw-worm remedy, smear 62.

During the screw-worm season stock growers make daily examinations of their animals to detect infestations. They find it helpful to have hospital corrals or pens where infested animals can be conveniently and gently handled and treated. Wounds are treated twice the first week then at seven-day intervals until healed. Generally two or three treatments suffice.

Employing a novel method of insect control, entomologists of the United States Department of Agriculture have made good progress in eliminating the screw-worm menace in southeastern states. They expose screw-worm pupae to gamma rays of Cobalt-60 which sterilizes both males and females. They then release large numbers of sterilized flies throughout the year.

When a female fly, that has developed naturally in the area, mates with a sterile male, she produces only infertile eggs which never hatch.

By swamping the natural populations with sterilized males beginning July 1958, entomologists apparently eliminated screw-worms in south-eastern United States in a year's time. At present they consider the method not justifiable for control of screw-worms in the southwest because of the large size of the infested area and because of the invasion of this area by migrating flies from Mexico.

Sheep ked
Melophagus ovinus (Linnaeus) [Diptera:Hippoboscidae]

The sheep ked, often called sheep-tick by American wool growers, is a world-wide pest of sheep. It obtains nourishment by piercing the skin of its host and sucking blood. In feeding it causes irritation and annoyance which prompts the infested sheep to rub, bite, and scratch. Sheep may also roll to the ground in relieving irritation, particularly in spring. Some animals get on their backs and are unable to right themselves. Unless they are found and are helped to their feet, their attempt to relieve irritation ends fatally. In a test conducted in South Africa, entomologists found that keds did not cause any apparent damage to sheep fed an adequate and nutritious diet, but that keds caused a 20 per cent mortality among poorly fed sheep. Several experiments in America have shown that keds do not depress weight gains of lambs fed fattening rations.

Sheep grazed throughout the year on pasture or range acquire heavy burdens of keds during winter and early spring. Though as yet undetermined, damage should be greatest at these times because of the consumption of large amounts of blood by the keds and the irritation caused by the bites. In spring injury may occur after transfer of large numbers of keds from ewes to new-born lambs. Losses caused by sheep keds have been variously assigned monetary values, but facts upon which they are based do not seem to be too reliable.

Description. Because eggs and larvae develop entirely within the uterus of the female ked, only two stages, the pupal and the adult, are visible on the sheep. Adult keds are large, about ¼ in. long, wingless parasites. They have brownish heads, thorax, and legs and a grayish abdomen. The puparia are dark red, barrel shaped, and about ⅛ in. long (Fig. 18:17).

Life history. The sheep ked is a permanent external parasite of sheep, since it lives upon the host for its entire life. If by accident a ked falls from its host, it does not survive longer than four or five days. Adult keds feed upon the sheep's blood which they obtain by piercing the skin.

Adult females are able to mate 24 hours after they emerge from the puparium, but fertilization of eggs does not occur until the fifth or sixth day. Following pupal emergence at least 12 to 14 days elapse before a young female deposits her first larva. This, as well as subsequent offspring, she glues to several wool fibers. Only one larva develops at a time. During

Fig. 18:17. The sheep ked, often called sheep-tick by ranchers. A, adult; B, puparium. *A, courtesy Cornell University; B, courtesy University of Wyoming.*

A   B

the female's life of 100 to 130 days, she produces around 10 to 15 young, giving birth every eight or nine days. Male keds do not mate before they are 10 to 11 days old. They have a shorter life than females, living for about 80 days.

At birth the larva is a light cream color, but within 12 hours it transforms to the red puparium. The pupal stage lasts from 18 to 30 days and averages 22 days.

There appears to be a wide range of susceptibility among sheep to infestation. Lambs and sheep in poor condition bear the heaviest numbers. As many as 1,000 adults may parasitize an old weak ewe.

Keds seem to prefer the neck, shoulder, and crutch regions of the sheep, but during warm weather many infest the belly. Few are ever found in the dense wool of the back. Size of populations varies with the seasons. Keds are most abundant during the winter and early spring and lowest during summer. In spring many of the young keds migrate from the ewes to the lambs.

Control. Treating all sheep in a range band or a farm flock with an insecticidal dip, spray, or dust controls sheep keds. Dipping is the most widely recommended practice, as it is generally the surest way to eradicate an infestation. A highly effective yet inexpensive insecticide for use in dip vats is ground cubé or derris root. It is used at the rate of 8 to 16 oz. of 5 per cent rotenone content powder to each 100 gal. of water. In America rotenone has been found to achieve complete eradication with a single dipping, but in Australia rotenone dips have been reported as not being sufficiently persistent to kill all young keds that emerge from puparia.

Chlorinated hydrocarbons are even more effective as dips than rotenone since they provide greater residual action. Toxaphene and DDT are effective at 0.25 per cent concentrations and lindane at 0.025 to 0.03 per cent gamma isomer. Where sheep lice as well as keds infest a flock the chlorinated hydrocarbons are preferable to rotenone, as the latter has failed to adequately control all cases of lice.

Wool growers often spray sheep to control keds, but spraying is not as effective as dipping because of the difficulty of thoroughly and completely wetting all sheep. The concentrations of the insecticide are generally doubled in sprays over those recommended for dips. In addition to the previously mentioned insecticides, sprays of 0.5 per cent malathion or ronnel or 0.25 per cent Co-Ral are also recommended. Delnav at 0.15 per cent has been recommended as a spray or dip.

A new simple way of controlling keds on small farm flocks is the "sprinkler can" method. An emulsion of 0.5 per cent ronnel is sprinkled on the backs of sheep with an ordinary garden sprinkle can. For convenience about 25 head are crowded into a small pen and the operator walks through them and dispenses six gallons of the insecticide over the heads, necks, tops, and

Fig. 18:18. Power dusting a large range flock of sheep in spring after shearing to control the sheep ked. *Courtesy University of Wyoming.*

sides of the sheep. The operation is repeated until all sheep in a flock have been treated.

Power dusting has been found useful for short term control of keds on feeder lambs. An effective and safe dust for this purpose is 0.5 per cent rotenone. Cubé or derris is diluted with pyrophyllite and 2 per cent of motor oil is added to cut down fluffiness.

Power dusting of large range bands of sheep after shearing in spring has proved successful in controlling keds (Fig. 18:18). The most effective dust is 1.5 per cent dieldrin in pyrophyllite to which 2 per cent of No. 10 motor oil has been added. One thorough dusting of a flock eradicates an infestation. This method has the advantage of being both rapid and safe, since two or three thousand sheep can be dusted in one hour without ever exposing them in a wet condition to inclement weather.

Winter tick
Dermacentor albipictus (Packard) [Acarina:Ixodidae]

The winter tick is a widespread, indigenous tick of North America. Though cattle are seriously attacked, it is chiefly a pest of horses and of big game—moose, elk, and deer (Fig. 18:19). The direct injury of the winter tick results from its feeding and withdrawing large amounts of blood. After five to six months of severe infestation during the winter, animals become exceedingly emaciated and weak. Colts are especially vulnerable to attack and often die. One of the chief factors contributing to mortality among moose and elk is gross infestation by this tick combined with feed shortages in late winter and early spring.

The winter tick is a vector of serious diseases among cattle, deer, and moose. It has been shown to be capable of spreading anaplasmosis among cattle.

Description. The winter tick has 4 life stages, egg, larva, nymph, and adult. The eggs are laid in masses of several thousand and are coated with a viscid secretion. Eggs are ovoid, smooth, shiny, and yellowish brown. Their longest dimension ranges from 0.45 to 0.5 mm. When first hatched, larvae are pale yellow but soon become dark reddish brown. They are six-legged and when replete with a blood meal measure 1 to 2 mm. long. On molting to the nymphal stage, the ticks become eight-legged. Size of engorged nymphs ranges from 3 to 5.4 mm. Newly emerged adults of both sexes range in length from 4 to 6 mm. (Fig. 18:20). Females increase their size tremendously as they engorge themselves on blood of the host. They are olive-green in color and when replete measure ⅓ to ⅔ in. long. Males

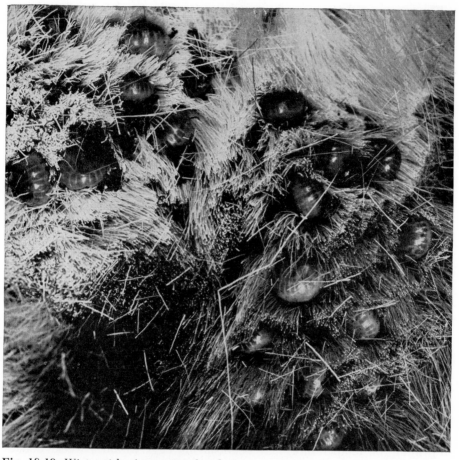

Fig. 18:19. Winter ticks (engorging females) on a yearling elk. Nearly 1400 ticks infested this animal. *Courtesy USDHEW.*

are reddish brown with pale yellow markings on the dorsum. They neither engorge nor increase in size like the females.

Life history. The life cycle of the winter tick is interesting because of its peculiar habit of feeding during the winter months rather than in spring and summer as do nearly all other ticks of the same family. It is seldom found on hosts in fall earlier than September or in spring later than June. In fall larval ticks coming out of summer dormancy begin to appear on the ends of grasses and twigs. There they hang head downward waiting for a host to pass by. The larvae are highly tolerant of snow and cold and unless they attach themselves to a host, they may remain in position till spring.

The winter tick is a one-host tick as it will complete its larval and nymphal development and become an adult on one and the same host. Larvae that succeed in obtaining a host attach to the skin and begin to suck blood. They feed to repletion in about nine days, remain quiescent

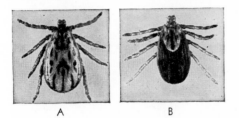

Fig. 18:20. Winter ticks, unengorged adults. A, male; B, female. *Courtesy USDHEW.*

for eleven days, then molt to the nymphal stage. In molting a transverse slit in the cuticula appears near the end of the body. The caudal end of the nymph protrudes from the slit and the nymph backs out leaving the exuviae hanging to the host by the inserted mouthparts.

Most of the nymphs crawl about for approximately half a day before they settle down close to the site of larval attachment. Although the winter tick is a one-host tick, nymphs while wandering about are able and often do transfer to another host when animals are in close proximity. After settling down they feed to repletion in about seven days. They then remain quiescent for six to eight days before molting to the adult stage.

After attachment adult female ticks become replete in five to 14 days. Adult males feed irregularly, crawl about and mate with the feeding females. Females have been observed to copulate as many as three times and males two or more times. Replete, mated females drop to the ground and, depending on temperature, may begin laying eggs within a week. Usually egg-laying commences in spring, each female producing about 4,000 eggs in a single mass over a period of several weeks. The eggs hatch in about six weeks into larval ticks, which remain bunched together and in a torpid state during summer.

Control. Stockmen control the winter tick as well as other ticks such as the lone star, Gulf Coast tick and Rocky Mountain wood tick by either dipping or spraying infested animals. For horses and beef cattle one may use 0.025 per cent lindane or 0.5 per cent toxaphene, as sprays or dips; or 0.5 per cent malathion or Co-Ral or 0.75 per cent ronnel as sprays. Dairymen may treat their cattle only with sprays of pyrethrins and synergist or with rotenone. A single treatment for the winter tick is usually sufficient, but if numbers of the pest are large a second treatment six to eight weeks later may be necessary. A second treatment may also be necessary when the first treatment is made early and animals become reinfested.

Hog itch mite

Sarcoptes scabiei suis (Gerlach) [Acarina:Sarcoptidae]

Swine are not plagued with many different kinds of external parasites. One species of lice, two species of mites, and one or two species of fleas are the only external parasites commonly found on hogs. Nevertheless, two of these, the hog louse (Fig. 18:21) and the hog itch mite, are both common and serious pests in North America as well as in many other parts of the world. The hog itch mite causes **sarcoptic mange,** a serious skin disease. The mites produce sores and intense irritation by their burrowing and feed-

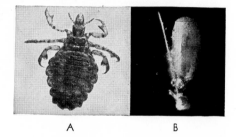

Fig. 18:21. The hog louse, *Haematopinus suis* (L.). A, adult; B, egg attached to hair. *Courtesy USDA.*

A   B

ing in the upper layer of the skin of the host. Small vesicles develop over the burrows, eventually rupture and allow serum to ooze over the area. As the mites increase, the infected area expands and the skin takes on the characteristic dry, scabby appearance of mange (Fig. 18:22).

The irritation set up by the mites induces hogs to rub and scratch and produce raw, bleeding areas. Infested swine neither grow nor gain properly and some actually die of the condition. When hogs with advanced cases are slaughtered, the meat is of inferior quality, requires special handling, and sells for less.

Hog itch mites are spread from one hog to another by direct contact. The habit of hogs sleeping close together aids the transmission of the disease. Though sarcoptic mange may start on any part of the body, lesions usually appear first on the head around eyes, ears, and nose. The lesions then spread backward over neck, shoulders, back, and sides and in severe cases involve the entire body.

Mange spreads slowly during warm weather when animals are on pasture. At such time lesions and mites can be found on the inner surface of the ear of infected animals. During winter when animals are confined and their resistance low, sarcoptic mange erupts and spreads rapidly. Young pigs and hogs in poor condition are more susceptible to the disease than

Fig. 18:22. Hog with an advanced case of sarcoptic mange. Note wrinkled, scabby skin of animal. *Courtesy USDA.*

thrifty mature animals. Positive diagnosis of mange is made by taking skin scrapings of lesions and finding the mites.

Description. The life stages of the hog itch mite are egg, larva, nymph, adult male, and immature and mature female. Eggs are ovoid in shape and about 0.2 mm. long. The motile stages are small, circular, whitish parasites. Larvae have three pairs of legs and are about 0.2 mm. long. Nymphs and adults have four pairs of short legs. Adult females are about 0.5 mm. long and adult males about 0.4 mm. The skin has many fine striae often interrupted by scaly areas or by areas of backward pointing spines (Fig. 18:23).

Life history. The hog itch mite lives its entire life on the hog. Eggs, laid in the burrows by the female mites, hatch in about five days. The larvae leave the burrows and wander over the skin looking for shelter and food. Both larvae and nymphs enter skin follicles of the host. The developmental period from egg to adult is from four to six days long. Although males make short burrows, they spend most of their time on the skin surface searching for unfertilized females. Unfertilized females make short burrows in which they stay for a day or two. Mating probably takes place on the skin surface. To form its burrow, the fertilized female cuts its way into the skin of the host using its mouthparts and legs. Females lay single eggs a few hours after forming tunnels and then at intervals of two to three days for about

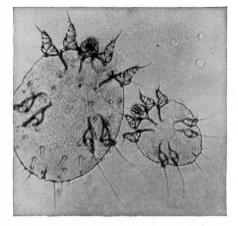

Fig. 18:23. Photomicrograph of the hog itch mite, *Sarcoptes scabiei suis* (Gerlach). *Courtesy USDA.*

one or two months stringing them out behind as they expand their burrows. They produce 10 to 25 eggs each before dying.

Control. The modern way of treating for both hog mange and hog lice is by dipping or spraying infested herds with certain of the new synthetic insecticides. A greater number of insecticides are recommended for louse control than for mange control. Lindane sprays or dips at 0.05 to 0.06 per cent concentration have been found effective for control of both conditions. If only lice are a problem, 0.5 per cent sprays or dips of DDT or methoxychlor or 0.5 per cent sprays of toxaphene are effective remedies. In addition some of the new phosphate systemic insecticides are effective for control of external parasites of swine.

Treatments are ideally made in early fall so that infestation of fall and spring pig crops is prevented. A farmer should make sure to treat all hogs on his place, as one untreated animal will eventually reinfest the others. Because mange mites can survive for four to six weeks off the host in moist bedding, control suggestions sometimes include the cleaning and the disinfecting of shelters and houses with chemicals, steam, or boiling water.

It is advisable to keep treated hogs out of cold, inclement weather until completely dry to prevent chilling and out of sunlight to prevent skin blistering.

Selected References

Anon., *Cattle Lice: How to Control Them,* USDA Leaflet 456, 1960.

Anon., *Eradicating Sheep Scabies,* USDA PA-458, 1961.

Bishopp, F. C., and W. E. Dove, *The Horse Bots and Their Control,* USDA Farmers' Bul. 1503, 1926.

———, E. W. Laake, H. M. Brundrett, and R. W. Wells, *The Cattle Grubs or Ox Warbles, Their Biologies and Suggestions for Control,* USDA Dept. Bul. 1369, 1926.

Bruce, W. G., *The Horn Fly and its Control,* USDA Leaflet 205, 1940.

Camin, J. H., and W. M. Rogoff, *Mites Affecting Domesticated Mammals,* So. Dak. Agr. Exp. Sta. Tech. Bul. 10, 1952.

Gregson, J. D., *The Ixodoidea of Canada,* Can. Dept. Agr. Publ. 930, 1956.

Haufe, W. O., *Control of Cattle Lice,* Can. Dept. of Agr. Publ. 1006, 1960.

James, M. T., *The Flies that Cause Myiasis in Man,* USDA Misc. Publ. 631, 1947.

Kemper, H. E., *Sheep Scab,* USDA Farmers' Bul. 713, 1952.

———, *The Sheep Tick and Its Eradication,* USDA Farmers' Bul. 2057, 1953.

———, and H. O. Peterson, *Cattle Lice and How to Eradicate Them,* USDA Farmers' Bul. 909, 1953.

———, and ———, *Cattle Scab and Methods of Control and Eradication,* USDA Farmers' Bul. 1017, 1953.

———, and ———, *Hog Lice and Hog Mange: Methods of Control and Eradication,* USDA Farmers' Bul. 1085, 1952.

———, and ———, *The Spinose Ear Tick and Methods of Treating Infested Animals,* USDA Farmers' Bul. 980, 1953.

Lancaster, J. L., *Cattle Lice,* Ark. Agr. Exp. Sta. Bul. 591, 1957.

Roberts, F. H. S., *Insects Affecting Livestock* (Sydney, Australia: Angus and Robertson, 1952).

Rogoff, W. M., *Cable-Type Backrubbers for Horn Fly Control on Cattle,* So. Dak. Agr. Exp. Sta. Bul. 418, 1952.

Schwardt, H. H., and J. G. Matthysse, *The Sheep Tick,* Melophagus ovinus *L.: Materials and Equipment for Its Control,* Cornell Univ. Agr. Exp. Sta. Bul. 844, 1948.

Chapter 19 | POULTRY INSECTS AND
RELATED PESTS | *Deane P. Furman*

Poultry suffer from the attacks of a wide variety of arthropods. These range from temporary, nonspecific parasites, such as mosquitoes, to pests such as chewing lice, which spend their entire life on the bird and are normally closely restricted to poultry or related wild fowl.

The pests

Chewing lice, belonging to the order Mallophaga, are the most common and widely distributed poultry insects. Nine species of lice are reported from chickens in the United States, with two additional species reported from neighboring regions to the south. Of these, the **chicken body louse** (Fig. 19:1), **chicken head louse** (Fig. 4:8B), and **shaft louse** (Fig. 19:2) are the most common and troublesome, with the **fluff louse, wing louse,** and **large chicken louse** of occasional importance. Frequently two or three species are found infesting birds simultaneously.

Of the fleas attacking poultry, the **sticktight flea** is frequently encountered in the southern United States from the Atlantic to the Pacific coast (Fig. 19:11). Two others, the **European chicken flea** and **western chicken flea,** are of occasional importance in North America.

The **fowl tick** is a voracious pest of chickens and turkeys in the southern United States (Fig. 19:14). It is particularly pestiferous in warm, arid regions of the Southwest, where tremendous populations of the pest may build up in a short time during summer.

Of the many species of mites attacking fowl, three species are of primary significance in North America. The most commonly encountered species is the **chicken mite,** which normally spends most of its life hiding in cracks of the poultry housing, only emerging at night to suck blood from birds

(Fig. 19:3). The **northern fowl mite,** by contrast, normally spends its entire life on the avian host sucking blood at will (Fig. 19:16). In most parts of the United States it ranks a close second in importance to the chicken mite. The **tropical fowl mite** closely resembles the northern fowl mite in appearance and habits, but it does not normally spend its entire life on the bird. It wanders about on the poultry housing, where it lays its eggs. The feeding stages may attack the birds at any time of the day or night. Other but less important mites that attack poultry include the **scaly-leg mite, depluming mite, air-sac mite** (Fig. 19:4), **fowl cyst mite,** and various kinds of **chiggers,** or larvae of Trombiculidae.

The common **bed bug** (Fig. 17:1E) and at least three species of avian bed bugs occasionally attack poultry. These insects have habits similar to that of the fowl tick in that they normally hide in cracks in the housing during the day, and attack the birds to suck blood at night.

There are a host of insects which are of varying degrees of economic importance to the poultry industry, but which by no means exclusively are pests of poultry. These include blood sucking reduviid bugs, gnats and mos-

Fig. 19:1. The chicken body louse, *Menacanthus stramineus* (Nitzsch), and egg masses on feather. *Courtesy Steve Moore III.*

Fig. 19:2. The shaft louse, *Menopon gallinae* (L.), as they normally appear on a feather shaft. *Courtesy Steve Moore III.*

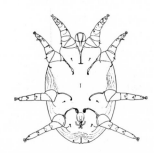

Fig. 19:3. Adult chicken mite, *Dermanyssus gallinae* (De G.). *Courtesy USDA.*

Fig. 19:4. Air-sac mite, *Cytodites nudus* (Vizioli). Ventral view of male. *From Baker* et al., *1956,* A Manual of Parasitic Mites, *by permission National Pest Control Association, Inc.*

quitoes; wound-invading fly maggots, such as the screw-worm (Fig. 18:16); house flies and related species which breed in manure, and beetles which serve as intermediate hosts of poultry tapeworms.

The injury

If any one feature may be said to be characteristic of successful parasites, it is the insidiousness with which they operate, frequently multiplying to produce tremendous populations before they are detected. During and subsequent to the development of heavy infestation of poultry insects and related pests, the damage caused is often difficult to see, since much of it takes places before, or without, accompanying death or marked illness of the birds. The economic significance of this damage is reflected in such factors as decreased egg production, decreased weight gains and increased susceptibility to disease agents. A recent estimate of the average annual cost of external parasites to the poultry industry of the United States was placed at 80 million dollars.

Poultry lice, with their chewing mouthparts, devour cast off skin fragments, feathers, and debris adhering to the birds. This is accompanied by scratching of the skin with the sharp spines and claws of the insects and, in some cases, by feeding on living skin and young quills. The importance of a few lice lies not so much in the damage they cause, but in their ability to multiply rapidly, with subsequent, serious, accumulative injury. Heavy louse populations produce generalized skin irritation and scabbing, damaged plumage, and poor condition. Affected birds become restless, lose sleep, and feed poorly. Egg production decreases and weight goes down. Young

birds are rapidly affected, becoming droopy and ruffled, developing diar-
rhea, and often dying.

The blood-sucking poultry mites include the most injurious of external
parasites. Their bites are extremely irritating to the birds, and heavily infested birds become scabby, anemic, droopy, and progressively emaciated.
Egg production is decreased and resistance to disease lowered. The fowl
tick produces much the same type of damage, but in addition it transmits
the causative agent of highly fatal fowl spirochaetosis, a disease now known
to occur in North America. On circumstantial evidence the chicken mite
has also been suspected of transmitting this pathogen. Piroplasmosis of
poultry caused by *Aegyptianella pullorum,* is transmitted by the fowl tick,
but the infection has not been encountered in the United States.

Attacks of fleas and bed bugs, both blood sucking insects, cause severe
irritation and anemia to which young birds may quickly succumb. The
sticktight flea may produce ulcers around the heads of birds which can
result in blindness and death (Fig. 19:5).

In the south and central United States, larval trombiculid mites, or chiggers, attach to poultry that are allowed to range over infested ground during the warm season. Groups of the mites, gathering beneath the wings
and on the breast, irritate the skin and induce the formation of abscesses.

A number of mites with chewing mouthparts invade the skin and even the
internal organs of poultry. The scaly-leg mite penetrates under the scales of
the leg, causing swellings and a rough appearance of the legs and feet due
to formation of scales and crusts (Fig. 19:6). Infested birds may be crippled.
A closely related form, the depluming mite, burrows into the skin around
the feather bases. The resulting intense irritation causes infested birds to
pluck out their feathers. The fowl cyst mite invades the loose, subcutaneous
tissues of the skin, forming small, caseous or calcified nodules which may
reduce the market value of affected fowl. The air-sac mite actually invades
the deepest portions of the respiratory tract of chickens, but it is evidently
well adapted to its host, for little damage has been attributed to it.

The problem created by filth-breeding flies differs from that caused by
poultry parasites. Flies do not normally cause direct losses in the form of
lower weight gains and decreased egg laying, but they are a nuisance to
the poultryman and, most importantly, they create a public health problem
for him and his neighbors. Furthermore, three common species of poultry
tapeworms reach their avian hosts through house flies. Fly larvae become
infected by ingesting tapeworm eggs passed in poultry droppings. Poultry
become infected with tapeworms by ingesting larval or adult flies in which
young tapeworms have developed to the infective, cysticercoid stage.

Fig. 19:5. An infestation of the stick-tight flea, *Echidnophaga gallinacea* (Westwood). *Courtesy USDA.*

Fig. 19:6. Legs of a chicken infested with the scaly-leg mite, *Knemidokoptes mutans* (R. & L.). *Courtesy USDA.*

Control through management

The problem of poultry pest control has been altered considerably in recent years by changing management procedures. In most instances such changes primarily have been directed at something other than poultry pests, and intelligent supervision is necessary to avoid the pitfalls while reaping the benefits associated with use of modern equipment and methods of poultry husbandry.

A few simple precautions will minimize the problems of introduction and control of poultry pests:

1. Isolate replacement birds from the flock for a period of time necessary to free them of those temporary parasites which will leave the birds. For example, in cases of parasitism by fowl tick larvae, a ten-day holding period should free the birds of the pests. The holding crates then may be scalded with steam or hot water, or treated with a suitable insecticide.

2. Treat replacement fowl infested with permanent or semi-permanent ectoparasites, such as lice, sticktight fleas, or northern fowl mites, with

an insecticide to eradicate the pests before bringing the new birds in contact with the flock.

3. Before partial or complete restocking of the poultry farm, clean housing thoroughly. If pests such as fowl ticks, chicken mites, bed bugs, or fleas are present, treat the housing with a suitable insecticide. Some of these pests may survive long starvation periods—up to three years for the fowl tick—so houses vacant a few weeks or months may contain hordes of hungry parasites.

4. Guard against introducing pests on used cages or other equipment, or on clothing of humans exposed to infested birds. Even insects such as lice may survive a few days off their hosts.

5. Provide tight, well constructed housing, free from cracks or loose boards, to aid in the control of those poultry pests which seek shelter in the housing. Easily removable roosts facilitate cleaning and insecticidal treatment. Do not allow poultry to roost in trees or sheds where pests may multiply undetected.

6. In chigger infested areas, restrict poultry from free range during the months of heavy mite populations. This will vary from one to two summer months in more northerly areas to practically the entire year in certain subtropical regions.

7. Discourage wild birds from nesting in and around poultry buildings, either by removing their nests as soon as constructed, or by screening out the birds with ¼ to ½ in. mesh hardware cloth.

Although house flies and related, filth-breeding flies are by no means restricted to poultry operations, the problems they create on poultry farms have become so critical that they can not be ignored. The control of such flies by insecticides alone is seldom satisfactory. Effective control requires good sanitation, as represented by the frequent, thorough clean-up and removal of manure, spilled feeds, and other materials that attract flies. Ways to decrease the fly breeding potential of such materials include the following: (1) open construction of buildings to aid rapid drying of droppings through free air circulation and sunlight; (2) drainage and farm construction to prevent wetting organic waste by leaky watering devices, rain, or ground water; (3) properly maintained, built up, litter floor, where fly breeding is greatly reduced by rapid turnover of droppings in the dry litter; (4) single-bird, wire-floored cages for laying flocks, rather than group, wire-floored cages; in hot, dry areas, the former procedure results in development of dry cones of manure; (5) compact compost piles with insecticidal treatment of the surface, or use of fly-tight manure boxes or houses; (6) weekly manure distribution in a thin layer on fields; (7) manure removal by a central agency for rapid mechanical composting, or storage in sanitary landfills or pit silos.

Since the lengths of the life cycles of filth-breeding flies are longer in cool than in warm weather, the weekly disposal period recommended for moist breeding materials may be correspondingly lengthened in cool periods, and dispensed with during months of frost or snow.

There is much room for improvement in management practices designed to control house flies. A recent resurgence of interest in the problem has produced some interesting leads. Recently entomologists in California have reported excellent fly control obtained through releasing 2-week old cockerels under wire floored cages containing adult hens. The cockerels turned over the droppings and ate the fly larvae encountered. Other work in California has demonstrated the practical use of the stratiomyid fly, *Hermetia illucens* (L.), in controlling house fly breeding in poultry droppings. The slowly maturing stratiomyid larvae competed successfully for available food, literally starving out house fly larvae. This represents a biological type of control.

Biological control of house fly breeding by means of microorganisms is a field which currently is receiving serious attention. Preliminary investigations have demonstrated that application of *Bacillus thuringiensis thuringiensis* spore powder as an additive to chicken feed resulted in 99 per cent reduction of adult fly emergence when 3 gm. per day were consumed by laying hens.

Chemical control

Recommendations for use of specific insecticides change from year to year, but most of the biological factors governing our choice remain constant. Thus we may apply contact insecticides such as DDT or related chlorinated hydrocarbon compounds to the housing to control fowl ticks, bed bugs, or other pests which rest on or in the housing. Surfaces treated with these materials retain, for weeks or months, a toxic effect for pests contacting them. Such applications of residual insecticides are designed to control existing infestations and to protect against reinfestations.

Materials having a relatively high vapor pressure with accompanying fumigant action on insects may be applied to poultry roosts for control of certain pests remaining permanently on the birds. Thus we may apply nicotine sulfate, in the form of "Black Leaf 40," to roosts for the control

Fig. 19:7. A small power sprayer used to treat poultry house with an acaricide for control of fowl ticks and chicken mites which inhabit cracks of the structure. *Courtesy University of California.*

of lice, and northern and tropical fowl mites. The warmth of the bodies of roosting fowl increases the fumigant action of the nicotine sulfate. Malathion or lindane, applied to roosts, works in similar fashion.

In contrast to the so-called housing and roost treatments, are those designed for direct application to poultry. The primary objective of such applications is to eliminate those poultry pests which normally spend their life on the birds; a secondary objective is to provide protection from reinfestation from outside sources. This combination of properties is difficult to achieve in view of the fact that many insecticides with residual characteristics may be absorbed through the skin of treated birds, some proving toxic to the birds or resulting in the accumulation of the insecticide in the tissues and even in the eggs. It is to prevent such possibly hazardous residues from reaching the dining room of man that the elaborate safeguards of Public Law 518 have been established.

Properties of some new insecticides have revived interest in the oral route of insecticide application for poultry pest control. This route offers singular advantages over currently used methods; application in the feed would eliminate individual, or even flock spraying, dusting or dipping, with the attendant drops in egg production. Preliminary experiments reported from California have demonstrated that effective control of the northern fowl mite has been obtained by adding to chicken feed the carbamate compound, Sevin. No ill effects were produced in the birds.

In applying insecticides around poultry one should follow the precautions given on the insecticide container and avoid contamination of feed and water troughs. Many insecticides are poisonous to man as well as animals if improperly used, so keep containers properly marked and store out of reach of irresponsible individuals.

Fig. 19:8. Treating individual birds with a hand duster (two puffs per bird) for control of northern fowl mite. *Courtesy University of California.*

Control equipment

Very little special equipment is required in the application of chemicals for control of poultry pests. For small farm flocks and for spot control of pests around larger flocks, a 2 to 5 gal., compressed air sprayer is most useful. When used in applying suspension-type sprays however, the sprayer must be shaken frequently to prevent settling of the insecticide. For larger flocks, a power sprayer provided with mechanical agitation is most suitable (Fig. 19:7). Either type of sprayer should have an adjustable nozzle to produce a coarse or fine spray. For most operations a power sprayer producing a nozzle pressure of from 50 to 100 p.s.i. is satisfactory, but in controlling pests such as fowl ticks in housing, pressures of up to 300 p.s.i. are more effective as they drive the spray into the deep crevices which harbor the pests. Both power and hand sprayers are suitable for treating birds or their housing.

Dusts may be applied directly to poultry by a small, hand-operated, plunger or puff-type duster provided with an adjustable swivel nozzle and extension tube (Fig. 19:8). These are particularly effective in treating individually caged laying hens. Flock dusting with larger, hand operated dusters of the rotary or bellows type is also practical, but such equipment fails to provide the penetration of the feathers needed by some dusts to assure control of pests.

Fig. 19:9. Painting the roosts with insecticide for control of lice and northern fowl mite. Insecticides with high vapor pressure provide a fumigant action that kills the parasites. *Courtesy USDA.*

In applying dusts to poultry house litter, the larger hand operated dusters are useful, but a large shaker-can may be used just as effectively.

For applying roost paints or sprays, the simplest device is a paint brush and can (Fig. 19:9). A faster device is a small compressed air sprayer provided with a nozzle producing a flat, fan-shaped spray pattern.

REPRESENTATIVE POULTRY PESTS

For detailed study we have chosen the following four poultry pests: the chicken body louse, the sticktight flea, the fowl tick, and the northern fowl mite.

Chicken body louse

Menacanthus stramineus (Nitzsch) [Mallophaga:Menoponidae]

The original host of the chicken body louse was probably the wild turkey, since the species has been found on this bird and no other wild host. It is now known as a common pest of domestic chickens as well as turkeys, and is also found on domestic guinea fowls, pea fowls, pheasants and quail when in contact with chickens. The geographic distribution includes North, Central and South America, Hawaii, Europe, East and South Africa, and Australia.

Conflicting opinions appear in the literature concerning the damage caused to poultry by lice. While the consensus of opinion is to the contrary, various workers, including some recent ones, believe lice cause no appreciable harm to poultry. It appears, however, that light breeds, such as the White Leghorn, are more susceptible to the effects of louse infestation than some of the heavier breeds, and this may account for the divergence of opinion. Of the several species of poultry lice, the body louse is considered the most harmful to adult birds. In a well-controlled and comprehensive series of tests, investigators in Alabama demonstrated that moderate infestation with the chicken body louse resulted in a 17 per cent decrease in egg production in White Leghorn hens. More heavily infested birds might logically be expected to show an even greater decrease in egg production. In heavy infestations chickens may carry populations well in excess of 8,000 lice per individual. The skin of such heavily infested birds becomes irritated and red with formation of localized scabs and blood clots. In addition to gnawing on the epidermis and feeding on skin fragments, feathers and debris, the chicken body louse attacks young quills and feeds on blood. Although this louse has been found naturally infected with the virus of eastern equine encephalomyelitis, it is not considered to have any epidemiological significance in the transmission of the pathogen.

Description. The adult chicken body louse is a small, yellowish insect 2.8 to 3.3 mm. long (Fig. 19:10A). The general appearance is that of an insect well adapted for clinging to the skin and feathers of the host. The body is flattened dorso-ventrally, with three pairs of short, two-clawed legs projecting horizontally from the thoracic region. The chewing mandibles are located on the ventral surface of the head, invisible from above, and the four-segmented antennae in repose are largely concealed in lateral grooves on the head.

Each abdominal segment is provided dorsally with two transverse rows of posteriorly directed setae. Males and females are of similar appearance but the terminal abdominal segments differ.

The immature stages, or nymphs, resemble the adults in general appearance, but are smaller and the genitalia are undeveloped. The eggs are readily visible to the naked eye and bear characteristic filaments on the anterior half of the shell and on the operculum (Fig. 19:10C).

Life history. In view of the fact that the body louse long has been recognized as one of the most harmful chicken lice, it is surprising that no detailed studies of the life history seem to have been reported. The characteristic eggs are usually attached to the basal barbs of the feathers (Fig. 19:1); masses of the eggs may often be seen attached to the small feathers below the vent. The eggs hatch in about a week, producing small, first instar nymphs. An additional 10 to 13 days are required for growth and development of the nymphal stage before the adults are produced.

Since all stages of the chicken body louse normally remain on or close to the skin of the host, the insect occupies a warm environment despite the season. Consequently large populations may develop very quickly and cause trouble at any time of the year. The louse survives off the host for very short periods, usually less than a day, so transmission from bird to bird primarily follows close contact.

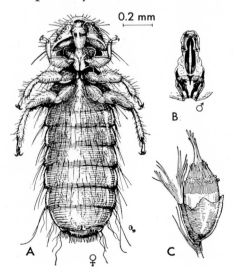

0.2 mm

A

B ♂

C

♀

Fig. 19:10. Chicken body louse. A, female, ventral view; B, male genitalia; C, egg fastened to feather barb. *Courtesy University of California.*

Control. All kinds of poultry lice, and particularly the chicken body louse, are easily controlled with insecticides. Treatment should be made before dense populations of lice develop in order to prevent losses. Birds should be examined frequently by parting the feathers and looking for body lice on the skin around the vent and breast. Other kinds of lice may be found on feathers of the head, body, and wings.

Some of the earliest used insecticides against poultry lice are still considered effective and are still recommended today. The major disadvantage of most of them is the time needed for application. In this category fall sodium fluoride and sodium fluosilicate dusts. These are applied to individual birds by the pinch method. A total of 11 pinches of dust, taken between the thumb and index finger are applied to the skin of the bird as follows: one pinch each on the tail, vent, breast, neck, head, each of the wings and thighs, and two pinches on the back. Both of these materials may also be applied as a dip using 1 oz. of dust in 1 gal. of warm water. Birds are immersed individually for about 20 seconds, ducking the head for only an instant. Another early remedy still occasionally used consists in dusting fowl liberally with flowers of sulfur. This provides effective control but occasionally causes severe irritation and blistering of the birds' skin, and likewise causes irritation of the applicator's eyes.

The recent trend in control of poultry lice is that of mass treatment of the flock, or application of insecticides to housing, litter and roosts. These techniques, however, are not new. Roost paints of nicotine sulfate (as Black Leaf 40) have been used for many years to control lice. The material is applied shortly before roosting time at the rate of one pint to 200 feet of roost. The fumigant action of the nicotine sulfate kills the lice as the birds roost. A second application seven days following the first is necessary to kill young lice hatching from eggs after the initial treatment. Although the chicken body louse is controlled well by this method, species such as the head louse often survive.

More effective roost paints include 3 per cent malathion or 1 per cent lindane in oil applied at the rate of 1 pint per 100 lineal feet of roost. A 1 per cent lindane water spray may also be used on roosts in wetting quantities.

To control lice with house sprays, the walls, ceilings and fixtures should be wetted with insecticide to the point of runoff, using a spray nozzle producing coarse droplets. One per cent malathion spray is effective, leaving the birds in the housing while treating. Lindane at 0.5 per cent may also be used, removing the birds from the housing while treating.

Turkeys infested with the chicken body louse may be treated rapidly by spraying 1 per cent malathion at 60 p.s.i. from a row-crop spray boom placed on the ground with nozzles directed upward. Driving the turkeys over the boom and through a curtain of spray treats them quickly.

Distribution of certain insecticidal dusts to deep litter floors usually provides effective control of poultry lice. Effective dusts include 4 per cent malathion or 1 per cent lindane at the rate of 1 lb. per 150 square feet of floor space.

The use of 4 per cent malathion dust in dust bath boxes is an effective self-treatment method for lice-infested hens. The method is particularly adapted for treatment of birds held on litter or in range type pens.

Mass dusting of poultry may be accomplished at night, using a hand-operated duster to distribute the dust over the roosting birds. Good control may be obtained with 2.5 per cent malathion or 1 per cent rotenone.

Although control of lice may be obtained through direct application to birds of DDT and certain other chlorinated compounds, their use involves the hazard of producing accumulations of toxicants in poultry tissues and hence is ill advised.

Sticktight flea

Echidnophaga gallinacea (Westwood) [Siphonaptera:Pulicidae]

Long known as a serious poultry pest in much of subtropical America, the sticktight flea commonly attacks a wide range of hosts. Dogs, cats, rats, and squirrels represent only a few of its mammalian hosts. It also attacks wild birds such as the English sparrow and Brewer's blackbird, and may be disseminated to domestic poultry by such alternative hosts. The geographic range of the flea includes much of the subtropical to tropical regions of the world. In the southern United States, the pest is common, occurring as far north as Oregon on the west coast.

The sticktight flea injures poultry through the semi-permanent attachment of female fleas to the skin of the bird, particularly around the eyes, ear lobes, wattles and comb. Irritation from clumps of attached fleas produces swelling of the host tissue and often results in ulcerations. Severely infested birds may be blinded, and even light infestations reduce egg production. Young birds may be killed in a short time by heavy infestations.

Description. Adult sticktight fleas are minute, wingless insects about 1 to 1.5 mm. long, with laterally compressed bodies of a dark brown color (Fig. 19:11). Of the three pairs of legs the posterior pair are elongated and adapted for jumping. The piercing-sucking mouthparts are prominently placed at the anterior, lower margin of the head. The head, thorax, and

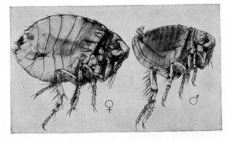

Fig. 19:11. Sticktight flea adults, female and male. *Courtesy University of California.*

abdomen form a compact unit, more or less oval in lateral view. The thoracic segments are greatly reduced, particularly dorsally. The male is readily distinguished from the female by the presence of the coiled, spring-like tendons of the male genital apparatus visible internally in cleared specimens, and by the characteristic protuberance at the posterior end representing the protruding genitalia.

The eggs are white and spherical, resembling miniature ping pong balls. The larvae are slender, white, legless, and wormlike (Fig. 19:12A). They have chewing mouthparts adapted for feeding on solid, particulate materials, in contrast to the sucking mouthparts of the adults. Full-grown larvae are 4 mm. long. The pupae are of the exarate type, that is, the appendages are free from secondary attachment to the body. In nature the pupa is swathed in a silken cocoon or envelope in which is incorporated bits of debris which make its detection difficult (Fig. 19:12B).

Life history. As with all fleas, only the adults are parasitic being provided with piercing-sucking mouthparts with which to penetrate skin and suck blood. Adult sticktight fleas are usually inactive for several days immediately following emergence from the puparium. Following this they attach to any of a variety of warm blooded hosts, including poultry. The mouthparts are inserted firmly in the tissues of the host, serving as an attachment organ as well as a food tube through which blood is sucked. Once attached, the fleas may remain in position as long as three weeks, and in this respect they differ from most other fleas, which remain attached for only a few moments at a time. Females will copulate while attached to the host, and egg production commences about a week following their first engorgement. The gravid female lays up to four eggs a day during its feeding period on the host.

The eggs usually drop to the ground unless held by the mass of swollen or ulcerated host tissue. They complete their incubation period in six to eight days at a temperature of 76° F. The worm-like larva is very active and feeds on excrementous matter such as flea feces, solid particles of which it manipulates with its chewing mouthparts. The larvae are found on the floor of infested poultry houses, in poultry nests and on ground near infested birds. Larvae emerging from eggs that adhere to the bird may feed directly on host tissue, but usually they drop to the ground. After two or

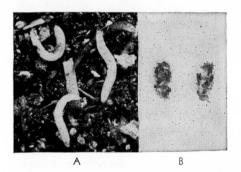

A   B

Fig. 19:12. Sticktight flea. A, larvae; B, cocoons. *Courtesy USDA.*

three weeks of feeding and developing, the larva becomes full grown and spins a silken cocoon in which the pupal stage is passed. After two to three weeks or more as a pupa, the adult flea emerges. The complete life cycle requires from 30 to 60 days, depending upon the prevailing temperature. Adult fleas may be found in infested debris for five months after all hosts have been removed.

Control. Sparrows, blackbirds, dogs, cats, rats and, in western areas of the United States, ground squirrels are among the most common hosts introducing sticktight fleas into poultry flocks in the United States. Where possible, measures should be taken to exclude these hosts from the poultry house.

Since the immature stages of fleas are passed on the floor, in nests, or on the ground, poultry maintained in wire floored cages with roll-away type nests are relatively safe from heavy flea infestations.

Where fleas are breeding, the ground of poultry runs and the floors of houses should be treated thoroughly with insecticide. Flea breeding in soil may be prevented by scattering salt freely about the yards and then thoroughly wetting the soil. Poultry should not be permitted to eat the salt, since it is toxic to them. Sprays of 5 per cent DDT, 5 per cent chlordane or 0.25 per cent lindane are also effective in preventing flea breeding when applied to floors, droppings, or ground. These should not be applied where they would be accessible to young chicks. Malathion applied to litter, ground, or floors provides excellent control of flea breeding. It may be applied as a 4 per cent dust at the rate of 5 lbs. per 100 square feet or as a 0.5 to 1 per cent spray in quantities to wet the treated surfaces. This method of treatment should also provide control of sticktight fleas attached to fowl, without the necessity of individual treatment of the birds.

Where rapid control of sticktight fleas on a few birds is desired, a 2 per cent carbolic ointment or 1 part of sulfur in 5 parts of lard or bland oil may be applied to the masses of attached fleas. Caution must be taken to keep the ointment out of the eyes of the birds.

Fowl tick

Argas persicus (Oken) [Acarina:Argasidae]

The most important tick infesting poultry is the fowl tick, also known by a variety of other names, such as bluebug, adobe tick, and tampan. The geographic distribution includes Europe, Asia, Africa, America and Australia; the tick thrives in warm weather and is most troublesome in dry regions. In the United States, the southwestern region is bothered most by the pest, although it occurs also in Florida and other southeastern states. Hosts for the tick include all species of domestic poultry, in addition to wild birds, such as quail, turkey, dove, vulture, golden crowned sparrow, and owls. On occasion man may be attacked, particularly if living close to abandoned roosting or nesting sites of birds.

The fowl tick is a voracious blood sucker in all active stages of its life cycle (Fig. 19:13). Poultry suffering from attacks of ticks, show the effects of anemia, becoming pale, weak, emaciated, and diarrheic. The feathers assume a dull, ragged appearance, and egg production is reduced or stopped. Young chicks brought into tick infested quarters are readily killed and growth of young birds is stunted. Turkeys suffer severely from attacks of the fowl tick.

The fowl tick serves as a vector of *Borrelia anserina*, the causative agent of avian spirochaetosis. This serious poultry disease occurs in the United States as well as in South America, Europe, Africa, India, Java, and Aus-

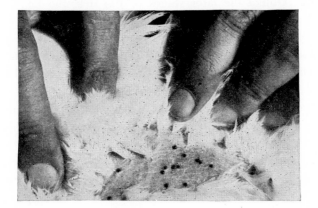

Fig. 19:13. First instar or seed ticks of the fowl tick, *Argas persicus* (Oken) attached to skin and feeding on the blood of a chicken. *Courtesy University of California.*

tralia. The disease frequently is transmitted in the absence of ticks, probably through infective bile droppings. The relatively non-pathogenic parasite, *Aegyptianella pullorum*, which has not been reported from America, is also transmissible by the fowl tick.

Description. Mature fowl ticks are dorsoventrally flattened, and suboval in outline viewed from above (Fig. 19:14). There is no subdivision of the body into head, thorax, and abdomen as in insects. Females average 8.5 mm. long by 5.5 mm. wide, and males slightly smaller. The color varies from light red to dark brown, and the body in general appears leathery and hairless, with more or less distinct cuticular discs arranged around the body margin as well as radially. The piercing-sucking mouthparts are anteroventrally placed and invisible from above. In common with other argasid ticks, there is very little difference in the gross appearance of the two sexes; the genital aperture in either case is located immediately behind the mouth parts. The eggs of the tick are shiny, reddish brown, and spherical in shape. The larvae are six-legged, active creatures about the size of a pin head before they feed. The two nymphal instars each have eight legs; except for the lack of a genital aperture and smaller size each of these instars resembles the adult tick in gross appearance.

Life history. The fowl tick deposits eggs in crevices about the poultry house, or under the bark of trees where these serve as roosting sites for fowl. The female tick produces as many as 900 eggs laying them in batches numbering up to 180. In the United States, the peak period of egg production is around July. The incubation period of the eggs is from eight to eleven days at 35° C, but at lower temperatures, it may be extended up to three months. The emerging six-legged larvae are ready to feed within a day after hatching, but in the absence of hosts may survive starvation for several months. Unlike the later stages of the tick, the larva remains attached to the avian host for four to nine days, occurring most abundantly on the sparsely feathered parts of the body. During feeding, the larva becomes globose in shape, but following complete engorgement it becomes flattened; at this time it seeks hiding places in crevices near the avian host nest or roost.

Seven to ten days after feeding the larva molts, producing the eight-legged, first nymphal stage. The nymph seeks an avian host at night, feeding to repletion in about two hours. It then hides in crevices for seven to ten days or longer after which it molts to the second stage nymph, which is similar in appearance, but larger than the preceding stage. After feeding and resting in a manner similar to that of the first nymphal stage, the second stage nymph molts to produce the adult male or female tick.

Fig. 19:14. Fowl tick adult is ½ in. long and one of the largest poultry parasites. *Courtesy University of California.*

A single mating suffices the female tick for life, but engorgement with blood must precede each successive batch of eggs deposited. Adult ticks normally engorge at night, requiring about one hour on the host. After each feeding they retire to nearby crevices in which to hide. Nymphs and adults may survive starvation up to three years or more.

Control. The general management procedures given earlier should be followed to avoid the introduction of fowl ticks to a poultry flock. It is simpler and less costly to prevent infestation than to eradicate an established population of ticks.

To control fowl ticks with chemicals, it is not necessary to treat the birds. The only ticks normally found on the birds during daylight hours are the larvae; these will drop off within a few days and will be killed by the residual action of acaricides applied to the housing. Before treating the housing, the nest boxes and roosts should be removed from walls to facilitate penetration of sprays into crevices. A coarse, driving acaricidal spray applied under pressures up to 300 lbs. p.s.i. is recommended for most effective results. Walls, ceiling, roosts and nests should be wetted thoroughly with the spray, using about ½ gal. per 1,000 square feet. A 2 per cent malathion spray is effective if applied under high pressure. At lower pressures, as obtained with a hand-pump type sprayer, a 3 per cent malathion emulsion should be used. One-half per cent lindane may be used similarly. Other effective sprays include 0.5 per cent toxaphene or chlordane, or 5 per cent DDT, but the use of these materials should be restricted to outside situations such as roosting trees or outbuildings infested with ticks. Painting or spraying walls and roosts with anthracine oil (carbolineum) is an old remedy which is effective, but its use may result in off odors in eggs of birds using the house shortly after treatment. If anthracine oil is used poultry should be excluded from the housing until the oil has dried into the wood.

Control measures effective against the fowl tick will also eliminate the common chicken mite and bed bugs, which hide in cracks of the housing, attacking the birds only for brief periods of feeding.

Northern fowl mite

Ornithonyssus sylviarum (Canestrini & Fanzago) [Acarina:Dermanyssidae]

This tiny mite is a pest of poultry in most temperate regions of the world. In warmer areas it is usually replaced by the closely related tropical fowl mite.

The northern fowl mite is particularly injurious to domestic chickens and turkeys, to which it may be introduced by a variety of wild bird hosts. The English sparrow and Brewer's blackbird, which frequent poultry yards in the United States, are two common hosts of the mite. Nests of the former, teeming with northern fowl mites, have been observed on rafters and eaves of poultry houses.

As with other serious, external parasites of poultry, infestations of northern fowl mites result in a serious decrease in egg production. An increase of 40 per cent or more in egg production following eradication of infestations is not uncommon. By sucking the blood of avian hosts, the mites produce marked weakening and even death of heavily infested birds. Bloody scabs form around the region of the vent as well as elsewhere on the body. The fluffy feathers around the tail become ragged and unkempt, matted with masses of mite eggs and feces, as well as with scabs from the skin (Fig. 19:15).

Viruses of western equine and St. Louis encephalitis as well as Newcastle disease have been recovered from northern fowl mites, but there is no indication that the viruses persist in the mites for any length of time, nor that they are important in the epidemiology of these diseases.

Description. The gross appearance of the northern fowl mite is similar to that of the tropical fowl mite and the common chicken mite. All are small, active, eight-legged organisms as adults, with a single dorsal plate covering only part of the body. The terminally located mouthparts are borne on a capitulum and are adapted for piercing and sucking by means of slender, paired, retractile chelicerae. Females of the northern fowl mite range from 0.6 to 0.75 mm. long and up to 0.5 mm. wide (Fig. 19:16). The color varies from bright red to black with white flecks, depending on the time elapsed since feeding. The northern fowl mite may be differentiated

Fig. 19:15. Feather of chicken matted with various stages and feces of the northern fowl mite. *Courtesy University of California.*

from the above mentioned closely related species by the presence of a single pair of posterior, dorsal plate setae extending to, or beyond, the tip of the plate. In addition the northern fowl and chicken mites bear two pairs of sternal plate setae as opposed to three pairs on the tropical fowl mite. The chelicerae of the two fowl mites bear prominent, paired, scissors-like digits, while the chelicerae of the chicken mite are long and needle-like, with only rudimentary digits.

Life history. All five stages in the life cycle of the northern fowl mite are normally passed on the feathers and skin of birds. In heavy infestations, however, mites may be found in nests and surrounding structures of the housing. The warmth of newly laid chicken eggs attracts the mites from feathers of the laying hen, and often the first indication of an infestation noted by the poultryman is the presence of dark red to black mites crawling on the eggs (Fig. 19:17).

The eggs of the northern fowl mite are sticky when laid and usually remain attached to feathers on the bird, often hatching in less than a day. The six-legged larva is a non-feeding stage which molts to produce an eight-legged protonymph in about one day at moderate temperature. The protonymph feeds two or more times by penetrating the host's skin to suck blood, finally engorging in about one to two days. In another two days it molts to produce the eight-legged, non-feeding deutonymph, which in

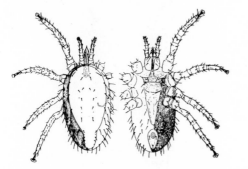

Fig. 19:16. Northern fowl mite, *Ornithonyssus sylviarum* (C. & F.), female. *From Baker,* et al., *1956,* A Manual of Parasitic Mites, *by permission National Pest Control Association, Inc.*

turn molts in about one day to produce an adult male or female. Adult mites are blood feeders. The complete life cycle requires less than a week but may be prolonged by unfavorable conditions. Mites removed from the host usually die within ten days, but some may survive up to three weeks.

The northern fowl mite will feed on the mouse and rabbit; hence, rodent infested premises may serve to prolong an infestation in an otherwise empty poultry house. Although the human being does not appear to be a suitable host, mites will occasionally bite man causing some itching.

Control. Many materials and techniques of application have been described for control of the northern fowl mite. Several of these are effective, but their applicability differs, depending upon such variables as prevailing climate, type of housing, and size of the poultry flock.

Sprays applied directly on poultry are best applied in mild weather. Rapid treatment can be made of birds caged singly or in small colony cages. A 0.5 per cent malathion emulsion spray is effective and recommended for use at the rate of 1 gal. per 100 birds. A 1 per cent Sulphenone spray is effective when applied at a rate of 1 gal. per 35 to 50 birds.

Dusts used for direct application on birds include 325 mesh sulfur, applied liberally by hand. This is an effective, but laborious and disagreeable procedure and may result in blistering the skin of birds. Four per cent malathion dust, applied by means of a hand operated, puff duster, is a superior treatment although less likely to eradicate infestation than the malathion spray treatment described above. Two puffs of dust are applied to each bird, directing the dust against the set of the feathers around the vent and breast. Preliminary information indicates that the dust also may

Fig. 19:17. Northern fowl mites and chicken mites crawling on warm, newly laid egg, an indication of heavy mite infestation. *Courtesy University of California.*

be applied effectively to poultry flocks with a rotary hand duster, allowing the dust to settle on the birds.

Litter and nest dusting has been recommended. Sulphur dust applied at the rate of 4 lbs. per 100 square feet of floor space has given excellent control. A 4 per cent malathion dust may be used at the rate of 1 lb. of dust per 50 square feet of floor space. This usually provides rapid reduction of mites unless cocks or cockerels are included in the pens. The efficiency of control by this method is dependent upon the degree to which the fowl dust themselves in such material as dry litter or dust in boxes provided for them. Since cockerels dust themselves less frequently than other fowl, litter treatment is probably less effective in control of their mite infestations.

Painting roosts with nicotine sulfate (Black Leaf 40), as described for louse control, provides rapid reduction of the northern fowl mite but eradication is seldom obtained, even when treatment is repeated after an interval of two weeks.

Selected References

Anon., *Chicken Lice: How to Control Them,* USDA Leaflet No. 474, 1960.

Baker, E. W., T. M. Evans, D. J. Gould, W. B. Hull, and H. L. Keegan, *A Manual of Parasitic Mites of Medical or Economic Importance,* National Pest Control Association, Technical Publication, 1956.

Benbrook, E. A., "External Parasites of Poultry," in Biester and Devries, *Diseases of Poultry* (Ames: Iowa State College Press, 1945).

Bishopp, F. C., and H. P. Wood, *Mites and Lice on Poultry,* USDA, Farmers' Bul. 801, 1931.

Briggs, J. D., "Reduction of Adult House-fly Emergence by the Effects of *Bacillus* spp. on the Development of Immature Forms," *J. Ins. Pathol.,* 2:418–32 (1960).

Cameron, D., "The Northern Fowl Mite (*Liponyssus sylviarum* C. and F. 1877)," *Canad. J. of Research D,* 16:230–54 (1938).

Chamberlain, R. W., and R. K. Sikes, "Laboratory Rearing Methods for Three Common Species of Bird Mites," *J. Parasitol.,* 36:461–5 (1950).

Crutchfield, C. M., and H. Hixson, "Food Habits of Several Species of Poultry Lice with Special Reference to Blood Consumption," *Florida Entomologist,* 26:63–66 (1943).

Emerson, K. C., "Mallophaga (Chewing Lice) Occurring on the Domestic Chicken," *J. Kans. Ent. Soc.,* 29:63–79 (1956).

Furman, D. P., and W. S. Coates, Jr., "Northern Fowl Mite Control with Malathion," *Poultry Sci.,* 36:252–5, 1957.

——, R. D. Young, and E. P. Catts, "*Hermetia illucens* (Linnaeus) as a Factor in the Natural Control of *Musca domestica* Linnaeus," *J. Econ. Ent.,* 52(5):917–21 (1959).

Gless, E. E., and E. S. Raun, "Insecticidal Control of the Chicken Body Louse on Range Turkeys," *J. Econ. Ent.,* 51:229–32 (1958).

Kraemer, P., and D. P. Furman, "Systemic Activity of Sevin in Control of *Ornithonyssus sylviarum* (C. and F.)," *J. Econ. Ent.* 52(1):170–1 (1959).

Loomis, E. C., "Avian Spirochaetosis in California Turkeys," *Am. J. Vet. Res.,* 14:612–15 (1953).

Parman, D. C., "Biological Notes on the Hen Flea, (*Echidnophaga gallinacea*)," *J. Agric. Res.,* 23:1007–09 (1923).

Reid, W. M., R. L. Linkfield, and G. Lewis, "Limitations of Malathion in Northern Fowl Mite and Louse Control," *Poultry Sci.,* 35:1397–98 (1956).

Reis, J., and P. Nobrega, *Tratado de Doencas das Aves,* Vol. III, Publ. Melhoramentos (1956).

Roberts, I. H., and C. L. Smith, *Poultry Lice,* USDA Yrbk. Agric., 1956.

Rodriguez, J. L. Jr., and L. A. Riehl, "Results with Cockerels for Housefly Control in Poultry Droppings," *J. Econ. Ent.,* 52(3):542–3 (1959).

Rodriguez, J. L. Jr., and L. A. Riehl, "The Malathion Dust-Bath for Control of Five Species of Lice on Chicken," *J. Econ. Ent.,* 53(2):328 (1960).

Sikes, R. K., and R. W. Chamberlain, "Laboratory Observations on Three Species of Bird Mites," *J. Parasitol.,* 40:691–7 (1954).

Warren, D. C., R. Eaton, and H. Smith, "Influence of Infestations of Body Lice on Egg Production in the Hen," *Poultry Sci.,* 27:641–2 (1948).

Chapter 20 | INSECTS OF MEDICAL
IMPORTANCE | *Wm. M. Rogoff*

The pests

The number of insects and other Arthropods that are of medical importance is very large, but the number of orders involved is relatively small. By far the largest number of these pests fall into the order Diptera, with relatively small numbers of forms in the Anoplura, Siphonaptera, Hemiptera, and Orthoptera. The arachnid order Acarina is second only to the Diptera in the number of species of medical importance (Fig. 20:1).

Among the Diptera are the house fly, the various myiasis-producing flies such as the blow flies (Fig. 18:16) and bot flies, and the many disease-carrying and discomfort-producing mosquitoes, sand flies, black flies (Fig. 20:2), eye gnats, horse flies, deer flies, and tsetse flies.

There are several species of house flies ubiquitously distributed throughout the world, but the common **house fly,** *Musca domestica* L., is the one most likely to be encountered (Fig. 20:7). Its relationship to disease transmission is essentially mechanical, but by virtue of the habits of this insect, its opportunities are ideal for transmitting many diseases of major and minor importance. House flies have been implicated as important carriers of typhoid fever, dysentery, and trachoma.

A common medical and veterinary phenomenon is the invasion of body tissues by dipterous larvae of various kinds. Such invasions are generically called **myiasis.** Myiasis-producing species may be specific, semispecific, or accidental. **Specific myiasis** producers are species whose larvae are found only in living tissues (Fig. 18:6). **Semispecific myiasis** forms are those species whose larvae normally breed in non-living organic matter, but which will occasionally lay eggs or deposit larvae in diseased tissues of man or other animals. The **accidental myiasis** producers are not clearly distinguishable from the semispecific forms but usually include species whose larvae may be ingested by the host along with food, or in a similar

Cone-nose Bugs
transmit: Chagas' Disease.

Fleas
transmit: Plague, Endemic Typhus, Dog Tapeworm.

Lice
transmit: Relapsing Fever, Epidemic Typhus Fever, Trench Fever.

Soft-backed Ticks
transmit: Relapsing Fever; *cause:* Tick Paralysis.

Hard-backed Ticks
transmit: Rocky Mtn. Spotted Fever, "Q" Fever, Tularemia, Colorado Tick Fever; *cause:* Tick Paralysis.

Mites
transmit: Tsutsugamushi (Scrub Typhus); *cause:* Dermatitus.

Nonbiting Flies
transmit: Yaws, Typhoid Fever, Dysenteries, Cholera, Conjunctivitis; *cause:* myiases.

Biting Flies
transmit: Tularemia, Sandfly Fever, Onchocerciasis, African Sleeping Sickness, Kala-azar, Bartonellosis.

Mosquitoes
transmit: Malaria, Yellow Fever, Dengue, Elephantiasis, Encephalitis.

Fig. 20:1. Types of arthropods that transmit pathogens of human diseases. *Courtesy U.S. Naval Medical School.*

unspecific manner. Over twenty species in at least six families are known as specific myiasis producers, with larger numbers of species in each of the other categories.

The **human bot fly** or torsalo (Fig. 20:3) is common in the tropical regions of South and Central America, and affects wild and domestic mammals in addition to human beings. It has a most unusual method of distribution. The gravid female fly captures mosquitoes of various species and deposits a single egg ventrally on the abdomen of the captive. The mosquito, upon release, carries the bot fly egg until she settles upon a mammal to feed. Heat from the body of the host initiates hatching of the egg and subsequent invasion of the host.

Mosquitoes (Fig. 20:9) are common throughout the world, from the tropics to the arctic. These insects, by virtue of their bloodsucking habits, enter into disease transmission in a highly specific manner. Among the more important diseases carried by mosquitoes are yellow fever, malaria, dengue or "breakbone fever," filariasis, and encephalitis. In addition to their importance as carriers of disease, mosquitoes are highly important because of the discomfort they produce.

Of the many genera of mosquitoes, three stand out in importance and are widely known. These are the genera *Anopheles*, *Aedes* and *Culex*. It would be entirely impractical in this chapter to list all or even most of the important species of mosquitoes. Typical of the medically important species are the following:

> *Anopheles freeborni* Aitken
> *Anopheles quadrimaculatus* Say (common malaria mosquito)
> *Anopheles albimanus* Wiedemann
> *Aedes dorsalis* (Meigen)
> *Aedes aegypti* (Linnaeus) (yellow-fever mosquito)
> *Culex pipiens pipiens* Linnaeus (northern house mosquito)
> *Culex pipiens quinquefasciatus* Say (southern house mosquito)
> *Culex tarsalis* Coquillett

Within the order Anoplura are two species that affect man. These are the two varieties of one species, *Pediculus humanus humanus* L., the **body louse,** and *P. humanus capitis* De G., the **head louse,** and the other species, *Phthirus pubis* (L.), the **crab louse** (Fig. 20:4). *P. humanus* is an important agent of human disease, being involved in the transmission of epidemic typhus, trench fever, and relapsing fever, as well as, but to a lesser degree, endemic typhus.

The order Siphonaptera includes a number of medically important species, among the most important being the **chigoe,** a tropical and subtropical flea that penetrates the skin; the **human flea** (Fig. 20:5); and the **oriental rat flea.** The latter two fleas are particularly important in the transmission of plague, and the oriental rat flea is involved additionally in the transmission of endemic typhus.

The order Acarina contains a very large number of important and diverse arthropods of medical importance. Elsewhere in this book have been discussions that introduced important ticks and mange mites. Many of these attack humans as well as livestock and wild animals. Of the numerous important Acarina, this chapter will treat only the **chiggers,** all within the family Trombiculidae. In many regions chiggers are of great importance as carriers of disease or as severe sources of irritation. Three examples will be considered: *Trombicula akamushi* (Brumpt) and *Trombicula deliensis* Walch the vectors of scrub typhus, and *Trombicula alfreddugesi* (Oudemans), the common North American chigger or redbug.

The injury

The most significant way in which insects affect the well-being of man is by the transmission of disease-causing organisms. In some instances this transmission is of a simple, mechanical nature, involving only the process of contamination. In other instances the disease organism maintains an intimate relationship to the insect and may actually require the insect in order to complete a part of its life history. The first of these methods of disease transmission is typified by the relationships of the house fly and similar

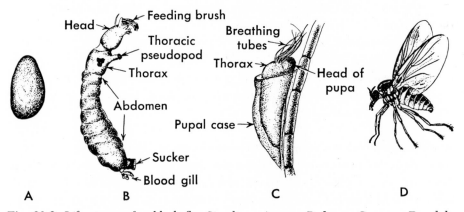

Fig. 20:2. Life stages of a black fly, *Simulium.* A, egg; B, larva; C, pupa; D, adult. Species of this genus are intermediate hosts for the filarial worm which causes onchocerciasis in parts of Africa, Mexico, and Central America. *Courtesy U.S. Naval Medical School.*

filth-inhabiting and filth-related flies to human health. A very large number of diseases caused by viruses, bacteria, and protozoa are transmitted by flies from one infected person to another, and from contaminated organic matter to humans. In most cases the relationship is based on the habits of the individual fly in exploring a great variety of organic materials and mechanically moving bits of this contamination from one site to another. In some cases the relationship is from the larval breeding medium, through the pupa, to the adult fly which effects the final transfer. Examples of diseases transmitted by flies include typhoid, dysentery, and trachoma, and to a lesser degree such diseases as leprosy, tularemia, cholera, yaws, tuberculosis, anthrax, trypanosomiasis, leishmaniasis, diphtheria, and poliomyelitis. Various species of flies have been implicated in the transmission of food poisoning organisms such as *Staphylococcus* and *Salmonella,* and of various species of *Streptococcus.* In none of these instances are flies as intermediaries necessary for the normal transmission of the diseases.

The mosquito-borne diseases also include representatives of the mechanical type of transmission, but included also are classical examples of intimate biological relationships between the disease organism, the mosquito, and the human. Among the important mosquito-borne diseases are malaria, yellow fever, dengue, filariasis, and encephalitis. Several of these diseases are actually complexes of several closely related diseases. For a clear understanding of the relationship of mosquitoes to disease we shall examine malaria and yellow fever in some detail.

Malaria is a disease, known from antiquity, with an essentially worldwide distribution in tropical, subtropical, and temperate regions. While still of tremendous importance, its range has been greatly reduced in recent years, largely by highly organized efforts of national and international forces. As an example of its former widespread nature, one study, published in 1932, indicated that over 17,750,000 cases had been treated in a single year, and that the actual number of cases would be numbered in terms of several hundreds of millions. The disease is caused by protozoa of the genus *Plasmodium.* At least five species of this genus are known to infect man, though three species are responsible for the overwhelming majority of cases. *Plasmodium* enters the red blood corpuscles where the individual parasites grow and reproduce asexually. This process eventually destroys many individual red cells and releases large numbers of infective forms that enter other red cells. The multiplication process continues many times. Later cells of a potentially sexual nature, called gametocytes, are produced. If during the time gametocytes are in the blood stream, an appropriate species of *Anopheles* mosquito takes a blood meal, a further cycle takes place in the body of the mosquito. The gametocytes participate in a sexual phase in the alimentary canal of the mosquito, and then undergo an asexual multiplication process in cysts in the stomach wall. The resultant parasites migrate to the salivary glands of the mosquito, from which they are introduced into the blood stream of the next victim. Thus, while it is possible to mechanically transmit malaria by moving blood from one person to another, the normal method of transmission involves an active biological participation by the mosquito.

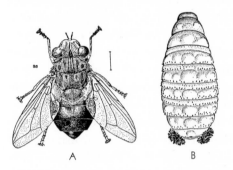

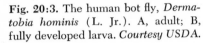
Fig. 20:3. The human bot fly, *Dermatobia hominis* (L. Jr.). A, adult; B, fully developed larva. *Courtesy USDA.*

While malaria has been known as one of the most important of human diseases since antiquity, details of its nature and transmission have become known only in modern times. The existence of the parasite was discovered by Laveran in 1880. The relationship of mosquitoes to malaria transmission was suggested by Manson in 1894. Within the next four years experimental transmission was demonstrated by Ross, and details of the life cycle of the parasite were worked out by Grassi and Bignami. Intelligent efforts at malaria control, therefore, have come only in the twentieth century.

Yellow fever was first described in the seventeenth century. This disease, apparently of African origin, is an acute infectious jaundice caused by a virus which, in the typical urban epidemics, is transmitted from man to man by the yellow-fever mosquito. Severe epidemics of this disease have been experienced in Philadelphia, Memphis, and New Orleans, but the greater number of epidemics have been seen in tropical and subtropical countries. The mosquito-transmission aspects of this disease were investigated by Finlay, starting in 1881 and elucidated in the following twenty years. In the period following 1900, Reed, Carroll, Lazear, and Agramonte, using human volunteers, discovered the essential features necessary for mosquito transmission of the disease. A method for mass vaccination for the control of yellow fever was developed in 1932. The combination of appropriate mosquito control measures in the early part of the century with the mass immunization procedures developed later, has greatly reduced the significance of the classical form of this disease.

It should not be assumed from what has been said that the injury caused by insects to the health of man is limited to the transmission of diseases caused by other organisms. An obvious feature, familiar to all, is the annoyance, sometimes extreme, caused by insects that bite or sting, or by arthropods that burrow partially or completely into epithelial layers, such as some mange mites and the chigoe flea.

Control through management of environment

The control of certain types of infestation by management of environment has been outstandingly successful. Most of these procedures are aimed at the larval breeding sites, but some are directed at adult insects. House fly larvae develop in a wide variety of decaying organic media, some accumulations of which are directly subject to management. Communities that are small enough to be located close to areas of cattle, swine, horse, or poultry production or maintenance, are frequently subject to infestation from these sources. The routine removal of fly-breeding materials is a necessary prerequisite to chemical control operations. Sanitation alone is rarely sufficient for control, but excesses of breeding materials greatly complicate the problems of fly control. Other large sources of fly breeding materials, subject to sanitation efforts, are garbage dumps, privies, compost heaps, and other accumulations of organic matter in the vicinity of homes and eating establishments.

Since water is necessary for the development of the larvae of many insects of medical importance, such as mosquitoes, major efforts to eliminate or modify such breeding areas is a normal part of routine control efforts. Filling areas that can be filled, or draining appropriate areas are common

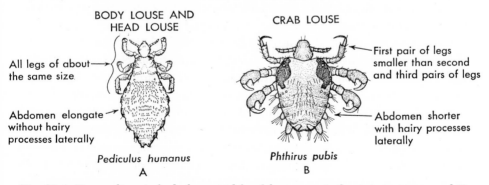

BODY LOUSE AND HEAD LOUSE

CRAB LOUSE

All legs of about the same size

First pair of legs smaller than second and third pairs of legs

Abdomen elongate without hairy processes laterally

Abdomen shorter with hairy processes laterally

Pediculus humanus
A

Phthirus pubis
B

Fig. 20:4. Human lice. A, body louse and head louse are similar in appearance and B, crab louse. *Courtesy USDHEW, Public Health Service.*

procedures. Although filling and drainage are ideal techniques, they have the obvious limitation that most bodies of water are otherwise desirable and hence not eliminable for the purposes of insect control. Much advantage can be gained by straightening streams and cleaning and grading shorelines to eliminate quiet pools especially suitable for breeding. Mosquitoes generally do better in water that has ample vegetation than in open water. This factor is one of high importance, and many mosquito control campaigns, such as the Tennessee Valley Authority project, utilize vegetation control as the primary technique in reducing mosquito populations. Shore line vegetation may be controlled by herbicides, by mechanical cutting, or by periodic, controlled fluctuation of lake water levels. In southeast Asia, where stream breeding species of *Anopheles* are important malaria vectors, periodic flushing of streams is accomplished by the use of automatic siphon dams that release impounded water as it reaches a critical depth.

Another approach to mosquito control is the use of predators, especially top-feeding minnows. In many regions a surprisingly large proportion of the diet of certain fish turns out to be the larvae of mosquitoes. In this connection, the control of vegetation is one way of permitting greater access of fish to larvae.

Management procedures aimed at adult insects are also widely practiced, the most obvious of these being the use of mesh screening on windows and doors. The removal or thinning of vegetation where it serves as adult resting places is also practiced, such as in mosquito control and in control of mite vectors of scrub typhus.

Chemical control

Although in many instances management of environment provides a high degree of effectiveness in the control of insects of medical importance, there is a preponderance of situations where the use of chemicals provides the only practical approach.

Chemicals can be used as attractants (materials that appear to attract), repellents (materials that appear to repel), and toxicants (materials that kill). These traditional terms are useful but not precise descriptions of chemical action. Attractants and repellents are behavior modifiers. The actual mechanism of operation may be quite different from what the name indicates. For instance ordinary sugar has almost no vapor tension and hence can have no directional influence on a fly that is at any distance from the sugar. Once a fly touches the sugar, however, locomotion is inhibited; hence when there are many flies in the vicinity, the number that collect around the sugar can give the impression of an actual attraction. Repellents, too, may have little or no directional influence at a distance from the chemical, but may simply induce locomotion, or inhibit feeding, when a fly or mosquito comes in contact with, or approaches close to one of these behavior modifying chemicals. Some chemicals, of course, do act in a directive manner at a distance. Attractants of this type, however, are not currently of practical value except in regard to trapping for survey purposes. Attractants (more properly "arrestants," materials that stop locomotion) are widely used in connection with bait applications for fly control. Repellents have achieved a position of importance where they can be applied frequently.

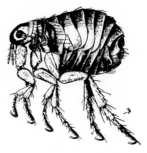

Fig. 20:5. Adult of the human flea, *Pulex irritans* L. *Courtesy USDA.*

The use of chemical procedures against mosquitoes is widespread. Attractants currently have only limited use in survey work rather than in control. Repellents of high efficiency against mosquitoes and other blood-sucking Diptera, as well as against chiggers, for use by individuals, have been developed. Dimethyl phthalate, ethyl hexanediol, dimethyl carbate, and Indalone have been in use for many years. More recently diethyl toluamide, an especially useful material, has come into use in the armed services and elsewhere. Toxicants are used against larvae as well as against adults of most forms.

As methods have evolved for control of mosquitoes in large areas, various oils have come into use to kill larvae. Initially kerosene and later diesel oil and other petroleum derivatives were sprayed on standing water. Except for the labor involved, oil spraying proved successful against *Culex* and *Aedes*, as well as *Anopheles*. Paris green, applied as a dust, was found to be successful against *Anopheles*, and much easier to handle than oils. Applied to the surface of standing water, the surface-feeding *Anopheles* consumed this poison readily, but the subsurface-feeding larvae of *Aedes* and *Culex* were virtually unaffected. Paris green became obsolete after the introduction of DDT, but surprisingly has begun to attract much favorable attention again as pellets against *Aedes*.

DDT proved to be an admirable mosquito larvicide that could be applied easily to large areas and that would persist for long periods of time. Soon dieldrin and other cyclodienes joined DDT as mosquito larvicides. As mosquitoes developed resistance to these chemicals, malathion, Diazinon, and other organophosphates were adapted for use as larvicides. An important development in mosquito larviciding came with the development of granular materials which could penetrate overhanging vegetation to reach larval breeding sites.

The problem of insecticide resistance has been an especially troublesome one relative to the control of insects of medical importance. Some of the most elaborate experimental studies have been directed at the house fly and at various species of mosquitoes. Problems of resistance have been most acute with the various chlorinated hydrocarbons, but significant resistance to many organic phosphates has also been seen. Although resistance has made many materials essentially obsolete for certain insects, other important species or races retain their susceptibility.

Control equipment

The treatment of adult flies and mosquitoes involves a wide variety of procedures. The choice of insecticide is strongly influenced by the choice of procedure. A time-honored and highly effective method of attack is the space spray. Here a finely divided mist is dispersed throughout the area to be protected, each insect then absorbing the insecticide through its cuticula and by way of its respiratory system. Space sprays can be achieved by hand sprayers, low pressure bombs, electric or gasoline powered atomizers, or by fixed installations that provide centralized operation and sometimes centralized supply of insecticide under pressure delivered to strategically placed nozzles. The space-spray application problem has been attacked by a particularly large number of special purpose commercial devices. In general space sprays provide almost immediate relief from current problems, but achieve relatively small long-term effects. Coupled with adequate screening and sanitation, space sprays can be the method of choice when frequent application is economically justified. Insecticides used as space sprays tend to be low-hazard materials, since the most appropriate places for their use are places of human or livestock occupancy. Synergized pyrethrum or allethrin combinations are among the most commonly used materials for space sprays, though Lethane, and Thanite are also important.

Fig. 20:6. A fog generator dispensing a smoke screen of insecticide. *From Curtis Automotive Devices, Inc., Westfield, Indiana.*

Fog generators have achieved wide use in protection of outdoor areas from the activity of adult mosquitoes and other bloodsucking Diptera. A wide variety of commercial fog generating equipment is currently available (Fig. 20:6). Many of these devices were adapted from military smoke screen generators. Some of these systems depend on direct heating of oil solutions, some involve secondary heating systems such as introducing the oil solutions into a stream of steam or into the exhaust system of an internal combustion engine, while some depend on direct mechanical atomization.

Mist blowers have been a particularly interesting recent development. These devices depend on the introduction of small quantities of concentrated insecticide solution into a large volume air blast. The air blast serves as the carrier for the finely divided insecticide solution. Mist blowers range from small wheelbarrow mounted units to large skid-mounted devices for use in trucks or boats. Many of these larger units are turret-mounted to permit ease in directing the discharge.

Insecticide vaporizers have had a period of popularity in recent years. Here an insecticide such as lindane is gently warmed and the resultant vapors are allowed to disperse in rooms, stores, barns, etc. It is usually recommended that appropriate thermostats be included with vaporizers to avoid excessive vaporization that might be a hazard to health.

REPRESENTATIVE PESTS OF MEDICAL IMPORTANCE

We have selected for detail study the house fly, mosquitoes, and chiggers.

House fly

Musca domestica Linnaeus [Diptera:Muscidae]

The house fly is a cosmopolitan species. It is intimately associated with humanity, thriving best where people are careless in the disposal of organic wastes. House flies are by no means limited to association with humans, though both house flies and humans tend to maintain high populations in similar general environments. As has been described earlier, house flies are highly important mechanical vectors of a great variety of human diseases.

Description. The house fly egg is of a pearly white color, elongate, and approximately 1 mm. long (Fig. 20:7A). The larva is a typical maggot, blunt at the posterior end and tapering to a point anteriorly (Fig. 20:7B). The cuticula is transparent, except toward the end of the larval period when the maggot assumes a creamy or yellowish appearance. When full grown the maggot may be 12 mm. or more in length. The large, black, posterior spiracles are D-shaped, with the straight margins directed toward the midline. The puparium, which is shorter and more robust than the larva, is slightly over 6 mm. long and, when mature, is dark brown in color (Fig. 20:7C). The adult fly is dark, mottled gray, and 6 to 7 mm. long (Fig. 20:7D). When retracted the adult mouthparts are inconspicuous, but during feeding they are protruded and capable of acting as an efficient swabbing device.

Life history. The house fly, like other Diptera, has a complete metamorphosis. The small, white eggs are laid in considerable numbers in decaying organic matter. A single gravid female fly may lay from 100 to 150 eggs at a time, and up to 600 or more eggs in two months of active adult life, though in midsummer longevity is thought to be under a month.

The development of the egg is rapid, the larva hatching within a day in normal summer temperatures. The larva feeds in the organic matter in which it hatches and grows rapidly. It goes through three instars in five to 15 days before pupating. The pupa remains within the shed integument of the last larval instar, which is referred to as a puparium. The pupal stage lasts from four to ten days. The newly transformed adult has a flexible membrane on the anterior portion of the head. This saclike membrane, called the ptilinum, pushes out from the head as it is filled with fluid. Pulsation of the abdomen causes a corresponding pulsation of the ptilinum,

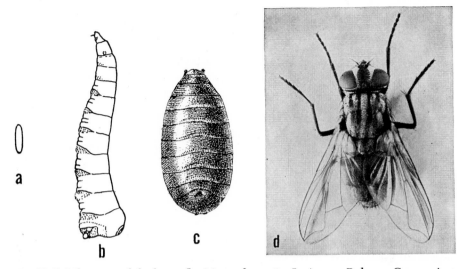

Fig. 20:7. Life stages of the house fly, *Musca domestica* L. A, egg; B, larva; C, puparium; D, adult. *Courtesy USDA.*

which is used as a tool in forcing open the puparium and in opening a passageway for the newly emerged fly to reach the open air. Two to 12 days after emergence the adults are ready to mate, and within two to three additional days the gravid female is ready to lay her first batch of eggs.

It is apparent that the reproductive potential of the house fly is very great. Assuming ideal reproducing conditions it is interesting to engage in the game of "how many at the end of the season?" Using conservative numbers (but total survival) the offspring of a single gravid female would easily reach 2×10^{20} flies. This ridiculous number would fill over 2,000 cubic miles! Obviously one limiting factor in this sequence is the amount of nutrient material available to the developing larvae. In a general way it can be stated that house flies will reproduce to the limit of the available food supply. This tends to emphasize the importance of sanitation in house fly control programs.

Control. There are three important general procedures in house fly control: sanitary, mechanical, and chemical. Sanitary practices by themselves are rarely effective in providing adequate control under farm conditions. They are, however, the key to most successful programs. Heavy breeding pressure is very difficult to overcome by attacks on the adults alone. The agriculturist should plan to dispose of fly-breeding materials to as great an extent as practicable.

In some situations mechanical practices such as screening, supplemented by traps or sticky paper, can be very valuable. On poultry farms the use of cockerels to search out and eat maggots has proven highly effective in appropriate situations.

By far the largest use of chemicals is as toxicants or poisons. These may be used against the larvae or against the adults. Larval treatments are less employed than adult treatments, and are used when breeding materials are of a localized nature. An effective treatment is 0.125 per cent Diazinon at the rate of one gallon per 100 square feet of surface.

The development of DDT opened a new era in fly control. It was the first of a series of residual products that provided long-term control. These residues were particularly effective against the house fly for several reasons. The swabbing mode of feeding made this fly especially vulnerable to residues. Of at least equal importance, however, is the sensitivity of the fly's tarsi to certain types of toxicants, such as DDT, that easily penetrate the cuticle and seemingly incapacitate the fly by overstimulating sensory end-organs. This last factor is enhanced by the house fly's habit of moving about on a resting surface, thereby coming in contact with a larger amount of residue. The earlier procedures involved over-all sprays both in interiors and outside. It was soon recognized that it was wasteful and unnecessary to spray all surfaces. The house fly has a tendency to rest on edges of doors or windows, edges of cracks between boards, pipes, or electric light cords. Anyone can see where house flies have rested during a season by the profusion of black feces-spots where the flies have been. This knowledge of fly behavior led to the use of localized applications. Such applications are as effective as over-all sprays, but offer great savings in material and permit use of much less elaborate equipment. Instead of high pressure, high gallonage equipment, simple compressed air sprayers or similar equipment can be used.

The residual applications of DDT in its first few years of use were so outstandingly successful that some people were convinced that the house fly was about to be eradicated. Fly control was one of the largest uses of DDT and other chlorinated hydrocarbons such as lindane, dieldrin, and toxaphene until the widespread development of resistance. These insecticides were replaced by various organophosphates such as malathion, Diazinon and Dipterex, and later supplemented by Korlan, DDVP, and Dibrom. While organophosphate resistance has also developed now, residual applications are still generally effective.

A specialized type of localized residual application is the impregnated cord technique. This procedure involves the use of cord, impregnated with materials such as parathion or Diazinon, draped in out of the way locations inside premises to be protected. This technique takes advantage of the resting behavior of the fly and permits the use of some materials which would otherwise be too hazardous for these situations.

Another localized treatment that became popular again with the widespread use of the organophosphates is the bait application. One of the first recent materials to be used in this connection was TEPP, mixed with molasses and water and distributed with a sprinkling can. Dipterex, Diazinon, and malathion soon replaced TEPP in this manner of use and also as dry baits, impregnated on sugar or other materials. These bait treatments, sprinkled in alleyways, gutters, and on sills, require almost no equipment for their application and have proven to be highly practical.

The topic of resistance is particularly important in house fly control. This aspect of the resistance problem has attracted wide attention throughout the world. The economic importance of this insect, coupled with the ease of quickly rearing large numbers of flies, has resulted in a tremendous research literature on house fly resistance. The rapid evolution of resistant flies has attracted wide attention among geneticists and evolutionists as well as among entomologists.

Mosquitoes

Anopheles freeborni Aitken
Anopheles quadrimaculatus Say   common malaria mosquito
Anopheles albimanus Wiedemann
Aedes dorsalis (Meigen)
Aedes aegypti (Linnaeus)   yellow-fever mosquito
Culex pipiens pipiens Linnaeus   northern house mosquito
Culex pipiens quinquefasciatus Say   southern house mosquito
Culex tarsalis Coquillett
[Diptera:Culicidae]

Mosquitoes, like house flies, are known around the world. There is, however, considerable variability in this group of insects, such that a great many species and genera have been discovered. Mosquitoes tend to be relatively independent of human activities, becoming important only as these are near breeding sites.

The mosquito family, Culicidae, contains at least 110 genera and over 2,400 species. A very large number of these species are so like other species that they are grouped into "complexes" below the generic level. Actually there are so many degrees of variation within the family Culicidae that taxonomic schemes frequently make use of the subdivisions "subfamily" within the family, "tribe" within the subfamily, "genus" within the tribe and so on to subgenus, group, species, and variety. The critical identification of these many forms is important because of the specific efficiency of mosquitoes in transmitting disease.

Of the many genera recognized, three stand out in importance and are widely known. These are the genera *Anopheles, Aedes,* and *Culex.* The discussion that follows will be limited to these three genera.

Description. The larval mosquito (Fig. 20:8B) is elongate and has the body clearly differentiated into a head, thorax, and abdomen. The head is distinct and freely moveable on the thorax. It has a pair of short antennae projecting forward. The eyes are of two types: the eyes of the first instar larva are small spots on each side of the head; as the larva grows, a pair of crescent-shaped compound eyes develop anterior to these original larval eyes. By the fourth instar these crescent-shaped compound eyes (which are the developing compound eyes of the adult) are much larger than the original larval eyes, and are essentially the active optic apparatus of the late larva.

The larval mouthparts are distinctly of a chewing type, though the actual function varies considerably among different species in relation to dietary habit. The mouthpart structures are well defined and include a particularly well developed labrum, mandibles, maxillae, hypopharynx, and labium.

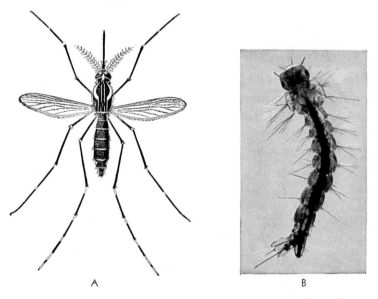

A   B

Fig. 20:8. The yellow-fever mosquito, *Aedes aegypti* (L.). A, adult; B, larva. *Courtesy USDA.*

Attached to the labrum are the prominent, long-haired mouth-brushes which are used in various ways, sweeping for microorganisms or holding larger particles for nibbling.

The larval thorax has no appendages other than a variety of hairs located in regularly defined groups. The nature and disposition of these hairs is of considerable use to taxonomists.

The first seven segments of the elongate abdomen are similar to each other and undistinguished. The eighth and ninth segments are worth special comment. The only spiracles of the larva are located dorsally on the eighth segment. In *Anopheles*, surrounding the spiracles, there is a very short projection which breaks through the surface film. In *Aedes* and *Culex* this projection is greatly elongated and is known as the siphon. The ninth segment has a variety of hairs, a saddle-like plate, and terminates in four large projections, the anal gills.

The mosquito pupa (Fig. 20:9) is an unusual form, frequently described as "comma-shaped." The main portion of the body contains the developing head and thorax of the adult, and is called the cephalothorax. The functional compound eyes are readily visible. On the dorsal part of the cephalothorax are two respiratory trumpets which connect to the developing thoracic spiracles of the adult. The abdomen is composed of nine segments and is terminated by a pair of conspicuous, overlapping plates, the "paddles." The abdomen is freely moveable on the cephalothorax, and by utilizing a crayfish-like abdominal motion, the pupa can quickly make an avoidance reaction in response to vibration or shadow.

The adult mosquito (Fig. 20:8A) is a slender, graceful insect, well adapted to independent flight for locating food, a mate, or an oviposition site. The mosquito head is a globular structure, freely moveable on the thorax. The largest part of its surface is covered by the two large compound eyes. The antennae are elongate and covered by whorls of hairs. At the base of each antenna is a globular structure, the Johnston's organ, a vibration-sensitive device. The mouthparts are elongate, sword-like structures that fit together as a single proboscis. The only mouthpart outside the proboscis is the pair of maxillary palpi, which vary in length with different genera as well as with sex. Both the antennae and maxillary palpi of male mosquitoes tend to be much more hairy than those of the females, a difference that is usually easily seen with the naked eye.

The proboscis of the female mosquito is an efficient piercing and sucking device (Fig. 2:7). The labium is an outer sheath which does not enter the wound. The hollow labrum-epipharynx is the heaviest of the penetrating structures and serves as the food intake tube. The hypopharynx is a flat-bladed structure that carries the salivary duct. The mandibles and maxillae consist of a pair each of the elongate, rodlike styli. In male mosquitoes the maxillae are somewhat shortened, while the mandibles are usually much shorter or lacking. The male mosquito is unable to pierce and suck blood.

The thorax of the adult mosquito is a well-developed area, specialized to provide locomotion for the mosquito. The legs are delicate, elongate structures that serve more for support than for transportation. The two wings are narrow and gently corrugated in the long axis. The wing veins are fringed with scales both above and below, as is also the posterior margin of each wing. The halteres are prominent and well developed.

The abdomen is narrow and elongate, generally longer than the head and thorax together. Following a blood meal the abdomen of the female can swell considerably. The tip of the abdomen of the male is distinguished by elaborate clasping devices.

Life history. Adult mosquitoes generally lay their eggs on the surface of water or in damp locations. Some species of *Aedes* may lay their eggs out of water, but usually in areas that are periodically flooded. In *Anopheles* and *Aedes* the eggs are laid singly, but in *Culex* they are laid in "rafts" of up to several hundred eggs each. These rafts, composed of elongate eggs, stacked vertically in a single layer, float on the surface of the water in which they are laid. Mosquito eggs laid on water usually hatch in from two to three days, but the eggs of *Aedes*, laid in damp situations may either hatch in a similar period or be delayed for varying periods even up to a year in length. (See Figure 20:9 for mosquito life histories.)

Wherever the eggs are laid, the larvae require water in which to complete their development. Mosquito larvae, however, are primarily air breathers and are usually found just beneath the surface film, with their spiracles open to the air above. The larvae feed on bacteria, yeasts, protozoans, and particles of organic matter, but may also depend on food materials in solution in the water. There are four larval instars between the egg and the pupa. The larval period may be passed in as little as three or four days, though more commonly in a week to ten days, or up to half a year or more in species that can overwinter as larvae.

The pupae are unusual in that they remain motile and responsive to external stimuli. They are probably the most active insect pupae. The pupal period lasts roughly from one to four days, depending on temperature as well as species differences. At the end of the pupal period air is swallowed, the abdomen straightens, the pupal skin splits, and the adult mosquito extricates itself and stands on the old pupal skin or on adjacent vegetation for a short period before flying away.

Ordinarily a few days are necessary after emergence before sexual maturity is attained. Depending on the time of year and on the species, adult mosquitoes may live from a few weeks to over half a year. Many species of mosquitoes have only one generation per year; others may have two to five or more depending on climatic conditions.

Mosquito larvae have relatively simple behavior patterns. Most of them spend their time just below the water surface, with the surface film broken only by the spiracles of *Aedes* and *Culex* and in addition by float hairs, notched organ, and maxillary palpi of *Anopheles*. The larvae of *Anopheles* feed on materials floating on the surface of the water while larvae of *Aedes* and *Culex* hang head down and feed below the water surface. Shadow or vibration initiates an alarm or scatter reaction, the larvae leaving the water surface and swimming downward by means of wide swinging motions of the abdomen. In some species at least, mosquito larvae are positively phototropic, this attraction being so powerful that a light placed below a breeding dish can cause the larvae to descend and remain until they are asphyxiated. Mosquito pupae exhibit a scatter reaction similar to that seen among the larvae.

Adult mosquitoes on the wing orient to visual stimuli as well as to air movement. While many mosquitoes, such as *Anopheles* species tend to remain localized within a half mile or so, many others, such as *Aedes* species, may range upward of 10 miles or more. High wind, of course, may greatly increase these figures.

Male and female mosquitoes exhibit quite different flight patterns, the former having a tendency to swarm, the latter remaining solitary. Male swarms tend to orient to dark objects below them and to maintain heights above these signals that are characteristic of the species. Females, locating these male swarms, enter them, mate, and then depart. Many species exhibit highly characteristic flight habits related to time of day or amount of light present. Feeding habits, too, can vary characteristically with the time of day or night.

Among *Anopheles* at least, the female that has just taken a blood meal tends to remain in the immediate vicinity for a significant period of time. It is this characteristic that has made the routine spraying of houses in malarious areas with insecticidal residues so effective in reducing or eliminating malaria transmission.

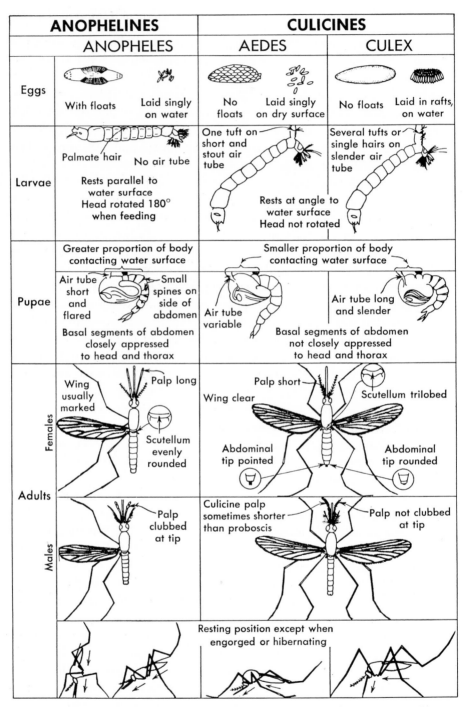

Fig. 20:9. Illustration of the life histories of three genera of mosquitoes. *Courtesy USDHEW, Public Health Service.*

Control. Activities related to mosquito control are sometimes of a localized nature, but more commonly they involve communities, districts, or even nations. Mosquitoes are attacked by a wide variety of procedures, from the elimination of breeding areas, through biological control agents, to a multitude of chemical procedures. Specific mention of many of these procedures was made in the introductory portions of this chapter.

The relationships of mosquito control activities to wildlife, make it necessary to take these factors into account in choosing chemicals for larviciding. Under such conditions, larvicides of a temporary nature must be used. DDT at 0.05 to 0.2 lb. per acre, or dieldrin, chlordane, heptachlor, or lindane at 0.1 lb. per acre can be regarded as reasonably safe to vertebrate wildlife. Where chlorinated hydrocarbon resistance has become a factor, malathion at 0.25 to 0.5 lb. per acre or parathion at 0.1 lb. per acre are useable. Paris green pellets at the rate of 15 lbs. of 5 per cent granules per acre are also recommended. Floodwater mosquitoes in irrigated pastures and rice fields may be controlled with parathion at 0.01 to 0.1 p.p.m., Phosdrin at 1.0 p.p.m., or Dipterex at 0.5 p.p.m.

Where protection of wildlife is not a factor, residual larvicides of much longer duration than the temporary larvicides mentioned above may be used. Examples of this type of treatment are BHC at the rate of 1 lb. of gamma isomer per acre, DDT at 3 lbs. per acre, and dieldrin at 1 lb. per acre.

Adult mosquitoes can be controlled by space sprays or by residual applications. Outdoor space sprays are utilized chiefly against species of *Aedes* and *Culex,* with DDT, chlordane, and lindane the materials of choice where resistance is not a factor. In the event of resistance, malathion or other organophosphate insecticides may be used.

Residual applications of insecticide to the interior of houses are widely employed in malaria control operations. Common materials and rates of application are DDT at 100 or 200 mg. per square foot, dieldrin at 50 mg. per square foot, and BHC at 50 mg. per square foot. The recent gigantic campaigns against malaria have taken the form, almost entirely, of residual applications to the interior of dwellings. Such applications, made once or twice a year, have had little effect in reducing total mosquito populations, but have had overwhelming success in killing those *Anopheles* that have fed on human beings in malarious areas. The result has been a sharp reduction in malaria cases, with the high hope of eventual elimination of this disease. That this goal is ambitious cannot be denied, but it is supported by the earlier example of success against yellow fever. The development of resistant strains of mosquitoes may slow the rate of progress, but it is not anticipated that this will prevent the eventual control of malaria.

Chiggers

Trombicula akamushi (Brumpt)
Trombicula deliensis Walch
Trombicula alfreddugesi (Oudemans)
[Acarina:Trombiculidae]

Two types of effect on humans are caused by chiggers. The first is a direct result of the feeding activities of the larval mite, the second is a result of the transmission of disease organisms. Chigger larvae feed on a wide variety of terrestrial vertebrates, including amphibians, reptiles, birds, and mammals. Man appears to be a host of relatively minor importance to the chigger. The larva attaches itself by means of its chelicerae to folds of skin or to the edges of hair follicles. It secretes a fluid that digests a localized portion of the skin and at the same time induces the underlying tissue to become organized as an elongate tube, frequently as long as the body of the chigger itself. This tube, called the stylostome or histosiphon, is formed over a period of several hours. The chigger remains attached, for a variable length of time, until it is engorged upon the predigested fluid (not blood) that it draws through the histosiphon. Between three and 24 hours after exposure, the lesion induced by the mite becomes an urticarial papule that itches intensely. The lesions may be from 0.4 to 2 cm. in diameter and may persist for several weeks, during which time they may itch intermittently. The itching frequently induces scratching which may be followed by secondary infection.

In the Asiatic Pacific area chiggers are the vectors of scrub typhus and suspected vectors of hemorrhagic fever. Ranging from Japan to Singapore, *T. akamushi* is the prime vector of scrub typhus, while in Burma, Sumatra, and New Guinea, *T. deliensis* is the major vector of this disease. Scrub typhus, known also as tsutsugamushi disease, is one of the rickettsial diseases, and is important in Japan and throughout southeast Asia. The disease is frequently fatal and is sufficiently common to be of major importance.

Chiggers, such as *T. alfreddugesi,* are often common on lawns as well as in the wild in areas with a hot, moist climate. They are particularly common in southeastern and south central regions of the United States and on the islands of the Carribean. Many similar species are found in most parts of the world.

Description. Trombiculid mites pass through four life stages during the course of their development. The spherical eggs are small (100 to 200 microns diameter) and for some species are unknown except as dissected from the gravid female adult. Some may be ovoviviparous. The first motile,

Fig. 20:10. A chigger or larva of the mite, *Trombicula alfreddugesi* (Oudemans), the stage which attacks man and other vertebrates. *Courtesy USDHEW, Public Health Service.*

free living stage is a six-legged larva, from 150 to 300 microns long and red to pale yellow or white depending on the species (Fig. 20:10). It is the larval stage that parasitizes vertebrates. The next stage consists of an eight-legged nymph, 600 to 1,000 microns long, hirsute, and resembling the adult. The adult closely resembles the nymph but is much larger (Fig. 4:5C).

Life history. Chigger eggs are commonly laid on the ground, or in the soil. Some species have been observed to spend from four to ten days in the egg and deutovum stage (the deutovum appears within a secondary chitinous envelope within the egg shell and persists after the egg shell breaks). The larvae move up onto grass or weeds, often in great numbers, and make contact with vertebrate hosts as they brush past. On humans the larvae settle mostly in the groin, under armpits, or where clothing is constricted as at the belt line or under socks. The larvae may remain attached for up to three to six days, occasionally longer, until engorged, and then drop from the hosts to the ground. The nymphal stage apparently lasts several weeks before transformation to the adult. Adults have been kept alive for at least 45 days. It has been estimated that chigger life cycles may last from two to 12 months or longer, with from one to three generations per year in temperate zones, and with continuous production in more tropical regions.

Control. Two major approaches in chigger control have been followed. The first is by the use of repellents, applied either directly to the person or by clothing impregnation. The second is an attack on the chigger itself, by increasing the difficulties of contacting a vertebrate host, or by the use of toxicants broadcast on the soil or vegetation harboring the chiggers.

Sulfur dust has been widely used for many years, applied directly to the body or broadcast on infested areas. Superior repellents and toxicants have come into use within the last two decades. Among the repellents are dimethyl phthalate, dibutyl phthalate, and benzyl benzoate, the latter two making especially good clothing impregnants, retaining their effectiveness even after several launderings. Liquid repellents are also used as band treatments on cuffs, seams, and tops of socks. In many instances these standard repellents appear to act also as toxicants.

While clothing repellents provide excellent protection of the individual, it is frequently desirable to eliminate the chiggers themselves from campsites or lawns. Several residual insecticides are good for this purpose. Chlordane, toxaphene, BHC, dieldrin, and aldrin at 2 lbs. or less per acre, have been successfully used against many species of chiggers. The ease of use of toxicants makes this method highly practical for chigger control, but where economic poisons are undesirable, the clearing and removal of vegetation reduces chigger populations by increasing the difficulties of the chiggers in finding suitable vertebrate hosts, and in reducing the presence of hosts other than man.

Selected References

Baker, E. W., T. M. Evans, D. J. Gould, W. B. Hull, and H. L. Keegan, *A Manual of Parasitic Mites* (New York: National Pest Control Association, 1956).

Bates, M., *The Natural History of Mosquitoes* (New York: Macmillan, 1949).

Brown, A. W. A., *Insecticide Resistance in Arthropods* (Geneva: World Health Organization, 1958).

Foote, R. H., and D. R. Cook, *Mosquitoes of Medical Importance*, USDA Agr. Handbook No. 152, 1959.

Herms, W. B., and M. T. James, *Medical Entomology* (New York: Macmillan, 1960).

Horsfall, W. R., *Mosquitoes: Their Bionomics and Relation to Disease* (New York: Ronald, 1955).

Howard, L. O., *The House Fly* (New York: Stokes, 1911).

Marshall, J. F., *The British Mosquitoes* (London: British Museum, 1938).

Matheson, R., *Handbook of the Mosquitoes of North America* (Ithaca, N. Y.: Comstock, 1944).

————, *Medical Entomology* (Ithaca, N. Y.: Comstock, 1950).

Stone, A., K. L. Knight, and H. Starke, *A Synoptic Catalog of the Mosquitoes of the World*. The Thomas Say Foundation, Vol. 6, Ent. Soc. Amer. Wash. D.C., 1959.

West, L. S., *The Housefly* (Ithaca, N. Y.: Comstock, 1951).

APPENDIX OF COMMON-SCIENTIFIC NAMES [1]

aedes mosquito * *Aedes* spp. Diptera:Culicidae
African sheep louse * *Linognathus africanus* Kellogg & Paine Anoplura:Lino-
gnathidae
air-sac mite * *Cytodites nudus* (Vizioli) Acarina:Cytoditidae
alder flea beetle *Altica ambiens* LeConte Coleoptera:Chrysomelidae
alfalfa caterpillar *Colias eurytheme* Boisduval Lepidoptera:Pieridae
alfalfa gall midge *Asphondylia websteri* Felt Diptera:Cecidomyiidae
alfalfa looper *Autographa californica* (Speyer) Lepidoptera:Noctuidae
alfalfa plant bug *Adelphocoris lineolatus* (Goeze) Hemiptera:Miridae
alfalfa snout beetle *Brachyrhinus ligustici* (Linnaeus) Coleoptera:Curculion-
idae
alfalfa webworm *Loxostege commixtalis* (Walker) Lepidoptera:Pyraustidae
alfalfa weevil *Hypera postica* (Gyllenhal) Coleoptera:Curculionidae
almond moth *Ephestia cautella* (Walker) Lepidoptera:Phycitidae
American cockroach *Periplaneta americana* (Linnaeus) Orthoptera:Blattidae
American dog tick *Dermacentor variabilis* (Say) Acarina:Ixodidae
American grasshopper *Schistocerca americana* (Drury) Orthoptera:Acrididae
angora-goat biting louse *Bovicola limbata* (Gervais) Mallophaga:Trichodec-
tidae
Angoumois grain moth *Sitotroga cerealella* (Olivier) Lepidoptera:Gelechiidae
angular-winged katydid *Microcentrum retinerve* (Burmeister) Orthoptera:Tet-
tigoniidae
anopheles mosquito * *Anopheles* spp. Diptera:Culicidae
apple aphid *Aphis pomi* De Geer Homoptera:Aphidae
apple curculio *Tachypterellus quadrigibbus* (Say) Coleoptera:Curculionidae
apple fruit miner *Marmara pomonella* Busck Lepidoptera:Gracilariidae
apple grain aphid *Rhopalosiphum fitchii* (Sanderson) Homoptera:Aphidae
apple leafhopper *Empoasca maligna* (Walsh) Homoptera:Cicadellidae
apple maggot *Rhagoletis pomonella* (Walsh) Diptera:Tephritidae
apple red bug *Lygidea mendax* Reuter Hemiptera:Miridae
apple rust mite *Vasates schlechtendali* (Nalepa) Acarina:Eriophyidae
apple sucker *Psylla mali* (Schmidberger) Homoptera:Psyllidae
apple twig beetle *Stephanoderes obscurus* (Fabricius) Coleoptera:Scolytidae

---

[1] Common names unmarked by asterisk are approved by Entomological Society of
America (*Bul. Ent. Soc. Amer.*, Vol. 6, No. 4, 1960); those marked by asterisk (*) are
common names that have been used in the literature but as yet have not been acted
upon or approved by the Society.

Argentine ant *Iridomyrmex humilis* (Mayr) Hymenoptera:Formicidae

Arid-land subterranean termite * *Reticulitermes tibialis* Banks Isoptera:Rhinotermitidae

army cutworm *Chorizagrotis auxiliaris* (Grote) Lepidoptera:Noctuidae

armyworm *Pseudaletia unipuncta* (Haworth) Lepidoptera:Noctuidae

Asiatic garden beetle *Autoserica castanea* Arrow Coleoptera:Scarabaeidae

asparagus beetle *Crioceris asparagi* (Linnaeus) Coleoptera:Chrysomelidae

asparagus miner *Melanagromyza simplex* (Loew) Diptera:Agromyzidae

asparagus spider mite * *Schizotetranychus asparagi* (Oudemans) Acarina:-Tetranychidae

Australian-pine borer *Chrysobothris tranquebarica* (Gmelin) Coleoptera:Buprestidae

azalea lace bug *Stephanitis pyrioides* Scott Hemiptera:Tingidae

azalea leaf miner *Gracilaria azaleella* Brants Lepidoptera:Gracilariidae

azalea whitefly *Pealius azaleae* (Baker & Moles) Homoptera:Aleyrodidae

balsam-fir sawyer *Monochamus marmorator* Kirby Coleoptera:Cerambycidae

banana root borer *Cosmopolites sordidus* (Germar) Coleoptera:Curculionidae

banded alder borer *Rosalia funebris* Motschulsky Coleoptera:Cerambycidae

banded woollybear *Isia isabella* (J. E. Smith) Lepidoptera:Arctiidae

Banks grass mite *Oligonychus pratensis* (Banks) Acarina:Tetranychidae

bean aphid *Aphis fabae* Scopoli Homoptera:Aphidae

bean leaf beetle *Cerotoma trifurcata* (Forster) Coleoptera:Chrysomelidae

bean leaf skeletonizer *Autoplusia egena* (Guenée) Lepidoptera:Noctuidae

bean thrips *Hercothrips fasciatus* (Pergande) Thysanoptera:Thripidae

bean weevil *Acanthoscelides obtectus* (Say) Coleoptera:Bruchidae

bed bug *Cimex lectularius* Linnaeus Hemiptera:Cimicidae

beet armyworm *Spodoptera exigua* (Hübner) Lepidoptera:Noctuidae

beet leafhopper *Circulifer tenellus* (Baker) Homoptera:Cicadellidae

beet webworm *Loxostege sticticalis* (Linnaeus) Lepidoptera:Pyraustidae

bella moth *Utetheisa bella* (Linnaeus) Lepidoptera:Arctiidae

big-headed grasshopper * *Aulocara elliotti* (Thomas) Orthoptera:Acrididae

birch leaf miner *Fenusa pusilla* (Lepeletier) Hymenoptera:Tenthredinidae

black blow fly *Phormia regina* (Meigen) Diptera:Calliphoridae

black carpenter ant *Camponotus pennsylvanicus* (De Geer) Hymenoptera:-Formicidae

black carpet beetle *Attagenus piceus* (Olivier) Coleoptera:Dermestidae

black cherry aphid *Myzus cerasi* (Fabricius) Homoptera:Aphidae

black cherry fruit fly *Rhagoletis fausta* (Osten Sacken) Diptera:Tephritidae

black cutworm *Agrotis ipsilon* (Hufnagel) Lepidoptera:Noctuidae

black grain stem sawfly *Cephus tabidus* (Fabricius) Hymenoptera:Cephidae

black-headed fireworm *Rhopobota naevana* (Hübner) Lepidoptera:Olethreutidae

Black Hills beetle *Dendroctonus ponderosae* Hopkins Coleoptera:Scolytidae

black-horned tree cricket *Oecanthus nigricornis nigricornis* Walker Orthoptera:-Gryllidae

black horse fly *Tabanus atratus* Fabricius Diptera:Tabanidae

black lady beetle *Rhizobius ventralis* (Erichson) Coleoptera:Coccinellidae

black-legged tick *Ixodes ricinus scapularis* Say Acarina:Ixodidae

black peach aphid *Anuraphis persicaeniger* (Smith) Homoptera:Aphidae

black pine leaf scale *Aspidiotus californicus* Coleman Homoptera:Diaspididae

black scale *Saissetia oleae* (Bernard) Homoptera:Coccidae

black vine weevil *Brachyrhinus sulcatus* (Fabricius) Coleoptera:Curculionidae

black widow spider *Latrodectus mactans* (Fabricius) Araneida:Theridiidae
blueberry blossom weevil * *Anthonomus musculus* Say Coleoptera:Curculion-
idae
blueberry fruit fly * *Rhagoletis pomonella* (Walsh) Diptera:Tephritidae
blueberry maggot *Rhagoletis pomonella* (Walsh) Diptera:Tephritidae
bluegrass aphid * *Rhopalosiphum poae* Gillette Homoptera:Aphidae
bluegrass webworm *Crambus teterrellus* (Zincken) Lepidoptera:Crambidae
blunt-nosed cranberry leafhopper *Scleroracus vaccinii* (Van Duzee) Homop-
tera:Cicadellidae
body louse *Pediculus humanus humanus* Linnaeus Anoplura:Pediculidae
Boisduval scale * *Diaspis boisduvalii* Signoret Homoptera:Diaspididae
boll weevil *Anthonomus grandis* Boheman Coleoptera:Curculionidae
bollworm *Heliothis zea* (Boddie) Lepidoptera:Noctuidae
booklice *Liposcelis* spp. Psocoptera:Liposcelidae
boxelder bug *Leptocoris trivittatus* (Say) Hemiptera:Coreidae
boxelder leaf roller *Gracilaria negundella* Chambers Lepidoptera:Gracilariidae
boxwood leaf miner *Monarthropalpus buxi* (Laboulbène) Diptera:Cecidomyi-
idae
boxwood psyllid *Psylla buxi* (Linnaeus) Homoptera:Psyllidae
bramble leafhopper *Ribautiana tenerrima* (Herrich-Schäffer) Homoptera:Ci-
cadellidae
broadbean weevil *Bruchus rufimanus* Boheman Coleoptera:Bruchidae
broad-horned flour beetle *Gnathocerus cornutus* (Fabricius) Coleoptera:Tene-
brionidae
broad mite *Hemitarsonemus latus* (Banks) Acarina:Tarsonemidae
broad-winged katydid *Microcentrum rhombifolium* (Saussure) Orthoptera:-
Tettigoniidae
bronze birch borer *Agrilus anxius* Gory Coleoptera:Buprestidae
brown-banded cockroach *Supella supellectilium* (Serville) Orthoptera:Blatti-
dae
brown cotton bug * *Euschistus impictiventris* Stål Hemiptera:Pentatomidae
brown cotton leafworm * *Acontia dacia* Druce Lepidoptera:Noctuidae
brown dog tick *Rhipicephalus sanguineus* (Latreille) Acarina:Ixodidae
brown soft scale *Coccus hesperidum* Linnaeus Homoptera:Coccidae
brown spider mite * *Bryobia rubrioculus* (Scheuten) Acarina:Tetranychidae
brown stink bug *Euschistus servus* (Say) Hemiptera:Pentatomidae
brown-tail moth *Nygmia phaeorrhoea* (Donovan) Lepidoptera:Lymantriidae
brown wheat mite *Petrobia latens* (Müller) Acarina:Tetranychidae
buffalo treehopper *Stictocephala bubalus* (Fabricius) Homoptera:Membrac-
idae
bulb mite *Rhizoglyphus echinopus* (Fumouze & Robin) Acarina:Acaridae
bulb scale mite *Steneotarsonemus laticeps* (Halbert) Acarina:Tarsonemidae
bumble flower beetle *Euphoria inda* (Linnaeus) Coleoptera:Scarabaeidae
burrowing nematode * *Radopholus similis* (Cobb) Tylenchida:Tylenchidae
cabbage aphid *Brevicoryne brassicae* (Linnaeus) Homoptera:Aphidae
cabbage butterfly * *Pieris rapae* (Linnaeus) Lepidoptera:Pieridae
cabbage looper *Trichoplusia ni* (Hübner) Lepidoptera:Noctuidae
cabbage maggot *Hylemya brassicae* (Bouché) Diptera:Anthomyiidae
cabbage seedpod weevil *Ceutorhynchus assimilis* (Paykull) Coleoptera:Cur-
culionidae
cabbage webworm *Hellula rogatalis* (Hulst) Lepidoptera:Pyraustidae
cadelle *Tenebroides mauritanicus* (Linnaeus) Coleoptera:Ostomatidae

California green lacewing * *Chrysopa californica* Coquillett Neuroptera:Chrysopidae
carnation bud mite * *Aceria paradianthi* Keifer Acarina:Eriophyidae
carnation leaf roller * *Platynota stultana* Walsingham Lepidoptera:Tortricidae
carnation tip maggot *Hylemya echinata* Séguy Diptera:Anthomyiidae
carpet beetle *Anthrenus scrophulariae* (Linnaeus) Coleoptera:Dermestidae
carpet moth *Trichophaga tapetzella* (Linnaeus) Lepidoptera:Tineidae
carrot beetle *Bothynus gibbosus* (De Geer) Coleoptera:Scarabaeidae
carrot rust fly *Psila rosae* (Fabricius) Diptera:Psilidae
carrot weevil *Listronotus oregonensis* (LeConte) Coleoptera:Curculionidae
casemaking clothes moth *Tinea pellionella* (Linnaeus) Lepidoptera:Tineidae
cat flea *Ctenocephalides felis* (Bouché) Siphonaptera:Pulicidae
cat louse *Felicola subrostrata* (Burmeister) Mallophaga:Trichodectidae
cattle biting louse *Bovicola bovis* (Linnaeus) Mallophaga:Trichodectidae
cattle follicle mite *Demodex bovis* Stiles Acarina:Demodicidae
cattle tail louse *Haematopinus quadripertusus* Fahrenholz Anoplura:Hematopinidae
cattle tick *Boophilus annulatus* (Say) Acarina:Ixodidae
celery leaf tier *Udea rubigalis* (Guenée) Lepidoptera:Pyraustidae
celery looper *Anagrapha falcifera* (Kirby) Lepidoptera:Noctuidae
cherry fruit fly *Rhagoletis cingulata* (Loew) Diptera:Tephritidae
cherry fruit sawfly *Hoplocampa cookei* (Clarke) Hymenoptera:Tenthredinidae
cherry fruitworm *Grapholitha packardi* Zeller Lepidoptera:Olethreutidae
chicken body louse *Menacanthus stramineus* (Nitzsch) Mallophaga:Menoponidae
chicken head louse *Cuclotogaster heterographus* (Nitzsch) Mallophaga:Philopteridae
chicken mite *Dermanyssus gallinae* (De Geer) Acarina:Dermanyssidae
chigoe *Tunga penetrans* (Linnaeus) Siphonaptera:Tungidae
chinch bug *Blissus leucopterus* (Say) Hemiptera:Lygaeidae
chorioptic mange mite * *Chorioptes bovis* (Hering) Acarina:Psoroptidae
chrysanthemum aphid *Macrosiphoniella sanborni* (Gillette) Homoptera:Aphidae
chrysanthemum gall midge *Diarthronomyia chrysanthemi* Ahlberg Diptera:Cecidomyiidae
chrysanthemum lace bug *Corythuca marmorata* (Uhler) Hemiptera:Tingidae
chrysanthemum leaf miner *Phytomyza atricornis* Meigen Diptera:Agromyzidae
chrysanthemum thrips *Thrips nigropilosus* Uzel Thysanoptera:Thripidae
cigarette beetle *Lasioderma serricorne* (Fabricius) Coleoptera:Anobiidae
citricola scale *Coccus pseudomagnoliarum* (Kuwana) Homoptera:Coccidae
citrophilus mealybug *Pseudococcus gahani* Green Homoptera:Pseudococcidae
citrus blackfly *Aleurocanthus woglumi* Ashby Homoptera:Aleyrodidae
citrus mealybug *Pseudococcus citri* (Risso) Homoptera:Pseudococcidae
citrus red mite *Panonychus citri* (McGregor) Acarina:Tetranychidae
citrus rust mite *Phyllocoptruta oleivora* (Ashmead) Acarina:Eriophyidae
citrus thrips *Scirtothrips citri* (Moulton) Thysanoptera:Thripidae
citrus whitefly *Dialeurodes citri* (Ashmead) Homoptera:Aleyrodidae
clay-colored weevil * *Brachyrhinus singularis* (Linnaeus) Coleoptera:Curculionidae
clear-winged grasshopper *Camnula pellucida* (Scudder) Orthoptera:Acrididae
clouded sulphur *Colias philodice* Latreille Lepidoptera:Pieridae
clover aphid *Anuraphis bakeri* (Cowen) Homoptera:Aphidae

clover hayworm *Hypsopygia costalis* (Fabricius) Lepidoptera:Pyralidae
clover head caterpillar *Grapholitha interstinctana* (Clemens) Lepidoptera:-
Olethreutidae
clover head weevil *Hypera meles* (Fabricius) Coleoptera:Curculionidae
clover leafhopper *Aceratagallia sanguinolenta* (Provancher) Homoptera:Cica-
dellidae
clover leaf weevil *Hypera punctata* (Fabricius) Coleoptera:Curculionidae
clover mite *Bryobia praetiosa* Koch Acarina:Tetranychidae
clover root borer *Hylastinus obscurus* (Marsham) Coleoptera:Scolytidae
clover root curculio *Sitona hispidula* (Fabricius) Coleoptera:Curculionidae
clover seed chalcid *Bruchophagus gibbus* (Boheman) Hymenoptera:Eurytom-
idae
clover seed midge *Dasyneura leguminicola* (Lintner) Diptera:Cecidomyiidae
clover seed weevil *Miccotrogus picirostris* (Fabricius) Coleoptera:Curculion-
idae
cluster fly *Pollenia rudis* (Fabricius) Diptera:Calliphoridae
codling moth *Carpocapsa pomonella* (Linnaeus) Lepidoptera:Olethreutidae
Colorado potato beetle *Leptinotarsa decemlineata* (Say) Coleoptera:Chryso-
melidae
columbine leaf miner *Phytomyza minuscula* Goureau Diptera:Agromyzidae
common cattle grub *Hypoderma lineatum* (de Villers) Diptera:Hypodermat-
idae
common malaria mosquito *Anopheles quadrimaculatus* Say Diptera:Culicidae
common wood cockroach ° *Parcoblatta pennsylvanica* (De Geer) Orthoptera:-
Blattidae
composite thrips *Microcephalothrips abdominalis* (D. L. Crawford) Thysanop-
tera:Thripidae
conchuela *Chlorochroa ligata* (Say) Hemiptera:Pentatomidae
confused flour beetle *Tribolium confusum* Jacquelin duVal Coleoptera:Tene-
brionidae
convergent lady beetle *Hippodamia convergens* Guérin-Méneville Coleoptera:-
Coccinellidae
Cooley spruce gall aphid *Chermes cooleyi* Gillette Homoptera:Chermidae
corn blotch leaf miner *Agromyza parvicornis* Loew Diptera:Agromyzidae
corn earworm *Heliothis zea* (Boddie) Lepidoptera:Noctuidae
cornfield ant *Lasius alienus* (Förster) Hymenoptera:Formicidae
corn flea beetle *Chaetocnema pulicaria* Melsheimer Coleoptera:Chrysomelidae
corn leaf aphid *Rhopalosiphum maidis* (Fitch) Homoptera:Aphidae
corn planthopper *Peregrinus maidis* (Ashmead) Homoptera:Delphacidae
corn root aphid *Anuraphis maidiradicis* (Forbes) Homoptera:Aphidae
corn root webworm *Crambus caliginosellus* Clemens Lepidoptera:Crambidae
corn sap beetle *Carpophilus dimidiatus* (Fabricius) Coleoptera:Nitidulidae
corn silk beetle *Luperodes brunneus* (Crotch) Coleoptera:Chrysomelidae
corn wireworm ° *Melanotus communis* Gyllenhal Coleoptera:Elateridae
cotton aphid *Aphis gossypii* Glover Homoptera:Aphidae
cotton blister mite *Aceria gossypii* (Banks) Acarina:Eriophyidae
cotton fleahopper *Psallus seriatus* (Reuter) Hemiptera:Miridae
cotton leaf perforator *Bucculatrix thurberiella* Busck Lepidoptera:Lyonetiidae
cotton leafworm *Alabama argillacea* (Hübner) Lepidoptera:Noctuidae
cotton square borer *Strymon melinus* (Hübner) Lepidoptera:Lycaenidae
cotton stainer *Dysdercus suturellus* (Herrich-Schäffer) Hemiptera:Pyrrhocori-
dae

cottony camellia scale * *Pulvinaria floccifera* Westwood Homoptera:Coccidae
cottony-cushion scale *Icerya purchasi* Maskell Homoptera:Margarodidae
cottony peach scale *Pulvinaria amygdali* Cockerell Homoptera:Coccidae
coulee cricket *Peranabrus scabricollis* (Thomas) Orthoptera:Tettigoniidae
cowpea aphid *Aphis medicaginis* Koch Homoptera:Aphidae
cowpea curculio *Chalcodermus aeneus* Boheman Coleoptera:Curculionidae
cowpea weevil *Callosobruchus maculatus* (Fabricius) Coleoptera:Bruchidae
crab louse *Phthirus pubis* (Linnaeus) Anoplura:Pediculidae
cranberry fruitworm *Acrobasis vaccinii* Riley Lepidoptera:Phycitidae
cranberry girdler *Crambus topiarius* Zeller Lepidoptera:Crambidae
cranberry rootworm *Rhabdopterus picipes* (Olivier) Coleoptera:Chrysomelidae
cranberry spanworm *Anavitrinella pampinaria* (Guenée) Lepidoptera:Geometridae
cranberry tipworm * *Dasyneura vaccinii* (Smith) Diptera:Cecidomyiidae
crescent-marked lily aphid *Myzus circumflexus* (Buckton) Homoptera:Aphidae
curled rose sawfly *Allantus cinctus* (Linnaeus) Hymenoptera:Tenthredinidae
currant aphid *Capitophorus ribis* (Linnaeus) Homoptera:Aphidae
currant borer *Ramosia tipuliformis* (Clerck) Lepidoptera:Aegeriidae
currant bud mite *Cecidophyes ribis* (Nalepa) Acarina:Eriophyidae
currant fruit fly *Epochra canadensis* (Loew) Diptera:Tephritidae
currant stem girdler *Janus integer* (Norton) Hymenoptera:Cephidae
cyclamen mite *Steneotarsonemus pallidus* (Banks) Acarina:Tarsonemidae
dark-lipped lacewing * *Chrysopa rufilabris* Burmeister Neuroptera:Chrysopidae
depluming mite *Knemidokoptes gallinae* (Railliet) Acarina:Sarcoptidae
desert locust * *Schistocerca gregaria* Forskål Orthoptera:Acrididae
desert spider mite *Tetranychus desertorum* Banks Acarina:Tetranychidae
devastating grasshopper *Melanoplus devastator* Scudder Orthoptera:Acrididae
diamondback moth *Plutella maculipennis* (Curtis) Lepidoptera:Hyponomeutidae
dictyospermum scale *Chrysomphalus dictyospermi* (Morgan) Homoptera:Diaspididae
differential grasshopper *Melanoplus differentialis* (Thomas) Orthoptera:Acrididae
dog biting louse *Trichodectes canis* (De Geer) Mallophaga:Trichodectidae
dog flea *Ctenocephalides canis* (Curtis) Siphonaptera:Pulicidae
dog follicle mite *Demodex canis* Leydig Acarina:Demodicidae
dog sucking louse *Linognathus setosus* (Olfers) Anoplura:Linognathidae
dogwood spittlebug *Clastoptera proteus* Fitch Homoptera:Cercopidae
Douglas-fir beetle *Dendroctonus pseudotsugae* Hopkins Coleoptera:Scolytidae
Douglas-fir tussock moth *Hemerocampa pseudotsugata* McDunnough Lepidoptera:Lymantriidae
dried-fruit mite *Carpoglyphus lactis* (Linnaeus) Acarina:Carpoglyphidae
dried-fruit moth *Vitula edmandsae serratilineella* Ragonot Lepidoptera:Phycitidae
drone fly * *Eristalis tenax* (Linnaeus) Diptera:Syrphidae
drugstore beetle *Stegobium paniceum* (Linnaeus) Coleoptera:Anobiidae
dryberry mite *Phyllocoptes gracilis* (Nalepa) Acarina:Eriophyidae
dry-land wireworm *Ctenicera glauca* (Germar) Coleoptera:Elateridae
dusky sap beetle *Carpophilus lugubris* Murray Coleoptera:Nitidulidae
ear tick *Otobius megnini* (Dugès) Acarina:Argasidae
eastern field wireworm *Limonius agonus* (Say) Coleoptera:Elateridae
eastern raspberry fruitworm *Byturus rubi* Barber Coleoptera:Byturidae

eastern spruce gall aphid *Chermes abietis* Linnaeus   Homoptera:Chermidae
eastern subterranean termite *Reticulitermes flavipes* (Kollar)   Isoptera:Rhino-
termitidae
eastern tent caterpillar *Malacosoma americanum* (Fabricius)   Lepidoptera:-
Lasiocampidae
eggplant lace bug *Gargaphia solani* Heidemann   Hemiptera:Tingidae
eggplant leaf miner *Keiferia glochinella* (Zeller)   Lepidoptera:Gelechiidae
elm leaf beetle *Galerucella luteola* (Müller)   Coleoptera:Chrysomelidae
elm spanworm *Ennomos subsignarius* (Hübner)   Lepidoptera:Geometridae
elongate flea beetle *Systena elongata* (Fabricius)   Coleoptera:Chrysomelidae
Engelmann spruce beetle *Dendroctonus engelmanni* Hopkins   Coleoptera:Scoly-
tidae
English grain aphid *Macrosiphum granarium* (Kirby)   Homoptera:Aphidae
European chicken flea *Ceratophyllus gallinae* (Schrank)   Siphonaptera:Cera-
tophyllidae
European corn borer *Ostrinia nubilalis* (Hübner)   Lepidoptera:Pyraustidae
European earwig *Forficula auricularia* Linnaeus   Dermaptera:Forficulidae
European fruit lecanium *Lecanium corni* Bouché   Homoptera:Coccidae
European grain moth *Nemapogon granella* (Linnaeus)   Lepidoptera:Tineidae
European pine shoot moth *Rhyacionia buoliana* (Schiffermüller)   Lepidoptera:-
Olethreutidae
European red mite *Panonychus ulmi* (Koch)   Acarina:Tetranychidae
European wheat stem sawfly *Cephus pygmaeus* (Linnaeus)   Hymenoptera:-
Cephidae
eyed click beetle *Alaus oculatus* (Linnaeus)   Coleoptera:Elateridae
eye-spotted bud moth *Spilonota ocellana* (Denis & Schiffermüller)   Lepidop-
tera:Olethreutidae
face fly *Musca autumnalis* De Geer   Diptera:Muscidae
fall armyworm *Laphygma frugiperda* (J. E. Smith)   Lepidoptera:Noctuidae
fall cankerworm *Alsophila pometaria* (Harris)   Lepidoptera:Geometridae
fall webworm *Hyphantria cunea* (Drury)   Lepidoptera:Arctiidae
false chinch bug *Nysius ericae* (Schilling)   Hemiptera:Lygaeidae
fern scale *Pinnaspis aspidistrae* (Signoret)   Homoptera:Diaspididae
fern whitefly * *Aleurotulus nephrolepidis* Quaintance   Homoptera:Aleyrodidae
field cricket *Acheta assimilis* Fabricius (complex of species)   Orthoptera:Gryl-
lidae
fiery hunter *Calosoma calidum* (Fabricius)   Coleoptera:Carabidae
fig mite *Aceria ficus* (Cotte)   Acarina:Eriophyidae
fig scale *Lepidosaphes ficus* (Signoret)   Homoptera:Diaspididae
filament bearer *Nematocampa limbata* (Haworth)   Lepidoptera:Geometridae
filbert bud mite *Phytoptus avellanae* Nalepa   Acarina:Eriophyidae
filbertworm *Melissopus latiferreanus* (Walsingham)   Lepidoptera:Olethreutidae
fire ant *Solenopsis geminata* (Fabricius)   Hymenoptera:Formicidae
fir engraver *Scolytus ventralis* LeConte   Coleoptera:Scolytidae
flat grain beetle *Cryptolestes pusillus* (Schönherr)   Coleoptera:Cucujidae
flatheaded apple tree borer *Chrysobothris femorata* (Olivier)   Coleoptera:Bu-
prestidae
flatheaded fir borer *Melanophila drummondi* (Kirby)   Coleoptera:Buprestidae
floodwater mosquito *Aedes sticticus* (Meigen)   Diptera:Culicidae
Florida red scale *Chrysomphalus aonidum* (Linnaeus)   Homoptera:Diaspididae
Florida wax scale *Ceroplastes floridensis* Comstock   Homoptera:Coccidae
flower thrips *Frankliniella tritici* (Fitch)   Thysanoptera:Thripidae

fluff louse *Goniocotes gallinae* (De Geer) Mallophaga:Philopteridae
follicle mite *Demodex folliculorum* (Simon) Acarina:Demodicidae
forage looper *Caenurgina erechtea* (Cramer) Lepidoptera:Noctuidae
foreign grain beetle *Ahasverus advena* (Waltl) Coleoptera:Cucujidae
forest tent caterpillar *Malacosoma disstria* Hübner Lepidoptera:Lasiocampidae
fork-tailed bush katydid *Scudderia furcata* Brunner von Wattenwyl Orthoptera:Tettigoniidae
four-lined plant bug *Poecilocapsus lineatus* (Fabricius) Hemiptera:Miridae
four-spotted spider mite *Tetranychus canadensis* (McGregor) Acarina:Tetranychidae
four-spotted tree cricket *Oecanthus nigricornis quadripunctatus* Beutenmüller Orthoptera:Gryllidae
fowl cyst mite * *Laminosioptes cysticola* (Vizioli) Acarina:Laminosioptidae
fowl tick *Argas persicus* (Oken) Acarina:Argasidae
foxglove aphid *Myzus solani* (Kaltenbach) Homoptera:Aphidae
fruit-tree leaf roller *Archips argyrospilus* (Walker) Lepidoptera:Tortricidae
fungus moth * *Tinea defectella* Zeller Lepidoptera:Tineidae
furniture carpet beetle *Anthrenus flavipes* LeConte Coleoptera:Dermestidae
garden symphylan *Scutigerella immaculata* (Newport) Symphyla:Scutigerellidae
garden webworm *Loxostege similalis* (Guenée) Lepidoptera:Pyraustidae
geminate leafhopper * *Colladonus geminatus* Van Duzee Homoptera:Cicadellidae
German cockroach *Blattella germanica* (Linnaeus) Orthoptera:Blattidae
gladiolus thrips *Taeniothrips simplex* (Morison) Thysanoptera:Thripidae
glassy cutworm *Crymodes devastator* (Brace) Lepidoptera:Noctuidae
goat sucking louse *Linognathus stenopsis* (Burmeister) Anoplura:Linognathidae
golden-eye lacewing *Chrysopa oculata* Say Neuroptera:Chrysopidae
gooseberry fruitworm *Zophodia convolutella* (Hübner) Lepidoptera:Phycitidae
goose body louse *Trinoton anserinum* (Fabricius) Mallophaga:Menoponidae
grain mite *Acarus siro* Linnaeus Acarina:Acaridae
grain rust mite *Abacarus hystrix* (Nalepa) Acarina:Eriophyidae
grain thrips *Limothrips cerealium* (Haliday) Thysanoptera:Thripidae
granary weevil *Sitophilus granarius* (Linnaeus) Coleoptera:Curculionidae
granulate cutworm *Feltia subterranea* (Fabricius) Lepidoptera:Noctuidae
grape berry moth *Paralobesia viteana* (Clemens) Lepidoptera:Olethreutidae
grape blossom midge *Contarinia johnsoni* (Slingerland & Johnson) Diptera:Cecidomyiidae
grape colaspis *Maecolaspis flavida* (Say) Coleoptera:Chrysomelidae
grape erineum mite *Eriophyes vitis* (Pagenstecher) Acarina:Eriophyidae
grape leaf folder *Desmia funeralis* (Hübner) Lepidoptera:Pyraustidae
grape leafhopper * *Erythroneura comes* (Say) Homoptera:Cicadellidae
grape mealybug *Pseudococcus maritimus* (Ehrhorn) Homoptera:Pseudococcidae
grape phylloxera *Phylloxera vitifoliae* (Fitch) Homoptera:Chermidae
grape root borer *Vitacea polistiformis* (Harris) Lepidoptera:Aegeriidae
grape rootworm *Fidia viticida* Walsh Coleoptera:Chrysomelidae
grape sawfly *Erythraspides vitis* (Harris) Hymenoptera:Tenthredinidae
grape scale *Aspidiotus uvae* Comstock Homoptera:Diaspididae
grape seed chalcid *Evoxysoma vitis* (Saunders) Hymenoptera:Eurytomidae
grape trunk borer *Cerasphorus albofasciatus* (Laporte & Gory) Coleoptera:Cerambycidae

grapevine aphid   *Aphis illinoisensis* Shimer   Homoptera:Aphidae
grapevine looper   *Lygris diversilineata* (Hübner)   Lepidoptera:Geometridae
grape whitefly   *Trialeurodes vittatus* (Quaintance)   Homoptera:Aleyrodidae
grass mite *   *Siteroptes graminum* (Reuter)   Acarina:Pyemotidae
grass sawfly   *Pachynematus extensicornis* (Norton)   Hymenoptera:Tenthredinidae
grass thrips   *Anaphothrips obscurus* (Müller)   Thysanoptera:Thripidae
gray field slug   *Deroceras laeve* (Müller)   Stylommatophora:Limacidae
gray garden slug   *Deroceras reticulatum* (Müller)   Stylommatophora:Limacidae
Great Basin tent caterpillar   *Malacosoma fragile* (Stretch)   Lepidoptera:Lasiocampidae
Great Basin wireworm   *Ctenicera pruinina* (Horn)   Coleoptera:Elateridae
great carpenter bee *   *Xylocopa virginica* (Linnaeus)   Hymenoptera:Apidae
greater wax moth   *Galleria mellonella* (Linnaeus)   Lepidoptera:Galleriidae
greenbottle fly *   *Phaenicia sericata* (Meigen)   Diptera:Calliphoridae
greenbug   *Toxoptera graminum* (Rondani)   Homoptera:Aphidae
green cloverworm   *Plathypena scabra* (Fabricius)   Lepidoptera:Noctuidae
greenfly *   *Rhopalosiphum rufomaculatum* (Wilson)   Homoptera:Aphidae
green fruitworm   *Lithophane antennata* (Walker)   Lepidoptera:Noctuidae
greenhouse leaf tier   *Udea rubigalis* (Guenée)   Lepidoptera:Pyraustidae
greenhouse slug   *Milax gagates* (Linnaeus)   Stylommatophora:Limacidae
greenhouse thrips   *Heliothrips haemorrhoidalis* (Bouché)   Thysanoptera:Thripidae
greenhouse whitefly   *Trialeurodes vaporariorum* (Westwood)   Homoptera:Aleyrodidae
green June beetle   *Cotinis nitida* (Linnaeus)   Coleoptera:Scarabaeidae
green peach aphid   *Myzus persicae* (Sulzer)   Homoptera:Aphidae
green stink bug   *Acrosternum hilare* (Say)   Hemiptera:Pentatomidae
gregarious oak leaf miner   *Cameraria cincinnatiella* (Chambers)   Lepidoptera:-Gracilariidae
ground mealybug   *Rhizoecus falcifer* Kunckel d'Herculais   Homoptera:Pseudococcidae
Gulf Coast tick   *Amblyomma maculatum* Koch   Acarina:Ixodidae
Gulf wireworm   *Conoderus amplicollis* (Gyllenhal)   Coleoptera:Elateridae
gypsy moth   *Porthetria dispar* (Linnaeus)   Lepidoptera:Lymantriidae
hairy chinch bug   *Blissus leucopterus hirtus* Montandon   Hemiptera:Lygaeidae
hairy flower bee *   *Anthophora occidentalis* Cresson   Hymenoptera:Apidae
hairy spider beetle   *Ptinus villiger* (Reitter)   Coleoptera:Ptinidae
Hall scale   *Nilotaspis halli* (Green)   Homoptera:Diaspididae
harlequin bug   *Murgantia histrionica* (Hahn)   Hemiptera:Pentatomidae
head louse   *Pediculus humanus capitis* De Geer   Anoplura:Pediculidae
hemispherical scale   *Saissetia hemisphaerica* (Targioni-Tozzetti)   Homoptera:-Coccidae
hemlock looper   *Lambdina fiscellaria* (Guenée)   Lepidoptera:Geometridae
Hessian fly   *Phytophaga destructor* (Say)   Diptera:Cecidomyiidae
hickory shuckworm   *Laspeyresia caryana* (Fitch)   Lepidoptera:Olethreutidae
hickory tussock moth   *Halisidota caryae* (Harris)   Lepidoptera:Arctiidae
hide beetle   *Dermestes maculatus* De Geer   Coleoptera:Dermestidae
hog follicle mite   *Demodex phylloides* Csokor   Acarina:Demodicidae
hog itch mite *   *Sarcoptes scabiei suis* (Gerlach)   Acarina:Sarcoptidae
hog louse   *Haematopinus suis* (Linnaeus)   Anoplura:Haematopinidae
hollyhock plant bug   *Melanotrichus althaeae* (Hussey)   Hemiptera:Miridae

holly leaf miner *Phytomyza ilicis* (Curtis) Diptera:Agromyzidae
holly scale *Aspidiotus britannicus* Newstead Homoptera:Diaspididae
honey bee *Apis mellifera* Linnaeus Hymenoptera:Apidae
hop aphid *Phorodon humuli* (Schrank) Homoptera:Aphidae
hop flea beetle *Psylliodes punctulata* Melsheimer Coleoptera:Chrysomelidae
horned squash bug *Anasa armigera* (Say) Hemiptera:Coreidae
horn fly *Haematobia irritans* (Linnaeus) Diptera:Muscidae
horse biting louse *Bovicola equi* (Linnaeus) Mallophaga:Trichodectidae
horse bot fly *Gasterophilus intestinalis* (De Geer) Diptera:Gasterophilidae
horse follicle mite *Demodex equi* Railliet Acarina:Demodicidae
horse sucking louse *Haematopinus asini* (Linnaeus) Anoplura:Haematopinidae
house cricket *Acheta domesticus* (Linnaeus) Orthoptera:Gryllidae
house fly *Musca domestica* Linnaeus Diptera:Muscidae
human bot fly *Dermatobia hominis* (Linnaeus, Jr.) Diptera:Cuterebridae
human flea *Pulex irritans* Linnaeus Siphonaptera:Pulicidae
hydrangea spider mite ° *Tetranychus hydrangeae* Pritchard & Baker Acarina:-
  Tetranychidae
imported cabbageworm *Pieris rapae* (Linnaeus) Lepidoptera:Pieridae
imported currantworm *Nematus ribesii* (Scopoli) Hymenoptera:Tenthredini-
  dae
imported fire ant *Solenopsis saevissima richteri* Forel Hymenoptera:Formicidae
Indian-meal moth *Plodia interpunctella* (Hübner) Lepidoptera:Phycitidae
iris borer *Macronoctua onusta* Grote Lepidoptera:Noctuidae
iris thrips *Iridothrips iridis* (Watson) Thysanoptera:Thripidae
iris whitefly ° *Aleyrodes spiraeoides* Quaintance Homoptera:Aleyrodidae
Italian pear scale *Epidiaspis piricola* (Del Guercio) Homoptera:Diaspididae
itch mite *Sarcoptes scabiei* (De Geer) Acarina:Sarcoptidae
Japanese beetle *Popillia japonica* Newman Coleoptera:Scarabaeidae
juniper webworm *Dichomeris marginella* (Fabricius) Lepidoptera:Gelechiidae
khapra beetle *Trogoderma granarium* Everts Coleoptera:Dermestidae
lantana leaf miner *Cremastobombycia lantanella* Busck Lepidoptera:Gracilari-
  idae
lappet moth *Epicnaptera americana* (Harris) Lepidoptera:Lasiocampidae
larch sawfly *Pristiphora erichsonii* (Hartig) Hymenoptera:Tenthredinidae
larder beetle *Dermestes lardarius* Linnaeus Coleoptera:Dermestidae
large chicken louse *Goniodes gigas* (Taschenberg) Mallophaga:Philopteridae
large duck louse *Trinoton querquedulae* (Linnaeus) Mallophaga:Menoponidae
large milkweed bug *Oncopeltus fasciatus* (Dallas) Hemiptera:Lygaeidae
larger cabinet beetle ° *Trogoderma inclusum* LeConte Coleoptera:Dermestidae
large turkey louse *Chelopistes meleagridis* (Linnaeus) Mallophaga:Philop-
  teridae
latrine fly *Fannia scalaris* (Fabricius) Diptera:Anthomyiidae
leaf crumpler *Acrobasis indigenella* (Zeller) Lepidoptera:Phycitidae
leaf curl plum aphid ° *Anuraphis helichrys* (Kaltenbach) Homoptera:Aphidae
leaf-footed bug *Leptoglossus phyllopus* (Linnaeus) Hemiptera:Coreidae
legume bug ° *Lygus hesperus* Knight Hemiptera:Miridae
lesser bud moth *Recurvaria nanella* (Hübner) Lepidoptera:Gelechiidae
lesser bulb fly *Eumerus tuberculatus* Rondani Diptera:Syrphidae
lesser clover leaf weevil *Hypera nigrirostris* (Fabricius) Coleoptera:Curculion-
  idae
lesser cornstalk borer *Elasmopalpus lignosellus* (Zeller) Lepidoptera:Phycitidae
lesser grain borer *Rhyzopertha dominica* (Fabricius) Coleoptera:Bostrichidae

lesser mealworm   *Alphitobius diaperinus* (Panzer)   Coleoptera:Tenebrionidae
lesser peach tree borer   *Synanthedon pictipes* (Grote & Robinson)   Lepidoptera:Aegeriidae
lesser wax moth   *Achroia grisella* (Fabricius)   Lepidoptera:Galleriidae
lilac leaf miner   *Gracilaria syringella* (Fabricius)   Lepidoptera:Gracilariidae
lima-bean pod borer   *Etiella zinckenella* (Treitschke)   Lepidoptera: Phycitidae
lined spittlebug   *Philaenus lineatus* (Linnaeus)   Homoptera:Cercopidae
little black ant   *Monomorium minimum* (Buckley)   Hymenoptera:Formicidae
little blue cattle louse °   *Solenopotes capillatus* Enderlein   Anoplura:Linognathidae
little house fly   *Fannia canicularis* (Linnaeus)   Diptera:Anthomyiidae
locust borer   *Megacyllene robiniae* (Forster)   Coleoptera:Cerambycidae
lodgepole cone beetle   *Conophthorus contortae* Hopkins   Coleoptera:Scolytidae
lone star tick   *Amblyomma americanum* (Linnaeus)   Acarina:Ixodidae
long-headed flour beetle °   *Latheticus oryzae* Waterhouse   Coleoptera:Tenebrionidae
long-nosed cattle louse   *Linognathus vituli* (Linnaeus)   Anoplura:Linognathidae
long-tailed mealybug   *Pseudococcus adonidum* (Linnaeus)   Homoptera:Pseudococcidae
lubber grasshopper   *Brachystola magna* (Girard)   Orthoptera:Acrididae
luden spider mite °   *Tetranychus ludeni* Zacher   Acarina:Tetranychidae
lygus bugs °   *Lygus* spp.   Hemiptera:Miridae
maize billbug   *Sphenophorus maidis* Chittenden   Coleoptera:Curculionidae
McDaniel spider mite °   *Tetranychus mcdanieli* McGregor   Acarina:Tetranychidae
meadow plant bug   *Leptopterna dolabratus* (Linnaeus)   Hemiptera:Miridae
meadow spittlebug   *Philaenus leucophthalmus* (Linnaeus)   Homoptera:Cercopidae
meal moth   *Pyralis farinalis* (Linnaeus)   Lepidoptera:Pyralidae
mealy plum aphid   *Hyalopterus pruni* (Geoffroy)   Homoptera:Aphidae
Mediterranean flour moth   *Anagasta kühniella* (Zeller)   Lepidoptera:Phycitidae
Mediterranean fruit fly   *Ceratitis capitata* (Wiedemann)   Diptera:Tephritidae
melon aphid   *Aphis gossypii* Glover   Homoptera:Aphidae
melon fly   *Dacus cucurbitae* Coquillett   Diptera:Tephritidae
Mexican bean beetle   *Epilachna varivestis* Mulsant   Coleoptera:Coccinellidae
Mexican fruit fly   *Anastrepha ludens* (Loew)   Diptera:Tephritidae
Mexican mealybug   *Phenacoccus gossypii* Townsend & Cockerell   Homoptera:-Pseudococcidae
migratory grasshopper   *Melanoplus bilituratus* (Walker)   Orthoptera:Acrididae
Mormon cricket   *Anabrus simplex* Haldeman   Orthoptera:Tettigoniidae
mushroom mite   *Tyrophagus putrescentiae* (Schrank)   Acarina:Acaridae
narcissus bulb fly   *Lampetia equestris* (Fabricius)   Diptera:Syrphidae
navel orangeworm   *Paramyelois transitella* (Walker)   Lepidoptera:Phycitidae
northern cattle grub   *Hypoderma bovis* (Linnaeus)   Diptera:Hypodermatidae
northern corn rootworm   *Diabrotica longicornis* (Say)   Coleoptera:Chrysomelidae
northern fowl mite   *Ornithonyssus sylviarum* (Canestrini & Fanzago)   Acarina:-Dermanyssidae
northern house mosquito   *Culex pipiens pipiens* Linnaeus   Diptera:Culicidae
nose bot fly   *Gasterophilus haemorrhoidalis* (Linnaeus)   Diptera:Gasterophilidae
oblique-banded leaf roller   *Archips rosaceanus* (Harris)   Lepidoptera:Tortricidae

620 | Fundamentals of Applied Entomology

odorous house ant *Tapinoma sessile* (Say) Hymenoptera:Formicidae
old-house borer *Hylotrupes bajulus* (Linnaeus) Coleoptera:Cerambycidae
oleander scale *Aspidiotus hederae* (Vallot) Homoptera:Diaspididae
olive scale *Parlatoria oleae* (Colvée) Homoptera:Diaspididae
omnivorous leaf tier *Cnephasia longana* (Haworth) Lepidoptera:Tortricidae
omnivorous looper *Sabulodes caberata* Guenée Lepidoptera:Geometridae
onion maggot *Hylemya antiqua* (Meigen) Diptera:Anthomyiidae
onion plant bug *Labopidea allii* Knight Hemiptera:Miridae
onion thrips *Thrips tabaci* Lindeman Thysanoptera:Thripidae
orange tortrix *Argyrotaenia citrana* (Fernald) Lepidoptera:Tortricidae
orchidfly *Eurytoma orchidearum* (Westwood) Hymenoptera:Eurytomidae
oriental beetle *Anomala orientalis* Waterhouse Coleoptera:Scarabaeidae
oriental cockroach *Blatta orientalis* Linnaeus Orthoptera:Blattidae
oriental fruit fly *Dacus dorsalis* Hendel Diptera:Tephritidae
oriental fruit moth *Grapholitha molesta* (Busck) Lepidoptera:Olethreutidae
oriental house fly *Musca domestica vicina* Macquart Diptera:Muscidae
oriental rat flea *Xenopsylla cheopis* (Rothschild) Siphonaptera:Pulicidae
ornate aphid ° *Myzus ornatus* Laing Homoptera:Aphidae
oxalis spider mite ° *Petrobia harti* (Ewing) Acarina:Tetranychidae
oystershell scale *Lepidosaphes ulmi* (Linnaeus) Homoptera:Diaspididae
Pacific Coast tick *Dermacentor occidentalis* Marx Acarina:Ixodidae
Pacific Coast wireworm *Limonius canus* LeConte Coleoptera:Elateridae
Pacific spider mite *Tetranychus pacificus* McGregor Acarina:Tetranychidae
pale legume bug ° *Lygus elisus* Van Duzee Hemiptera:Miridae
pale-sided cutworm *Agrotis malefida* Guenée Lepidoptera:Noctuidae
pale-striped flea beetle *Systena blanda* Melsheimer Coleoptera:Chrysomelidae
pale western cutworm *Agrotis orthogonia* Morrison Lepidoptera:Noctuidae
palmerworm *Dichomeris ligulella* Hübner Lepidoptera:Gelechiidae
papaya fruit fly *Toxotrypana curvicauda* Gerstaecker Diptera:Tephritidae
parlatoria date scale *Parlatoria blanchardi* (Targioni-Tozzetti) Homoptera:-
  Diaspididae
parsnip webworm *Depressaria heracliana* (Linnaeus) Lepidoptera:Oecophor-
  idae
pavement ant *Tetramorium caespitum* (Linnaeus) Hymenoptera:Formicidae
pea aphid *Macrosiphum pisi* (Harris) Homoptera:Aphidae
peach bark beetle *Phloeotribus liminaris* (Harris) Coleoptera:Scolytidae
peach silver mite *Aculus cornutus* (Banks) Acarina:Eriophyidae
peach tree borer *Sanninoidea exitiosa* (Say) Lepidoptera:Aegeriidae
peach twig borer *Anarsia lineatella* Zeller Lepidoptera:Gelechiidae
pea leaf weevil *Sitona lineata* (Linnaeus) Coleoptera:Curculionidae
pea moth *Laspeyresia nigricana* (Stephens) Lepidoptera:Olethreutidae
pear lace bug ° *Stephanitis pyri* Fabricius Hemiptera:Tingidae
pear leaf blister mite *Eriophyes pyri* (Pagenstecher) Acarina:Eriophyidae
pear midge *Contarinia pyrivora* (Riley) Diptera:Cecidomyiidae
pear psylla *Psylla pyricola* Förster Homoptera:Psyllidae
pear-slug *Caliroa cerasi* (Linnaeus) Hymenoptera:Tenthredinidae
pear thrips *Taeniothrips inconsequens* (Uzel) Thysanoptera:Thripidae
pea weevil *Bruchus pisorum* (Linnaeus) Coleoptera:Bruchidae
pecan bud moth *Gretchena bolliana* (Slingerland) Lepidoptera:Olethreutidae
pecan nut casebearer *Acrobasis caryae* Grote Lepidoptera:Phycitidae
pecan phylloxera *Phylloxera devastatrix* Pergande Homoptera:Chermidae
pecan weevil *Curculio caryae* (Horn) Coleoptera:Curculionidae

pepper maggot *Zonosemata electa* (Say) Diptera:Tephritidae
pepper weevil *Anthonomus eugenii* Cano Coleoptera:Curculionidae
periodical cicada *Magicicada septendecim* (Linnaeus) Homoptera:Cicadidae
persimmon psylla *Trioza diospyri* (Ashmead) Homoptera:Psyllidae
phalaenopsis mite * *Tenuipalpus pacificus* Baker Acarina:Tenuipalpidae
Pharaoh ant *Monomorium pharaonis* (Linnaeus) Hymenoptera:Formicidae
pickleworm *Diaphania nitidalis* (Stoll) Lepidoptera:Pyraustidae
pigeon fly *Pseudolynchia canariensis* (Macquart) Diptera:Hippoboscidae
pineapple mealybug *Pseudococcus brevipes* (Cockerell) Homoptera:Pseudococcidae
pine bark aphid *Pineus strobi* (Hartig) Homoptera:Chermidae
pine butterfly *Neophasia menapia* (Felder & Felder) Lepidoptera:Pieridae
pine needle miner *Exoteleia pinifoliella* (Chambers) Lepidoptera:Gelechiidae
pine spittlebug *Aphrophora parallela* (Say) Homoptera:Cercopidae
pink bollworm *Pectinophora gossypiella* (Saunders) Lepidoptera:Gelechiidae
pitch twig moth *Petrova comstockiana* (Fernald) Lepidoptera:Olethreutidae
plains false wireworm *Eleodes opaca* (Say) Coleoptera:Tenebrionidae
plum curculio *Conotrachelus nenuphar* (Herbst) Coleoptera:Curculionidae
plum gouger *Anthonomus scutellaris* LeConte Coleoptera:Curculionidae
plum leafhopper *Macropsis trimaculata* (Fitch) Homoptera:Cicadellidae
poplar-and-willow borer *Sternochetus lapathi* (Linnaeus) Coleoptera:Curculionidae
potato aphid *Macrosiphum euphorbiae* (Thomas) Homoptera:Aphidae
potato leafhopper *Empoasca fabae* (Harris) Homoptera:Cicadellidae
potato psyllid *Paratrioza cockerelli* (Sulc) Homoptera:Psyllidae
potato stem borer *Hydroecia micacea* (Esper) Lepidoptera:Noctuidae
potato tuberworm *Gnorimoschema operculella* (Zeller) Lepidoptera:Gelechiidae
poultry bug *Haematosiphon inodorus* (Dugès) Hemiptera:Cimicidae
prairie grain wireworm *Ctenicera aeripennis destructor* (Brown) Coleoptera:-
Elateridae
privet leaf miner *Gracilaria cuculipennella* (Hübner) Lepidoptera:Gracilariidae
privet mite *Brevipalpus obovatus* Donnadieu Acarina:Tenuipalpidae
Puget Sound wireworm *Ctenicera aeripennis aeripennis* (Kirby) Coleoptera:-
Elateridae
purple-backed cabbageworm *Evergestis pallidata* (Hufnagel) Lepidoptera:-
Pyraustidae
quince treehopper *Glossonotus crataegi* (Fitch) Homoptera:Membracidae
ragweed plant bug *Chlamydatus associatus* (Uhler) Hemiptera:Miridae
rain beetles * *Pleocoma* spp. Coleoptera:Scarabaeidae
raisin moth *Ephestia figulilella* Gregson Lepidoptera:Phycitidae
rapid plant bug *Adelphocoris rapidus* (Say) Hemiptera:Miridae
raspberry aphid * *Amphorophora rubi* (Kaltenbach) Homoptera:Aphidae
raspberry cane borer *Oberea bimaculata* (Olivier) Coleoptera:Cerambycidae
raspberry cane maggot *Pegomya rubivora* (Coquillett) Diptera:Anthomyiidae
raspberry crown borer *Bembecia marginata* (Harris) Lepidoptera:Aegeriidae
raspberry sawfly *Monophadnoides geniculatus* (Hartig) Hymenoptera:Tenthredinidae
red-backed cutworm *Euxoa ochrogaster* (Guenée) Lepidoptera:Noctuidae
red-banded leaf roller *Argyrotaenia velutinana* (Walker) Lepidoptera:Tortricidae

red-banded thrips *Selenothrips rubrocinctus* (Giard) Thysanoptera:Thripidae
redberry mite *Aceria essigi* (Hassan) Acarina:Eriophyidae
red flour beetle *Tribolium castaneum* (Herbst) Coleoptera:Tenebrionidae
red harvester ant *Pogonomyrmex barbatus* (F. Smith) Hymenoptera:Formicidae
red-legged grasshopper *Melanoplus femurrubrum* (De Geer) Orthoptera:-Acrididae
red-necked cane borer *Agrilus ruficollis* (Fabricius) Coleoptera:Buprestidae
red-necked peanutworm *Stegasta basqueella* (Chambers) Lepidoptera:Gelechiidae
red-shouldered plant bug * *Thyanta custator* (Fabricius) Hemiptera:Pentatomidae
red-tailed tachina * *Winthemia quadripustulata* (Fabricius) Diptera:Tachinidae
red turpentine beetle *Dendroctonus valens* LeConte Coleoptera:Scolytidae
relapsing-fever tick *Ornithodoros turicata* (Dugès) Acarina:Argasidae
Rhodes-grass scale *Antonina graminis* (Maskell) Homoptera:Pseudococcidae
rhododendron borer *Ramosia rhododendri* (Beutenmüller) Lepidoptera:Aegeriidae
rhododendron lace bug *Stephanitis rhododendri* Horvath Hemiptera:Tingidae
rhododendron whitefly *Dialeurodes chittendeni* Laing Homoptera:Aleyrodidae
rhubarb spittlebug * *Aphrophora permutata* Uhler Homoptera:Cercopidae
rice stalk borer *Chilo plejadellus* Zincken Lepidoptera:Crambidae
rice stink bug *Oebalus pugnax* (Fabricius) Hemiptera:Pentatomidae
rice water weevil *Lissorhoptrus oryzophilus* (Kuschel) Coleoptera:Curculionidae
rice weevil *Sitophilus oryzae* (Linnaeus) Coleoptera:Curculionidae
Rocky Mountain grasshopper *Melanoplus spretus* (Walsh) Orthoptera:Acrididae
Rocky Mountain wood tick *Dermacentor andersoni* Stiles Acarina:Ixodidae
rose aphid *Macrosiphum rosae* (Linnaeus) Homoptera:Aphidae
rose budworm * *Pyrrhia umbra* (Hufnagel) Lepidoptera:Noctuidae
rose chafer *Macrodactylus subspinosus* (Fabricius) Coleoptera:Scarabaeidae
rose curculio *Rhynchites bicolor* (Fabricius) Coleoptera:Curculionidae
rose grass aphid * *Macrosiphum dirhodum* (Walker) Homoptera:Aphidae
rose leaf beetle *Nodonota puncticollis* (Say) Coleoptera:Chrysomelidae
rose leafhopper *Edwardsiana rosae* (Linnaeus) Homoptera:Cicadellidae
rose leaf tier * *Archips rosaceanus* (Harris) Lepidoptera:Tortricidae
rose midge *Dasyneura rhodophaga* (Coquillett) Diptera:Cecidomyiidae
rose scale *Aulacaspis rosae* (Bouché) Homoptera:Diaspididae
rose-slug *Endelomyia aethiops* (Fabricius) Hymenoptera:Tenthredinidae
rose stem girdler *Agrilus rubicola* Abeille Coleoptera:Buprestidae
rosy apple aphid *Anuraphis rosea* Baker Homoptera:Aphidae
rough strawberry root weevil * *Brachyrhinus rugosostriatus* (Goeze) Coleoptera:Curculionidae
roundheaded apple tree borer *Saperda candida* Fabricius Coleoptera:Cerambycidae
rusty grain beetle *Cryptolestes ferrugineus* (Stephens) Coleoptera:Cucujidae
rusty plum aphid *Hysteroneura setariae* (Thomas) Homoptera:Aphidae
rusty tussock moth *Orgyia antiqua* (Linnaeus) Lepidoptera:Lymantriidae
salt-marsh caterpillar *Estigmene acrea* (Drury) Lepidoptera:Arctiidae
salt-marsh mosquito *Aedes sollicitans* (Walker) Diptera:Culicidae

sand wireworm *Horistonotus uhlerii* Horn Coleoptera:Elateridae
San Jose scale *Aspidiotus perniciosus* Comstock Homoptera:Diaspididae
Saratoga spittlebug *Aphrophora saratogensis* (Fitch) Homoptera:Cercopidae
satin moth *Stilpnotia salicis* (Linnaeus) Lepidoptera:Lymantriidae
saw-toothed grain beetle *Oryzaephilus surinamensis* (Linnaeus) Coleoptera:-
Cucujidae
Say stink bug *Chlorochroa sayi* Stål Hemiptera:Pentatomidae
scab mite * *Psoroptes ovis* (Hering) Acarina:Psoroptidae
scaly-leg mite *Knemidokoptes mutans* (Robin & Lanquentin) Acarina:Sar-
coptidae
Schoene spider mite *Tetranychus schoenei* McGregor Acarina:Tetranychidae
screw-worm *Callitroga hominivorax* (Coquerel) Diptera:Calliphoridae
scurfy scale *Chionaspis furfura* (Fitch) Homoptera:Diaspididae
secondary screw-worm *Callitroga macellaria* (Fabricius) Diptera:Calliphoridae
seed-corn beetle *Agonoderus lecontei* Chaudoir Coleoptera:Carabidae
seed-corn maggot *Hylemya cilicrura* (Rondani) Diptera:Anthomyiidae
serpentine leaf miner *Liriomyza brassicae* (Riley) Diptera:Agromyzidae
shaft louse *Menopon gallinae* (Linnaeus) Mallophaga:Menoponidae
sheep biting louse *Bovicola ovis* (Linnaeus) Mallophaga:Trichodectidae
sheep bot fly *Oestrus ovis* Linnaeus Diptera:Oestridae
sheep follicle mite *Demodex ovis* Railliet Acarina:Demodicidae
sheep foot louse * *Linognathus pedalis* (Osborn) Anoplura:Linognathidae
sheep itch mite * *Psorergates ovis* Womersley Acarina:Cheyletidae
sheep ked *Melophagus ovinus* (Linnaeus) Diptera:Hippoboscidae
short-nosed cattle louse *Haematopinus eurysternus* (Nitzsch) Anoplura:Haema-
topinidae
shot-hole borer *Scolytus rugulosus* (Ratzeburg) Coleoptera:Scolytidae
silverfish *Lepisma saccharina* Linnaeus Thysanura:Lepismatidae
silver-spotted tiger moth *Halisidota argentata* Packard Lepidoptera:Arctiidae
sinuate pear tree borer *Agrilus sinuatus* (Olivier) Coleoptera:Buprestidae
six-spotted leafhopper *Macrosteles fascifrons* (Stål) Homoptera:Cicadellidae
slender goose louse *Anaticola anseris* (Linnaeus) Mallophaga:Philopteridae
smaller European elm bark beetle *Scolytus multistriatus* (Marsham) Coleop-
tera:Scolytidae
small milkweed bug *Lygaeus kalmii* Stål Hemiptera:Lygaeidae
small pigeon louse *Campanulotes bidentatus compar* (Burmeister) Mallo-
phaga:Philopteridae
snapdragon plume moth * *Platyptilia antirrhina* Lange Lepidoptera:Pterophor-
idae
snowball aphid *Anuraphis viburnicola* (Gillette) Homoptera:Aphidae
snowy tree cricket *Oecanthus niveus* (De Geer) (complex of species) Orthop-
tera:Gryllidae
solitary oak leaf miner *Cameraria hamadryadella* (Clemens) Lepidoptera:-
Gracilariidae
sorghum midge *Contarinia sorghicola* (Coquillett) Diptera:Cecidomyiidae
southern armyworm *Prodenia eridania* (Cramer) Lepidoptera:Noctuidae
southern cabbageworm *Pieris protodice* Boisduval & LeConte Lepidoptera:-
Pieridae
southern corn rootworm *Diabrotica undecimpunctata howardi* Barber Coleop-
tera:Chrysomelidae
southern cornstalk borer *Diatraea crambidoides* (Grote) Lepidoptera:Cram-
bidae

southern fire ant *Solenopsis xyloni* McCook Hymenoptera:Formicidae
southern garden leafhopper *Empoasca solana* DeLong Homoptera:Cicadellidae
southern green stink bug *Nezara viridula* (Linnaeus) Hemiptera:Pentatomidae
southern house mosquito *Culex pipiens quinquefasciatus* Say Diptera:Culicidae
southern masked chafer *Cyclocephala immaculata* (Olivier) Coleoptera:Scarabaeidae
southern pine beetle *Dendroctonus frontalis* Zimmerman Coleoptera:Scolytidae
southern pine sawyer *Monochamus titillator* (Fabricius) Coleoptera:Cerambycidae
southern red-legged grasshopper * *Melanoplus femurrubrum propinquus* Scudder Orthoptera:Acrididae
southern red mite *Oligonychus ilicis* (McGregor) Acarina:Tetranychidae
southwestern corn borer *Zeadiatraea grandiosella* (Dyar) Lepidoptera:Crambidae
soybean cyst nematode * *Heterodera glycines* Ichinohe Tylenchida:Heteroderidae
spinach flea beetle *Disonycha xanthomelas* (Dalman) Coleoptera:Chrysomelidae
spinach leaf miner *Pegomya hyoscyami* (Panzer) Diptera:Anthomyiidae
spined soldier bug *Podisus maculiventris* (Say) Hemiptera:Pentatomidae
spotted alfalfa aphid *Therioaphis maculata* (Buckton) Homoptera:Aphidae
spotted asparagus beetle *Crioceris duodecimpunctata* (Linnaeus) Coleoptera:-Chrysomelidae
spotted cucumber beetle *Diabrotica undecimpunctata howardi* Barber Coleoptera:Chrysomelidae
spotted garden slug *Limax maximus* Linnaeus Stylommatophora:Limacidae
spotted tussock moth *Halisidota maculata* (Harris) Lepidoptera:Arctiidae
spring cankerworm *Paleacrita vernata* (Peck) Lepidoptera:Geometridae
spruce budworm *Choristoneura fumiferana* (Clemens) Lepidoptera:Tortricidae
spruce spider mite *Oligonychus ununguis* (Jacot) Acarina:Tetranychidae
square-necked grain beetle *Cathartus quadricollis* (Guérin-Méneville) Coleoptera:Cucujidae
squash beetle *Epilachna borealis* (Fabricius) Coleoptera:Coccinellidae
squash bug *Anasa tristis* (De Geer) Hemiptera:Coreidae
squash vine borer *Melittia cucurbitae* (Harris) Lepidoptera:Aegeriidae
stable fly *Stomoxys calcitrans* (Linnaeus) Diptera:Muscidae
stalk borer *Papaipema nebris* (Guenée) Lepidoptera:Noctuidae
steel-blue lady beetle *Orcus chalybeus* (Boisduval) Coleoptera:Coccinellidae
sticktight flea *Echidnophaga gallinacea* (Westwood) Siphonaptera:Pulicidae
stink beetle *Nomius pygmaeus* (Dejean) Coleoptera:Carabidae
strawberry aphid *Pentatrichopus fragaefolii* (Cockerell) Homoptera:Aphidae
strawberry crown borer *Tyloderma fragariae* (Riley) Coleoptera:Curculionidae
strawberry crown miner *Aristotelia fragariae* Busck Lepidoptera:Gelechiidae
strawberry crown moth *Ramosia bibionipennis* (Boisduval) Lepidoptera:Aegeriidae
strawberry flea beetle * *Altica ignita* Illiger Coleoptera:Chrysomelidae
strawberry leaf beetle * *Paria canella* Fabricius Coleoptera:Chrysomelidae
strawberry leaf roller *Ancylis comptana fragariae* (Walsh & Riley) Lepidoptera:Olethreutidae
strawberry root aphid *Aphis forbesi* Weed Homoptera:Aphidae

strawberry root weevil *Brachyrhinus ovatus* (Linnaeus) Coleoptera:Curculionidae

strawberry rootworm *Paria fragariae* Wilcox Coleoptera:Chrysomelidae

strawberry spider mite *Tetranychus atlanticus* McGregor Acarina:Tetranychidae

strawberry weevil *Anthonomus signatus* Say Coleoptera:Curculionidae

strawberry whitefly *Trialeurodes packardi* (Morrill) Homoptera:Aleyrodidae

striped blister beetle *Epicauta vittata* (Fabricius) Coleoptera:Meloidae

striped cucumber beetle *Acalymma vittata* (Fabricius) Coleoptera:Chrysomelidae

striped horse fly *Tabanus lineola* Fabricius Diptera:Tabanidae

suckfly *Cyrtopeltis notatus* Distant Hemiptera:Miridae

sugar-beet crown borer *Hulstia undulatella* (Clemens) Lepidoptera:Phycitidae

sugar-beet root aphid *Pemphigus betae* Doane Homoptera:Aphidae

sugar-beet root maggot *Tetanops myopaeformis* (Röder) Diptera:Otitidae

sugar-beet wireworm *Limonius californicus* (Mannerheim) Coleoptera:Elateridae

sugarcane beetle *Euetheola rugiceps* (LeConte) Coleoptera:Scarabaeidae

sugarcane borer *Diatraea saccharalis* (Fabricius) Lepidoptera:Crambidae

sugarcane leaf roller *Hedylepta accepta* (Butler) Lepidoptera:Pyraustidae

sunflower maggot *Strauzia longipennis* (Wiedemann) Diptera:Tephritidae

superb plant bug *Adelphocoris superbus* (Uhler) Hemiptera:Miridae

swallow bug *Oeciacus vicarius* Horvath Hemiptera:Cimicidae

sweetclover weevil *Sitona cylindricollis* Fåhraeus Coleoptera:Curculionidae

sweetpotato flea beetle *Chaetocnema confinis* Crotch Coleoptera:Chrysomelidae

sweetpotato hornworm *Agrius cingulatus* (Fabricius) Lepidoptera:Sphingidae

sweetpotato leaf beetle *Typophorus nigritus viridicyaneus* (Crotch) Coleoptera:Chrysomelidae

sweetpotato leaf roller *Pilocrocis tripunctata* (Fabricius) Lepidoptera:Pyraustidae

sweetpotato weevil *Cylas formicarius elegantulus* (Summers) Coleoptera:Curculionidae

sweetpotato whitefly *Bemisia tabaci* (Gennadius) Homoptera:Aleyrodidae

tarnished plant bug *Lygus lineolaris* (Palisot de Beauvois) Hemiptera:Miridae

ten-lined June beetle *Polyphylla decemlineata* (Say) Coleoptera:Scarabaeidae

terrapin scale *Lecanium nigrofasciatum* Pergande Homoptera:Coccidae

Texas leaf-cutting ant *Atta texana* (Buckley) Hymenoptera:Formicidae

thief ant *Solenopsis molesta* (Say) Hymenopera:Formicidae

thistle aphid *Anuraphis cardui* (Linnaeus) Homoptera:Aphidae

three-banded leafhopper *Erythroneura tricincta* Fitch Homoptera:Cicadellidae

three-cornered alfalfa hopper *Spissistilus festinus* (Say) Homoptera:Membracidae

three-lined potato beetle *Lema trilineata* (Olivier) Coleoptera:Chrysomelidae

throat bot fly *Gasterophilus nasalis* (Linnaeus) Diptera:Gasterophilidae

tobacco budworm *Heliothis virescens* (Fabricius) Lepidoptera:Noctuidae

tobacco flea beetle *Epitrix hirtipennis* (Melsheimer) Coleoptera:Chrysomelidae

tobacco hornworm *Protoparce sexta* (Johannson) Lepidoptera:Sphingidae

tobacco moth *Ephestia elutella* (Hübner) Lepidoptera:Phycitidae

tobacco stalk borer *Trichobaris mucorea* (LeConte) Coleoptera:Curculionidae

tobacco thrips *Frankliniella fusca* (Hinds) Thysanoptera:Thripidae

tobacco wireworm *Conoderus vespertinus* (Fabricius) Coleoptera:Elateridae

tomato fruitworm *Heliothis zea* (Boddie) Lepidoptera:Noctuidae
tomato hornworm *Protoparce quinquemaculata* (Haworth) Lepidoptera:Sphingidae
tomato pinworm *Keiferia lycopersicella* (Busck) Lepidoptera:Gelechiidae
tomato psyllid *Paratrioza cockerelli* (Sulc) Homoptera:Psyllidae
tomato russet mite *Vasates lycopersici* (Massee) Acarina:Eriophyidae
toothed flea beetle *Chaetocnema denticulata* (Illiger) Coleoptera:Chrysomelidae
tropical fowl mite *Ornithonyssus bursa* (Berlese) Acarina:Dermanyssidae
tropical rat mite *Ornithonyssus bacoti* (Hirst) Acarina:Dermanyssidae
tuber flea beetle *Epitrix tuberis* Gentner Coleoptera:Chrysomelidae
tule beetle *Agonum maculicolle* Dejean Coleoptera:Carabidae
tulip bulb aphid *Anuraphis tulipae* (Fonscolombe) Homoptera:Aphidae
tuliptree scale *Toumeyella liriodendri* (Gmelin) Homoptera:Coccidae
tumid spider mite *Tetranychus tumidus* Banks Acarina:Tetranychidae
turnip aphid *Rhopalosiphum pseudobrassicae* (Davis) Homoptera:Aphidae
turnip maggot *Hylemya floralis* (Fallén) Diptera:Anthomyiidae
tussock moth tachina * *Compsilura concinnata* Meigen Diptera:Tachinidae
twice-stabbed lady beetle *Chilocorus stigma* (Say) Coleoptera:Coccinellidae
twig girdler *Oncideres cingulata* (Say) Coleoptera:Cerambycidae
two-lined chestnut borer *Agrilus bilineatus* (Weber) Coleoptera:Buprestidae
two-marked treehopper *Enchenopa binotata* (Say) Homoptera:Membracidae
two-spotted lady beetle *Adalia bipunctata* (Linnaeus) Coleoptera:Coccinellidae
two-spotted spider mite *Tetranychus telarius* (Linnaeus) Acarina:Tetranychidae
two-striped grasshopper *Melanoplus bivittatus* (Say) Orthoptera:Acrididae
ugly-nest caterpillar *Archips cerasivoranus* (Fitch) Lepidoptera:Tortricidae
varied carpet beetle *Anthrenus verbasci* (Linnaeus) Coleoptera:Dermestidae
variegated cutworm *Peridroma saucia* (Hübner) Lepidoptera:Noctuidae
variegated leafhopper * *Erythroneura variabilis* Beamer Homoptera:Cicadellidae
vedalia *Rodolia cardinalis* (Mulsant) Coleoptera:Coccinellidae
vegetable weevil *Listroderes costirostris obliquus* (Klug) Coleoptera:Curculionidae
velvetbean caterpillar *Anticarsia gemmatalis* Hübner Lepidoptera:Noctuidae
vetch bruchid *Bruchus brachialis* Fåhraeus Coleoptera:Bruchidae
Virginia-creeper leafhopper *Erythroneura ziczac* (Walsh) Homoptera:Cicadellidae
Virginia-creeper sphinx *Ampeloeca myron* (Cramer) Lepidoptera:Sphingidae
walnut aphid *Chromaphis juglandicola* (Kaltenbach) Homoptera:Aphidae
walnut blister mite *Aceria erinea* (Nalepa) Acarina:Eriophyidae
walnut husk fly *Rhagoletis completa* Cresson Diptera:Tephritidae
walnut sphinx *Cressonia juglandis* (J. E. Smith) Lepidoptera:Sphingidae
webbing clothes moth *Tineola bisselliella* (Hummel) Lepidoptera:Tineidae
western bumble bee * *Bombus occidentalis* Greene Hymenoptera:Apidae
western chicken flea *Ceratophyllus niger* Fox Siphonaptera:Ceratophyllidae
western chinch bug *Blissus occiduus* Barber Hemiptera:Lygaeidae
western corn rootworm *Diabrotica virgifera* LeConte Coleoptera:Chrysomelidae
western flower thrips * *Frankliniella occidentalis* (Pergande) Thysanoptera:-Thripidae

western grape leafhopper * *Erythroneura elegantula* Osborn Homoptera:Cicadellidae

western grape rootworm *Adoxus obscurus* (Linnaeus) Coleoptera:Chrysomelidae

western horse fly * *Tabanus punctifer* Osten Sacken Diptera:Tabanidae

western peach tree borer *Sanninoidea exitiosa graefi* (Hy. Edwards) Lepidoptera:Aegeriidae

western pine beetle *Dendroctonus brevicomis* LeConte Lepidoptera:Scolytidae

western raspberry fruitworm *Byturus bakeri* Barber Coleoptera:Byturidae

western strawberry leaf roller * *Anacampsis fragariella* Busck Lepidoptera:-Gelechiidae

western striped cucumber beetle *Acalymma trivittata* (Mannerheim) Coleoptera:Chrysomelidae

western subterranean termite *Reticulitermes hesperus* Banks Isoptera:Rhinotermitidae

western tent caterpillar *Malacosoma pluviale* (Dyar) Lepidoptera:Lasiocampidae

western tree-hole mosquito *Aedes varipalpus* (Coquillett) Diptera:Culicidae

western yellow-striped armyworm *Prodenia praefica* Grote Lepidoptera:Noctuidae

wheat curl mite *Aceria tulipae* (Keifer) Acarina:Eriophyidae

wheat head armyworm *Faronta diffusa* (Walker) Lepidoptera:Noctuidae

wheat jointworm *Harmolita tritici* (Fitch) Hymenoptera:Eurytomidae

wheat midge *Sitodiplosis mosellana* (Gehin) Diptera:Cecidomyiidae

wheat stem maggot *Meromyza americana* Fitch Diptera:Chloropidae

wheat stem sawfly *Cephus cinctus* Norton Hymenoptera:Cephidae

wheat straw-worm *Harmolita grandis* (Riley) Hymenoptera:Eurytomidae

wheat wireworm *Agriotes mancus* (Say) Coleoptera:Elateridae

white-fringed beetles *Graphognathus* spp. Coleoptera:Curculionidae

white garden snail *Theba pisana* (Müller) Stylommatophora:Helicidae

white-lined sphinx *Celerio lineata* (Fabricius) Lepidoptera:Sphingidae

white-marked tussock moth *Hemerocampa leucostigma* (J. E. Smith) Lepidoptera:Lymantriidae

white-pine weevil *Pissodes strobi* (Peck) Coleoptera:Curculionidae

Willamette spider mite * *Eotetranychus willamettei* (McGregor) Acarina:Tetranychidae

willow shoot sawfly *Janus abbreviatus* (Say) Hymenoptera:Cephidae

wing louse *Lipeurus caponis* (Linnaeus) Mallophaga:Philopteridae

winter tick *Dermacentor albipictus* (Packard) Acarina:Ixodidae

w-marked cutworm *Spaelotis clandestina* (Harris) Lepidoptera:Noctuidae

woolly apple aphid *Eriosoma lanigerum* (Hausmann) Homoptera:Aphidae

woolly whitefly *Aleurothrixus floccosus* (Maskell) Homoptera:Aleyrodidae

yellow bumble bee * *Bombus fervidus* (Fabricius) Hymenoptera:Apidae

yellow-fever mosquito *Aedes aegypti* (Linnaeus) Diptera:Culicidae

yellow-headed fireworm *Acleris minuta* (Robinson) Lepidoptera:Tortricidae

yellow-headed leafhopper *Carneocephala flaviceps* (Riley) Homoptera:Cicadellidae

yellow mealworm *Tenebrio molitor* Linnaeus Coleoptera:Tenebrionidae

yellow scale *Aonidiella citrina* (Coquillett) Homoptera:Diaspididae

yellow spider mite *Eotetranychus carpini borealis* (Ewing) Acarina:Tetranychidae

yellow-striped armyworm *Prodenia ornithogalli* Guenée Lepidoptera:Noctuidae

yellow woollybear   *Diacrisia virginica* (Fabricius)   Lepidoptera:Arctiidae
zebra caterpillar   *Ceramica picta* (Harris)   Lepidoptera:Noctuidae
Zimmerman pine moth   *Dioryctria zimmermani* (Grote)   Lepidoptera:Phyciti-
dae

GLOSSARY |

Abdomen. The posterior of the three main body divisions of insects (Fig. 2:1).

Acaricide. A chemical employed to kill and control mites and ticks.

Acetyl choline. A substance present in many parts of the body of animals and important to the function of nerves.

Acidic. Acid in reaction resulting from excess of hydrogen ions over hydroxyl (OH) ions in solution.

Adsuki bean. A kind of bean, *Phaseolus angularis,* extensively grown in Japan and occasionally for home use in the United States.

Aerosol. Finely dispersed particles in air, such as smoke or fog.

Air sac. A dilated portion of a trachea.

Alate. Winged; having wings.

Aldrin (common name). A synthetic insecticide; a chlorinated hydrocarbon of not less than 95 per cent 1,2,3,4,10,10-hexachloro-1,4,4a,5,8,8a-hexahydro-1,4-*endo-exo*-5,8-dimethanonaphthalene; moderately toxic to mammals, acute oral LD_{50} for rats 44 mg/kg; phytotoxicity: none when properly formulated, but some crops are sensitive to solvents in certain formulations.

Aliphatic. A term applied to the "open chain" or fatty series of hydrocarbons.

Alkaline. Having the reaction of an alkali resulting from an excess of hydroxyl ions (OH) over hydrogen ions in solution; pH greater than 7.0.

Alkaloids. Substances found in plants, many having powerful pharmacologic action, and characterized by content of nitrogen and the property of combining with acids to form salts.

Allethrin. A synthetic insecticide related to the plant derived pyrethrins; relatively harmless to warmblooded animals, acute oral LD_{50} for rats 920 mg/kg.

Alsike clover. A perennial clover, *Trifolium hybridum,* adapted to cool climates with abundant moisture, especially suited for pasture mixtures and also grown for hay.

Althea. A tall shrub of the mallow family with showy flowers of white, pink, red, or purple.

Ametabola. The insects which develop without metamorphosis, namely the Protura, Thysanura, and Collembola.

Amide. Compound derived from carboxylic acids by replacing the hydroxyl of the $-COOH$ by the amino group, $-NH_2$.

Amine. An organic compound containing nitrogen, derived from ammonia, NH_3, by replacing one or more hydrogen atoms by as many hydrocarbon radicals.

Amino acid. Organic compounds that contain the amino (NH_2) group and the carboxyl (COOH) group. Amino acids are the "building stones" of proteins.

Ammonia. A colorless alkaline gas, NH_3, soluble in water.

629

Anal. Pertaining to last abdominal segment which bears the anus.

Anaplasmosis. Infection with *Anaplasma,* a genus of Sporozoa that infests red blood cells.

Anasa wilt. A wilt disease of cucurbits caused solely by the feeding of the squash bug, no parasitic microorganism involved.

Anemic. Deficient in blood quantity or quality.

Annulate. Formed in ringlike segments.

Antenna (pl., antennae). Pair of segmented appendages located on the head and usually sensory in function (Fig. 2:1).

Anterior. Front; toward the front.

Anther. Flower part which develops and contains the pollen.

Anthrax. Malignant anthrax a fatal infectious disease of cattle and sheep caused by a bacterium, *Bacillus anthracis,* and characterized by hard ulcers at point of inoculation and by symptoms of collapse. It also occurs in man.

Antibiosis. An association between two or more organisms that is detrimental to one or more of them.

Anticoagulin. A substance antagonistic to the coagulation of blood.

Anus. The posterior opening of the digestive tract (Fig. 2:19).

Aorta. The anterior, nonchambered, narrow part of the insect heart which opens into the head (Fig. 2:19).

Apterous. Wingless.

Apterygota. A subclass of primitively wingless insects which include the Protura, Thysanura, and Collembola.

Aquatic. Living in water.

Arachnida. A class of arthropods which include the scorpions, spiders, mites, ticks, and several other groups.

Aramite (trade name). A synthetic acaricide, a sulfite; chemically, 2-(*p-tert-*butylphenoxy) isopropyl 2-chloroethyl sulfite; acute oral LD_{50} for rats 3,900 mg/kg; phytotoxicity low except to some pear varieties.

Aromatic. In chemistry, compounds which have a nuclear structure similar to that of benzene.

Arboreal. Living in, on, or among trees.

Arthropoda. A phylum of animals with segmented body, exoskeleton, and jointed legs.

Arthropods. Animals belonging to the phylum Arthropoda.

Aschelminthes. A phylum of invertebrate animals that include roundworms, rotifers, and several other classes.

Asymmetrical. Organs or body parts not alike on either side of a dividing line or plane.

Aster yellows. A virus disease of many kinds of plants transmitted by the six-spotted leafhopper and characterized by stunting of plants, sterility, and chlorosis in foliage.

Atomization. Process of breaking a liquid into a fine spray.

Atropine. A poisonous, crystalline alkaloid used in medicine; a specific antidote for poisoning by organic phosphate insecticides.

Attapulgite. A magnesium silicate clay mined in Florida and Georgia and used as a dust carrier.

Attractants. Substances which elicit a positive directive response; chemicals having positive attraction for animals such as insects, usually in low concentration and at considerable distances.

Axon. The process of a nerve cell that conducts impulses away from the cell body.

Azobenzene (common and chemical name). A synthetic acaricide, $C_6H_5N=NC_6H_5$, used by volatilizing from hot water pipes of greenhouse, or by ignition in a pyrotechnic mixture, or as a spray, either emulsion or suspension; chronic toxicity 1,000 ppm in diet kills rats in a few days; phytotoxicity: has injured roses and asparagus fern.

Bacterial wilts. Plant diseases in which the causative bacteria produce slime that plugs the water conducting tissue of the invaded plant.

Barley yellow dwarf. A virus disease of cereals, marked by leaves rapidly turning light green and yellow, beginning at the tips; transmitted by certain species of aphids.

Basic. Having the property of ionizing in solution to form hydroxyl ions and of neutralizing acids to form salts.

Bentonite. A clay composed mainly of silica and aluminum silicate; mined in Mississippi, Wyoming and elsewhere; used as dust diluent and for lining ponds to hold water.

Benzene hexachloride (chemical name). See BHC.

Berseem. Egyptian clover, *Trifolium alexandrinum,* grown as a winter annual in southern Arizona and southern California.

BHC (common name). A synthetic insecticide, a chlorinated hydrocarbon, 1,2,3,-4,5,6-hexachlorocyclohexane of mixed isomers; slightly more toxic to mammals than DDT, acute oral LD_{50} for rats about 200 mg/kg; phytotoxicity: more toxic than DDT, interferes with germination, suppresses growth and reduces yields except at low concentration; certain crop plants, as potato absorb crude BHC with consequent tainting of tubers.

Bilateral symmetry. Similarity of form, one side with the other.

Biological control. The control of pests by employing predators, parasites, or disease; the natural enemies are encouraged and disseminated by man.

Bionomics. The study of the habits, breeding, and adaptations of living forms.

Bisexual. Having two sexes distinct and separate; with males and females.

Black spot. A fungus disease of roses caused by *Diplocarpon rosae* and characterized by black spots on the leaves and yellowing and premature dropping of leaves.

Boll. The pod in which the lint and seeds of cotton develop.

Book lung. A respiratory cavity containing a series of leaflike folds.

Boot leaf. The leaf arising from the protective sheath enclosing the young inflorescence of grain.

Bordeaux mixture. Primarily a fungicide but also a repellent to many insects; a popular formula consists of copper sulfate 6 lb., hydrated lime 10 lb., and water 100 gal.; ingestion of large quantities may cause fatal gastroenteritis in mammals; toxic to some plants, particularly at low temperatures.

Bot. The larva of certain flies that are parasitic in the body of mammals.

Brachypterous. With short wings that do not cover the abdomen.

Bract. A small leaf at the base of the flower.

Brood. In insects, a group of individuals of a given species which have hatched into young or which have become adult at approximately the same time and which live together in a defined and limited area.

Bubonic plague. A bacterial disease of rodents and man caused by *Pasteurella pestis* and transmitted chiefly by the oriental rat flea; marked by chills, fever, and inflammatory swelling of lymphatic glands.

Caecum (pl., caeca). A sac or tubelike structure open at only one end (Fig. 2:19).

Calyx. The outer usually green, leaflike parts of a flower.

Campodeiform larva. A larva shaped like the thysanuran *Compodea*, that is elongate, flattened, with well-developed legs and antennae, and usually with filaments on end of abdomen, and usually active (Fig. 2:2A).

Capitate. With an apical knoblike enlargement.

Capitulum. Headlike structure of ticks which bears the feeding organs.

Captan (trade name). A protective fungicide, particularly for foliage application; chemically, *N*-trichloromethylmercapto-4-*cyclo*hexene-1, 2-dicarboximide; low acute toxicity to warm-blooded animals, acute oral LD_{50} for rats greater than 15,000 mg/kg; no evidence of phytotoxicity.

Carabiform larva. A larva shaped like the larva of a carabid beetle, that is elongate, flattened, and with well-developed legs; filaments lacking on end of abdomen (Fig. 2:2B).

Carbohydrate. Any of a group of neutral compounds made up of carbon, hydrogen, and oxygen; for example, sugar, starch, cellulose.

Carbon disulfide. Insecticidal fumigant for treatment of stored grain, also a soil fumigant for Japanese and Asiatic beetles, also used to rid horses of bots and roundworms; empirical formula CS_2; highly toxic to mammals and toxic to plants and certain seeds.

Carbon tetrachloride. Insecticidal fumigant for treatment of stored grain; empirical formula CCl_4; MLD for man 3 to 4 cc.; vapors may cause acute poisoning at 1,000 ppm; phytotoxicity: does not affect germinating qualities of wheat.

Carnivorous. Preying or feeding on animals.

Carpel. Structural unit of the pistil in which the seed develop.

Caste. A form or type of adult in a social insect such as among termites and ants (Figs. 17:20 and 17:21).

Caterpillar. The larva of a moth, butterfly, or sawfly (Fig. 9:11).

Catfacing. The injury caused by the feeding of such insects as plant bugs and stink bugs on developing fruit which results in uneven growth and a deformed mature fruit.

Cattle tick fever. A specific infectious disease of the blood of cattle caused by a protozoan *Babesia bigemina* which attacks the red blood cells; characterized by fever, anemia, jaundice, and red urine; transmitted by the bite of the cattle tick.

Cement layer. A thin layer on the surface of insect cuticles formed by the hardened secretion of the dermal glands.

Cellulose. An inert carbohydrate, the chief component of the solid framework or woody part of plants.

Cauda. The pointed end of the abdomen in aphids.

Cephalothorax. A body region consisting of head and thoracic segments, as in spiders.

Cercus (pl., cerci). One of a pair of appendages at the end of the abdomen (Fig. 2:1).

Chain. In chemistry, a series of atoms connected by bonds, forming the skeleton of a number of compounds.

Chelicera (pl., chelicerae). The anterior pair of appendages in arachnids (Fig. 2:8).

Chigger. The parasitic larva of trombiculid mites.

Chitin. A nitrogenous polysaccharide occurring in the cuticle of arthropods and certain other invertebrates. Probably occurs naturally only in chemical combination with protein.

Chlorbenside (common name). A synthetic acaricide, a sulfide; chemically, *p*-chlorobenzyl, *p*-chlorophenyl sulfide; single dose of 3,000 mg/kg administered to rats without signs of systemic toxicity; phytotoxicity, none reported, but some harm may be caused to cucurbits.

Chlordane (common name). A synthetic insecticide; a chlorinated hydrocarbon, 1,2,4,5,6,7,8,8-octachloro-3a,4,7,7a-tetrahydro-4, 7-methanoindane; moderately toxic to mammals, oral LD_{50} for rats about 250 mg/kg; phytotoxicity: high concentrations injurious to some vegetables, residues in soil depress germination.

Chlorobenzilate (trade name). A synthetic acaricide, a chlorinated hydrocarbon and relative of DDT; chemically, ethyl 4, 4'-dichlorobenzilate; relatively nontoxic to mammals, acute oral LD_{50} for rats about 1,900 to 3,200 mg/kg.

Chloropicrin. Insecticidal fumigant for treatment of stored grain and cereal products and for soil treatment to control insects, nematodes, weeds, fungi; empirical formula CCl_3NO_2; 0.05 oz./1,000 cu. ft. lethal in 10 minutes to mammals; very toxic to plants when injected into soil.

Chlorosis. In plants, yellowness of normally green tissues due to partial failure of chlorophyll to develop or to removal of chlorophyll.

Cholinesterase. An enzyme (or enzymes) present in body tissues which hydrolyzes or breaks down acetylcholine.

Chorion. The outer shell or covering of the insect egg.

Chromosomes. At cell division the dark-staining, rod-shaped structures which contain the hereditary units called genes.

Chrysalis. The pupa of a butterfly.

Class. A division of the animal kingdom lower than a phylum and higher than an order, for example the class Insecta.

Clavate. Clublike; thickening gradually toward the tip (Fig. 2:4C).

Coarctate pupa. A pupa enclosed in a hardened case formed from the next to the last larval skin; found among higher Diptera (Fig. 3:13C).

Cocoon. A silken case inside which the pupa develops.

Cockerel. A young domestic rooster.

Collard. A kind of edible kale.

Combine. A farm machine which cuts, threshes, and cleans grain while moving over the field.

Commissure. A bridge connecting any two bodies or structures.

Complete metamorphosis. Same as complex metamorphosis. See definition below and Fig. 3:10.

Complex metamorphosis. Metamorphosis in which the insect develops by four distinct stages, namely egg, larva, pupa, and adult; the wings (when present) develop internally during the larval stage.

Compound eye. An eye consisting of many individual elements or ommatidia each of which is represented externally by a facet (Fig. 2:26).

Connective. A longitudinal cord of nerve fibers connecting successive ganglia.

Co-Ral (trade name). An animal systemic insecticide; a synthetic organic phosphate, O, O-diethyl O-3-chloro-4-methyl-2-oxo-2H-1-benzopyran-7-yl phosphorothioate; moderately toxic to mammals, oral LD_{50} for rats 90 to 150 mg/kg.

Cornicles. The pair of dorsal tubular processes on the posterior part of the abdomen, as in aphids (Fig. 4:11A).

Corpora allata. A pair of small endocrine glands located just behind the brain (Fig. 2:28).

Cosmopolitan. Occurring throughout most of the world.

Coxa (pl., coxae). The basal segment of the leg (Fig. 2:3).

Crawler. The active first instar of a scale insect (Fig. 13:23D).

Crochets (Pronounced croshays). Hooked spines at tip of the prolegs of lepidopterous larvae.

Crop. The dilated section of the foregut just behind the esophagus (Fig. 2:19).

Cruciferous. Belonging to the mustard family which includes cabbage, turnip, mustard, radish, and others.

Cryolite. An inorganic insecticide, sodium fluoaluminate; useful in controlling codling moth, orange tortrix, and several other chewing insects; low acute mammalian toxicity; phytotoxicity: may seriously injure peach trees, corn, or grapes, otherwise little plant injury.

Cryptobiotic. Leading a hidden or concealed life.

Cubé powder. The finely ground roots of certain leguminous trees and shrubs, *Lonchocarpus* spp., which contain rotenone, an insecticidal substance.

Cucurbit. A plant belonging to the gourd family, Cucurbitaceae, such as pumpkin, squash, and cucumber.

Cuneus. A small triangular section of the hemelytra at the leading margin and next to the membrane.

Curly top. A virus disease of sugar beets, beans, tomatoes, and other plants transmitted by the beet leafhopper.

Cuticle. The outer noncellular layers of the insect integument secreted by the epidermis (Fig. 2:13).

Cyclic. In chemistry, atoms linked together to form a ring structure.

Cyclodienes. Synthetic insecticides belonging to the cyclodiene group of cyclic hydrocarbons, for example chlordane, heptachlor, aldrin, dieldrin, and endrin.

Cyclorrhaphous Diptera. The group of flies which emerge from the puparium through a circular opening at one end of the puparium. These flies belong to the more advanced families.

Cyst. A sac normal or abnormal, especially one containing a liquid or semisolid.

Cysticercoid. A form of larval tapeworm.

D-D (trade name). A soil fumigant for controlling nematodes; a mixture of 1,3-dichloropropene and 1,2-dichloropropane; moderately toxic to mammals by ingestion or by inhalation, acute oral LD_{50} for rats 140 mg/kg, inhalation LC_{50} for rats 1,000 ppm; toxic to plants and germinating seeds.

DDT (common name). A widely used synthetic insecticide; a chlorinated hydrocarbon, dichloro diphenyl trichloroethane; moderately toxic to mammals, acute oral LD_{50} for rats about 250 mg/kg; phytotoxicity: injures cucurbits, young tomato plants, and beans.

DDVP (common name). A synthetic insecticide and space fumigant; an organic phosphate, O,O-dimethyl 2,2-dichlorovinyl phosphate; moderately toxic to mammals, acute oral LD_{50} for rats 50 to 80 mg/kg; phytotoxicity: none to wide variety of plants at insecticidal concentrations.

Dealate. Wingless as a result of the insect casting or breaking off its own wings.

Delayed dormant spray. An orchard spray applied during the period from swollen bud to late green tip of bud development; often called "swollen bud" in stone fruit work.

Delnav (trade name). A synthetic insecticide and acaricide; an organic phosphate, 2,3-*p*-dioxanedithiol S,S-bis(O,O-diethyl phosphorodithioate); moderately toxic to mammals, acute oral LD_{50} for rats 110 mg/kg; not phytotoxic at recommended rates of application.

Demeton (common name). A contact and plant systemic insecticide and acaricide; an organic phosphate, O,O-diethyl O(and S)-2-(ethylthio)ethyl phosphorothioates; extremely toxic to mammals, acute oral LD_{50} for rats 12 mg/kg; little phytotoxicity at recommended dosages, but "pink" and "petal fall" application to McIntosh apples should be avoided. It has trade name, Systox.

Dengue (pronounced deng'e). A virus disease of man marked by severe pains in head, eyes, muscles, and joints and transmitted by certain mosquitoes.

Dermatitis. Inflammation of the skin.

Derris powder. The finely ground roots of the leguminous shrub, *Derris elliptica,* which contains rotenone, an insecticidal substance.

Deutonymph. The third instar of a mite.

Deutovum. The quiescent, undeveloped larval stage which hatches from the egg of certain mites and from which, after six or seven days, the active, six-legged larva emerges.

Diapause. A state of an animal, such as an insect, in which a reduction of growth processes or maturation occurs which is not necessarily caused by immediate environmental influence, does not depend for its continuance on unsuitable conditions, and is not easily or quickly altered by change to a more favorable environment. However, once the state of diapause comes to an end normal growth and development are resumed.

Diaphragm. A horizontal membranous partition of the body cavity.

Diazinon (trade name). A synthetic insecticide and acaricide; an organic phosphate, O,O-diethyl O-(2-isopropyl-6-methyl-4-pyrimidyl) thiophosphate; moderately toxic to mammals, acute oral LD_{50} for rats about 150 mg/kg; phytotoxicity: toxic to Stephanotis and African violets and may cause russeting of certain varieties of apples.

Dibrom (trade name). A synthetic insecticide and acaricide; an organic phosphate, 1,2-dibromo-2, 2-dichloroethyl dimethyl phosphate; moderately toxic to mammals, acute oral LD_{50} for rats 430 mg/kg; phytotoxicity: injury may occur on some varieties of pome and stone fruits.

Dieldrin (common name). A highly residual insecticide; a chlorinated hydrocarbon of not less than 85 per cent of 1,2,3,4,10,10-hexachloro-6, 7-epoxy-1,4,4a,-5,6,7,8,8a-octahydro-1,4-*endo-exo*-5, 8-dimethanonaphthalene; somewhat more toxic to mammals than DDT, acute oral LD_{50} for rats 100 mg/kg; phytotoxicity: none when properly formulated, but some crops are sensitive to solvents in certain formulations.

Differentiation. Increase in visible distinctive morphology.

Dilan (trade name). A synthetic insecticide; a chlorinated hydrocarbon, 2-nitro 1, 1-bis(p-chlorophenyl)propane and butane mixture (1 to 2 ratio); only ¼ as toxic to mammals as DDT; acute oral LD_{50} for rats about 1,100 mg/kg; no evidence of phytotoxicity even on cucurbits.

Dimethoate (common name). A synthetic insecticide and acaricide, both an animal and plant systemic; an organic phosphate, O,O-dimethyl S(N-methyl-carbamoylmethyl) phosphorodithioate; moderately toxic to mammals, acute oral LD_{50} for rats 245 mg/kg; slight phytotoxicity to some fruit and field crops.

Dimite (trade name). A synthetic acaricide, a chlorinated hydrocarbon and relative of DDT; chemically, 1, 1-bis(p-chlorophenyl)ethanol; moderately toxic to mammals, acute oral LD_{50} for rats 500 mg/kg.

Dimorphic. Occurring in two distinct forms.

Dimorphism. A difference in size, form, or color, between individuals of the same species, characterizing two distinct types.

Dinitrocresol (common name). A synthetic insecticide; a nitrophenyl compound, 4, 6-dinitro-o-cresol, sodium salt; highly toxic to man, acute oral LD_{50} for rats 30 mg/kg; phytotoxicity: very great, can be used as weed killer.

Diphtheria. A highly contagious bacterial disease due to presence of *Corynebacterium diphtheriae* characterized by fever, heart weakness, anemia, and great prostration; often fatal.

Dipterex (trade name). Chemically the same as Dylox.

Disk. A type of plow with a rolling disk bottom.

Di-Syston (trade name). A synthetic insecticide and acaricide, plant systemic absorbed through the roots; an organic phosphate, *O, O*-diethyl S-2-(ethylthio) ethyl phosphorodithioate; extremely toxic to mammals, acute oral LD_{50} for rats 2 to 9 mg/kg; high dosages can injure seed.

DMC. See Dimite.

Dockage. Foreign material in harvested grain such as weed seeds, chaff, and dust.

Dormancy. A state of quiescence or inactivity.

Dormant spray. A spray applied to trees in true dormancy, before the buds begin to swell.

Dorsal. Top or uppermost; pertaining to the back or upper surface.

Dorsal ocellus. The simple eye in adult insects and in nymphs and naiads (Fig. 2:26).

Dorsal shield. The scutum or sclerotized plate covering all or most of the dorsal surface in males and the anterior portion in females, nymphs, and larvae of hard-backed ticks (Fig. 18:20).

Dorsum. The back or top side.

Downy mildew. Any plant disease caused by species of fungi in the family Peronosporaceae and characterized by the downy growth on host lesions.

Drone. The male honey bee.

Drupelet. A small drupe; the small individual fleshy fruits which make up the berry as in blackberries and raspberries.

Dylox (trade name). A synthetic insecticide; an organic phosphate, dimethyl (2,2,2-trichloro-1-hydroxyethyl) phosphonate; moderately toxic to mammals, acute oral LD_{50} for rats 450 to 500 mg/kg; phytotoxicity: varying degrees of injury to fruit of several apple varieties.

Ectoderm. The outer embryological layer which gives rise to the nervous system, integument, and several other parts of an insect.

Ectohormone. A substance secreted by an animal to the outside causing a specific reaction, such as determination of physiological development, in a receiving individual of the same species.

Ectoparasite. A parasite that lives on the outside of its host.

Egg pod. A capsule which encloses the egg mass of grasshoppers and which is formed through the cementing of soil particles together by secretions of the ovipositing female (Fig. 8:8).

Elateriform larva. A larva with the form of a wireworm; that is long, slender, heavily sclerotized, with short thoracic legs, and with few body hairs (Fig. 2:2E).

Elytra (sing., elytron). Thickened, horny or leathery front wings as in beetles and earwigs (Fig. 8:18C).

Emmer. A type of wheat cultivated from very early times; in America grown for livestock feed.

Emulsifiable concentrate. A liquid formulation of insecticide which contains an emulsifier so that water may be added to form an emulsion.

Emulsion. A suspension of fine droplets of one liquid in another, such as oil in water. Emulsions are milky in appearance.

Encephalitis. Inflammation of the brain.

Endemic typhus. See Murine Typhus Fever.

Endocrine. Secreting internally, applied to organs whose function is to secrete into blood or lymph a substance which has an important role in metabolism.

Endocuticle. The innermost layer of the cuticle (Fig. 2:13).

Endosperm. A food storage tissue in seeds.

Endrin (common name). A highly residual insecticide, particularly effective against lepidopterous larvae; a chlorinated hydrocarbon, the *endo-endo* isomer of dieldrin; highly toxic to mammals, acute oral LD_{50} for rats 10–12 mg/kg; phytotoxicity: none when properly formulated, but some crops are sensitive to solvents in certain formulations.

Entoleter. A centrifugal force machine to kill insects infesting grain.

Entomogenous. Growing in or on an insect, for example certain fungi.

Enzyme. An organic catalyst formed by a living cell.

Epicuticle. The thin, nonchitinous, surface layers of the cuticle (Fig. 2:13).

Epidemic typhus. Same as Typhus Fever.

Epidermis. The cellular layer of the integument that secretes or deposits a comparatively thick cuticle on its outer surface (Fig. 2:13).

Epipharynx. A mouthpart structure on the inner surface of the labrum or clypeus.

Epithelium. The layer of cells that covers a surface or lines a cavity.

EPN (common name). A synthetic insecticide and acaricide; an organic phosphate, ethyl *p*-nitrophenyl benzene thiophosphonate; highly toxic to mammals, acute oral LD_{50} for rats 35 to 45 mg/kg; phytotoxicity: may injure McIntosh and related varieties of apples.

EQ 335. A screw-worm remedy consisting of the following (per cent by weight): lindane 3, pine oil 35, mineral oil 42, emulsifier 10, and silica aerogel 10.

Erinose. Any plant disease in which an abnormal growth of hairs occurs in patches on the leaves, such as caused by the attack of certain gall mites (genus *Eriophyes*).

Eruciform larva. A caterpillar, a larva with cylindrical body, well-developed head, and thoracic legs and abdominal prolegs (Fig. 2:2C).

Erythrocyte. A red blood corpuscle.

Escutcheon. An area on a cow just above the rear part of the udder and below the vulva.

Esophagus. The narrow part of the alimentary canal immediately posterior to the pharynx and mouth.

Esters. Esters are chemical compounds formed by the elimination of water between a molecule of an alcohol and a molecule of an acid.

Estivate. To enter a dormant state during summer.

Ethers. Ethers are organic compounds in which two hydrocarbon radicals are joined through an atom of oxygen.

Ethion (common name). A synthetic insecticide and acaricide; an organic phosphate, O,O,O',O',-tetraethyl S,S'-methylene bisphosphorodithioate; moderately toxic to mammals, acute oral LD_{50} for rats 96 mg/kg; phytotoxicity: safe on all crops except defoliation may result when applied to Wealthy apples.

Ethylene dibromide. Insecticidal fumigant for treatment of stored grain, also a soil insecticide and nematocide; empirical formula $C_2H_4Br_2$; acute oral LD_{50} for male rats 146 mg/kg and for female rats 420 mg/kg; toxic to plants.

Ethylene dichloride. Insecticidal fumigant for use against stored grain insects and peach tree borers; empirical formula $C_2H_4Cl_2$; exposure to 4,000 ppm for one hour produces serious illness in man.

Exarate pupa. A pupa which has its appendages free and not glued to the body (Fig. 3:13B).

Excretion. The elimination of waste products of metabolism.

Exocuticle. The hard and usually darkened layer of the cuticle lying between endocuticle and epicuticle (Fig. 2:13).

Exoskeleton. Collectively the external plates of the body wall.

Facet. The external surface of an individual unit (ommatidium) of the compound eye (Fig. 2:26).

Fallow. Land, ordinarily used for crops, allowed to lie idle during the growing season.

Family. A taxonomic subdivision of an order, suborder, or superfamily that contains a group of related genera, tribes, or subfamilies. Family names end in *-idae.*

Fascicle. A small bundle; the bundle of piercing stylets of insects with piercing-sucking mouthparts (Fig. 2:7).

Fat. The oily substance that covers the connective tissue of an animal.

Fat body. An organ in the insect body with multiple functions in metabolism, food storage, and excretion. "Fat body" is a misnomer, for protein and glycogen are stored as well as fat.

Femur (pl., femora). The third segment of the insect leg (Fig. 2:3).

Fenson (trade name). A synthetic acaricide; a sulfonate, *p*-chlorophenyl benzene sulfonate; moderately toxic to mammals, acute oral LD_{50} for rats around 1,535 mg/kg; little information on phytotoxicity but safe as recommended for use.

Ferbam (trade name). A protective fungicide used for foliage application; chemically, ferric dimethyldithiocarbamate; of low acute mammalian toxicity, acute oral LD_{50} for rats greater than 11,000 mg/kg; generally nonphytotoxic.

Feterita. A group of grain sorghums.

Filariasis. A disease state due to infection with filarial roundworms (nematodes of the superfamily Filarioidea).

Filiform. Threadlike; slender and of equal diameter (Fig. 2:4A).

Flax. An annual herbaceous plant, *Linum usitatissimum,* grown for seed or fiber from which linseed oil or linen and cigarette paper are made.

Flaxseed. The puparium of the Hessian fly.

Floret. A small flower, usually one of a dense cluster.

Fluke. A parasitic flatworm of the class Trematoda.

Forb. Any herbaceous plant other than grass.

Foregut. The anterior part of the alimentary canal from the mouth to the midgut (Fig. 2:19).

Fumigant. A substance or mixture of substances which produce gas, vapor, fume, or smoke intended to destroy insect and other pests.

Fungicide. Any substance that kills fungi or inhibits the growth of the spores or hyphae.

Gall. An abnormal growth of plant tissues induced by the presence and stimulus of an animal or another plant.

Gametocyte. A sex cell stage of *Plasmodium,* the malarial parasite.

Ganglion. A nerve mass that serves as a center of nervous influence (Fig. 2:19).

Gastric caeca. The sac-like diverticula at the anterior end of the midgut (Fig. 2:19).

Gastroenteritis. Inflammation of the stomach and intestines.

Generation. The group of individuals of a given species that have been reproduced at approximately the same time; the group of individuals of the same genealogical rank.

Geniculate. Elbowed or abruptly bent (Fig. 2:4E).

Genital claspers. Organs of the male genitalia which serve to hold the female during copulation.

Genitalia. The reproductive organs; the external structures which enable the sexes to copulate and the females to deposit eggs, strictly these are the external genetalia.

Genite (trade name). A synthetic acaricide; a sulfonate, 2,4-dichlorophenyl benzenesulfonate; acute oral LD_{50} for rats approximately 1,650 mg/kg; phytotoxicity: may cause leaf yellowing and damage to apples when applied after pre-blossom stages.

Genus (pl., genera). A group of closely related species.

Germ. The embryo within a seed.

Glycogen. A carbohydrate synthesized by animals, also called "animal starch."

Gnathosoma. The anterior part of the body of mites and ticks which bears the mouth and mouthparts (Fig. 2:8).

Gonad. The ovary or testis or the embryonic rudiment of either.

G.p.m. Gallons per minute.

Gradual metamorphosis. See simple metamorphosis.

Granular viruses. Viruses causing insect diseases characterized by the presence in large numbers of very small but microscopically discernible granular inclusions in infected cells, and particularly visible in the cytoplasm of the host. The granules consist of proteinaceous material within which the virus particle is located.

Granulosis. Virus disease of insects characterized by the presence of granular inclusions.

Granules. An insecticidal formulation in which the insecticide is impregnated on small particles of clay. Size of particles is expressed in terms of the number of openings per linear inch of two limiting screens. Four common mesh sizes are $\frac{8}{15}$, $\frac{15}{30}$, $\frac{24}{48}$, $\frac{30}{60}$.

Gregarious. Living in groups.

Ground bed. A plat of soil at or near ground level in greenhouses, in contrast to soil in raised benches.

Grub. A scarabaeiform larva, that is a thick bodied larva with thoracic legs and well developed head; usually sluggish.

Guthion (trade name). A synthetic insecticide; an organic phosphate, O,O-dimethyl S-4-oxo-1,2,3-benzotriazin-3(4-H)-ylmethyl phosphorodithioate; extremely toxic to mammals, acute oral LD_{50} for rats 15 to 25 mg/kg.

Haltere. A slender knobbed structure on each side of the metathorax in place of the hind wings.

Harrow. A farm implement used to level the ground and crush clods, to stir the soil, and to prevent and destroy weeds. Five principal kinds are the disk, spike-tooth, spring-tooth, rotary cross-harrow, and soil surgeon.

Heart. The chambered, pulsatile portion of the dorsal blood vessel (Fig. 2:19).

Head. The anterior body region of insects which bears the mouthparts, eyes, and antennae (Fig. 2:1).

Hematophagous. Feeding or subsisting on blood.

Hemelytron (pl., hemelytra). The front wing of Hemiptera in which the basal portion is thickened and the distal portion membranous.

Hemimetabola. Insects with simple metamorphosis, with immature stages aquatic and adults terrestrial; insects of the orders Odonata, Ephemeroptera, and Plecoptera; young are called naiads.

Hemoglobin. Oxygen carrying red pigment.

Hemolymph. The blood plasma or liquid part of the blood, though generally synonymous for blood of insects.

Heptachlor (common name). A synthetic insecticide; a chlorinated hydrocarbon, 1,4,5,6,7,8,8-heptachloro-3a,4,7,7a-tetrahydro-4,7-methanoindene; moderately toxic to mammals, acute oral LD_{50} for rats 130 mg/kg; nontoxic to plants at recommended concentrations.

Herbicide. A chemical for killing weeds.

Hermaphroditic. Containing the sex organs of both sexes in one individual.

Heterometabola. Insects with simple metamorphosis including the Paurometabola and Hemimetabola.

HETP (common name). A synthetic insecticide and acaricide; an organic phosphate, a mixture of ethyl polyphosphates containing 12 to 20 per cent of tetraethyl pyrophosphate (TEPP); extremely toxic to mammals, acute oral LD_{50} for rats 7 mg/kg.

Hibernation. Dormancy during the winter.

Hindgut. The posterior part of the alimentary canal between the midgut and anus (Fig. 2:19).

Histosiphon. Same as stylostome.

Holometabola. The higher insects which have complex metamorphosis.

Homologous. Organs or parts which exhibit similarity in structure, in position with reference to other parts, and in mode of development, but not necessarily similarity of function, are said to be homologous.

Honeydew. A sugary liquid discharged from the anus of certain Homoptera.

Hopperburn. A disease of potato, alfalfa, and other plants resulting from the feeding of the potato leafhopper, a toxicogenic insect.

Hormone. A chemical substance formed in some organ of the body, secreted directly into the blood, and carried to another organ or tissue where it produces a specific effect.

Host. The organism in or on which a parasite lives; the plant on which an insect or other arthropod feeds.

Hybrid. The offspring of two plants or animals of different races, varieties, or species.

Hydrocarbons. Compounds that contain carbon and hydrogen only.

Hydrolysis. Chemical reaction in which a compound reacts with water to produce a weak acid, a weak base, or both.

Hypermetamorphosis. A type of complex metamorphosis in which the larval instars in their development assume the form of two or more types of larvae.

Hyperparasite. A parasite whose host is also a parasite.

Hypopharynx. A tonguelike mouthpart arising on the upper surface of the labium; in piercing-sucking insects it may be stylet-shaped and contain the salivary channel.

Hypopus. A nymphal stage in the development of certain mites in which the organism is small and has developed suckers or claspers for grasping insects and thereby effecting dispersal.

Hypostome. In ticks, the median ventral dartlike mouthpart that is immovably attached to basal part of the capitulum (Fig. 2:8).

Hysterosoma. In mites, the posterior part of the body when there is a demarcation of the body between the second and third pair of legs.

Imago (pl., imagoes or imagines). The adult stage of an insect.

Indigo. Any of a group of plants of the pea family that yield indigo, a blue dye; indigo is mostly the product of *Indigofera tinctoria*.

Insect. A member of the class Insecta.

Insecta. A class of phylum Arthropoda distinguished by adults having three body regions: head, thorax, and abdomen; and by having the thorax three-segmented with each segment bearing a pair of legs.

Insecticide. A toxic chemical substance employed to kill and control insects.

Instar. The form of an insect between successive molts, the first instar being the form between hatching and the first molt.

Integrated control. Control of pests which combines and integrates chemical methods with natural and biological control. Chemical control is applied as necessary and in a manner which is least disruptive to natural and biological control.

Integument. The covering layers of an animal.

Intermediate host. The host which harbors the immature stages or the asexual stages of a parasite.

Internode. The length of stem between two successive nodes.

Intima. The cuticular membrane lining the tracheae.

Invertebrates. Animals without a spinal column or backbone.

Isomer. Any of two or more chemical compounds having like constituent atoms, but differing in physical or chemical properties because of differences in arrangement of the atoms.

Johnston's organ. A sense organ located in the second antennal segment of many insects and particularly well developed in male mosquitoes and certain other Diptera.

Joint. In plants, a node; to develop distinct nodes and internodes in a grass stem.

Juvenile hormone. The hormone, secreted by the corpora allata, that maintains the immature form of an insect during early molts.

Kafir. A group of sorghums grown for both grain and forage.

Kale. A plant, *Brassica oleracea* var. *acephala,* belonging to the mustard family and grown for forage.

Kelthane (trade name). A synthetic acaricide, a chlorinated hydrocarbon and relative of DDT; chemically, 1,1-bis(*p*-chlorophenyl)2,2,2-trichloroethanol; moderately toxic to warm-blooded animals, acute oral LD_{50} for rats around 750 mg/kg; little evidence of phytotoxicity except on eggplant and avocado.

Keratitis. Inflammation of the cornea of the eyes of man or livestock.

Korlan (trade name). See ronnel which is common name for this chemical.

Kudzu. A leguminous perennial plant, *Pueraria thunbergiana,* adapted to warm climates and grown for hay or pasture or for soil improvement or erosion control.

Keratin. A protein forming the principal matter of hair, horns, and nails.

Labellum. The expanded fleshy tip of the labium.

Labial palpus (pl., labial palpi). One of the pair of sensory appendages (feeler-like and 2 to 5 segmented) of the insect labium.

Labium. The posterior mouthpart or lower lip of an insect (Fig. 2:1).

Labrum. The anterior mouthpart or upper lip of an insect (Fig. 2:1).

Labrum-epipharynx. A mouthpart composed of the labrum and epipharynx and usually elongate (Fig. 2:7).

Lamellate. Platelike or sheetlike; composed of or covered with thin sheets.

Larva. The immature insect hatching from the egg and up to the pupal stage in orders with complex metamorphosis; the six-legged first instar of mites and ticks.

Lateral ocellus. The simple eye in holometabolus larvae. Also called stemma (pl., stemmata).

Lateral oviduct. In insects, one of the paired lateral ducts of the female genital system connected with the ovary.

LD_{50}. Lethal dose to 50 per cent of the test animals. Usually expressed in terms of milligrams (mg.) of toxicant per kilogram (kg.) of body weight of the test animal (mg/kg).

Leaf miner. An insect which lives in and feeds upon the leaf cells between the upper and lower surfaces of a leaf.

Leaf sheath. The lower part of the leaf that encloses the stem.

Legal control. Control of pests through the enactment of legislation that enforces control measures or imposes regulations, such as quarantines, to prevent the introduction or spread of pests.

Legume. A member of the plant family, Leguminosae, which includes bean, pea, alfalfa, clover, peanut, and many other species.

Leguminous. Having the nature of or bearing a legume.

Leishmaniasis. Any disease due to infection with species of *Leishmania*, a genus of Protozoa in the class Flagellata.

Leprosy. A chronic, transmissible disease due to a specific bacterium, *Mycobacterium leprae*.

Lethane 384 (trade name). A synthetic insecticide; a thiocyanate, β-butoxy-β′-thiocyanodiethyl ether; moderately toxic to mammals, acute oral LD_{50} for rats 90 mg/kg; somewhat phytotoxic.

Life history. Habits and changes undergone by an organism from the egg stage to its death as an adult.

Lime-sulfur. An insecticide and fungicide made by boiling sulfur and lime together in water, which react to form both soluble and insoluble salts of calcium polysulfide; irritating to eyes, nose, and skin; phytotoxicity: injurious to peach trees and on "sulfur-shy" varieties.

Lindane (common name). A synthetic insecticide; a chlorinated hydrocarbon containing 99 per cent or more of the gamma isomer of BHC; somewhat more toxic to mammals than DDT, acute oral LD_{50} for rats 125 mg/kg; nonphytotoxic at insecticidal concentrations, can damage plants if used in excess.

Lint. The fiber surrounding the seed of unginned cotton.

Listed corn. Corn planted in a furrow or trench or below the general level of the ground.

Lister. A plow with double moldboard that heaps soil on both sides of the furrow; it may also be combined with a drill that plants seed in the same operation.

Litter floor. The floor of a poultry house which is composed of straw, shavings, or ground corncobs, etc. and droppings and other waste materials and builds up during one laying year.

Lock. A locule or ovary cavity.

Locust. A migratory grasshopper.

Lodge. To throw or beat down, as growing grain.

Looper. A caterpillar with two or more of the ventral prolegs wanting; crawls by looping its body.

Macropterous. Long or large winged.

Maggot. A vermiform larva; a larva without legs and without well-developed head capsule (Fig. 2:2G).

Malaria. An infectious febrile disease of man caused by Protozoa of the genus *Plasmodium* which invade the red blood corpuscles and which are transmitted by mosquitoes of the genus *Anopheles*.

Malathion (common name). A synthetic insecticide; an organic phosphate, *O,O*-dimethyl dithiophosphate of diethyl mercaptosuccinate; moderately toxic to mammals, acute oral LD_{50} for rats 1,500 mg/kg; phytotoxicity: tolerated by most plants at concentrations used for insect control, a slight damage under greenhouse conditions to poled string bean, squash, and cucumber.

Malpighian tubes. Excretory tubes of insects arising from the anterior end of the hindgut and extending into the body cavity (Fig. 2:19).

Mandibles. The anterior paired mouthparts in insects; stout and toothlike in chewing insects, needle or sword shaped in piercing-sucking insects (Figs. 2:1, 2:6, and 2:7).

Mange. A group of contagious skin diseases in livestock caused by certain parasitic mites.

Mastitis. Inflammation of the mammary gland.

Maxillae (sing., maxilla). The paired mouthparts behind the mandibles; the second pair of jaws in chewing insects (Figs. 2:1, 2:6, and 2:7).

Mechanical control. Control of pests by mechanical means such as window screens, earth barriers, etc.

Median oviduct. In insects, the single duct formed by the merging of the paired lateral oviducts; this duct opens posteriorly into a genital chamber or vagina (Fig. 2:19).

Melanistic. Characterized by excessive pigmentation or blackening of the integument or tissues.

Membranous. Thin and transparent (in reference to wings); thin and pliable (in reference to integument).

Mesoderm. In insects, the embryological tissue that forms a middle layer and gives rise to muscles, heart, blood cells, fat body, reproductive organ, and others.

Mesothorax. The middle or second segment of the thorax (Fig. 2:1).

Metaldehyde (chemical name). A chemical with slug-killing properties; empirical formula $(CH_3CHO)_4$; moderately toxic to mammals.

Metamorphosis. Change in form during the development of an insect.

Metathorax. The third or posterior segment of the thorax (Fig. 2:1).

Methoxychlor (common name). A synthetic insecticide; a chlorinated hydrocarbon related to DDT, 1,1,1-trichloro-2,2-bis(p-methoxyphenyl) ethane; less toxic to mammals than DDT, acute oral LD_{50} for rats about 1,000 mg/kg; generally nonphytotoxic to crop plants.

Methyl bromide. Insecticidal fumigant for treatment of mills, warehouses, vaults, ships, freight cars; also a soil fumigant; empirical formula, CH_3Br; exposure to 2,000 ppm for one hour causes serious injury to mammals; toxic to growing plants.

Methyl parathion (common name). A synthetic insecticide and acaricide; an organic phosphate, O,O-dimethyl O-p-nitrophenyl phosphorothioate, extremely toxic to mammals, acute oral LD_{50} for rats 9 to 25 mg/kg; little phytotoxicity in recommended doses.

MGK 264 (trade name). A synergist for pyrethrum; chemically, N-(2-ethylhexyl)-bicyclo [2.2.1]-hept-5-ene-2, 3-dicarboximide; relatively nontoxic to mammals, acute oral LD_{50} for rats 2,800 mg/kg.

Microflora. Microscopic plant life of an area.

Micron. One-thousandth part of a millimeter.

Micropyle. A minute opening or group of openings into the insect egg through which the spermatozoa enter in fertilization.

Microtrichia. Minute hairs projecting from the integument, they are formed around cellular filaments.

Midgut. The middle part of the alimentary canal and the main site of digestion and absorption (Fig. 2:19).

Millet. A cereal grass, *Setaria italica*, of minor importance in America.

Millimeter. One thousandth of a meter or approximately 0.04 inch.

Milo. A sorghum group grown strictly for grain.

Mineral. An inorganic homogenous substance; an inorganic foodstuff.

Mite. Any minute invertebrate belonging to the phylum Arthropoda and order Acarina except the ticks (Fig. 4:4).

Miticide. Any poisonous substance used to kill and control mites.

Mitochondria. Small granules or rodlike structures found in cytoplasm of cells after differential staining.

Mitox (trade name). See chlorbenside which is common name for this chemical.

mm. A millimeter.

Mollusca. A phylum of animals containing snails, slugs, clams, oysters, octopus, and others.

Molt. Process of shedding the skin; to shed the skin.

Moniliform. Beadlike, with rounded segments, as in moniliform antennae (Fig. 2:4E).

Monophagous. Feeding upon only one kind of food, for example one species or one genus of plants.

Murine typhus fever. A human disease caused by a bacterium-like microorganism, *Rickettsia mooseri* and transmitted from rats to man by the oriental rat flea. Clinically similar to typhus fever except with milder symptoms.

Mycetome. In insects, a group of cells that harbor specific microorganisms.

Myiasis. Infestation of the body by the larvae of flies.

Naiad. An aquatic, gill-bearing nymph.

Naphthalene (chemical name). A coal tar derivative long used as a fumigant for clothes moth, also employed as a soil fumigant; relatively nontoxic to mammals; very toxic to plants.

Nasutus (pl., nasuti). A type of soldier caste in certain termites; this form bears a median frontal rostrum through which it ejects a defensive fluid; the jaws are small or vestigial.

Natural control. The reduction of pest populations by the forces of nature such as climatic factors, parasites, predators, and disease.

Nectar. The sugary liquid secreted by many flowers.

Nectary. A floral gland which secretes nectar.

Neguvon (trade name). A product prepared for use as an animal medicament, chemically the same as Dylox.

Nematodes. Unsegmented worms with cylindrical, elongate bodies.

Neurone. The entire nerve cell including all its processes.

Neurosecretory. Pertaining to the secretion of hormones by nerve cells.

Newcastle disease. An acute, rapidly spreading respiratory and nervous disease of domestic poultry and other birds caused by a virus and characterized by rales, coughing, sneezing, and nervous manifestations.

Nicotine (common name). A botanical insecticide derived from leaves and stems of the tobacco plant; an alkaloid, l-1-methyl-2-(3′-pyridyl)-pyrrolidine; highly toxic to mammals, acute oral LD_{50} for rats 50 to 60 mg/kg, phytotoxicity: safe on most plants.

Nit. The egg of a louse.

Nocturnal. Active at night.

Node. The joint of a stem where a leaf is attached.

Notum (pl., nota). In insects the dorsal surface of a body segment.

Nubbin. A small or imperfect ear of corn.

Nucleus. The spheroid body within a cell that has the major role in controlling and regulating the cell's activities and contains the hereditary units or genes.

Nurse cells. Cells that are located in the ovarian tubes of certain insects and that furnish nutriment to the developing eggs.

Nymph. A young insect of a species with simple or no metamorphosis; an eight-legged immature mite or tick.

Obtect pupa. A pupa in which the appendages are closely appressed to the body (Fig. 3:13A).

Ocellus (pl., ocelli). The simple eye of an insect or another arthropod.

Okra. A tall plant of the mallow family with sticky green pods used in soups, stews, etc.

Ommatidium (pl., ommatidia). A single unit or visual section of a compound eye (Fig. 2:26).

Onchocerciasis. Infection with a genus of filarial nematodes, *Onchocerca*. The adults live and reproduce in subcutaneous fibroid nodules; the young, called microfilariae, are carried by the lymph and found chiefly in the skin and eyes; transmitted by certain black flies.

Ootheca (pl., oothecae). An egg case formed by the secretions of accessory genital glands or oviducts, as in cockroaches.

Order. A subdivision of a class or subclass containing a group of related families.

Organophosphates. Organic compounds containing phosphorous; an important group of synthetic insecticides belong to this class of chemicals.

Oribatid mite. A mite belonging to the Oribatei, a large unit of mites containing about 35 families in the suborder Sarcoptiformes.

Osmotic pressure. The maximum pressure which can be developed in a solution which is separated from pure water by a rigid membrane permeable only to water.

Ovex (common name). A synthetic acaricide; a sulfonate, *p*-chlorophenyl *p*-chlorobenzenesulfonate; acute oral LD_{50} for rats 2,050 mg/kg; phytotoxicity: injures hops and causes russeting of stem end of some varieties of apples and pears.

Oviduct. The duct leading from the ovary through which the eggs pass (Fig. 2:19).

Oviparae. In aphids, the oviparous females.

Oviparous. Producing eggs which are hatched outside the body of the female.

Oviposition. The act of laying or depositing eggs.

Ovipositor. The tubular or valved structure of the female by means of which the eggs are deposited.

Ovoviviparous. Producing living young by the hatching of the egg while still within the female.

Palpus (pl., palpi). A segmented feeler-like process borne by the maxilla or labium.

Paradichlorobenzene. Insecticidal fumigant for control of clothes moth, also soil fumigant for peach tree borer; empirical formula $C_6H_4Cl_2$; doses over 300 mg/kg for humans begin to be harmful, low acute oral toxicity for rats as latter survive 1,000 mg/kg; phytotoxicity: seriously injures seed germination.

Parasite. Any animal or plant that lives in or on and at the expense of another organism.

Parathion (common name). A widely used agricultural insecticide and acaricide; an organic phosphate, *O,O*-diethyl *O-p*-nitrophenyl phosphorothioate; extremely toxic to mammals, oral LD_{50} to rats 2 to 6 mg/kg; phytotoxicity: injurious to certain ornamentals, pears and McIntosh and related apples under certain weather conditions.

Parenchyma. A plant tissue composed of thin walled cells which often store food and usually retain the capacity to divide.

Paris green. An arsenical compound which came into use as an insecticide around 1867; chemically, copper acetoarsenite; highly toxic to mammals; toxic to tender plants and fruit trees.

Parthenogenesis. Reproduction by the development of an egg without its being fertilized by a sperm.

Pathogenic. Giving origin to disease.

Paurometabola. Insects with simple metamorphosis and with young and adults living in the same habitat; young are called nymphs.

Pectinate. Comblike; with branches or processes like the teeth of a comb, as in pectinate antennae (Fig. 2:4G).

Pedipalp. The second pair of appendages of an arachnid, used to crush prey.

Pentachlorophenol (chemical name). A wood preservative, used to control termites and to protect cut timber from wood-boring insects and from fungal rots, moderately toxic to mammals, acute oral LD_{50} for rats 210 mg/kg; toxic to plants at point of contact, but not translocated, used as a herbicide.

Perthane (trade name). A synthetic insecticide; a chlorinated hydrocarbon related to DDT; 1,1-dichloro-2,2-bis(*p*-ethylphenyl)ethane; low mammalian toxicity, oral LD_{50} for rats around 8,000 mg/kg; not phytotoxic.

Pesticide. A chemical that is used to poison and control pests, either animal or plant.

Petiole. A leaf stalk.

Phagocytic. Pertaining to any cell that ingests microorganisms or other cells and substances.

Pharynx. The anterior part of the foregut between the mouth and the esophagus.

Pheromone. See ectohormone.

Phorate (common name). A synthetic insecticide and acaricide, a plant systemic with high contact activity; an organic phosphate, *O,O*-diethyl S-ethylthiomethyl phosphorodithioate; extremely toxic to mammals, oral LD_{50} for rats 4 mg/kg; phytotoxicity: seed of wheat, oats, corn, peas, cucumbers and beans will not tolerate higher dosage than 4 to 8 oz. per 100 lbs.; injures tobacco and apples.

Phosdrin (trade name). A synthetic insecticide and acaricide, a plant systemic; an organic phosphate, 1-methoxycarbonyl-1-propen-2-yl dimethyl phosphate; extremely toxic to mammals, acute oral LD_{50} for male rats alpha isomer 3 mg/kg, beta isomer 46 mg/kg.

Phosphamidon (common name). A plant systemic insecticide and acaricide; an organic phosphate, 2-chloro-2-diethylcarbamoyl-1-methylvinyl dimethyl phosphate; highly toxic to mammals acute oral LD_{100} for rats 50 mg/kg; some phytotoxicity to apples, peaches, and walnuts.

Phostex (trade name). A synthetic insecticide and acaricide; a phosphorous-containing compound, bis(dialkoxyphosphinothioyl) disulfides (alkyl ratio 25 per cent isopropyl, 75 per cent ethyl); low toxicity to mammals, acute oral LD_{50} for rats 2,500 mg/kg; phytotoxicity causes shotholing of stone-fruit foliage, toxic to Wealthy apples.

Phylum (pl., phyla). A major division of the animal kingdom.

Physical control. Control of pests by physical means such as heat, cold, electricity, sound waves, etc.

Phytophagous. Feeding upon plants.

Phytotoxic. Poisonous to plants.

Pink eye. In cattle an infectious disease of the eyes in which the eye and its protective membranes become inflamed.

Piperonyl butoxide (common name). A synergist for pyrethrum; chemically, *a*-[2-(2-butoxyethoxy)ethoxy]-4,5-methylenedioxy-2-propyltoluene; relatively nontoxic to mammals, acute oral LD_{50} for rats 7,500 to 12,800 mg/kg.

Piperonyl cyclonene (common name). A synergist for pyrethrum; chemically, a mixture of 3-alkyl-6-carbethoxy-5-(3,4-methylenedioxyphenyl)-2-cyclohexen-1-one and 3-alkyl-5-(3,4-methylenedioxyphenyl)-2-cyclohexen-1-one; relatively nontoxic to mammals, acute oral LD_{50} for rats 5,200 mg/kg.

Piroplasmosis. Infection with piroplasma, genus *Babesia*, parasitic protozoans that attack the red blood corpuscles of cattle, dogs, and other animals and cause a high fever, destruction of red blood corpuscles, enlarged spleen, engorged liver, emaciation, and often death; the organism is transmitted by ticks.

Plague. See bubonic plague.

Platyform larva. A very flattened larva (Fig. 2:2F).

Platyhelminthes. The phylum containing the flatworms, such as tapeworms and flukes.

Plumose. Featherlike, as in plumose antennae (Fig. 2:4H).

Poliomyelitis. Inflammation of the gray matter of the spinal cord; an acute infectious virus disease attended with fever, motor paralysis, and atrophy of groups of muscles.

Pollen. The mass of microspores or male fertilizing elements of flowering plants.

Pollinate. To transfer pollen grains from a stamen to a stigma or ovule of a plant.

Polyembryony. The production of several embryos from a single egg, as in some chalcids.

Polyhedral viruses. Viruses which cause insect disease characterized by the presence of polyhedral (many sided) inclusions in the infected cells of the host.

Polyphagous. Feeding on a variety of plants or animals.

Polyhedrosis. Virus disease of insects characterized by the presence of polyhedral inclusions.

Population. A group of individuals of the same species living in a limited and defined area.

Posterior. Hind or rear.

Potassium ammonium selenosulfide. An inorganic acaricide; used as a spray on ornamental plants; highly toxic to mammals.

ppm. Parts per million.

Predaceous. Preying on other animals.

Predator. An animal that attacks and feeds on other animals, usually smaller and weaker than itself.

Preovipositional period. The period between the emergence of an adult female and the start of its egg laying.

Prepupa. The last larval instar after it ceases to feed; often it takes on a distinctive appearance and becomes quiescent.

Presumptive organization. Arrangement of cells in the embryo into groups which in normal development become a particular organ or tissue.

Pretarsus. In insects the terminal segment of the leg bearing the pretarsal claws.

Primary parasite. A parasite which establishes itself in or upon a free-living host, that is, the host is not a parasite.

Primary reproductives. See reproductives.

Proctodeal valve. In insects, a valve in the anterior end of the hindgut that serves as an occlusor mechanism.

Proleg. A fleshy abdominal leg of certain insect larvae.

Propupa. In thrips, the next to the last nymphal instar in which the wing pads are present and the legs short and thick. Also in male scale insects.

Protein. Any one of a group of nitrogen containing compounds consisting of a union of amino acids and also containing carbon, hydrogen, oxygen, and frequently sulfur; proteins occur in all animal and vegetable matter and are essential to the diet of animals.

Proterosoma. In mites, the anterior part of the body when there is a demarcation of the body between the second and third pair of legs.

Prothoracic gland. One of a pair of endocrine glands located in the prothorax near the prothoracic spiracles.

Prothorax. The first or anterior segment of the thorax (Fig. 2:1).

Protonymph. The second instar of a mite.

Protozoa. The phylum containing the one-celled animals.

Proventriculus. The posterior section of the foregut.

Pseudoscorpions. Small arachnids, seldom over 5 mm. long, scorpion-like in general appearance but without sting.

Pseudovipositor. The slender tube to which the posterior part of the abdomen is reduced in the female of certain insects.

Psi. Pounds per square inch.

Pterygota. A subclass of insects which are primarily winged but sometimes secondarily wingless.

Ptilinum. In Diptera an organ that can be inflated to a bladder-like structure and thrust out through a frontal suture of the head at the time of emergence from the puparium.

Pubescent. Covered with short fine hairs.

Pupa (pl., pupae). The stage between the larva and the adult in insects with complex metamorphosis, a nonfeeding and usually inactive stage.

Puparium (pl., puparia). In higher Diptera, the thickened, hardened barrel-like larval skin within which the pupa is formed.

Pyrethrum (common name). A botanical insecticide derived from the flowers of *Chrysanthemum*, primarily *C. cinerariaefolium;* relatively harmless to warm-blooded animals; nontoxic to plants.

Pyrophyllite. A mineral used as a dust carrier for insecticides; chemically, $H_2O \cdot Al_2O_3 4SiO_2$.

Queen cell. The special cell in which a queen honey bee develops from egg to the adult stage.

Quinones. Organic compounds, benzene derivatives, known to play a role in the hardening and darkening of arthropod cuticle.

Race. A variety of a species; a subspecies.

Rape. A plant, *Brassica napus* var. *biennis,* belonging to the mustard family and grown chiefly as a pasture crop for forage.

Receptacle. The enlarged end of the flower stalk.

Rectum. In insects, the posterior expanded part of the hindgut, typically pear-shaped (Fig. 2:19).

Relapsing fever. Any one of a group of acute infectious diseases caused by various bacteria of the genus *Borrelia*. The European epidemic fever is caused by *Borrelia recurrentis*, which is transmitted by the human body louse. The disease is marked by alternating periods of fever.

Repellents. Substances which elicit an avoiding reaction.

Reproductives. In termites the caste of kings and queens. They have compound eyes, fully developed wings (before dealation) and are usually heavily pigmented.

Resistance. Of insects to insecticides, the ability of strains of insects to survive normally lethal doses of insecticide, the ability having resulted from selection of tolerant individuals in populations exposed to the toxicant for several generations.

Of plants to insect attack, the ability of certain varieties to produce a larger crop of good quality than do ordinary varieties at the same level of insect infestation.

Rickettsia. An obligate intracellular parasite of arthropods, many types of which are pathogenic for man and other animals. They are thought to be intermediate between bacteria and viruses, because they have features in common with both.

Rocky Mountain spotted fever. A human disease caused by a bacteriumlike micro-organism, *Rickettsia rickettsi,* characterized by a rash, fever, headache, back-ache, and marked malaise; transmitted by the Rocky Mountain wood tick and the American dog tick.

Ronnel (common name). A synthetic insecticide, an animal systemic and contact insecticide; an organic phosphate, *O,O*-dimethyl *O*-2,4,5-trichlorophenyl phos-phorothioate; low toxicity to mammals, acute oral LD_{50} for rats 1,700 to 1,740 mg/kg. Trolene and Korlan are trade names of this insecticide.

Rotary tiller. A cultivator made up of two gangs of hoe wheels.

Rotenoids. A group of related toxic compounds (rotenone, elliptone, etc.) that are found in certain leguminous plants.

Rotenone (common name). A botanical insecticide; the main toxic constituent in the roots of certain leguminous plants, such as *Derris elliptica* and *Loncho-carpus utilis* and *L. urucu;* moderately toxic to mammals, acute oral LD_{50} for rats 132 mg/kg; nontoxic to plants.

Roundworm. A cylindrical, unsegmented worm tapered toward both ends; a member of the phylum Aschelminthes and the class Nematoda.

Rudimentary. Imperfectly developed.

Ruelene (trade name). A synthetic insecticide and anthelmintic, an animal sys-temic; an organic phosphate, *O*-4-*tert*-butyl-2-chlorophenyl *O*-methyl methyl-phosphoramidate; moderately toxic to mammals, acute oral LD_{50} for rats 1,000 mg/kg.

Ryania (common name). A botanical insecticide consisting of the ground stem-wood of *Ryania speciosa;* active ingredient is the alkaloid ryanodine; moderately toxic to mammals, acute oral LD_{50} for rats of the ground *Ryania* stems 1,200 mg/kg.

Sabadilla (common name). A botanical insecticide made from the ground seeds of a lily, *Schoenocaulon officinale;* active ingredient is a crude mixture of alka-loids termed veratrine; relatively nontoxic to warm-blooded animals.

Salivary glands. Glands that open into the mouth and secrete a fluid with diges-tive, irritant, or anticoagulatory properties.

Saprophytic. Living on dead or decaying organic matter.

Saturated. In chemistry, having all valences of the constituent atoms of a com-pound fully satisfied.

Scab. A contagious skin disease of animals caused by certain parasitic mites.

Scale. A scale insect; a member of the order Homoptera.

Scarabaeiform larva. A grublike larva, body thick and cylindrical, well-developed head and thoracic legs, and no prolegs, usually sluggish (Fig. 2:2D).

Scavanger. An animal that feeds on dead plants or animals, on decaying organic matter, or on animal wastes.

Schradan (common name). A synthetic insecticide and acaricide, a plant sys-temic; an organic phosphate, octamethylpyrophosphoramide; extremely toxic to mammals, acute oral LD_{50} for rats 8 to 10 mg/kg; phytotoxicity: not markedly toxic at insecticidal concentrations, but over 4 lb. per acre injurious to some crops.

Sclerite. A hardened body wall plate delimited by sutures or membranous areas.

Sclerotization. The hardening and darkening processes in the cuticle (involves the epicuticle and exocuticle).

Scorpion. Any member of the arachnid order Scorpionida; they have an elongate body and a poison sting at the end of abdomen.

Scrub typhus. A disease prevalent in the Far East and caused by a bacterium-like microorganism, *Rickettsia tsutsugamushi,* which is transmitted by the chigger,

Trombicula akamushi; the disease is characterized by headache, apathy, general malaise, and fever.

Scutum. In ticks, the sclerotized plate covering all or most of the dorsum in males, and the anterior portion in females, nymphs, and larvae of the Ixodidae.

Sebaceous gland. A gland producing a greasy lubricating substance.

Secondary parasite. A parasite which establishes itself in or upon a host that is a primary parasite.

Segment. A subdivision of the body or of an appendage between joints or areas of flexibility.

Segmentation. The embryological process by which the insect body becomes divided into a series of parts or segments.

Selocide (trade name). An acaricide containing about 30 per cent potassium ammonium selenosulfide.

Semilooper. A caterpillar with one or two pairs of the ventral prolegs wanting; in crawling small loops of the body are formed.

Sessile. Attached and incapable of moving from place to place.

Seta (pl., setae). A slender, hairlike outgrowth of the integument.

Sesamin (common name). A synergist for pyrethrum; chemically, 2,6-bis(3,4-methylenedioxyphenyl)-3,7-dioxabicyclo[3.3.0]octane; nontoxic to mammals.

Sevin (trade name). A synthetic insecticide; a carbamate, 1-naphthyl methylcarbamate; moderately toxic to mammals, acute oral LD_{50} for rats 500 to 700 mg/kg; no evidence of phytotoxicity in use at normal rates.

Shingling. The placing of shingles or pieces of lumber among crop plantings to become daytime hiding places for slugs, squash bugs, earwigs, etc., which can then be destroyed.

Silica aerogel. A sorptive dust that is insecticidal, killing insects by desiccation; prepared by treating sodium silicate with sulfuric acid, drying, and then grinding to small particle size.

Simple dorsal eyes. See Dorsal ocellus.

Simple eye. See Ocellus.

Simple lateral eye. See Lateral ocellus.

Simple metamorphosis. Metamorphosis in which the wings (when present) develop externally during the immature stage and there is no prolonged resting stage preceding the last molt; stages included are the egg, nymphal, and adult. Also called gradual or partial metamorphosis, and paurometabolous development (Fig. 3:8).

Sinus. A recess, cavity, or hollow space; an air cavity in a cranial bone.

Skeletal muscle. In insects, a muscle that stretches across the body wall and serves to move one segment on another.

Slug. A relative of snails but having the shell rudimentary or entirely wanting.

Slurry. A thin mixture of water and any of several fine insoluble materials, as clay, derris or cubé powder, etc.

Small grains. Any cereal having small kernels, as wheat, oats, barley, or rye.

Smear 62. A screw-worm remedy consisting of the following (parts by weight): diphenylamine 3.5, benzol 3.5, turkey red oil 1, and lamp black 2.

Snail. A member of the phylum Mollusca having a single, usually coiled shell and a broad, flat foot.

Social. Living in more or less organized communities of individuals.

Sodium selenate. An inorganic systemic insecticide and acaricide that is applied to soil; empirical formula, Na_2SeO_4; highly toxic to warm-blooded animals; limited to treatment of ornamentals; phytotoxic to chrysanthemums at doses about 250 mg/sq ft, carnations stunted by use of selenate for more than a year.

Solanaceous. Belonging to the nightshade family, of which potato is a common example.

Soldier. In termites, sterile males or females with large heads and mandibles; they function to protect the colony.

Solitary. Occurring singly or in pairs, not in colonies.

Sorghum. An annual cereal grass, *Sorghum vulgare* and other related species that are grown for grain, fodder, or sirup.

Sorgo. Sweet or cane sorghum grown for forage, silage, and sirup.

Species. A group of individuals or populations which are similar in structure and physiology and are capable of interbreeding and producing fertile offspring, and which differ in structure and/or physiology from other such groups and normally do not interbreed with them.

Specific miticides. Chemicals that are used to control mites but are relatively non-toxic to insects.

Spelt. A type of wheat, in America grown for livestock feed.

Spermatozoon (pl., spermatozoa). The mature male sexual cell or sperm cell, whose function is the fertilization of the egg.

Spermatheca. The sperm storage receptacle of the female insect.

Spine. A multicellular, thornlike process or outgrowth of the integument not separated from it by a joint.

Spiracle. An external opening of the tracheal system through which diffusion of gases takes place.

Spiracular plate. A platelike sclerite next to or surrounding a spiracle.

Spirochaetosis. Infection with spirochetes, organisms that are regarded as a connecting link between bacteria and protozoa.

Spittle. In insects, a frothy fluid produced by the nymphs of spittlebugs (Cercopidae).

Spur. A spinelike process of the integument connected to the body wall by a joint.

Square. An unopened flower bud of cotton with its subtending involucre bracts.

Stadium (pl., stadia). The time interval between molts in a developing insect.

Stage. A distinct, sharply different period in the development of an insect, e.g., egg stage, larval stage, pupal stage, adult stage; in mites and ticks, each instar.

Stemma (pl., stemmata). The simple eye in holometabolous larvae. Also called lateral ocellus.

Sterols. Mostly large molecular alcohols, found in plant and animal cells combined with fatty acids and soluble in fat solvents.

Stewart's disease. Bacterial wilt of corn caused by *Bacterium stewartii* and transmitted by the feeding of flea beetles.

Stipe. A small, stalklike structure.

St. Louis encephalitis. A virus disease affecting the brain, producing languor, apathy, lethargy, and death; transmitted by certain mosquitoes and mites.

Stomodeal valve. In insects, the cylindrical or funnel-shaped invagination of the foregut into the midgut.

Stover. Corn stalks used as fodder for animals.

Striate. A virus mosaic disease of wheat transmitted by the painted leafhopper.

Striated muscle. Muscle that is composed of fibers with alternate light and dark bands.

Strobane (trade name). A synthetic insecticide; a chlorinated hydrocarbon, terpene polychlorinates containing 65 per cent chlorine; moderately toxic to mammals, acute oral LD_{50} for rats 200 mg/kg; toxic to cucurbits, prunes, and peaches.

Stubble. The stumps of small grain, corn, etc., left standing after harvest.

Stylet. A needlelike structure.

Stylostome. The tube formed by the host as a result of the feeding of a chigger; in secreting salivary fluids, the chigger partially digests skin tissues, which induces the host to form a proteinaceous tube walling off the injury.

Subterranean. Living in the ground.

Sulfoxide (common name). A synergist for pyrethrum; chemically, 1,2-methylenedioxy-4-[2-(octylsulfinyl) propyl]benzene; relatively nontoxic to warm-blooded animals, acute oral LD_{50} for rats about 2,000 mg/kg; nonphytotoxic.

Sulfotepp (common name). A synthetic insecticide and acaricide; an organic phosphate, tetraethyl dithiopyrophosphate; highly toxic to mammals, acute oral LD_{50} for rats 5 mg/kg.

Sulphenone (trade name). A synthetic acaricide, a sulfone; chemically, p-chlorophenyl phenyl sulfone and related sulfones; relatively non-toxic to mammals, acute oral LD_{50} for rats approximately 3650 mg/kg; toxic to grapes, most varieties of pears, sensitive greenhouse plants, cucurbits, and some varieties of apples.

Superfamily. A group of closely related families; superfamily names end in -*oidea*.

Superior oil. A dormant spray oil of high paraffinic and low aromatic content, characteristics which provide increased plant safety and satisfactory insecticidal action.

Supplementary reproductives. In termites the caste of males and females with short wings, light pigmentation, and small compound eyes. The females lay eggs in the colony supplementing the work of the queen.

Suspension. A system of solid particles dispersed in a liquid.

Suture. A linelike external groove in the body wall or a narrow membranous area between sclerites; a line where adjacent parts have united.

Swine pox. A virus disease of swine characterized by small, red skin lesions, weakness, loss of appetite, chills and fever; transmitted by the hog louse.

Swollen joints. An acute infectious disease, commonly called navel ill, caused by certain bacteria which often gain entrance into the navel soon after birth, becoming septicemic and localizing in the joints.

Symmetry. Similarity of organs or body parts on either side of a dividing line or plane.

Synapse. The region of contact between processes of two adjacent neurons, forming the place where a nervous impulse is transmitted from one neuron to another.

Synergist. A chemical substance that when used with an insecticide, drug, etc. will result in greater total effect than the sum of their individual effects.

Systemic insecticide. An insecticide capable of absorption into plant sap or animal blood and lethal to insects feeding on or within the treated host.

Talc. Powdered soapstone, anhydrous magnesium silicate.

Tapeworm. A parasitic intestinal flatworm (phylum Platyhelminthes).

Tarsus (pl., tarsi). The foot; the distal part of the insect leg, consisting of from one to five segments.

Tassel. The staminate inflorescence of corn.

TDE (common name). A synthetic insecticide; a chlorinated hydrocarbon related to DDT; dichlorodiphenyl dichloroethane; from ⅕ to ¹⁄₁₀ as toxic to mammals as DDT, acute oral LD_{50} for rats 2,500 mg/kg; nonphytotoxic at insecticidal concentrations except possibly to cucurbits.

Tectocuticle. See Cement layer.

Tedion (trade name). A synthetic acaricide, a sulfone; chemically, p-chlorophenyl

2,4,5-trichlorophenyl sulfone; relatively nontoxic to mammals, 14,700 mg/kg administered to rats without signs of systemic toxicity: nonphytotoxic.

Tegmen (pl., tegmina). The thickened leathery forewing of an orthopteran.

TEPP (common name). A synthetic insecticide and acaricide; an organic phosphate, tetraethyl pyrophosphate; extremely toxic to mammals, acute oral LD_{50} for rats 2 mg/kg; toxic to some varieties of tomato and chrysanthemum; blemishes some plants and fruits if applied by aircraft in less than 10 gallon water per acre.

Texas cattle fever. See cattle tick fever.

Thanite (trade name). A synthetic insecticide; a thiocyanate, 82 per cent isobornyl thiocyanoacetate and 18 per cent other related terpenes; low mammalian toxicity, acute oral LD_{50} for rat 1,000 mg/kg; highly toxic to plants.

Thiodan (trade name). A synthetic insecticide and acaricide; a chlorinated hydrocarbon, 6,7,8,9,10,10-hexachloro-1,5,5a,6,9,9a-hexahydro-6,9-methano-2,4,3-benzodioxathiepin 3-oxide; moderately toxic to mammals, acute oral LD_{50} for rats 110 mg/kg; no phytotoxicity experienced on citrus and deciduous trees and on many row crops.

Thimet (trade name). See phorate, the common name for this chemical.

Thiram (trade name). Protective fungicide suitable for foliage application or seed treatment; chemically, bis (dimethylthiocarbamoyl) disulfide; moderately toxic to mammals, acute oral LD_{50} for rats 865 mg/kg; phytotoxicity relatively low when used as directed.

Thylate (trade name). Same as Thiram.

Tibia (pl., tibiae). The fourth segment of the leg, between femur and the tarsus.

Tick. A blood-sucking arachnid parasite of the family Ixodidae or Argasidae (Fig. 18:20).

Tick paralysis. A flaccid, afebrile (without fever), ascending, motor paralysis produced by the attachment of certain species of ticks and believed to be due to a neurotoxin secreted by the salivary glands of the feeding female tick.

Tiller. An erect shoot arising from the crown of a grass.

Tolerance. The amount of a pesticide that may safely and legally remain as a residue on a food plant or in meat or fat.

Toxaphene (common name). A synthetic insecticide; a chlorinated hydrocarbon, chlorinated camphene containing 67 to 69 per cent of chlorine; somewhat more toxic to mammals than DDT, acute oral LD_{50} for rats 60 mg/kg; toxic to cucurbits, causes off-color in some cured tobaccos.

Toxicogenic. Capable of producing a toxin; insects that introduce a toxin into a plant while feeding are said to be toxicogenic.

Toxin. Any of various unstable poisonous compounds produced by some microorganisms and causing certain diseases; any of various similar poisons secreted by plants and animals.

Trachea (pl., tracheae). A tube of the respiratory system in insects.

Trachoma. A contagious form of conjunctivitis, caused by virus and characterized by formation of inflammatory granulations on the inner eyelid.

Trade name. Trade name is a registered trade mark of the company manufacturing the product and is capitalized in this book for identification.

Trench fever. A human disease caused by a bacterium-like microorganism, *Rickettsia quintana,* nonfatal and characterized by sudden onset of fever, headache, dizziness, and pains in muscles and bones; transmitted by the body louse through its feces.

Trithion. A synthetic insecticide and acaricide; an organic phosphate, S-(p-chlorophenylthio) methyl *O,O*-diethyl phosphorodithioate; highly toxic to mammals, acute oral LD_{50} for rats 30 mg/kg; slightly injurious to fruit and foliage of certain apple varieties, isolated cases of injury to citrus and to greenhouse roses.

Trochanter. The second segment of the leg, between coxa and femur.

Trolene (trade name). See ronnel, common name for this chemical.

Trypanosomiasis. The disease caused by the presence in the body of a protozoan parasite of the genus *Trypanosoma*, marked by fever, anemia, and redness of the skin; transmitted by tsetse flies.

Tubercle. A small knoblike or rounded protuberance.

Tularemia. A bacterial disease occurring mainly in rabbits but also in certain rodents, ungulates, carnivores, birds, livestock, and man; caused by *Pasturella tularensis* and transmitted by arthropod vectors (ticks, lice, fleas, biting flies) and by contact of skin with infected material; marked by inflammation of lymph glands, headache, chills, and fever.

Typhoid fever. An acute infectious disease caused by a bacterium, *Salmonella typhosa*, characterized by continued fever, inflammation of intestine, intestinal ulcers, a rose-spot on the abdomen, and enlarged spleen; food and water-borne but may be transmitted by house flies.

Typhus fever. A human disease caused by a bacterium-like microorganism; *Rickettsia prowazeki*, and transmitted by the body louse, *Pediculis humanus humanus* L. The disease is characterized by high fever, backache, intense headache, bronchial disturbances, mental confusion, and congested face. Mortality may range from 15 to 75 per cent.

Unsaturated. In chemistry, not having all valences of the constituent atoms of a compound fully satisfied.

Urea. Chief nitrogenous constituent of the urine of mammals and the final product of decomposition of proteins in the body; chemically, NH_2CONH_2.

Uric acid. The chief nitrogenous waste of birds, reptiles and insects; chemically, $C_5H_4N_4O_3$.

Urticarial papule. A small solid elevation of the skin which itches and stings.

Vascular tissues. The fluid conducting tissues of a plant including both xylem (water) and phloem (food) tissues.

Veins. In insects, the riblike tubes that strengthen the wings.

Venation. The arrangement of veins in the wings of insects.

Ventral. Lower or underneath, pertaining to the under side of the body.

Vermiform larva. A legless wormlike larva without a well developed head (Fig. 2:2G).

Vertebrates. Animals with a spinal column or backbone, such as fishes, birds, mammals, etc.

Vestigial. Having the nature of a degenerate or atrophied organ, more fully functional in an earlier stage of development of the individual or species.

Vetch. A group of leguminous plants of the genus *Vicia* grown for cover, green manure crops, or for hay.

Visceral muscle. A muscle which invests an internal organ.

Vitamin B complex. The group of water soluble vitamins, including thiamine, riboflavin, nicotinic acid, and others.

Viviparae. Female aphids which bear living young (do not lay eggs).

Volunteer growth. Plants that spring up from unplanted seed, usually lost before or during harvest.

Western equine encephalitis. A virus disease of horses communicable to man, marked by fever, convulsions, and coma and transmitted by certain species of mosquitoes.

Wettable powder. Insecticidal dusts to which have been added wetting agents as well as insecticide, thus making the product dispersible and suspensible in water.

Wheat streak mosaic. A virus disease of wheat and other grasses marked by yellow streaking of leaves, stunted growth, and reduced seed set, transmitted by the wheat curl mite.

Whorl. An arrangement of organs, such as leaves, in a circle around the stem of a plant.

Wilt. Loss of freshness and drooping of leaves of plants due to inadequate water supply or excessive transpiration or to a vascular disease which interferes with utilization of water or to a toxin produced by an organism.

Wing pads. The undeveloped wings of nymphs and naiads, which appear as two flat structures on each side.

Woollybear. A very hairy caterpillar belonging to the family Arctiidae, the tiger moths.

Workers. In termites, the sterile males and females that perform most of the work of the colony; they are pale, wingless, and usually lack compound eyes; in social Hymenoptera, females with undeveloped reproductive organs that perform the work of the colony.

Yaws. A tropical infectious disease caused by a spirochete, *Treponema pertenue*, marked by raspberry-like excrescences and ulcerations on face, hands, feet, and external genitals; transmitted by certain flies or gnats (*Hippelates*).

Yeast. Unicellular fungi of the family Saccharomycetaceae.

Yellow fever. An acute infectious disease due to a virus transmitted by certain mosquitoes and marked by fever, jaundice, and albumin and globulin in the urine.

Yellows. A plant disease characterized by yellowing and stunting of the affected plant; caused by a fungus, virus, or insect toxin.

Zineb. A protective fungicide used for foliage application; chemically, zinc ethylene bisdithiocarbamate; of low mammalian toxicity, acute oral LD_{50} for rats greater than 5,200 mg/kg; toxic to zinc sensitive plants.

Selected References

Torre-Bueno, J. R. *A Glossary of Entomology* (Brooklyn: Brooklyn Ent. Soc., 1937).

Tullock, G. S. *Torre-Bueno's Glossary of Entomology—Supplement A* (Brooklyn: Brooklyn Ent. Soc., 1960).

Index |

Abdomen, of insects, 33
 of mites and ticks, 60
Acalymma trivittata, 356
A. vittata, 356–359
Acaridae, 91
Acarid mites, 91
Acarina, 85–92
Accessory pulsating structures, 48
Aceria essigi, 424
Acetyl choline, 54
Acrididae, 99
Acts, 18, 154–156
 Department of Agriculture Organic Act
  1944, 155
 Federal Food, Drug, and Cosmetic Act
  1938, 18
 Federal Insecticide 1910, 18
 Federal Insecticide, Fungicide, and Ro-
  denticide 1947, 18
 Federal Plant Pest Act 1957, 156
 Incipient and Emergency Outbreak Reso-
  lution 1938, 155
 Insect Pest Act 1905, 156
 Mexican Border Act 1942, 154
 Miller Amendment, 18
 Plant Quarantine Act 1912, 154
 Public Law 518, 18
 Terminal Inspection Act 1915, 156
Aedeagus, 33
Aedes, 4, 600, 602
 aegypti, 599
 dorsalis, 599
Aegeriidae, 119
Aeolus mellillus, 245
Aerosols, 162
Agricultural Extension Service, 141, 328
Agriotes mancus, 243
Agromyzidae, 133
Agrotis ipsilon, 341–344
Aldrin, 184
Aleyrodidae, 108
Alfalfa caterpillar, 287
Alfalfa insects. *See* Legume insects

Alfalfa snout beetle, 285
Alfalfa webworm, 287
Alfalfa weevil, 13, 299–302
Allethrin, 177
American Association of Economic En-
 tomologists, 16
American cockroach, 507
American Entomological Society, 16
Ametabola, 76
Amnion, 70
Angoumois grain moth, 492–494
Annand, P. N., 10
Anopheles, 4, 600, 602
 albimanus, 599
 freeborni, 599
 quadrimaculatus, 599
Anoplura, 102
Antennae, 26
Anthomyiidae, 135
Anthonomus grandis, 325–332
Ants, 128, 514–518
 black carpenter, 514
 control of, 517
 fire, 514
 imported fire, 516
 little black, 515
 Pharaoh, 515
 southern fire, 516
 thief, 516
Aorta, 48, 72
Aphidae, 109
Aphids, 109
 greenbug, 213, 239
 spotted alfalfa, 283
Apidae, 129
Apis mellifera, 2
Application equipment, 191–211
 aircraft, 201
 classification, 192
 dusters, 207
 granule applicators, 210
 performance (table), 194
 sprayers, 193

Apterygota, 31, 92
Arachnida, 85
Aramite, 189
Araneida, 85
Arctiidae, 122
Argasidae, 86
Argas persicus, 577–580
Arid land subterranean termite, 518–525
Armored scales, 110
Army cutworm, 287
Armyworm, 4, 123, 213, 229–233
Arthropoda, 81–84
    characteristics, 82
    classes, 84
Aspidiotus perniciosus, 399–403
Attractants, 190
Aulocara elliotti, 220–229
Aurelian Society, 16

Bark aphids, 108
Bark beetles, 117
Barley yellow dwarf, 215
Basement membrane, 35
Bathyplectes curculionis, 293
Bean beetle, Mexican, 359–363
Bed bugs, 5, 105
Bees, 129
Beet leafhopper, 369–374
Beetles, 111
Benzene hexachloride, 184
BHC, 184
Big-headed grasshopper, 220–229
Biological control, 144–149
    advantages, 145
    agents, 147
    problems, 146
    weeds, 148
Black carpenter ant, 514
Black cherry fruit fly, 403–406
Black cutworm, 341–344
Black vine weevil, 418–421
Blastoderm, 68
Blastokinesis, 70
Blatta orientalis, 506
Blattella germanica, 505
Blattidae, 93
Blissus leucopterus, 260–265
Blister mites, 89
Blood, 48
Blood cells, 47, 48, 72
Blow flies, 135
Body louse, 2
Boll weevil, 325–332
Bollworm, 315
Book-lungs, 85
Bordeaux mixture, 172
Botanical insecticides, 174–180
Bot flies, 133

Bovicola bovis, 536–540
Brachyrhinus ligustici, 285
B. ovatus, 418–421
B. rugosostriatus, 418–421
B. sulcatus, 418–421
Braconidae, 127
Brain, 53, 71
Brown-banded cockroach, 508
Brown spider mite, 392
Bruchidae, 116
Bruchophagus gibbus, 307–310
Bruchus brachialis, 287
Bryobia rubrioculus, 392
Bubonic plague, 3
Bud moths, 120
Bugs, 104
Bumble bees, 129
Buprestidae, 112
Bursa copulatrix, 51
Butoxy polypropylene glycol, 189
Butterflies, 118
Byturidae, 114
Byturus bakeri, 421–423
B. rubi, 421–423

Cabbageworm, imported, 363–366
Cadelle, 491–492
Calliphoridae, 135
Callitroga hominivorax, 547–551
Camnula pellucida, 220–229
Campodeiform larva, 79
Camponotus pennsylvanicus, 514
Capitulum, 60
Carabidae, 111
Carabiform larva, 79
Carbon disulfide, 187
Carbon tetrachloride, 188
Cardiac valve, 41
Carpenter bees, 129
Carpocapsa pomonella, 387–392
Carter, W., 14
Cattle biting louse, 536–540
Cattle grubs, 540
Cattle insects. *See* Livestock insects
Cattle lice, 536
Cattle tail louse, 536–540
Cecidomyiidae, 130
Cephalothorax, 60
Cephidae, 127
Cerambycidae, 115
Cercopidae, 107
Cereal mites, 91
Chalcididae, 128
Chalcidoidea, 128
Chapman, R. N., 14
Chelicerae, 30
Chelonethida, 85
Chemical control, 159–190

Chermidae, 108
Cherry fruit fly, 403–406
Chewing lice, 102
Chicken body louse, 571–574
Chicken insects. *See* Poultry insects
Chicken mites, 88
Chiggers, 90, 606–608
Chinch bug, 105, 213, 260–265
Chitin, 35, 37
Chlordane, 184
Chlorobenzilate, 189
Cholinesterase, 54
Chorion, 51, 66
Chrysalis, 80
Chrysomelidae, 115
Chrysopidae, 110
Cicadellidae, 107
Cimicidae, 105
Circulatory system, insects, 47–49
  mites, 62
Circulifer tenellus, 369–374
Claspers, 33
Clear-winged grasshopper, 220–229
Clearwing moths, 119
Click beetles, 112
Clothes moths, 5, 119, 511–513
Clover aphid, 284
Clover head caterpillar, 288
Clover head weevil, 287
Clover insects. *See* Legume insects
Clover leaf weevil, 284
Clover root borer, 285
Clover root curculio, 285
Clover seed chalcid, 307–310
Clover seed midge, 288
Clover seed weevil, 287
Coarctate pupa, 80
Coccidae, 110
Coccinellidae, 113
Coccoidea, 110
Cockroaches, 5, 93, 505–510
  control, 509
Cocoon, 79
Codling moth, 387–392
Coleoptera, 111
Commercial entomology, 13
Common cattle grub, 540–545
Common malaria mosquito, 599
Community projects, 140
Compound eye, 55–56
  adaptation, 55
  perception of movement, 56
Comstock, J. H., 9, 12
Confused flour beetle, 489–490
Consumer pressure, 140
Control of insects,
  biological, 144–149
  chemical, 159–190

Control of Insects (*Cont.*):
  combination, 147
  cultural, 149–152
  integrated, 296
  legal, 154–157
  mechanical, 153
  natural, 142
  physical, 153
  preventive, 140
  principles, 138–157
Coreidae, 104
Corn earworm, 265–270
Corn insects, 249–280
  chemical control, 257
  control equipment, 258
  cultural control, 255
  injury, 251
  kinds, 249
Corn maggot, seed, 366–369
Corn rootworms, 276–280
  control, 278
  description, 277
  injury, 276
  kinds, 276
  life history, 277
Corn wireworm, 243
Corpora allata, 59
Corpus cardiacum, 59
Cotton aphid, 315
Cotton fleahopper, 338–340
Cotton insects, 315–344
  chemical control, 321
  control equipment, 323
  cultural control, 320
  injury, 318
  kinds, 315
Cotton leafworm, 317
Cottony-cushion scale, 9
Crambidae, 121
Crickets, 99
Crop, insects, 42
Crop values, 139
Crown borers, 119
Cryolite, 171
Crystalline cone, 56
Ctenicera aeripennis destructor, 243–248
C. pruinina, 243
Cucujidae, 113
Cucumber beetles, 356
Culex, 600, 602
  pipiens pipiens, 599
  pipiens quinquefasciatus, 599
  tarsalis, 599
Culicidae, 129
Cultural control, 149–152
  clean culture, 152
  location, 151
  resistant plant varieties, 152

Cultural control (*Cont.*):
  rotation, 151
  tillage, 151
  timing, 152
  trap crop, 151
Curculionidae, 116
Cutworms, 123, 341
  black cutworm, 341–344
  kinds, 341

Darkling beetles, 114
D-D mixture, 188
DDT, 181
Deer flies, 131
Demeton, 186
Demodicidae, 88
Department of Agriculture Organic Act
  1944, 155
Dermacentor albipictus, 554–556
Dermanyssidae, 88
Dermanyssid mites, 88
Dermaptera, 100
Dermestidae, 113
Deroceras laeve, 458–464
D. reticulatum, 458–464
Desert locust, 2, 3,
Diabrotica longicornis, 276–280
D. undecimpunctata howardi, 276–280
D. virgifera, 276–280
Diaspididae, 110
Dibutyl succinate, 189
Dichloropropene-Dichloropropane mixture,
  188
Dieldrin, 184
Diethyl toluamide, 189
Differential grasshopper, 220–229
Differentiation, 71
Digestive enzymes, 43, 44
Digestive system, insects, 41–44
  mites, 62
Dimethyl phthalate, 189
Diptera, 129
Di-Syston, 186
Dorsal diaphragm, 48
Dryberry mite, 424
Ducts,
  ejaculatory, 52
  vas deferens, 52
  lateral oviduct, 51
  common oviduct, 51
Dung beetles, 2
Dusters, 207–210
  parts, 207–210
Dusts, 160

Earwigs, 100
Eastern raspberry fruitworm, 421–423
Eastern subterranean termite, 518–525

Echidnophaga gallinacea, 574–577
Ectodermal derivatives, 71–72
Ectohormones, 60
Egg pod, 65
Eggs of insects, 51, 64–74
  appearance, 65
  fertilization, 51, 67
  hatching, 73–74
  numbers, 65
  sites, 64
Elateridae, 112
Elateriform larva, 79
Elytra, 32
Emulsifiable concentrates, 161
Encyrtidae, 128
Endocuticle, 35
Endoderm, 73
Endodermal derivative, 73
Endrin, 184
Entomological societies, 16
Entomological Society, of America, 16
  of Canada, 16
  of London, 16
Entomology,
  commercial, 13
  in Canada, 15
  in colonial America, 4
  in federal service, 8
  in the states, 11
  professional, 6
  societies, 16
  volunteer, 5
Entomology Research Division, 10
Eotetranychus carpini borealis, 392
Epicuticle, 35
Epidemic typhus, 4
Epidermis, 35
Epilachna varivestis, 359–363
Epipharynx, 27
Equipment, 191–211
Eriophyidae, 89
Eriophyid mites, 89
Eruciform larva, 79
Erythroneura comes, 426
E. dolosa, 426
E. elegantula, 426
E. octonotata, 426
E. tricincta, 426
E. variabilis, 426
E. vitifex, 426
E. vitis, 426
E. vulnerata, 426
E. ziczac, 426
Esophagus, 42
Ethylene dichloride, 188
Eulophidae, 128
European corn borer, 270–276
European red mite, 392

Eurytomidae, 128
Exarate pupa, 80
Excretion, in insects, 46–47
    in mites, 62
Exocuticle, 35
Exoskeleton, 34
Eyes, 55

Facets, 57
False wireworms, 114
Fascicle, 28
Fat body, 47, 72
Feather chewing lice, 102
Federal Food, Drug, and Cosmetic Act of
    1938, 18
Federal Insecticide Act of 1910, 18
Federal Insecticide, Fungicide, and Ro-
    denticide Act of 1947, 18
Federal Plant Pest Act of 1957, 156
Fenson, 189
Fertilization of eggs, 51, 66, 67
Fire ant, 516
Fitch, A., 7
Flagellum, 26
Flat bark beetles, 113
Flatheaded wood borers, 112
Flea beetles, 115
Fleas, 136
    sticktight, 574
Fletcher, J., 15
Flies, 129
Flight in insects, 57–58
Floricultural insects, 430–464
    biological control, 440
    chemical control, 441
    control equipment, 445
    cultural control, 440
    injury, 437
    kinds, 430–437
Flour beetles, 114, 489
Flower flies, 131
Flower thrips, 452–455
Follicle mites, 88
Foregut of insects, 42
Forficulidae, 101
Formicidae, 128
Four-spotted spider mite, 392
Fowl tick, 577–580
Frankliniella tritici, 452–455
Froghoppers, 107
Fruit flies, 132
Fruit insects, small fruits, 408–429
    tree fruits, 376–406
Fruit moths, 120
Fruitworm beetles, 114
Fumigants, 162, 187
Fumigation of stored grain, 480–485
    dosage rates, 483

Fumigation of stored grain (*Cont.*):
    fumigants, 481
    methods, 481
    precautions, 484
Fungus mites, 91

Gall aphids, 108
Galleriidae, 121
Gall midges, 130
Gall mites, 89
Ganglion in insects, 53–54
    abdominal, 71
    frontal, 54
    hypocerebral, 54
    ingluvial, 54
    occipital, 54
    subesophageal, 53, 71
    thoracic, 71
Garden symphylan, 449–452
Garden webworm, 287
Gasterophilidae, 133
Gastric caeca, 43
Gelechiidae, 119
Genitalia, 33
Genite, 189
Geometridae, 124
German cockroach, 505
Gibson, A., 15
Gills of insects, 41
    blood, 41
    physical, 41
    tracheal, 41
Glands in insects,
    accessory, 52
    colleterial, 51
    corpora allata, 59
    oviducal, 52
    prothoracic, 59
    salivary, 43, 72
Glover, T., 6
Gnathosoma, 60
Gracilariidae, 118
Grain beetles, 113
Grain, fumigation, 480
    protectants, 478
    storage, 474
Granary weevil, 485–488
Granular formulations, 160
Granule applicators, 210–211
Grape leafhopper, 426–429
Grape phylloxera, 8
Grasshoppers, 4, 99, 220–229
    control, 226
    description, 223
    injury, 221
    kinds, 220
    life history, 224
Grass moths, 121

Gray field slug, 458–464
Gray garden slug, 458–464
Great Basin wireworm, 243
Greenbug, 213, 239–243
Greenhouse insects. *See* Floricultural insects
Greenhouse slug, 458–464
Ground beetles, 111
Growth of insects, 64–80
Gryllidae, 99

Haematobia irritans, 545–547
Haematopinidae, 103
Haematopinus eurysternus, 536–540
H. quadripertusus, 536–540
Hagen, H., 12
Halteres, 32
Hard-backed ticks, 86
Harris, T. H., 5
Harvest mites, 90
Hatching spine, 74
Head of insects, 25–30
Heart of insects, 47, 48, 72
Heliothis zea, 265–270, 315
Hellebore, 180
Hemelytra, 32
Hemimetabola, 77
Hemiptera, 104
Hemoglobin, 48
Hemolymph, 47
Heptachlor, 184
Hessian fly, 5, 15, 213, 233–239
Heterometabola, 76
Hewitt, C. G., 15
Hindgut of insects, 43
Hippoboscidae, 136
Hog itch mite, 557–559
Hog louse, 557
Holometabola, 77
Homoptera, 106
Honey bee, 1, 2, 5, 129
Hormonal mechanisms, in insects, 58–60
  in mites, 63
Horn fly, 545–547
Hornworms, 124
Horse bots, 133
Horse flies, 131
Horse insects. *See* Livestock insects
House fly, 135, 596–599
Household insects, 495–525
  chemical control, 502
  control equipment, 503
  control precautions, 504
  control through sanitation, 501
  damage, 497
  kinds, 495
Hover flies, 131
Howard, L. O., 9

Hoyt, A. S., 10
Human flea, 2
Human louse, 4
Hydrogen cyanide, 187
Hylastinus obscurus, 285
Hylemya cilicrura, 366–369
Hymenoptera, 126
Hypera meles, 287
H. nigrirostris, 287
H. postica, 299–302
H. punctata, 284
Hypoderma bovis, 540–545
H. lineatum, 540–545
Hypodermatidae, 134
Hypolithus nocturnus, 244
Hypopharynx, 27
Hypostome, 30
Hysterosoma, 60

Ichneumonidae, 127
Ichneumonoidea, 127
Imago, 76
Imported cabbageworm, 363–366
Imported fire ant, 516
Incipient and Emergency Outbreak Resolution 1938, 155
Inorganic insecticides, 171
Insect, characteristics, 92
  classification, 81–137, 138
  embryology, 68–73
  external form, 22
  flight, 57
    direction, 57
    frequency of wing beat, 58
    initiation, 57
    maintenance, 57
  growth, 64–80
  immature characteristics, 98
  in colonial America, 4
  introduced pests, 139
  numbers, 83
  orders, 94–97
  outbreaks, 141
  Pest Act of 1905, 156
  structure and function, 22–60
Insecticides, 159–188
  application equipment, 191
  botanical, 174
  chlorinated hydrocarbons, 181
  classification, 170
  compatibility, 163
  compatibility chart, 164
  factors influencing effectiveness, 163
  fertilizer mixtures, 161
  formulations, 160
  fumigants, 162, 187
  hazards, 168
  inorganic, 171

Insecticides *(Cont.)*:
  laws, 17–20
  mode of action, 166
  oils, 172
  organic phosphates, 185
  synergists, 167
  synthetic organic, 180
  tolerance, 19
Instar, 75
Integrated control, 296
Integument, insects, 34–38
  mites, 61
Intima, 38
Invertebrates, 81
Isoptera, 101
Itch mites, 92
Ixodidae, 86

Jumping plantlice, 108
June beetles, 114
Juvenile hormone, 59

Katydids, 99
Kelthane, 189
Knipling, E. F., 10

Labellum, 29
Labium, 27
Labrum, 27
Lacewings, 110
Lady beetles, 113
Larva, 60, 77
Larval forms, 79
Lasiocampidae, 125
Laws on insecticides, 17–20
Lead arsenate, 171
Leaf beetles, 115
Leaf blotch miners, 118
Leafhoppers, 107
Leaf miner flies, 133
Leaf rollers, 121
Legal control, 154–157
Leg, of insects, 31
  of mites and ticks, 60–61
Legume bug, 302
Legume insects, 282–313
  beneficial, 291
  biological control, 293
  chemical control, 295
  control equipment, 298
  cultural control, 291
  injury, 288
  kinds, 282
  natural control, 293
Lepidoptera, 118
Lesser clover leaf weevil, 287
Lice, body, 587
  cattle, 536

Lice *(Cont.)*:
  chewing, 102
  chicken body louse, 571
  crab, 587
  head, 587
  hog louse, 557
  sucking, 102
Limax maximus, 458–464
Lime-sulfur, 171
Lindane, 184
Linognathus vituli, 536–540
Lipoprotein layer, 35
Little black ant, 515
Little blue cattle louse, 536–540
Livestock insects, 526–559
  chemical control, 531
  control equipment, 532
  control precautions, 535
  control through management, 529
  injury, 527
  kinds, 526, 528
Locust, 2, 3
Long-horned beetles, 115
Longhorn grasshoppers, 99
Long-nosed cattle louse, 536–540
Loopers, 124
Louse flies, 136
Lygaeidae, 105
Lygus bugs, 302–307, 315, 338
  control, 305
  description, 303
  injury, 303
  kinds, 303
  life history, 305
Lygus elisus, 302
L. hesperus, 302
L. lineolaris, 302
Lymantriidae, 123

Malaria, 4, 5, 589
Malathion, 186
Mallophaga, 102
Malpighian tubes, 43, 46, 72
Mammal chewing lice, 102
Management control, 152
Mandibles, 27
Mange mites, 92
Marlatt, C. L., 10
Maxillae, 27
Maxon, A. C., 13
McDaniel spider mite, 392
Meadow spittlebug, 310–313
Mealybugs, 110
Measuringworms, 124
Mechanical control, 153
Medical insects, 585–608
  chemical control, 592
  control equipment, 594

Medical insects (*Cont.*):
  control through management, 591
  injury, 588
  kinds, 585
Melanoplus bilituratus, 220–229
M. bivittatus, 220–229
M. differentialis, 220–229
M. femurrubrum, 220–229
M. spretus, 8
Melanotus communis, 243
Melophagus ovinus, 551–554
Membracidae, 106
Menacanthus stramineus, 571–574
Menoponidae, 102
Mercurous chloride, 172
Meroblastic cleavage, 68
Mesodermal derivatives, 72–73
Metallic wood borers, 112
Metamorphosis, 48, 75–79
  complex, 77
  hyper, 78
  no, 76
  simple, 76
Methoxychlor, 183
Methyl bromide, 188
Methylparathion, 186
Mexican bean beetle, 359–363
Mexican Border Act of 1942, 134
Miccotrogus picirostris, 287
Micropylar pores, 66
Micropyle, 66
Microtrichia, 38
Midgut of insects, 43, 73
Migratory grasshopper, 213, 220–229
Milax gagates, 458–464
Miller amendment, 18
Millers, 123
Minute egg parasites, 128
Miridae, 106
Mites, 87–92
  characteristics, 86, 87
  chiggers, 606
  dryberry mite, 424
  external form, 60
  hog itch mite, 557
  internal form and function, 62–63
  mouthparts, 30
  northern fowl mite, 580
  numbers, 83
  on fruit, 392, 409
  redberry mite, 424
  spider mites, 89, 392
  two-spotted spider mite, 392, 455
Miticides, 188
Mitox, 189
Molting, 36
Monomorium minimum, 515
M. pharaonis, 515

Mormon cricket, 99
Mosquitoes, 4, 129, 599–606
Moths, 118
Mouthparts, insects, 27–29
  mites, 30
  ticks, 30
Musca domestica, 596–599
Muscidae, 135
Muscular system, insects, 49–50
  mites, 63
Mycetomes, 45

Naiad, 77
Naphthalene, 188
Narrow-winged thrips, 103
Natural control, 142–144
  climatic factors, 142
  natural enemies, 143
  topographic factors, 142
Neoptera, 93
Nerve, afferent, 71
  connectives, 71
  cord, 53, 71
  efferent, 71
  transmission, 54
Nervous system, insects, 53–57
  mites, 63
Neural groove, 71
  ridges, 71
Neurilemma, 54
Neuroptera, 110
Neurosecretory cells, 59
Nicotine, 174
Noctuidae, 123
Nomenclature system, 82
Northern, cattle grub, 540–545
  corn rootworm, 276–280
  fowl mite, 580–583
  house mosquito, 599
Notum, 30
Nurse cells, 51
Nutrition of insects, 45
Nymph, 60, 76

Obtect pupa, 80
Ocelli, 55
Oestridae, 133
Oil insecticides, 172–174
  dormant, 173
  summer, 173
  superior, 173
Olethreutidae, 120
Ommatidium, 55
Oogonia, 51
Ootheca, 52, 65
Operculum, 73
Organ development, 71–73
Oriental cockroach, 506

Oriental rat flea, 4
Ornithonyssus sylviarum, 580–583
Orthoptera, 93
Ostia, 48
Ostrinia nubilalis, 270–276
Ovarioles, 50, 73
Ovary, 50
Ovex, 188
Oviduct, 51
Ovipositor, 34
Owlet moths, 123

Pale legume bug, 302
Paleoptera, 93
Panonychus ulmi, 392
Paradichlorobenzene, 188
Parathion, 185
Parks, T. H., 13
Parthenogenesis, 50, 67
Pea aphid, 283
Pea weevil, 5
Peck, W. D., 5
Pectinophora gossypiella, 332–338
Pedicel, 26
Pediculus humanus, 2
Pedipalps, 30
Pentatomidae, 104
Periplaneta americana, 507
Periplasm, 66
Peritrophic membrane, 43
Perthane, 183
Phalangida, 85
Pharaoh ant, 515
Pharynx, 42
Pheromones, 60
Philaenus leucophthalmus, 310–313
Philopteridae, 102
Phosphorus, 172
Phycitidae, 122
Phyla, 81
Phylloxeras, 108
Physical control, 153
Phytophaga destructor, 233–239
Phytoseiidae, 87
Pieridae, 125
Pieris rapae, 363–366
Pigments, 35
Pink bollworm, 332–338
Plant bugs, 106
Plantlice, 109
Plant Quarantine Act of 1912, 154
Plastron, 41
Platyform larva, 79
Pleura, 31
Pleuropodia, 73
Polyembryony, 66
Polyphenol layer, 35
Potato leafhopper, 283

Poultry body lice, 102
Poultry insects, 561–583
    chemical control, 567
    control equipment, 569
    control through management, 565
    injury, 563
    kinds, 561
Poultry lice control, 573
Prairie grain wireworm, 243–248
Predator mites, 87
Prepupa, 79
Proctodaeal valve, 42
Prolegs, 33
Proterosoma, 60
Prothoracic glands, 59
Proventriculus, 42
Psallus seriatus, 338–340
Pseudaletia unipuncta, 229–233
Pseudococcidae, 110
Pseudovipositor, 34
Psilidae, 132
Psoroptidae, 91
Psyllidae, 108
Psyllids, 108
Pteromalidae, 128
Pterygota, 31, 92
Public Law 518, 18
Pulex irritans, 2
Pulicidae, 136
Pupa, 77
Pupal forms, 80
Pyralidae, 121
Pyralidoidea, 121
Pyraustidae, 121
Pyrethrum, 176

Quarantines, 154–157
    eradication and control, 155
    export certification, 156
    terminal inspection, 156

Raspberry fruitworms, 421–423
Rectal pads, 43
Rectal papillae, 43
Recurrent nerve, 54
Redberry mite, 424
Redbugs, 90
Red flour beetle, 489–490
Red-legged grasshopper, 220–229
Repellents, 189
Reproductive system, insects, 50–53
    mites, 63
Resistant plant varieties, 152
    antibiosis, 152
    nonpreference, 152
    tolerance, 152
Respiratory movements, 40
Respiratory system, insects, 38–41

Respiratory system (*Cont.*):
  mites, 63
Reticulitermes flavipes, 518–525
R. hesperus, 518–525
R. tibialis, 518–525
Retinula cells, 56
Rhabdom, 56
Rhagoletis cingulata, 403–406
R. fausta, 403–406
Rhinotermitidae, 101
Rice weevil, 485–488
Riley, C. V., 8, 11
Rocky Mountain grasshopper, 8
Rodolia cardinalis, 9
Root maggots, 135
Root mites, 91
Rotenone, 178
Rough strawberry root weevil, 418–421
Roundheaded wood borers, 115
Rust flies, 132
Rust mites, 89
Ryania, 180

Sabadilla, 180
San Jose scale, 399–403
Sarcoptes scabiei suis, 557–559
Sarcoptidae, 92
Sawflies, 126
Scab mites, 91
Scape, 26
Scarab, 2, 114
Scarabaeidae, 114
Scarabaeiform larva, 79
Scarabaeus sacer, 2
Schistocerca gregaria, 2
Schoene spider mite, 392
Scientific name, 82
Sclerites, 37
Sclerotization, 37
Scolytidae, 117
Scorpionida, 85
Screw-worm, 547–551
Scutigerella immaculata, 449–452
Seed beetles, 116
Seed-corn maggot, 366–369
Segmentation, 69
Semiloopers, 123
Seminal, duct, 51
  vesicle, 52
Sensory, hair, 55
  neurone, 55
  receptors, 55
Serosa, 70
Setae, 37
Sexual, dimorphism, 22
  reproduction, 67
Sheep insects. *See* Livestock insects
Sheep ked, 551–554

Short-nosed cattle louse, 536–540
Simple eye, dorsal, 55
  lateral, 55
Siphonaptera, 136
Sitona cylindricollis, 285
S. hispidula, 285
Sitophilus granarius, 485–488
S. oryzae, 485–488
Sitotroga cerealella, 492–494
Skeletal muscles of insects, 49, 72
Skin beetles, 113
Sleeping sickness, 4
Slugs, 458–464
Small fruit insects, 408–429
  chemical control, 414
  control equipment, 417
  cultural control, 413
  disease transmission, 413
  injury, 410
  kinds, 408
Small grain insects, 213–248
  chemical control, 218
  control equipment, 219
  cultural control, 216
  injury, 215
  kinds, 213
Snout beetles, 116
Sodium fluoride, 171
Sodium fluosilicate, 171
Sodium selenate, 172
Soft-backed ticks, 86
Soft scales, 110
Solenopotes capillatus, 536–540
Solenopsis geminata, 516
S. molesta, 516
S. saevissima richteri, 516
S. xyloni, 516
Solutions, insecticide, 161
Somatic mesoderm, 72
Southern, corn rootworm, 276–280
  fire ant, 516
  house mosquito, 599
Specific miticides, 188
Sperm, 51, 67
Spermatheca, 51
Spermatogonia, 52
Spermatophore, 63
Spermatozoa, 52
Sperm tubes, 73
Sphingidae, 124
Sphinx moths, 124
Spider mites, 89, 316, 392–399
Spines, 37
Spiracles, 38–39
Spiral pore canals, 36
Spittlebugs, 107
Splanchnic mesoderm, 72
Spotted alfalfa aphid, 283

Spotted garden slug, 458–464
Sprayers, 193–207
    calibration, 206
    care, 205
    parts, 202
Spur, 38
Squash bugs, 104
Stadium, 75
Stage, 76
Stemmata, 55
Stem sawflies, 127
Sternum, 30
Sticktight flea, 574–577
Stink bugs, 104
Stomodaeal valve, 41
Storage excretion, 47
Stored grain insects, 466–494
    adaptive characteristics, 470
    chemical control, 477
    control by management, 476
    damage, 471
    environment, 470
    field infestations, 473
    food, 469
    fumigation, 480
    incidental pests, 469
    kinds, 466
    major pests, 467
    minor pests, 467
    original sources, 466
    parasites and predators, 469
Strawberry root weevil, 418–421
Striped cucumber beetle, 356–359
Strong, L. A., 10
Structural insects. See Household insects
Stylets, mandibular, 28
    maxillary, 28
Styli, 33
Subesophageal ganglion, 53, 71
Subterranean termites, 101, 518–525
Sucking lice, 102
Sulfur, 171
Sulfur butterflies, 125
Supella supellectilium, 508
Sutures, 37
Sweetclover weevil, 285
Swezey, O. H., 13
Swine insects. See Livestock insects
Symbiotic microorganisms, 44, 45
Symphylan, garden, 449–452
Syrphidae, 131
Systox, 186

Tabanidae, 131
Tachina flies, 134
Tachinidae, 134
Taenidia, 38
Tarnished plant bug, 302

Tarsonemidae, 90
Tarsonemid mites, 90
TDE, 183
Tectocuticle, 35
Tedion, 189
Tegmina, 32
Tenebrionidae, 114
Tenebroides mauritanicus, 491–492
Tent caterpillars, 125
Tenthredinidae, 126
Tephritidae, 132
TEPP, 186
Terminal Inspection Act of 1915, 156
Terminal ligament, 50
Termites, 101, 518–525
Testes, 52
Testicular follicles, 52
Tetranychidae, 89
Tetranychus canadensis, 392
T. mcdanieli, 392
T. schoenei, 392
T. telarius, 392, 455–458
Tettigoniidae, 99
Thallous sulfate, 172
Thief ant, 516
Thorax, 30–32
Thread-footed mites, 90
Three-banded leafhopper, 426–429
Thripidae, 103
Thrips, 103
    in greenhouses, 452–455
Thysanoptera, 103
Ticks, 86
    characteristics, 86
    external form, 60
    fowl tick, 577
    mouthparts, 30
    winter tick, 554
Tiger moths, 122
Tineidae, 119
Tineola bisselliella, 2, 511–513
Tolerance, insecticide, 19
Tormogen cell, 37
Tortricidae, 121
Toxaphene, 183
Toxoptera graminum, 239–243
Tracheae, 38–39, 72
Tracheal end cell, 38
Tracheoles, 38
Tree fruit insects, 376–406
    chemical control, 383
    control equipment, 385
    cultural control, 381
    disease transmission, 381
    injury, 378
    kinds, 376
Treehoppers, 106
Tribolium castaneum, 489–490

T. confusum, 489–490
Trichodectidae, 102
Trichogen cell, 37
Trichogrammatidae, 128
Trombicula akamushi, 606–608
T. alfreddugesi, 606–608
T. deliensis, 606–608
Trombiculidae, 90
Tsetse fly, 4
Tussock moths, 123
Two-spotted spider mite, 392, 455–458
Two-striped grasshopper, 220–229

Urate cells, 47
U.S. Entomological Commission, 8

Vagina, 51
Variegated leafhopper, 426–429
Vas deferens, 52
Vegetable insects, 346–374
    chemical control, 353
    control equipment, 355
    cultural control, 352
    injury, 349
    kinds, 346
Ventral, diaphragm, 48
    plate, 68
Vermiform larva, 79
Vertebrates, 81
Vetch bruchid, 287
Virginia-creeper leafhopper, 426–429
Visceral muscles, 49, 72
Vitelline membrane, 66
Vittelophags, 73

Walsh, B. W., 11
Warble flies, 134
Wax moths, 121
Webbing clothes moth, 2, 511–513
Weevils, 116
Western, corn rootworm, 276–280
    grape leafhopper, 426–429
    raspberry fruitworm, 421–423
    striped cucumber beetle, 356
    subterranean termite, 518–525
Wettable powders, 161
Wheat insects. *See* Small grain insects
Wheat, midge, 15
    wireworm, 243
White butterflies, 125
Whiteflies, 108
White grubs, 114
Wings of insects, 31–32
Wing venation, 32
Winter tick, 554–556
Wireworms, 112, 214, 243–248
    control, 247
    description, 245
    injury, 244
    kinds, 243
    life history, 245
Woollybears, 122
Wrinkled sucking lice, 103

Yellow fever, 4, 5, 590
Yellow-fever mosquito, 599
Yellow spider mite, 392

Xenopsylla cheopis, 4